A PERIL AND A HOPE

Suddenly the day of judgment was the next day and has been ever since.

I. I. RABI, 1962

When the late war ended in a thunderclap, it left two noteworthy developments in its wake. Science had become politically interesting, and scientists had become interested in politics.

J. H. RUSH, 1947

A PERIL
AND A HOPE

THE SCIENTISTS' MOVEMENT
IN AMERICA: 1945–47

Alice Kimball Smith

Chicago and London

THE  UNIVERSITY OF CHICAGO PRESS

LIBRARY OF CONGRESS CATALOG CARD NUMBER: 65–17300
THE UNIVERSITY OF CHICAGO PRESS, CHICAGO & LONDON
THE UNIVERSITY OF TORONTO PRESS, TORONTO 5, CANADA
© 1965 BY THE UNIVERSITY OF CHICAGO. ALL RIGHTS
RESERVED. PUBLISHED 1965. COMPOSED AND PRINTED IN
THE UNITED STATES OF AMERICA

Introduction

THIS BOOK RECORDS an early stage of the dramatic change in the relation of scientists to public affairs. It is true that anxiety about the application of nuclear fission was but one of several factors propelling them into closer association with government and policy-making and that other influences helped to produce a more explicit acknowledgment of the human values attaching to research. But the death and suffering that attended the introduction of atomic energy acted upon some members of the scientific profession with the force of spiritual revelation. What quickly came to be known as the scientists', or atomic scientists', movement represented joint action toward a new purpose and on a new scale. Scientists, says a recent commentator on the Oppenheimer hearings, Cushing Strout, have begun to act into history as they once acted into nature.

The message that the adherents of the postwar movement proclaimed—and it was a message in the sense of being both monitory and prophetic—seemed at the time, as far as the American public was concerned, to fall largely on deaf ears. And yet nearly two decades later their ideas and their phraseology had so far permeated the general thinking about international problems that in preparing this book it was often necessary to remind myself whether I was reading the first mimeographed declarations of worried Manhattan Project scientists or the columns of the daily paper in 1964.

Scientists have not always been regarded as apolitical or as constitutionally unsuited to public life. Earlier generations did not find it strange that Isaac Newton should direct the Mint or that Benjamin Franklin should represent his country in France. But in more recent times, with specialization and a tendency of research men to dissociate themselves from the cruder forms of applied science and technology, it was generally assumed that one of the marks of a first-class scientist was exclusive preoccupation with research. Private indulgence in music, travel, or mountain climbing was acceptable, but public display of interest in things other than science required special justification.

In Britain between the two world wars hundreds of scientists challenged this assumption by subscribing to the social-relations-in-science movement, which admitted responsibility for application of discoveries. In America this change had scarcely begun when the war drew virtually all scientists into the task of national defense, but at its conclusion an articulate and influential portion of the American scientific community made a desperate effort to establish guaranties that science should henceforth be primarily an instrument of peace and dedicated to human welfare. With this as their basic motivation, they adopted the slightly more finite objective of finding solutions to the problems created or aggravated by the release of atomic energy, forming first the Federation of Atomic Scientists and then the more broadly based Federation of American Scientists. Much of the scientists' activity in the first critical year after the war focused in the FAS; hence the following account devotes a good deal of space to its development and operation. But it is intended to be less a history of the organization than a record of reactions and attempts to influence policy-making in the broad field of atomic energy.

The scientists' movement early acquired an aura of importance not least because of the magnitude and global ramifications of the problem with which it tried to grapple. A certain epic quality attaches to any experience by which men are so stirred as to be wrenched from their accustomed patterns of behavior, and in addition this particular experience stemmed from a decision in which elements of immediate and ultimate good, of right and wrong and expediency appeared in all their baffling complexity—a decision that threw into sharp relief man's unevenly developed powers over the realms of matter and of spirit. Mankind now faced a common destiny of destruction as represented once before by the universal story of the flood. And the scientists' own world was abruptly enlarged. Science, once the exclusive province of a dedicated few, seemed suddenly to be of interest to everybody, and just as suddenly scientists found that they themselves possessed a hitherto unrecognized aptitude for practical things, whether it was makng bombs or persuading legislators to espouse a particular course of action.

To readers who feel that the following account does not explore in sufficient depth the multiple meanings of the scientists' movement I would say that the decision to present as nearly as possible an unvarnished tale was a deliberate one, taken in the currently unfashionable belief that recreating the past is a respectable and fascinating end in itself and that a mere patina of terms borrowed from sociology, psychology, or political science does not necessarily enrich the historical narrative. At the same time I hope that the book may be useful to experienced practitioners in these and other fields who wish to explore more adequately such large and important topics as the moral responsibility of science or the scientists' effectiveness in a political role.

There remain, however, many questions of the utmost relevance to the place of science and scientists in our political society that are at least illuminated if not finally answered by developments of 1945 and 1946, for it was a period in which practical aspects of the scientist's dilemma were amply demonstrated. If he devotes himself intensively to public affairs, how can he maintain the scientific competence on which his usefulness rests? When only a few individuals have access to all the technical data needed to decide a given point, how can collective scientific wisdom play its part, and how can it be effectively expressed when the natural spokesmen for the profession become confidential advisers to government? What happens to the authority of science when scientists do not agree on the answer to a given question? And where, if at all, do they draw the line between their roles as scientists and citizens? And there are questions of more specific relevance to the scientists' movement—its effect upon postwar policy and upon the attitude of scientists toward participation in public affairs—upon which one must render some account even though the answers cannot be quantitative or complete.

It is not possible to remind the reader at every point that the developments here recorded took place amidst a host of other adjustments that followed the war and that to most newspaper readers items about atomic energy were subordinate in interest to news of returning troops, of the Pearl Harbor investigation, of revelations of the horrors of Bataan and Buchenwald and the trials of their perpetrators, of strikes and threats of strikes, of growing estrangement from our ally Russia, and of the formation of the United Nations. But for the scientists with whom this story is concerned atomic energy overshadowed all other topics because they felt so certain that unless its implications were understood civilization would not survive. To the extent that their view was a distorted one—a matter of judgment and still a subject of debate—this account also is distorted, for it is written largely from their own files and their own recollections. A history of the development of atomic energy through the year 1946 is to be found in the admirable volume, *The New World*, prepared by the Atomic Energy Commission's historians, Richard G. Hewlett and Oscar E. Anderson, Jr., which was published in 1962 when I was midway through the first draft of this book. While its thorough coverage of events has at points reduced the novelty of what I intended to say—has even, where we used the same sources, anticipated my phraseology—at the same time I have gratefully taken advantage of the summaries and interpretations of classified documents to which the authors had access to place the scientists' activities more accurately in the context of official developments than I could otherwise have done.

Although this book has been written from the scientists' point of view—even, in part, as a tribute to what they tried to accomplish— one cannot assume that many of them will read it, for although they love to reminisce about the days when they so blithely cultivated the skills of politician and publicist and have done so for me most generously, when it comes to systematic history they tend to glance at a few paragraphs in a bookstore or thumb through an index, then commit their dissent or elaboration to the limbo of casual comment. The historian of nearly contemporary events must hope that his readers will help in the well-nigh limitless task of rounding out the documents with personal recollections and in this particular case that the scientists who shaped the atomic age will take some responsibility for seeing that it is accurately recorded.

I have chosen the autumn of 1946 as the terminal point of the detailed story. Extending it further would have involved much tedious repetition and the elimination of detail in the early period where the excitement and the real significance of the movement lie. The passage of the McMahon bill in midsummer, 1946, assuring civilian control and reasonable freedom of research, and the acceptance at the end of September of the principle of inspection and control by the scientific and technical committee of the United Nations Atomic Energy Commission provide landmarks in domestic and international policy relating to atomic energy. Up to this point scientists could claim that their technical knowledge gave them special competence to inform and advise; beyond lay those admittedly far more vexing political issues upon which they could speak only as informed citizens and upon which, in fact, their remarkable unanimity would soon break down. The inclination of many scientists to regard these initial successes as points beyond which they preferred to play a less active political role was fortified by growing impatience with the distraction from research or teaching that organizational activity entailed. A nucleus of capable and respected scientists continued to support the Federation of American Scientists, and on several occasions in the next few years it served as a focus of protest when the freedom of science was threatened, but after the autumn of 1946 its activities began to contract and it gradually assumed the watchdog role that it continues to play.

The term "atomic scientists" (and "atomic scientists' movement") was used very early after the war by headline writers to designate those who had worked on the bomb. The phrase was retained by the scientists themselves in the title of their first loose federation with what has been described as "a finer appreciation of the journalists' art than of the niceties of English usage."[1] Like many spontaneously derived phrases, it was not exact and its pre-emption by technical personnel of the Manhattan Project, as also their complacent references to "the Project," was the subject of caustic comment from other scientists, who pointed out that while many pioneer students of the atom were working on radar or the proximity fuse during the war scores of physicists, chemists, biologists, metallurgists, and engineers with only a peripheral understanding of the nucleus were acquiring distinction as "atomic scientists." Some restraint has been exercized in the use of this term in the following account, but without awkward circumlocution it is not possible to avoid it entirely, and the reader is asked to bear in mind that the sanction is one of usage rather than precise definition.

Another terminological trap exists in the terms "scientists" and "scientific community." The extent and nature of support given to the activities I describe are discussed at appropriate points. Here I point out only that this is not a quantitative study of opinion and action but a description of what a highly vocal and temporarily influential group of American scientists and engineers thought, and said, and

---

[1] James R. Newman and Byron S. Miller, *The Control of Atomic Energy* (New York: McGraw-Hill Book Company, 1948), p. 217. Used by permission of the publisher.

did about the problems arising from the release of atomic energy. The reader who feels that the term "scientists" is used in too all-embracing a fashion is reminded that no countermovement or organization sprang up and is assured that recorded expressions of dissent and disapproval by scientists have been scrupulously included.

It was with satisfaction, though not with surprise, that I found the title of the book in words of Robert Oppenheimer, who, speaking to his associates at Los Alamos in November, 1945, referred to atomic energy as a field in which there lay "not only a great peril but a great hope . . . of beginning to realize those changes which are needed if there is to be any peace."

I am deeply indebted to the hundred or so busy scientists and their associates in the movement who took time to talk or write to me and to W. A. Higinbotham and Lyle Borst, who have kindly allowed me to cite their diaries. Much useful material came from personal files, especially those of Thorfin Hogness, Zay Jeffries, Eugene Rabinowitch, John Simpson, and J. H. Rush. I also acknowledge the kindness of friends who read parts of the manuscript, particularly that of Higinbotham and Rush, whose extensive and meticulous comment was invaluable. Robert Rosenthal, curator of Special Collections at the University of Chicago's Harper Library, made it possible for me to use a confusing accumulation of material with a minimum of trouble.

Much of the writing was done between 1962 and 1964 as a scholar in the Radcliffe Institute for Independent Study, and my gratitude for the uniquely rewarding association with its members and staff would be hard indeed to express. And finally, without the confidence and prompting of Eugene Rabinowitch this book would not have been undertaken, and it would not have been carried far without the unrelenting encouragement of my husband and his continuing assurance that the job in hand was worthwhile.

Contents

PART IV
TO STUDY AND INFORM

PART V
DOMESTIC LEGISLATION AND INTERNATIONAL CONTROL

PART VI
HOPE DEFERRED

APPENDIXES

NOTE ON SOURCES

INDEX

List
of Abbreviations

Associations, governmental agencies, laboratories, and plants:

AAAS	American Association for the Advancement of Science
AAScW	American Association of Scientific Workers
AEOR	Atomic Engineers of Oak Ridge (at K-25)
ALAS	Association of Los Alamos Scientists
Alsos	Scientific intelligence mission to Germany in the spring of 1945
AORES	Association of Oak Ridge Engineers and Scientists (formed in June, 1946, by the merger of AORS and ORES)
AORS	Association of Oak Ridge Scientists
AORSCL	Association of Oak Ridge Scientists at Clinton Labs ("CL" was dropped in November, 1945)
APSOR	Atomic Production Scientists of Oak Ridge (at Y-12)
ASAE	Association of Scientists for Atomic Education
ASC	Atomic Scientists of Chicago
ECAS	Emergency Committee of Atomic Scientists
FAmS	Federation of American Scientists (used for a time to distinguish it from FAtS)
FAS	Federation of American Scientists
FAtS	Federation of Atomic Scientists
ICC	Independent Citizens Committee of the Arts, Sciences and Professions
K-25	Gaseous diffusion plant at Oak Ridge
NCAI	National Committee for Atomic Information

ORES   Oak Ridge Engineers and Scientists (formed in December, 1945, by the merger of AEOR and APSOR)
OSRD   Office of Scientific Research and Development
OWMR   Office of War Mobilization and Reconversion
SAM   Manhattan Project laboratory at Columbia University, standing for the code name "Substitute Alloy Materials"
X-10   Designation of the area in which Clinton Labs was situated
Y-12   Electromagnetic plant at Oak Ridge

Files of scientists' associations deposited in Harper Memorial Library at the University of Chicago:

ALAS   Association of Los Alamos Scientists
AORES   Association of Oak Ridge Engineers and Scientists
ASC   Atomic Scientists of Chicago
Camb.   Association of Cambridge Scientists
FAS   Federation of American Scientists

In references to these files, Roman numerals indicate boxes, and arabic numerals indicate folders within boxes. (In a few references to ASC files, the second roman numeral, preceded by "Vol.," indicates a folder.)

PART I

Protest
and Prophecy
1943–45

CHAPTER 1

War Years

Для a society which seeks peace it is important to explore the springs of action that lead to war. Henceforth scientists, no less than soldiers and statesmen, will be subjected to that inquiry. But in the war of 1939 to 1945 their professional responsibility was not yet fully admitted. In the hope of winning a desperate fight, like a majority of their fellow citizens, they did the job for which their talents and experience best suited them.

When scientists talk about their reaction to the use of atomic bombs against Japan in August, 1945, and their subsequent efforts to control atomic energy, laymen are likely to envision Pandora's box or the genie in the bottle and to inquire why scientists worked on a bomb in the first place. Some answer to this natural question, though it has often been given, must preface the story of the scientists' movement for which the fact of the bomb provided by far the major motivation.

The compelling reason among British and American scientists for trying to develop a bomb was fear that Hitler's Germany would get one first and deal the Allies a paralysing blow. The last scientific visitors to Berlin in 1939 reported work on the separation of the uranium isotope 235. News and rumors over the next four years indicated

German interest in the thermal diffusion method of isotope separation and also in heavy water, a possible moderator in a nuclear reactor producing plutonium. These ominous rumors were capped by a report from Niels Bohr, after his escape from Denmark in late 1943, that the eminent German physicist Werner Heisenberg was heading atomic research in Germany.

One of the few who denies that fear of a German bomb was for himself a primary motive is Robert F. Bacher, a physicist on leave from Cornell and the ranking member of a large contingent which left the Radiation Laboratory at Massachusetts Institute of Technology for Los Alamos in the spring of 1943. Better informed than the average scientist, Bacher interpreted reports of a drastic curtailment of the German radar project as evidence that industrial shortages would make an atomic bomb impossible. Others construed the radar cutback to mean that Germany was concentrating on some other project, probably an atomic one, and felt their fears confirmed. Bacher's main reason for transferring to the Manhattan Project was the possibility, which seemed very real in early 1943, that without a decisive weapon war in both Europe and the Pacific might drag on for years. And for many others, still anxious about German developments, this consideration provided added incentive and justification. Only rarely did any of the scientists consider what would happen if Germany was defeated before the bomb was ready and it became not a defensive weapon against a probable competitor but an offensive weapon against Japan, whose handful of excellent nuclear physicists could clearly not command the necessary industrial backing.

A few early workers on S-1, as the project was known before the organization of the Manhattan Engineer District in August, 1942, found comfort in the hope that some insuperable obstacle might demonstrate the impossibility of an atomic weapon, but by 1943, when major recruitment began, this was highly unlikely. People were saying rather that if a bomb could be made the fact should be settled once and for all. And with Hitler threatening all Europe and Japan's militarists spreading over Asia, it was easy to argue that such knowledge was most safely lodged with the United States and Britain.

But as scientists try to reconstruct their feelings in those desperate and yet in a way innocent days, they freely admit the presence of nonmilitary factors which, if not completely persuasive, reconciled them to working on the bomb. Robert Oppenheimer hinted at these when he later explained how he had staffed the Los Alamos Laboratory despite its isolation and restrictions and the prior involvement of most scientists in useful war research. "Almost everyone," he recalled in 1954,

realized that this was a great undertaking. Almost everyone knew that if it were completed successfully and rapidly enough, it might determine the outcome of the war. Almost everyone knew that it was an unparalleled opportunity to bring to bear the basic knowledge and art of science for the benefit of his country. Almost everyone knew that this job, if it were achieved, would be a part of history. This sense of excitement, of devotion and of patriotism in the end prevailed.[1]

One component in this excitement was curiosity. And if a historic development was inevitable, why not share in it? "I worked on the bomb," says one usually independent physicist with a touch of bitterness, "because everybody I knew was doing it." Perhaps a few scientists thought quite early that atomic weapons might provide the *reductio ad absurdum* for major wars, but for most this was a later rationalization. In the category of justifications the most common was the belief that peaceful applications of atomic energy to power, medicine, agriculture, and industry would in the long run far outweigh destruction. Very little in the following account is based upon the author's personal recollections, but I remember vividly the succinct explanation that covered our own migration to an undesignated spot in the western mountains: the project would almost certainly end the war and afterward promised almost limitless benefits to mankind. Amidst the fears and uncertainties of the winter of 1942 and 1943, so easily blurred and forgotten in later knowledge of victory, what more could one ask?

1. BOHR AND BUSH

The subject of this book is not, however, the development of the bomb but what scientists tried to do to control it. So long as the war lasted the chief impulses to consider the future development and control of the atom now appear to have come from Niels Bohr, Vannevar Bush, and a group at the Manhattan Project's Metallurgical Laboratory in Chicago. Because of the necessary limitations on discussion the influence of neither Bohr nor Bush was recognized at the time by more than a handful of their colleagues. Yet Bohr had an enormous, if usually indirect, influence upon the thinking of his fellow scientists, and Bush upon official policy.

---

[1] U.S. Atomic Energy Commission, *In the Matter of J. Robert Oppenheimer*, Transcript of Hearing before Personnel Security Board (Washington, D.C.: Government Printing Office, 1954), p. 13.

To Bohr's laboratory in Copenhagen the prewar generation of physicists from Europe, Asia, and America had been drawn by his brilliant contributions to nuclear theory and had departed fond admirers of a sensitive spirit as well as of a towering intellect. It was Bohr who had brought news to the United States early in 1939 of the Hahn-Strassmann-Meitner work on fission of the uranium atom, precipitating a rash of confirmatory experiments at Columbia, Berkeley, and other laboratories and leading in October, 1939, to Albert Einstein's letter to President Franklin D. Roosevelt urging the importance of developing an atomic weapon.

After a few months at the Institute for Advanced Study in Princeton, Bohr had returned to Copenhagen. He did not know of the British-American atomic weapons project—or at least did not have any idea of its scope—until he escaped from Nazi-occupied Denmark to Sweden in the autumn of 1943 and at the request of British scientists was flown to England. There Bohr was asked to join the British delegation which, through arrangements made at the Quebec Conference in August, 1943, had gone to the United States to work with the Manhattan Project. Most of the British scientists were at Los Alamos, and in December Bohr, with his son Aage, also arrived there. On the mesa where some world-renowned scientific figure had been turning up every other day or so, Bohr's appearance created uncommon excitement. Former associates welcomed him with delight, and their affectionate conversion of his Project pseudonym of Nicholas Baker to Uncle Nick was quickly adopted by new friends and admirers.

Bohr's technical insights were extremely helpful, and his more recent contacts with German scientists, though guarded on both sides, provided grounds for speculation about what lines of nuclear development they might be pursuing. But according to Oppenheimer, Bohr's great contribution was on another level:

He made the enterprise, which often looked so macabre, seem hopeful; he spoke with contempt of Hitler who with a few hundred tanks and planes had hoped to enslave Europe. He said nothing like that would ever happen again; and his own high hope that the outcome would be good, and that in this the role of objectivity, friendliness, cooperation, incarnate in science, would play a helpful part: all this was something we wished very much to believe.[2]

---

[2] J. Robert Oppenheimer, "Three Lectures on Niels Bohr and his Times; Part III: The Atomic Nucleus" (Pegram Lectures, Brookhaven National Laboratory, August,

In his elaboration of these themes Bohr revealed his true purpose in coming to the United States. For it was his fervent hope that he might persuade Churchill and Roosevelt of the vital importance of early communication with Stalin about the possibility of an atomic bomb and of making a generous offer to share its control. The very act of making and accepting such a gesture might, Bohr thought, produce a radical alteration in the world view of the actors in the drama and create a new pattern in international relationships. Only by a policy of true "openness" could accelerated competition be avoided.

Bohr's proposal, which appears at first glance as rampant idealism, was, in fact, based on some highly realistic judgments. He recognized earlier than most people that the alliance of the western democracies and Russia was unlikely to survive the war; he knew that any real bargaining over power must be done by the statesmen in whom power resided; he thought in terms of prompt positive action comparable to the seizure of initiative in developing the bomb. And Bohr, with the freer prewar contacts made possible by his great prestige and citizenship in a neutral country, was in a unique position to assess the probabilities not only of German but of Russian nuclear progress. Without loss of substantial advantage to the United States and Britain Bohr thought than an offer might be so formulated as to contain benefits which Russia could not afford to ignore. Bohr's principal failure in realism, thinks Oppenheimer, was in not recognizing how monolithic Stalin's power was and how little he was influenced by the kind of Russian Bohr knew. One might add that Bohr failed to make clear how his policy of openness was to be reconciled with his insistence that no information should be exchanged until controls were accepted.

At Los Alamos it was a small circle that fell directly under Bohr's benign spell, listening with the rapt attention that his scrupulous regard for security, his elliptical phraseology, and his almost inaudible voice required. Despite these barriers his own clarity of thought and

---

1963). My information about Bohr's activities is drawn from an interview with him on February 4, 1958, from an interview with Oppenheimer on December 9, 1963, from Oppenheimer's third Pegram lecture at Brookhaven in August, 1963, and from correspondence and memorandums in Oppenheimer's files. See also Richard G. Hewlett and Oscar E. Anderson, Jr., *The New World, 1939–1946* (University Park: Pennsylvania State University Press, 1962), chap. x (referred to hereinafter as *The New World*); Ronald W. Clark, *The Birth of the Bomb* (London: Phoenix House, 1961), pp. 178–80. As this book goes to press, details of Bohr's negotiations in England are supplied in Margaret Gowing's *Britain and Atomic Energy, 1939–45* (London: Macmillan & Co., 1964).

his warm humanity made a deep impression. But Bohr could also
listen, and it was to some extent a composite view that he began to
write down in early 1944, recording for the first time ideas that would
later appear in Bush's memorandums to Secretary of War Henry L.
Stimson, in the Jeffries Report on the future of nucleonics, in the
Franck Report, in the numerous manifestoes of the scientists' organizations, and finally in the Acheson-Lilienthal Report, on which
was based the United States control plan of 1946.

On his way to Los Alamos Bohr had already conveyed to a few
people the outlines of his thinking about the impact of the bomb.
In England he had met with much sympathetic understanding from
Sir John Anderson, the cabinet member responsible for scientific
research. In Washington he had seen the minister of the Danish
government-in-exile, Dr. Henrik de Kauffman, and the British ambassador, Lord Halifax. Renewing a friendship with Justice Felix
Frankfurter begun ten years before in England and finding by careful
indirection that Frankfurter knew about the bomb project, Bohr told
him of his belief in the necessity of frank discussion with Russia. Early
in 1944 Frankfurter found an occasion to talk to Roosevelt about
Bohr's views. The President seemed receptive and told Frankfurter that
Bohr might talk to "friends" in London about exploration of safeguards. So in April Bohr returned to England to see if this sign of
Roosevelt's incipient interest would temper the vehement opposition
to Russian talks that Anderson had encountered when he broached
the matter to Winston Churchill. While Bohr sought an opportunity
to talk to the Prime Minister, he picked up a letter awaiting him at
the Soviet Embassy from his old friend the Russian physicist Peter Kapitza, who, after working for years in Cambridge, had been detained
on a visit to Russia in 1935. Kapitza had heard of Bohr's escape from
Denmark and extended a warm invitation to come to Moscow. He reminded Bohr of their mutual admiration for Lord Rutherford and
their long scientific and personal friendship and mentioned the names
of half a dozen other nuclear physicists who would welcome Bohr's
collaboration. Bohr replied cordially, and of course with full knowledge of British security officers, that he hoped conditions would soon
permit a reunion with his colleagues in Moscow which he had last
visited in 1937. But the names Kapitza mentioned were reminders,
which Bohr scarcely needed, of how quickly the Russians could push
ahead on nuclear research if news of work elsewhere kindled their
interest, and these things were in his mind as he again talked to

Anderson and other British leaders and finally in May to Churchill himself. This interview, from which Bohr hoped for so much, was a sad fiasco. Lord Cherwell, Churchill's scientific adviser, was also present, and he and the Prime Minister engaged in an argument that left Bohr on the sidelines unable to explain what he had in mind. Churchill expressed unalterable opposition to talks with Russia, and the episode was for Bohr a tragically frustrating experience. The only accomplishment of his London sojourn was agreement among Churchill's advisers that he and the President should discuss the future of atomic energy next time they met.

Bohr did not give up, however. He went back to the United States and Los Alamos, working on the memorandum begun the previous February, parts of which he had used for his talks with Anderson and Churchill. By July 3, 1944, he had revised and polished it for the interview with Roosevelt that his friend Frankfurter was arranging.

The consequences of the atomic energy project, explained Bohr, surpassed the imagination. New energy sources might revolutionize industry, transport, and warfare. Customary measures of control would not suffice, and the prevention of clandestine competition demanded "such concessions regarding exchange of information and openness about industrial efforts including military preparations as would hardly be conceivable unless at the same time all partners were assured of a compensating guarantee of common security against dangers of unprecedented acuteness." With a bitter fight against the aggressor nations still in progress, the present might seem ill suited to making continuing commitments, for in victory the nations united against aggression might find grave causes of disagreement in their conflicting attitudes toward social and economic problems.

By a closer consideration, however, it would appear that the potentialities of the project as a means of inspiring confidence just under these circumstances acquire most actual importance. Moreover the momentary situation would in various respects seem to afford quite unique possibilities which might be forfeited by a postponement awaiting the further development of the war situation and the final completion of the new weapon.... Without impeding the importance of the project for immediate military objectives, an initiative, aiming at forestalling a fateful competition about the formidable weapon, should serve to uproot any cause of distrust between the powers on whose harmonious collaboration the fate of coming generations will depend.[3]

---

[3] Bohr, Open Letter to the United Nations, June 9, 1950 (Copenhagen: J. H. Schultz Forlag, n.d.), pp. 5–6. The Open Letter, which was reprinted in Bulletin of the Atomic

These and other portions of his wartime memorandums that Bohr published in 1950 failed to do justice to the cogency of his argument which had included more specific references to Russia's probable interest and capacity for nuclear development than he cared to mention publicly after the cold war began. By the summer of 1944 he felt sure that Germany would not produce a bomb, but he was worried about what would happen to German technical knowledge during an Allied occupation. Again Bohr showed more realistic foresight than some who thought him vague and dreamy. He knew the limitations of security when it came to ideas, and either through the polite questions directed at him by officials at the Soviet Embassy in London or by some more intuitive process he sensed a strong Russian interest in nuclear developments. Something of this he must have tried to convey to Roosevelt in the hour and a half he spent with him on July 26, for Bohr a far happier occasion than the meeting with Churchill. Although he was dismayed to find that the President had not already discussed postwar controls with Bush and other advisers, he left with the impression that Roosevelt took a favorable view of talking to Russia before the bomb was used. Still Bohr thought he might not have made one point sufficiently clear, and early in September he sent the President a supplementary comment. Only responsible statesmen had insight into political possibilities, said Bohr, but "helpful support may perhaps be afforded by the world-wide scientific collaboration which for years has embodied such bright promises for common human striving. On this background personal connections between scientists of different nations might even offer means of establishing preliminary and non-committal contact."[4]

Perhaps Bohr overestimated the President's interest. He did not yet know how disturbed Roosevelt had been by the appearance of Frankfurter, who had no reason to know about the bomb, as Bohr's intermediary. In any case whatever inclination the President may have felt toward Russian talks vanished during private discussions on atomic energy which he had with Churchill on September 18, 1944, when the Prime Minister visited Hyde Park at the conclusion of the second Quebec conference. There the two leaders signed an *aide-memoire* stating that an atomic bomb, when available, "might perhaps, after mature consideration, be used against the Japanese, who should be

---

Scientists, (July, 1950), 213–17, 219, contained excerpts from Bohr's memorandums of July 3, 1944, and March 24, 1945.
　　[4] Bohr, *Open Letter to the United Nations,* p. 6.

warned that this bombardment will be repeated until they surrender," and that Anglo-American collaboration for commercial and military purposes should continue after the defeat of Japan unless specifically terminated.[5] But first they had dealt with Bohr's proposal, which they summarily dimissed on the grounds that the time had not yet come to tell the world about the bomb. What Bohr had in mind was not, of course, telling the world but a very private communication between Allied leaders. Oppenheimer thinks the Hyde Park decision was based on "a substantial if not total misunderstanding of what Bohr was after"; it is possible, he thinks, that Bohr's seemingly innocuous codicil on the contributions scientists could make to international amity was misinterpreted. Roosevelt's misgivings about Frankfurter's unauthorized involvement, combined with Churchill's intense dislike of the whole project, led to a supplementary decision to have Bohr carefully watched.[6]

Vannevar Bush learned of this suspicion of Bohr when he talked to the President a few days later in Washington and did his best to dispel it. In this he was backed up by British officials who knew how discreetly Bohr had handled the matter of the Kapitza letter, and Bohr's contacts with the Manhattan Project were not curtailed. The Yalta Conference in January, 1945, was probably the last time that the approach Bohr advocated had any chance of success, but with the San Francisco meeting to organize the United Nations scheduled for April he tried yet another appeal to Roosevelt. "It is significant," he wrote in a memorandum of March 24, 1945,

that the special character of the efforts which, irrespective of technical refinements, are required for the production of the active materials, and the peculiar conditions which govern their use as dangerous explosives, will greatly facilitate such control and should ensure its efficiency, provided only that the right of supervision is guaranteed.

Detailed proposals for the establishment of an effective control would have to be worked out with the assistance of scientists and technologists appointed by the governments concerned, and a standing expert committee, related to an international security organization, might be charged with keeping account of new scientific and technical developments and with recommending appropriate adjustments of the control measures.

[5] As quoted in The New World, p. 327.

[6] Because it used the British code name for the atomic project, "tube alloys," Roosevelt's copy of the aide-memoire was filed with naval documents and did not turn up until his papers were catalogued many years later. American Project officials learned of the agreement when shown a copy by the British after Roosevelt's death; see Leslie R. Groves, Now It Can Be Told (New York: Harper & Bros., 1962), pp. 401–2.

On recommendations from the technical committee the organizations would be able to judge the conditions under which industrial exploitation of atomic energy sources could be permitted with adequate safeguards to prevent any assembly of active material in an explosive state.

Those familiar with the Acheson-Lilienthal Report will see here the beginnings of some of its most important features—qualified reliance upon technological inspection, the necessity of keeping track of new developments, the distinction between safe and dangerous activities. Bohr repeated the points he had made previously about the wisdom of seizing the crucial moment, his hope "that an understanding about this vital matter might contribute most favorably towards the settlement of other problems where history and traditions have fostered divergent viewpoints," the help to be expected from the internationalism of science, and the advantage which nations would surely see in the assurance of security. "Looking back on those days," he wrote in 1950, "I find it difficult to convey with sufficient vividness the fervent hopes that the progress of science might initiate a new era of harmonious co-operation between nations, and the anxieties lest any opportunity to promote such a development be forfeited."[7] Bohr was trying to arrange another interview with Roosevelt to discuss the March memorandum when the President died.

Keenly aware of the delicacy of his position as a Danish citizen trying to influence the policy of the United States and Britain, Bohr was always extremely cautious in speaking of these wartime activities. But it is now evident that either through his influence or through parallel thinking, scientists with whom Bohr was in contact shared his conviction that Russia should have advance warning of the bomb even if they did not all dare to be as hopeful as Bohr about the effect of the communication upon the Russian attitude. H. D. Smyth, already at work on a report on the development of the bomb, proposed it to James B. Conant and Richard C. Tolman.[8] Oppenheimer was convinced of the advisability of Russian talks and shared his opinion with close associates, but as with other non-technical questions at Los Alamos, discretion and preoccupation with deadlines prevented much discussion.

Bohr was aware of these influential supporters; he knew that after Roosevelt's death his memorandums had been brought to Stimson's attention. But in his scheme time was of the essence, and in the spring

---

[7] Bohr, *Open Letter to the United Nations*, pp. 7, 8.
[8] H. D. Smyth to the author, June 18, 1957, quoting letters which he wrote to Tolman on November 13, 1944, and April 26, 1945.

of 1945 time was running out. In June he returned to England and later in the summer to Denmark. To the end of his life he felt that a magnificent opportunity had been lost.

Obviously this is not the whole story of the Bohr episode. Official documents on both sides of the Atlantic will some day reveal more about the deep suspicions that his activities inevitably aroused in those who had no special reason to trust him. Even among scientists, few knew at the time what he was trying to do. Many did not connect him until much later with the views they began so earnestly to espouse in August, 1945. Yet some of these ideas were first developed by Bohr, and at or near the center of a widening circle his influence was certainly very great.

But the scientist in the best position to influence policy was not Bohr, a foreigner noted for absent-mindedness and abstract thought, but Vannevar Bush, a native New Englander with a crisp direct manner and great talent in the application and administration of research, which he had employed as professor of electrical engineering and vice-president of the Massachusetts Institute of Technology, then as president of the Carnegie Institution in Washington, and after 1941 as director of the Office of Scientific Research and Development. In September, 1942, he was made chairman of the Manhattan Project Military Policy Committee. Bush's deputy on the committee and his close associate in the supervision of atomic research was James B. Conant, president of Harvard and chairman of the National Defense Research Council.

In the final year of the war Bush alone, or jointly with Conant, represented to Stimson and the President, the gravity of the problems that would accompany the achievement of atomic weapons and the need for advance planning on both the domestic and the international levels.[9] On September 30, 1944, Bush and Conant addressed to Stimson a careful examination of international problems, proposing that control should be placed in the hands of an international agency after the war. They had grave doubts about the exclusive Anglo-American hegemony that seemed to be evolving in the hands of Churchill and Roosevelt, believing that it would lead to intensive efforts by Russia to develop a bomb of her own. They strongly recommended the release of all basic scientific information and of all but

---

[9] Bush's activities are reported in detail in *The New World*, chap. x.

manufacturing and military details of the bomb as soon as the first one was dropped. Security did not lie in secrecy, they said, and the United States advantage was temporary. The possibility of a weapon based upon hydrogen meant that a monopoly of uranium ore was of limited value. With optimism tempered by a realistic appraisal of inevitable opposition and with a natural tendency to a more prosaic embodiment of ideas than Bohr's, these two seasoned administrators were yet ready to rest their case for radical action on the argument that the danger itself was unprecedented and to suggest that if people understood the unparalleled threat of atomic weapons they might never be used. On these two propositions the postwar scientists' movement was to be based, though Bush and Conant had little to do with it.[10]

When Stimson could detach himself sufficiently from other pressing problems, Bush found him a responsive listener. Stimson's assistant, Harvey Bundy, says that prior to the decision to use the bomb the Secretary had thought so long and painfully about the significance of atomic energy as to need no prodding from the scientists; but the documents seem to show that Stimson's advocacy of international control owed a great deal to Bush, and especially to a talk which Bundy himself, after briefing by Bush and Conant, had with Stimson as late as March 5, 1945.[11]

While Bush was trying to alert his political superiors to the implications of atomic developments he was also working for the appointment of a committee on long-range planning, a step which had been urgently commended to him for the past year or more by certain scientists in Chicago to whose sometimes disruptive activities we now turn.

2. Ferment and Forecast at the Met Lab

The genesis and interchange of thoughts on how to deal with the political atom is not easily traced in this period of necessarily private communication. Bush and Conant were familiar at least with the substance of Bohr's July, 1944, memorandum; that many of its ideas appeared soon afterward in their own September 30 memorandum to Stimson does not prove indebtedness to Bohr although such eminent advocacy may not have been without effect. When asked about this concurrence of thinking scientists insist that their technical

---

[10] *The New World*, pp. 325–30.
[11] Interview with Bundy, March 18, 1959; *The New World*, pp. 338–39.

knowledge and appreciation of the character of the new development led naturally to certain conclusions about its control, or they reply vaguely that these ideas were in the air.

Although it is now evident that Bush and Conant deserve credit for more liberal thinking on the political implications of atomic energy and for calling official attention to them than their critics among Project scientists have granted them, the documents confirm the earlier impression of close correspondence between each renewed effort on their part and agitation in Chicago.

In the summer of 1943—six months before Bohr arrived in the United States and a year before Bush began actively to promote a planning committee—a grass-roots movement at the Metallurgical Laboratory on the University of Chicago campus had revealed some sheer restiveness under wartime restraints and some genuine concern about the future of nuclear research. The Met Lab—the usual shortening of a code name that had turned out to be more appropriate than its sponsors intended—was organized in January, 1942, with a nucleus of groups transferred from Columbia and Princeton, for research on plutonium and the building of an experimental chain-reacting pile. December 2, 1942, saw the successful achievement, under Enrico Fermi's direction, of the first controlled chain reaction; the research on plutonium continued.

The Met Lab was part of the Metallurgical Project, directed by Arthur H. Compton, which also included research units at Ames, Berkeley, and after 1943 at the Clinton Labs at Oak Ridge, Tennessee. In the autumn of 1942, E. I. duPont de Nemours and Company had been selected to operate the proposed uranium separation plant at Oak Ridge, and while it was being built the Met Lab staff was augmented by duPont scientists and engineers. Since the war, industrial and academic scientists have come to understand each other, but in 1943 there was an appreciable gulf between those accustomed to the directed efficiency of industrial research and those who throve in the more chaotic atmosphere of academic laboratories. Tension between the two groups at the Met Lab produced a highly critical attitude toward Project policy in the young academic scientists and an abortive attempt to organize in the summer of 1943.

As recalled sixteen years later by Nathan Sugarman, now a professor of chemistry at the University of Chicago's Enrico Fermi Institute, the agitation had two objectives: the elimination of a marked salary differential between duPont employees and others at the same level, and prevention of a postwar monopoly of atomic energy by some private interests like duPont. Youthful idealism, Sugarman maintains, was as strong as pecuniary interest. When Aaron Novick described the 1943 episode just after the war, he gave a more general cast to its motivation. "We were troubled," he said,

by the fact that except for the scientists and the Army there was no fore-knowledge of the tremendous implications of the atom bomb, and we felt someone should attempt to represent the public conscience and that at least we scientists should discuss among ourselves the tremendous social and political implications of atomic warfare.[12]

In a period of two months four or five meetings were held, with Project permission but with guards present. A manifesto incorporating the chief complaints received some fifty signatures. But the opposition of the military authorities to organized activity was clear from the beginning, and freedom of discussion within the laboratory was soon added to the other points at issue. A moving talk by James Franck, whose memory of suppression in German laboratories was still vivid, made a lasting impression on his young listeners. Things reached a climax when a local deputy of General Leslie R. Groves, the commanding officer of the Manhattan Engineer District, interrupted a conference between one of the laboratory leaders and the young scientists to say that they had better disband unless they wanted to be shipped off to Guadalcanal. Although Compton, as Project director, intervened to assure them that this would not happen, the movement was brought to an end—but with the resolve to revive it after the war—not by the threat of military service but by a plaintive appeal from the Met Lab's associate director, Samuel K. Allison, that the job of placating the authorities was taking too much of his time.

This disposed for the time being of the issue of organization, but it did not lay the specter of military-industrial domination of postwar research. The costly preparations which duPont was making at Oak Ridge for the production of plutonium—which the speedy success of the Clinton pile would soon justify—not only seemed extravagant but indicative of a long-term interest, and some months after the protest of mid-1943—largely a chemistry affair—a group of young physicists at the Met Lab prepared a petition asking that Harry L.

---

[12] Novick, "A Plea for Atomic Freedom," *New Republic*, CXIV (March 25, 1946), 399–400; and interviews with Charles D. Coryell, March 17, 1959, and Nathan Sugarman, October 8, 1959.

Hopkins or Secretary of the Interior Harold L. Ickes be delegated to spend several months on the Project to keep an eye on duPont's Oak Ridge development. Fearing that their request would fall into duPont hands if they used regular Project channels, on the spur of the moment one of them deposited a copy with a White House secretary through whom it promptly reached General Groves and oblivion.[13]

Although these two episodes could be dismissed as youthful defiance, it soon became evident that they were a symptom of anxieties shared by a cross section of senior men in Chicago. The completion of important work on plutonium, or its transfer to Oak Ridge, Hanford, or Los Alamos, gave rise in the summer of 1944 to review by Manhattan Project authorities of the function of the Met Lab; this in turn led to uneasy speculation by the staff that the laboratory would be disbanded or at most kept in stand-by condition. The preoccupation of Washington (meaning Groves, Bush, and Conant) with the immediate objective of completing the bomb appeared to be needlessly exclusive. War or no war the immobilizing of scientific talent and of a working laboratory organization seemed a poor way to realize the potential of a brave new atomic world. Metallurgical Project council members Richard L. Doan, associate director of Clinton Labs, and Thorfin R. Hogness, head of the Project's chemistry division, protested that curtailment would undermine morale and tempt young men to go elsewhere; consultant Zay Jeffries of General Electric opposed any cut in basic research until Germany was defeated.[14]

Compton relayed these opinions to Bush, and during July and August they agreed that planning for the future should be carried on, but in such a way as not to jeopardize work on the bomb. While these exchanges were in progress, but probably not due solely to them, the Military Policy Committee, of which Bush was chairman, appointed a committee under the chairmanship of Richard C. Tolman, a physicist from California Institute of Technology and a member of the National Defense Research Council, to study the relation of atomic energy to national security. Another physicist, H. D. Smyth of Princeton, a member of the Metallurgical Project staff, also served on the committee as did engineers and representatives of the armed services.

---

[13] Interviews with Coryell, March 17, 1959, and Irving Kaplan, April 3, 1962.

[14] The documents relating to the Met Lab reaction of the summer of 1944 are summarized in *The New World*, pp. 322–24. The University of Chicago, through the Metallurgical Project, continued in charge of Clinton Laboratories until the Monsanto Chemical Company took over its management July 1, 1945.

According to Smyth, the conclusion of the still classified Tolman Report, which was submitted on December 28, 1944, was in line with his own preliminary formulation that

the objective of all plans with regard to the future development of nuclear energy in this country must be primarily the achievement of such a strong scientific and technological position that the military supremacy of this country cannot be questioned. This is the sole objective of the recommendations which this committee is making.[15]

Smyth himself saw the problem in broad perspective and while the report was in preparation advised Tolman that

in order to give a basis for decision on these problems of administration and organization it is necessary to present to the government and perhaps ultimately to the people a statement of what has been accomplished during the war period, of what may be accomplished in the future, and of the nature and magnitude of the work which must be carried out in the future to maintain military supremacy.

From this conviction sprang Smyth's own report of August, 1945, on the work of the Manhattan Project.[16]

But during the summer of 1944, when the Tolman committee was appointed, pressure was mounting to look ahead on a much broader front than that of defense research. Bush knew of Bohr's current efforts to draw official attention to future international problems, and in August he heard from another world-famous scientist, James Franck, who added to Compton's earlier representations his personal entreaty that something be done to relieve anxieties in Chicago about the apparent lack of thought for the future.

It was against this background that Bush and Conant decided it was time to begin the indoctrination of officials in the government and prepared for Secretary Stimson their memorandum of September 30, 1944, on international control. These two men bore a tremendous responsibility, not only in development of the bomb, but for all aspects of war research. They woud have been criticized by their associates in the Manhattan Project had they shown any tendency to sub-

---

[15] Smyth to the author, June 18, 1957, quoting his letter to Tolman of November 13, 1944.

[16] Smyth to the author, June 18, 1957, quoting his letter to Tolman of November 13, 1944. Smyth's report was issued first as *A General Account of the Development of Methods of Using Atomic Energy for Military Purposes under the Auspices of the United States Government, 1940–45* (Washington, D.C.: August, 1945). It was reissued as Henry DeWolf Smyth, *Atomic Energy for Military Purposes* (Princeton, N.J.: Princeton University Press, 1945).

ordinate the bomb to more remote applications of atomic power. It has been argued that they fully understood the need for domestic and international planning but considered it futile to make specific studies and analyses until officials in the government were interested and able to use them.[17] It was the view of the Chicago critics that decisions were being made all the time, even with the end of the war not yet in sight, that required just that prior understanding of the significance of atomic energy that administration officials did not have. General reassurances about discussion within the administration may have been passed on to the Met Lab through Compton; they do not seem to have contained any definite information.

Meantime the summer's unrest had led Metallurgical Project leaders in Chicago to initiate their own appraisal of the future of nuclear research. The proposal ostensibly came from Zay Jeffries, of General Electric, who wrote to Compton on July 13, 1944, suggesting a prospectus on possible applications of what he called "nucleonics" so that problems arising therefrom could be intelligently faced. Jeffries' letter was clearly the fruit of discussions about Met Lab research, but he remembers it as inspired by worried young men who came to him asking whether there was any future in the field and also by an occasion a year earlier when Compton had marked the six months' anniversary of the first chain reaction by inviting a dozen people to dinner at a suburban restaurant, after which, on an open lawn with only a cloud of virulent mosquitoes within earshot, he had asked each one for ideas on postwar uses of atomic energy. From that time on, with Compton's encouragement, says Jeffries, we all began to think about this question.[18]

Jeffries was a distinguished metallurgist with a long career in industrial research. He naturally thought in terms of vast new developments in which private industry might participate: stimulation of research, encouragement of the nucleonics industry, and the harmonizing of these developments with military needs to assure maximum security. "Intelligent speculation is all that can be done now," Jeffries told Compton. "It is to be expected that five or ten years hence such a statement will seem amateurish." Jeffries' view was by no means parochial, but as things turned out, the report to which his

---

[17] *The New World*, p. 325.

[18] Jeffries to Compton, July 13, 1944 (supplied by Jeffries); Jeffries to the author, December 8, 1958.

name was attached became the vehicle for much broader consideration of the subject than he originally envisioned.

Before the end of July, Jeffries was authorized by Compton and the
Metallurgical Project council to carry out his study with a committee
consisting of Enrico Fermi, who had left Chicago and was now an
associate director of the Los Alamos Laboratory; James Franck, associate director of the chemistry division of the Met Lab; Thorfin R.
Hogness, director of chemistry for the Metallurgical Project; Robert S.
Stone, head of the Met Lab's health division; Charles A. Thomas,
research director of Monsanto Chemical Company and co-ordinator
of plutonium research for the Manhattan Project; and Robert S.
Mulliken, a physicist serving as information director of the Metallurgical Project.[19]

Mulliken, acting as secretary, wrote to group leaders throughout
the Project. The speed with which replies came in indicates previous
interest in both programs and organization of postwar research, and
the comments of a non-technical nature lend some support to scientists' later claim that they had been thinking about these problems
for some time.

An early August memorandum from Lothar W. Nordheim, physicist
and section chief at Clinton Labs, was at once a reflection of current discontents and prophetic of scientists' later activities. Wrote
Nordheim:

After the war there will undoubtedly be pressure from political and
commercial interests. The only group with real information and no direct
bias will be the scientists. Their opinion and recommendations will carry
weight according to how far it has been possible to unify their points of
view.

Final negotiations will have to be in the hands of a few. However, since
there is always room for honest difference of opinion, the weight carried
by the scientists will be proportionate to the extent to which common
ground has been established beforehand among themselves. All efforts
should be made, therefore, to find this common ground, and all workers
carrying out responsible research should be given the opportunity to obtain
information about future plans and to express their opinions....

The writer has found among project members a widespread and deep

---

[19] See Arthur Holly Compton, *Atomic Quest* (New York: Oxford University Press,
1956), p. 232. Compton was probably in error in describing subcommittees on industrial phases, health hazards, safeguards of the peace, and social consequences but correct
in stating that studies made for the Jeffries committee contributed to a report prepared
at the Met Lab in June, 1945, for the War Department's Interim Committee on Atomic
Energy.

concern about the questions of future policies. It would seem to be of great advantage to channel this very lively interest into the direction of active collaboration.

"Some Remarks on Nucleonics," submitted by M. C. Leverett, director of the engineering division of the Met Lab, dealing chiefly with uses of a chain reaction for power, suggested that a grasp of technical realities would provide a brake as well as a spur.

There is no intent to disparage the opinion that atomic power is a wonderful thing and has a revolutionary future.... Until we get it, we should not talk like magazine ads for postwar plastics.... The possibilities should be viewed with the greatest optimism, but any commitments as to one's ability actually to put atomic power to useful work should be made very conservatively....[20]

On the basis of these and other responses a draft was prepared by Mulliken and submitted to the full committee. With the title "Prospectus on Nucleonics," the Jeffries Report was turned over to Compton on November 18, 1944.[21]

The term "nucleonics" was selected from a list of possibilities, but it did not catch on even among scientists. "Atomic" energy was commonly used during the period covered by this book and has never been replaced in popular parlance by the more accurate term "nuclear." The first three sections described the development of atomic energy; the fourth and fifth dealt with possible new tools and methods, the sixth with social and political implications, and the last with aspects of postwar control.

Section VI, "The Impact of Nucleonics on International Relations and the Social Order," has particular relevance to the present inquiry. Other nations, said its authors, were undoubtedly pressing work in nucleonics, and it was therefore the duty of American scientists not to relax their efforts to develop the bomb lest our present strong hand be covered by a stronger. Atomic weapons would enormously increase the danger of a sudden attack and give greatly increased advantage to the aggressor. A central authority would be needed to control the use of nuclear power, and until such an authority could be set up, the United States could only cling to the fragile hope that fear of retaliation by us would act as a deterrent to attack.

---

[20] Copies of these memos are in Rabinowitch's files.

[21] Jeffries et al., "Prospectus on Nucleonics," November 18, 1944, in Manhattan Engineer District files; the report was declassified in 1957 and copies sent by Jeffries to committee members. Sections I, V, VI, and VII are printed in Appendix A.

The widening gap between technological progress and static political institutions posed a problem for which two solutions suggested themselves: the first, to take a step backward and abandon nucleonic developments, thus courting national suicide; the second, to combine intensive development of nucleonics and all its potential benefits with an effort to solve political problems on a world-wide scale. "Widespread scientific education must go hand in hand with education of the general public," said the authors, adding in an underlined passage:

The moral development necessary to prevent the misuse of nuclear energy can only be achieved if public opinion becomes fully aware of the catastrophic possibilities inherent in the development of nucleonics, and thus prepared to give its support to the decisions required to prevent the danger. . . .
     To sum up, we believe that the inevitability of the development of nucleonics by some if not all, nations shows compellingly, because of its potential military consequences the necessity for all nations to make every effort to cooperate now in setting up an international administration with police powers which can effectively control at least the means of nucleonic warfare.

Section VI, with its implied warning of a nuclear arms race, is a direct antecedent of the Franck Report. Two men were responsible for its inclusion in the Jeffries Report, Robert Mulliken, the secretary of the committee, and Eugene Rabinowitch, a Met Lab biophysicist. Rabinowitch's name will appear often in this book, first as principal formulator of and contributor to ideas and programs developed at the Met Lab, then as founder and editor of the *Bulletin of the Atomic Scientists*. After many others lost faith or patience he continued to explore ways in which science and scientists could contribute to international understanding and to encourage his colleagues to educate themselves in the broader implications of their work while helping others to understand the meaning of science. Having left Russia as a schoolboy after the revolution of 1917, Rabinowitch was trained as a chemist at the University of Berlin, later working on photosynthesis with Franck at Göttingen. In 1933 he moved to England and in 1938 to the United States. From Massachusetts Institute of Technology he had come to the Met Lab in 1943.

Repeated experience as a refugee had made of Rabinowitch not, as it so often does, a perennially displaced person but an adaptable cosmopolitan and an interested observer of international politics without the obsessive fears and prejudices that sometimes color the views of the expatriate. By 1944 he had an excellent English vocabu lary and was fully articulate in his latest adopted language except for some difficulty with its "shalls," "mights," and "woulds"—a difficulty that characterizes so much of the literature of the early atomic age because of the European background of its authors. Rabinowitch's older friend and associate, James Franck, although expressing himself eloquently in English, has never written it with ease, and it was in part as his trusted interpreter that Rabinowitch had the opportunity to make his first significant contributions to Met Lab discussions.

Although Rabinowitch was not a member of the Jeffries committee he had no trouble convincing Mulliken that political and social implications ought to be included in its report. Together they prepared a draft of Section VI for which Mulliken then obtained the committee's approval.[22]

Rabinowitch also made substantial contributions to Section VII, "The Post-War Organization of Nucleonics in America," in particular a final broad objective: "To strive for the establishment of an efficient international supervision over all military aspects of nucleonics." And he added the urgent recommendation (to which his own energies have been devoted without stint) that "enlightenment of public opinion on the scope and significance of nucleonics should start as soon as possible to bring about realization of the dangers for world security caused by the new scientific and technical developments, and to prepare for decisions which will have to be taken to meet this danger."[23]

Although Rabinowitch and Mulliken put these points into the Jeffries Report, they were only setting down ideas now commonly discussed by the research staff at the Met Lab. Three months earlier Compton himself had talked to the Metallurgical Project council about the need for international control. And while the Jeffries Report was being written, twenty-two Chicago scientists, headed by the Met Lab director, Samuel K. Allison, sent to Washington through Compton the recommendation that the United States forewarn its allies about the bomb.[24] In connection with the concurrent Tolman committee study (to which, according to Compton, the Jeffries committee gave what help they could), Smyth was stressing the need for an informed public opinion in almost the same words as Rabinowitch.

---

[22] Jeffries to the author, June 3, 1957; Mulliken to the author, May 6, 1957; discussions with Rabinowitch.
[23] Material in Rabinowitch's files.
[24] The New World, p. 341.

But the completion of the Jeffries Report underlined once again the fact that there did not yet exist any group specifically charged with developing atomic policy on a broad and long-term basis. Compton later recalled a certain perplexity about what to do with the report and that when he turned it over to General Groves it was with the renewed request that such a committee be appointed.[25]

3. SZILARD AND FRANCK SPEAK UP

The Jeffries Report is significant chiefly as evidence of the nature and extent of scientists' thinking at this period about nuclear research and its implications. By the time it was declassified thirteen years later its technical forecasts, although historically interesting and by no means all realized, had little value as a blueprint. As for its political analysis, it is true that as much as six weeks before the report was finished Bush and Conant, whom the authors must chiefly have hoped to influence, had already committed themselves to international control. But as they tried further to interest Stimson and the President, it would be strange indeed if they did not find it convenient to cite the unanimity with which the respected members of the Jeffries committee had supported some of the points they wished to make.

Although the full Jeffries Report was not generally available to Met Lab scientists, enough was learned of its generally constructive tone to relieve anxieties that vested industrial interests might obtain a strangle hold on atomic research. Still as a bloodletting to reduce fever at the Met Lab it was not an entire success, for interest in non-technical topics did not abate; it only shifted to the international problems raised in the report's final chapters. By the opening of 1945 these had been resolved into three questions which took on varying degrees of immediacy in the next six months: Should our allies be told about the bomb so that planning for postwar organization at the April San Francisco conference could be done with realistic appraisal of its impact? If Germany was defeated before the bomb was ready, as now seemed likely, should it then be used on Japan? And what form should international control assume?

People differ in their recollections of just when they became concerned about these various questions, and it was perhaps as much to equalize awareness as to stimulate discussion that a series of three

---

[25] Compton to the author, September 30, 1958.

or four "seminars" was held, principally by and for the younger men but with the sympathetic approval of Joyce Stearns, who had become director of the Met Lab when Allison left for Los Alamos. The leader of this discussion project, as of other scientists' activities in the next two years, was John A. Simpson, a twenty-eight-year-old physicist from Oregon who, like many of the other younger men, had just completed his graduate training when he joined the laboratory in 1943. A talk by Simpson to a selected group of academic personnel, probably on March 20, outlined some rudimentary ideas on the shape of postwar control. He recommended a scientific council, under the auspices of the proposed United Nations Security Council but not controlled by it, whose members would be elected by recognized scientists in their respective countries. The council would supervise an international laboratory on military nucleonics; investigate within all governments in the world advances in the art (or attempts to conceal advances) and report them in an intelligible form to the Security Council and the General Assembly; and act in an advisory capacity to the world organization. Simpson also suggested an international scientific laboratory under United Nations auspices.[26]

According to Simpson's usually reliable recollection, the question of using the bomb against Japan and the possibility of forming a scientists' organization were also discussed at these spring seminars. From them developed a committee on social and political implications which held more meetings during the summer, but a hiatus in organized discussion seems to have occurred after early April, and before it was resumed in July the initiative had been seized by more senior members of the Met Lab staff. Those in positions of responsibility knew that a bomb was forecast by midsummer. Fear of a German atomic bomb had disappeared some months before Germany surrendered on May 8, 1945. Although United States bases were pushing closer to Japan's home islands and fire raids were doing enormous damage to Japanese cities, it was assumed that the war would continue in the Pacific until Japan itself was invaded and that the cost to both sides would be tremendous. Left with what had for many of them been a secondary reason for working on the bomb—bringing the war to a speedier end—an increasing number of scientists at the Met Lab now asked whether it could not equally well serve this purpose if it was demonstrated to the Japanese leaders in some

---

[26] Notes for a meeting, March 20, 1945, in Simpson's files.

uninhabited area. If this did not induce surrender, another bomb could then be used on a Japanese city. They insisted that they raised this question in the context of its bearing on the establishment of a peaceful world, not as an isolated moral or political issue, but in a small circle at least, this aspect of the subject overshadowed all others during the final two months of the war.

The origin of the demonstration idea is obscure. In their memorandum to Stimson of September 30, 1944, Bush and Conant had suggested that the appropriate time to disclose all but the details of bomb manufacture would be immediately after its first demonstration. "This demonstration," they had said, "might be over enemy territory or in our own country, with subsequent notice to Japan that the materials would be used against the Japanese mainland unless surrender was forthcoming."[27] Bush and Conant later changed their minds about the feasibility of a non-military demonstration, though Conant in particular tried to leave the way open for scientists with different views to present them to the Interim Committee.

The economist Alexander Sachs, who had taken the Einstein letter to Roosevelt in 1939, later made public a memorandum which he had read to the President just before the November, 1944, election recommending that

following a successful test, there should be arranged (a) a rehearsal demonstration before a body including internationally recognized scientists from all Allied countries and, in addition, neutral countries, supplemented by representatives of the major (religious) faiths; (b) that a report on the nature and portent of the atomic weapon be prepared by the scientists and other representative figures; (c) that, thereafter, a warning be issued by the United States and its allies in the Project to our major enemies in the war, Germany and Japan, that atomic bombing would be applied to a selected area within a designated time limit for the evacuation of human and animal life; and, finally, (d) in the wake of such realization of the efficacy of atomic bombing, an ultimatum demand for immediate surrender by the enemies be issued, in the certainty that failure to comply would subject their countries and peoples to atomic annihilation.[28]

Sachs claimed that Roosevelt was favorably impressed. One can only speculate about possible connections between Sach's recommendation, the suggestion made by Bush and Conant a month earlier, and

---

[27] Quoted in *The New World*, p. 329.
[28] Quoted by Nat S. Finney, "How FDR Planned to Use the A-Bomb," *Look*, XIV (March 14, 1950), 24.

the talk of a demonstration which became common at the Met Lab, according to some recollections, very early in 1945. No written link is likely to appear, for this kind of thing had to be discussed with the utmost discretion.

As interest at the Met Lab focused on international problems Leo Szilard, whose influence may well have sparked some of the earlier agitation, emerged as a leading figure. Szilard, a Hungarian physicist, had contributed during the 1930's in Germany and England to nuclear theory and had also tried unsuccessfully to launch a foundation to control atomic energy when it became available. By 1939 he was doing research at Columbia University and with his fellow Hungarian, Eugene Wigner, persuaded Einstein to write the famous letter to Roosevelt from which the United States atomic energy project is usually assumed to have sprung.[29]

At Columbia, and after the spring of 1942 at the Met Lab, Szilard's ingenious mind had spawned a steady stream of suggestions. If the Project could have been run on ideas alone, says Wigner, no one but Szilard would have been needed. Szilard's more staid scientific colleagues sometimes had trouble adjusting to his mercurial passage from one solution to another; his army associates were horrified, and to make matters worse Szilard freely indulged in what he once identified as his favorite hobby—baiting brass hats. General Groves, in particular, had been outraged by Szilard's unabashed view that army compartmentation rules, which forbade discussion of lines of research that did not immediately impinge on each other, should be ignored in the interests of completing the bomb. Groves had tried to develop a certain tolerance for the peculiar ways of his strange charges, but this did not stretch to cover what he considered Szilard's tendency to loose talk. Groves felt, as he later told a reporter, that compartmentation was the only way to get the bomb done; otherwise, he said, the scientists would have spent all their time talking.

But those who found Szilard's brand of intellectual ferment at all appealing were themselves infected with it, and a number of his younger colleagues say that he was the one who first led them to think about the political impact of what they were doing. From the beginning Szilard had expressed dissatisfaction with the apparent absence of long-range thinking about atomic energy. Seeing no progress in this direction he decided early in 1945 to try to talk directly to

---

[29] Vannevar Bush told a *Boston Globe* interviewer, as reported in the issue of December 2, 1962, that "the show was going on before that letter was ever written."

Roosevelt and drew up a memorandum of what he wanted to say. Szilard assumed that atomic bombs would be used against Japan and did not specifically urge, as he would do a few weeks later, that this should be avoided, but he analyzed the adverse effect that the very existence of such weapons would have upon the postwar position of the United States—the early expiration of its atomic lead, the special vulnerability of its urban centers to surprise attack, the ineffectiveness under the new conditions of its huge productive capacity, and the temptation to preventive war that stockpiles of bombs would offer. Szilard went on to consider methods of control by which nations producing atomic energy for peaceful purposes might be prevented from turning it to military use. It might be feasible to denature fissionable materials, that is render them unsuitable for bombs, by adding certain isotopes which could not easily be removed. Or it might be necessary to forego the benefits of atomic power; for it was not clear, said Szilard, that the problem of having atomic energy for power but not for bombs could be solved within any control system that nations would accept. Such controls should, however, be carefully considered.[30]

To reach the President with this message Szilard again invoked the prestige of Einstein, who wrote to Roosevelt on March 25, recalling his letter of 1939 on the importance of uranium to national defense but cautiously explaining that secrecy prevented his knowing about Szilard's present work. "However," he continued,

I understand that he now is greatly concerned about the lack of adequate contact between scientists who are doing this work and those members of your Cabinet who are responsible for formulating policy. In the circumstances I consider it my duty to give Dr. Szilard this introduction and I wish to express the hope that you will be able to give his presentation of the case your personal attention.[31]

Without acting on Einstein's letter the President left for Warm Springs on March 29. Szilard had also arranged an interview with Mrs. Roosevelt as a step in reaching the President but had not yet seen her when the President died on April 12.

---

[30] With figures deleted this memorandum was printed in *Bulletin of the Atomic Scientists,* III (December, 1947), 351–53; the editorial note erred in describing it as the first discussion of international implications and control. Unknown to the editors, both Bohr and Bush had previously discussed these questions.

[31] Einstein to Roosevelt, March 25, 1945; printed in Otto Nathan and Heinz Norden, *Einstein on Peace* (New York: Simon & Schuster, 1960), pp. 304–5.

Soon Szilard began devising an approach to Truman. It is not easy to see a President in wartime, and in any case the Szilard legend includes a penchant for mild intrigue. With Albert Cahn, a young Met Lab mathematician who had earned money for graduate school by working for the Pendergast political machine, he traveled to Kansas City and convinced Truman's political associates there that he must see the President. A message was shortly conveyed to Truman that people at the University of Chicago wanted to talk to him about something top-secret. Muttering that he did not like the sound of this, Truman gave instructions that the emissaries from Chicago should see his secretary, Matthew J. Connelly. In the respectable company of Walter Bartky, associate dean of the physical sciences at the University, Szilard called on Connelly at the White House, only to learn that the President wished them to see his personal adviser, James F. Byrnes, then at his home in Spartanburg, South Carolina. Szilard phoned Harold C. Urey at the Mahattan Project's Columbia University Laboratory and Urey joined Szilard and Bartky for the interview at Spartanburg which took place on May 28.[32]

Byrnes, slated for the office of secretary of state, which he would assume on July 3, had been told about the Manhattan Project. Yet at no time, now or later, did he impress scientists by his grasp of the significance of atomic energy. He appeared to view the bomb as a nice thing to have on your hip when you met the Russians and was worried about justifying the expenditure of two billion dollars. The three men who called on him in Spartanburg found that he did not know about the potential use of atomic energy for power, and they spent much of the interview imparting what they conceived to be elementary information. There was little chance to discuss the contents of the March memorandum, which Szilard left with him, or the proposition that Szilard was currently weighing (with little encouragement from his colleagues) that in order to avoid a nuclear arms race it might be a good idea not to use the bomb against Japan and to let the Russians think that our work on it had not succeeded.

Byrnes, for his part, did not think highly of Szilard or of his complaint "that he and some of his associates did not know enough about the policy of the government with regard to the use of the bomb. He felt," said Byrnes,

---

[32] Interviews with Bartky, July 8, 1957; Szilard, June 2, 1957; Urey, July 23, 1958; and Cahn, March 5, 1963.

that scientists, including himself, should discuss the matter with the Cabinet, which I did not feel desirable. His general demeanor and his desire to participate in policy-making made an unfavorable impression on me, but his associates were neither as aggressive nor apparently as dissatisfied.[33]

General Groves was much disturbed by the trip to Spartanburg, of which he learned through the customary watch kept on the movements of leading Project scientists. It was useless to remonstrate with Szilard, but he summoned Bartky to Washington. Bartky, later vice-president of the University of Chicago and more of a trouble shooter than a trouble maker, used the opportunity to impress upon Groves how strong and how widespread was the feeling among Chicago scientists that any decision involving the bomb must be carefully weighed in the light of its international repercussions.

During Szilard's abortive negotiations, proof of Bartky's statement had been accumulating. One item of evidence is a seven-page unsigned memorandum, dated April 21, 1945, which James Franck later identified as the fruit of his intense concern "that plans for the future were being discussed at the United Nations meeting without the statesmen having been informed about the great changes in the world situation brought about by the development of the atomic bomb."[34]

James Franck, a brilliant physicist and a Nobel laureate of 1925 who had been driven from his native Germany by Nazi attacks on the integrity of science, would do honor to any fatherland or to any profession. Gentle and considerate, he was possessed of a strong moral sense and a keen mind that quickly disposed of personal or intellectual pretentiousness. His laboratory in Göttingen, like Bohr's in Copenhagen, had been a training ground for many young physicists and chemists, for Franck's own research overlapped both fields. During the 1920's, when Bohr and Franck were building their laboratories, they had become firm friends, but Bohr was strongly critical of the way in which Franck had first ignored the rise of German militarism and then, after 1914, had joined the German army. The individual, Bohr maintained, must be responsible for what society did.

So when Hitler came to power Franck spoke out against the attacks on individuals and protested the Nazi doctrine that the search for truth must be directed toward exclusively German ends, but when

---

[33] James F. Byrnes, *All in One Lifetime* (New York: Harper & Bros., 1958), p. 284.
[34] Franck to the author, July 22, 1958; conversations with Franck, June 3, 1957, and June 21, 1963.

it became clear that he would soon be unable to speak freely he left his comfortable and honorable post in Göttingen and came to the United States, first to Johns Hopkins, then in 1938 to the University of Chicago.

At the end of 1942 Franck was pursuing work in photosynthesis as a research professor at the University of Chicago when A. H. Compton begged him to take charge of the chemistry section of the Met Lab. He would join the Project, Franck told Compton, on one condition: that if the time came to use an atomic bomb and it had not been developed elsewhere he might present his views about its use to someone at the highest policy-making level. "I did not always agree with Compton," says Franck, "but he was an honest man and a gentleman." In April, 1945, the time had come to redeem the promise.

Accordingly, Franck proceeded to incorporate in a memorandum the ideas currently being discussed at the Met Lab. Asked years later whether these reflected Bohr's influence, Franck said that as far as he was concerned they did so only through Bohr's general views about individual responsibility. After Bohr came to the United States in late 1943 they met as old friends, but they did not talk atomic politics. In framing his April memorandum Franck turned for help to his associate in research, Eugene Rabinowitch, and ideas that Rabinowitch had put into the final chapters of the Jeffries Report were now more clearly defined and tailored to Franck's plea that statesmen recognize the obsolescence of traditional competition between nations.[35]

The basic principles of atomic energy were not secret, explained Franck by way of introduction; hence our advantage was at best temporary. Hereafter cities could be destroyed in one sudden devastating attack. Scientists could no longer remain in the comfortable isolation of their laboratories but had a duty to warn such political leaders as they could reach without breaking their oaths of secrecy that the implications of atomic power were alarming.

One of the warnings Franck felt impelled to give concerned the importance of continuing research. Scientists had the impression that the government was considering atomic energy solely as a weapon. If a bomb failed, nuclear research would stop and the world would lose enormous benefits; if a bomb succeeded and an armaments race

[35] Unsigned memorandum, April 21, 1945 (penciled heading "Washington trip memo,"), in Rabinowitch's files.

followed its use, then continued research and development would be vital to our security.

In the event of a nuclear arms race research would soon produce more devastating weapons. The only solution would be international control, for which, with its four- or five-year lead, the United States could offer a plan. Franck thought that wartime co-operation among the allies in controlling materials gave hope of success; at the same time it might be difficult (as Szilard had recently pointed out) to get both control and atomic power because of the close relation between weapons and power production.

Scientists were told, said Franck, that the secretary of war would shortly appoint a committee on long-range planning; they realized that under any program much of the work would remain under military supervision.

None of the scientists objects to these regulations as long as they only bring about personal inconveniences and restrictions in mutual information which would be useful for the work. These regulations become intolerable if a conflict is brought about between our conscience as citizens and human beings and our loyalty to the oath of secrecy. That is the situation in which we scientists now find ourselves. We read and hear about all the efforts which the best statesmen devote to peace planning in Dumbarton Oaks, San Francisco, etc., and we hear about plans to control industries, etc. in the aggressor states, but we know in our hearts that all these plans are obsolete, because the future war has an entirely different and a thousand times more sinister aspect than the war which is fought now. How is it possible that the statesmen are not informed that the aspect of the world and its future is entirely changed by the knowledge that atomic energy can be tapped, and how is it possible that the men who know these facts are prevented from informing the statesmen about the situation?

One of the grave political decisions that will have to be made, said Franck in conclusion, echoing both Smyth and the Jeffries Report, is how and when to inform the public about the bomb and its implications, since in a democracy effective political steps cannot be taken without enlightened public opinion. Franck had invoked his privilege of plain speaking; for the time being he made no comment on the use of the bomb against Japan.

Against the background of Bohr's and Bush's earlier representations to the government there is nothing original in this memorandum, but the fact that Franck—a trusted senior member of the Manhattan Project staff—did not know that it had been said before was a forceful illustration of his principal point that scientists were cut off from the shaping of policy on which their work and knowledge had a vital bearing. Whether in wartime scientists in general should have been allowed to know more was, and is, a matter of judgment. Bush, besides being a very busy man, was temperamentally something of an autocrat. In consulting a few key scientists whose opinions he respected, he felt that he was adequately tapping those of the scientific community. Many scientists viewed the situation quite differently. The world of the laboratory, though not exactly a classless society, is a place where people are accustomed to speaking out when they have something to say and to having the value of their ideas judged by a general consensus. Science has its own rigorous discipline, but this does not include, as in the military and to some extent the government bureaucracy, unquestioned adherence to decisions handed down from above. And, in addition, scientists like other intellectuals had justified this war as defending the integrity of knowledge and the freedom to express opinions. A man like James Franck did not want to dictate national policy, but he did want to make sure that it was decided on the basis of the fullest possible knowledge.

In further fulfilment of his promise Compton now arranged for Franck to go to Washington with his memorandum and to talk with Secretary of Commerce Henry A. Wallace, with whom Compton was on friendly terms. On or about April 21 the three men had breakfast at the Wardman Park Hotel. (Franck, who had fewer wartime breakfasts at the Wardman Park than the other two is the only one who remembered the occasion thirteen years later.) The discussion was hurried, for Wallace had other engagements, but Franck left a copy of the memo with him. This copy, or another, ended up in the files of the Office of Scientific Research and Development, where Bush was in command. If it crossed Bush's desk at the time, it is likely, given its eminent source and his correspondence with Franck on the same topic the previous summer, that he read it thoughtfully. For after frustrating delays Bush was currently engaged—as were Groves, Bundy, and another Stimson assistant, George L. Harrison—in preparing the Secretary to give President Truman his first full-scale briefing on the atomic bomb.

However, it is unlikely that the memorandum Stimson used when he talked to Truman on April 25 was altered by what Franck had said on the twenty-first, although the Stimson memo contained most of the points in this and other Met Lab statements and showed no less an understanding of the awesome nature of the challenge.

In the light of our present position with reference to this weapon, the question of sharing it with other nations and, if so shared, upon what terms, becomes a primary question of our foreign relations. Also our leadership in the war and in the development of this weapon has placed a certain moral responsibility upon us which we cannot shirk without very serious responsibility for any disaster to civilization which it would further.

On the other hand, if the problem of the proper use of this weapon can be solved, we would have the opportunity to bring the world into a pattern in which the peace of the world and our civilization can be saved.[36]

The Chicago scientists, had they known of it, could no longer have complained of what was being said at the highest level; but they would still have complained that it was being said so late.

4. THE INTERIM COMMITTEE AND THE DECISION

As a final point in his memorandum of April 25, Stimson proposed to the President the appointment of a committee "for recommending action to the executive and legislative branches of our government when secrecy is no longer in full effect." As a consequence there came into existence the Interim Committee of the War Department. A week later Stimson discussed its membership with Truman, in whose name the invitations were issued on May 4. Stimson himself was chairman, with his assistant, George L. Harrison, president of the New York Life Insurance Company, as deputy chairman. The other members were James L. Byrnes, serving as the President's personal representative; Ralph A. Bard, undersecretary of the Navy; William L. Clayton, assistant secretary of state; Vannevar Bush, director of the Office of Scientific Research and Development and president of the Carnegie Institution of Washington; Karl T. Compton, chief of the Office of Field Service in the Office of Scientific Research and Development and president of Massachusetts Institute of Technology; James B. Conant, chairman of the National Research Council and president of Harvard University.[37]

Conant at first demurred at accepting the appointment. He was perhaps more sensitive than Bush to the dissatisfaction of his fellow

---

[36] Henry L. Stimson, "The Decision to Use the Atomic Bomb," *Harper's Magazine*, CXCIV (February, 1947), 99–100.

[37] Stimson, "The Decision to Use the Atomic Bomb," p. 100; *The New World*, p. 345.

scientists and knew it was not confined to chronic dissenters like Szilard. Before consenting to serve, Conant asked permision to show to a few scientists the memorandum that he and Bush had submitted to Stimson the previous September so that their championship of certain views would be known, and he also got Stimson's assurance that there would be opportunity for scientists with strong views on international questions to present them to the Interim Committee.

With the advice of Conant and Bush a panel of four scientists was shortly appointed to assist the Interim Committee: Arthur H. Compton, Enrico Fermi, Ernest O. Lawrence, and J. Robert Oppenheimer. Again Conant recommended that other scientists be allowed to add their word on general policy to that of the technically competent panel members.[38]

Public attention was directed to the Interim Committee early in 1947 when Stimson published an article on the decision to use the bomb against Japan in which he reported the conclusion of a two-day meeting of the committee and its scientific panel on May 31 and June 1, 1945:

> On June 1, after its discussions with the Scientific Panel, the Interim Committee unanimously adopted the following recommendations: (1) The bomb should be used against Japan as soon as possible. (2) It should be used on a dual target—that is, a military installation or war plant surrounded by or adjacent to houses and other buildings most susceptible to damage, and (3) it should be used without prior warning [of the nature of the weapon]. One member of the committee, Mr. Bard, later changed his view and dissented from recommendation (3).

"In reaching these conclusions," commented Stimson, "the Interim Committee carefully considered such alternatives as a detailed advance warning or a demonstration in some uninhabited area. Both of these suggestions were discarded as impractical."[39]

Stimson took pains to point out the comprehensive framework within which the Interim Committee made this important recommendation:

> The discussions of the committee ranged over the whole field of atomic energy, in its political, military, and scientific aspects. That part of its work which particularly concerns us here relates to its recommendations for the use of atomic energy against Japan, but it should be borne in mind that

---

[38] The New World, pp. 345–46, based on Conant to Stimson, May 5, 1945, and Conant to Harrison, May 9, 1945.

[39] Stimson, "The Decision to Use the Atomic Bomb," p. 100.

these recommendations were not made in a vacuum. The committee's work included the drafting of the statements which were published immediately after the first bombs were dropped, the drafting of a bill for the domestic control of atomic energy, and recommendations looking toward the international control of atomic energy.

Stimson's account of this meeting was later supplemented by some not entirely accurate recollections of other participants, but it was fifteen years before scholars were permitted to report the meeting from the Interim Committee log and from notes taken for Manhattan files.[40]

To the May 31 session at the Pentagon, Stimson summoned General George C. Marshall, the chief of staff, General Groves, and Stimson's assistants, Harvey Bundy and Arthur W. Page (who was to prepare releases about the bomb) because he wanted them to hear what the three scientists on the committee and the four panel members had to say about the future of atomic weapons, non-military developments, research, and international competition and controls. The scientists, providing technical background, did most of the talking at the morning session. They discussed the brief duration of a United States monopoly (which A. H. Compton estimated as six years), the possibility of a thermonuclear bomb, the vital importance for United States' security of continued research and development and especially the need to restock the reservoir of basic knowledge on which war research had drawn heavily. Apparently Oppenheimer was not challenged when he said that human welfare was the goal of atomic energy development and that the United States would be in a stronger moral position if it offered free exchange of information, especially on the peaceful uses of atomic energy, before dropping the bomb. There was, however, some discussion about how complete exchange would affect security and the value of inspection as a means of enforcing control. The impossibility of concealing the secrets of nature and the possible contributions to international control of the international fraternity of scientists were also mentioned.

Oppenheimer had a chance to present the arguments in favor of telling Russia about the bomb (which he had often discussed with Bohr), among them that "Russia had always been friendly to science." General Marshall cited recent experience with Russian obstructive-

---

[40] These, with Stimson's diary entries, are the basis for the report of the meeting given in *The New World*, pp. 356–61; I follow closely the wording of its authors to avoid inaccurate paraphrasing.

ness in military matters as a warning not to expect too much, but he suggested that two Soviet observers might be invited to the forthcoming Alamogordo test. Byrnes, however, was strongly opposed to giving the Russians any information, though agreeing the United States should try to improve relations. The sense of the morning session as summarized by A. H. Compton was that the United States should permit as much freedom of research as was consistent with national security and military necessity, it should establish a combination of democratic powers for co-operation in atomic energy, and it should seek an understanding with Russia.

For some years prior to the opening of the documents it was clear that however painstaking may have been the examination by individual committee members of the wisdom of using the bomb it did not take the form of exhaustive exploration at that May 31 to June 1 meeting. Not all of the committee members were, in fact, prepared for such an examination, although it might be argued (and perhaps Stimson had this in mind in making the appointments) that a fresh look at the situation by a few people not influenced by long emotional involvement with the bomb was a useful thing. Just three days earlier Byrnes had shocked his scientist callers at Spartanburg by the superficiality of his information and understanding. And Ralph Bard later told the author that he had learned of the bomb only when he went to the May 31 meeting. On this point Bard's memory erred; he had been present at earlier meetings on May 9, 14, and 18, at the first of which Stimson had explained the basic facts for the benefit of Bard, Byrnes, and Clayton.[41] But his impression that he was not the only one who faced this momentous decision without much preparation, if not literally correct, was not far off the mark.

Compton later wrote that "throughout the morning's discussions it seemed to be a foregone conclusion that the bomb would be used. It was regarding only the details of strategy and tactics that differing views were expressed."[42] The use of the bomb was not, in fact, on the agenda. It was at lunch, with no record kept of the conversation, that a demonstration prior to use in combat was considered. The panel members were particularly involved, but their recollections—merged perhaps with those of a more intensive discussion among themselves three weeks later—do not agree.

---

[41] The New World, pp. 353–54.
[42] Compton, Atomic Quest, p. 238.

Oppenheimer was certain in later years that no discussion of use had taken place at this meeting, although he was quoted as saying he could think of no demonstration spectacular enough to be effective.[43] Fermi was not asked about the meeting before he died in 1954. Ernest Lawrence left the most nearly contemporary record. Replying on August 17 to an inquiry from a fellow physicist, K. K. Darrow, Lawrence wrote that Byrnes had asked him at lunch about a demonstration and that "the proposition was the subject of general discussion" for perhaps ten minutes.[44]

Writing some ten years later, A. H. Compton recounted how, seated next to Stimson, he had raised the question with the Secretary and gave the impression of a fairly exhaustive discussion of alternatives and their dismissal.[45] Compton himself was so deeply disturbed by the decision and involved in so many discussions of it in Chicago that he may well have forgotten the limits of this particular one, but it was quite in character that he should have brought up the subject. None of the statements emanating from Chicago, not even Franck's latest memorandum of April 21, had mentioned a demonstration because the scientists wished to avoid the charge of dictating political decisions, but in a forty-two-page memorandum on Met Lab problems which Compton had submitted to the Interim Committee three days before this meeting, he had described the question of how the bomb was to be used as "first in point of urgency." "This whole question," wrote Compton diplomatically, "may well have received the broad study it demands. I merely mention it as one of the urgent problems that have bothered our men because of its many ramifications and humanitarian implications."[46]

Stimson may not himself have seen every word of Compton's memorandum, but within the past few days he had read and noted in his diary a long letter on the use of the bomb which he thought important enough to call to the attention of the President, to whom it was addressed, and General Marshall. The writer of the letter was Oswald C. Brewster, an engineer employed by the Kellex Corporation in New York City, whose outstanding mechanical ingenuity had put him, back in 1942, in a small team with Manson Benedict that was

---

[43] Interview with Oppenheimer, November 11, 1957.
[44] Cited in *The New World*, p. 358 and n. 19.
[45] Compton, *Atomic Quest*, p. 238.
[46] Quoted in Fletcher Knebel and Charles W. Bailey, "The Fight Over the A-Bomb," *Look*, XXVII (August 13, 1963), 21.

doing early work on the gaseous diffusion process of uranium isotope separation. Known to his friends as "Owl," Brewster was a warm-hearted, explosive individual, totally unlike the popular concept of the imperturbable engineer. He seemed to be more aware of the end product of his work than his fellow employees at Kellex who had been told in effect that this was not their concern. Brewster was a person of firm convictions, strongly anti-Nazi and very apprehensive about possible German technical achievements. He worked at his job with great enthusiasm, but after Germany was defeated his friends observed that he was greatly upset about something. Benedict, for one, knew that Brewster was writing a letter, though he did not see it. Brewster showed it to his superiors at Kellex who did not try to dissuade him from sending it but pointed out that there were security angles to communicating with the President in wartime. Sure enough, a few days later Brewster was indignantly complaining that he was being shadowed and his phone was being tapped.

Brewster's three-thousand-word letter was dated May 24, 1945. He regarded the atomic bomb as too evil a thing to be entrusted either to men or to governments. He urged that it not be used in Japan without a demonstration and that development should be brought to a stop. Brewster had not been swept along by any tide of collective anxiety. According to Benedict, people at Kellex were not talking about the use of the bomb or its implications and Brewster did not have contacts with the Met Lab or Clinton. He spoke only for himself, and perhaps it was the strong note of personal passion that aroused Stimson's interest.[47]

What Brewster had to say, however, did not weigh as heavily with the Secretary as the points that were made at the Interim Committee luncheon table. The arguments later cited as deciding the demonstration issue on this occasion were that if the Japanese were notified in advance they would suspect a trick and interfere with the bomb's delivery; that if a demonstration failed (for the bomb had not yet been tested) the chance to administer a paralyzing shock to Japan's leaders would be lost; and that American prisoners might be brought to the demonstration site. Hitler's boasting of decisive weapons had

---

[47] Quotations from Brewster's letter in *The New World*, p. 355, and in Knebel and Bailey, "The Fight Over the A-Bomb," pp. 20–21, are accompanied by slightly different interpretations of what Brewster recommended. Information about Brewster and the background of the letter comes from an interview with Benedict, September 18, 1963.

strained credulity; and the fanaticism of Japan's militarists was be-lieved to be such that no mere sight of scorched earth would move them.[48]

In the afternoon of May 31 the Interim Committee considered the kind of target on which a bomb would be most effective (a list of cities was being drawn up by a special target committee), and the scientists offered opinions about the bomb's probable effects. The following day the committee heard testimony from industrialists.

During these two days the Committee was exposed to many of the ideas that the worried scientists in Chicago, as well as Bush and Conant in Washington and the peripatetic Bohr, had wanted for months to lay before the policy-makers, but the question of using the bomb did not come up again except toward the end of the final session when the recommendations regarding its use were confirmed. Stimson reported this recommendation to the President on June 6.[49]

Considering this Interim Committee action as it related to Stim-son's career, his biographer Elting E. Morison concluded that the Committee's task was not so much to weigh the pros and cons of using the bomb as to give "ordered form, some corporate structure" to "attitudes already developed by work on the common task. . . . The Interim Committee, insofar as the special matter of using the bomb was concerned, was, in a sense, a symbolic act to demonstrate with what care this enormous conclusion had been considered. That in its actual proceedings, as so far reported, there should be some real ambiguity is less surprising than the fact that in its symbolism it should have so closely verified, all things considered, the actual proc-ess of decision."[50]

---

[48] Compton, *Atomic Quest*, pp. 238–39; James F. Byrnes, *All in One Lifetime*, p. 285. I do not attempt to discuss all aspects of the decision to use the bomb as a weapon against Japan but rather wish to show how scientists expressed themselves on the question at various times. An excellent account with a perceptive evaluation is con-tained in Herbert Feis, *Japan Subdued* (Princeton, N.J.: Princeton University Press, 1961). More political and technical details are to be found in *The New World*, esp. chap. xi. Robert J. C. Butow's *Japan's Decision to Surrender* (Stanford, Calif.: Stanford University Press, 1954) tells the less familiar and most illuminating Japanese side of the story. A study by Gar Alperovitz of the relation of the atomic bomb to United States policy toward Russia during President Truman's first six months in office will be published by Simon & Schuster in 1965.

[49] This is the date given in Stimson's diary; Truman's memoirs say June 1 (see Harry S Truman, *Year of Decisions* [Garden City, N.Y.: Doubleday & Co., 1955], p. 419).

[50] Elting E. Morison, *Turmoil and Tradition* (Boston: Houghton Mifflin Co., 1960), pp. 629–30.

5. THE FRANCK REPORT

Full as the Interim Committee agenda was at that May 31 to June 1 meeting Compton insisted that consideration be given to the woes and plaints of the Met Lab. It is doubtful that committee members had read the forty-two pages that he had submitted for their perusal, but before adjournment on the first day he obtained their recommendation that research at the Met Lab should continue at the present level until the war ended.[51]

The scientific panel was not expected to attend the second day's meeting, but they were told that their opinions would be welcome at any time. They were asked to prepare a statement on postwar control. (They were not asked at this time, as later stated by Compton, to review the feasibility of a demonstration.)

Knowing how insistently he would be questioned when he returned to Chicago, Compton asked what panel members might tell their associates about the Interim Committee and its proceedings. According to the authors of *The New World*,

his question led to the understanding that they could say that the Secretary of War had appointed the committee to consider control, organization, legislation, and publicity. While they could indicate that Stimson was chairman, they should not identify the other members. They could explain that they had met with the committee and enjoyed complete freedom to present their views on any phase of the subject. They should make it clear that the Government was taking a most active interest.[52]

The panel had met with the Interim Committee on Thursday, and on Friday had pursued its directive to explore postwar controls. Compton was in Chicago, meeting with Met Lab leaders, on Saturday afternoon. He told them what he could about the Washington discussions and that the panel would again be considering control measures at Los Alamos the middle of the month; he would convey to the panel proposals that were ready when he left Chicago on June 14.

Committees were appointed immediately to co-ordinate ideas on several topics, and Compton reported this step the same day to Bush and Conant, with a list of five committee chairmen.[53] The agenda of another Met Lab meeting on June 4 included the reshuffling of com-

---

[51] Compton does not mention this May 28 memo in *Atomic Quest*; see *The New World*, p. 365, and Knebel and Bailey, "The Fight Over the A-Bomb," p. 21.

[52] *The New World*, p. 359.

[53] *The New World*, p. 366 and n. 33.

mittees; a sixth was added, and the membership of the various groups listed as follows:

(1) *Research Program*, Walter Zinn, chairman; Farrington Daniels, Eugene Wigner, Glenn Seaborg, Leon Jacobson, Kenneth Cole, John Howe.

(2) *Social and Political Implications*, James Franck, chairman; Leo Szilard, Donald Hughes, Seaborg, Joyce Stearns, J. J. Nickson, E. Rabinowitch.

(3) *Education*, R. S. Mulliken, chairman; Hughes, J. Warner, Arthur Dempster, Thorfin R. Hogness, Cole, Rabinowitch.

(4) *Production*, Szilard, chairman; Walter Bartky, Howe, Wigner, Jacobson, Daniels.

(5) *Controls*, Dempster, chairman; Hogness, Bartky, Stearns, Jacobson.

(6) *Organization*, Bartky, chairman; Hogness, Stearns, Zinn.[54]

The material collected by these Met Lab committees (their task greatly facilitated by the work done earlier for the Jeffries Committee) was incorporated by Norman Hilberry into a single report, dated July 17, 1945. Forwarded to the Interim Committee, it was used by the members of the War Department staff who were engaged during the summer in drafting the domestic atomic energy legislation which later emerged as the May-Johnson bill.[55]

The report from Franck's committee on social and political implications was set apart from the others by the immediacy of its contents and became in its way a famous document. There had been periods of tension before at the Met Lab, Hilberry later recalled; what happened now was the exclamation point at the end of the sentence. Being the man he was, Compton in all likelihood adhered to the letter of what he was authorized to say about the Interim Committee, and this did not include its decision about dropping the bomb. But he also had that prior commitment to James Franck that he might express a dissenting opinion if the bomb were about to be used, and Compton knew that Franck and others now wanted to add something to the April 21 memorandum. Franck's appointment as chairman of the social and political implications group (made, he says, because of Compton's earlier promise) was enough of a signal, had one been needed, that the time for influencing the decision about the bomb was getting short. Franck thinks he chose the members of the committee himself.

With knowledge of the June 2 meeting and committee appoint-

---

[54] Rough notes of the June 4 meeting are in Rabinowitch's files.
[55] *The New World*, p. 409 and n. 2.

ments, the once conflicting scraps of information regarding the origin of the Franck committee fit into place. Those committee members who like Donald Hughes placed discussion of the international implications of dropping the bomb earlier than June were certainly correct; as were Szilard, who later claimed that there had been no Franck committee when he went to Spartanburg on May 28, and Rabinowitch, who remembered the committee as one of several appointed for the purpose of collecting information for the Interim Committee. Hughes seems to have accurately reconstructed the development of thinking in Franck's circle when he wrote:

Actually, during the first meetings we were not so much interested in the possible use of the bomb in war but [in] the question of whether atomic energy would be developed after the war. We felt that if the war ended before the bomb was used there would be little attention paid to atomic energy and a post war economy drive might stop the development. It was only after the first few meetings that the use of the bomb became an important issue. However, I feel that we did talk about demonstrations on non-military targets earlier than June of '45. It seems to me that we discussed this possibility for several weeks at least and at a period about two months before the actual use of the bomb.[56]

Franck also has described the character and tempo of the thinking that came to be associated with his name:

...The factual information was available to all of us and our opinions too had been discussed back and forth between many of us and were by no means a sudden inspiration which could be dated and be ascribed to one person.[57]

On Monday, June 4, Franck committee members began to organize what they had previously talked about unofficially. Nickson, acting as secretary, made three pages of notes. Another three-page typed memorandum entitled "Conditions Under Which International Control Is Most Probable," a set of handwritten undated notes, and a two-page "Outline for Social and Political Considerations" in Rabinowitch's files also appear to pertain to the June 4 meeting, or to a second meeting on June 5.

The discussion on June 4 centered on the problem of international control: why it was essential, how it might be achieved, and

---

[56] Interviews with Szilard, June 2, 1957, Rabinowitch, September, 1958, and Nickson, April 22, 1959; Hughes to the author, October 1, 1957; Franck to the author, August 13, 1958.

[57] Franck to the author, August 13, 1958.

how it might be implemented—by control of raw materials, by inspection, by the pooling of fissionable materials, or by some combination of these methods. It was in connection with the second point, how international control might be achieved, that alternatives to the use of the bomb were discussed. "It is our opinion," states one of the summaries of the June 4 meeting, "that the manner in which this new weapon is introduced to the world will determine in large part the future course of events." The proposals that were later incorporated into the Franck Report were here freely discussed. Franck, Stearns, and Szilard had alternatives to suggest: refraining from use but building a stockpile for the future, announcing that we had the bomb but would not use it, or demonstrating the destructive effect of the bomb on an uninhabited island before our Allies and the Japanese, with the United Nations deciding about its use if Japan did not immediately surrender.

The final report rested its argument against dropping the bomb on a target in Japan solely on the ground that announcing its existence to the world in this way would make agreement about international control virtually impossible. The discussion on June 4 placed the emphasis upon the same point. With a nice economy, if not elegance, of expression the author of the handwritten notes concluded, "clear that if no agreement, are sunk," a conviction that many of his colleagues were to embroider and repeat over and over again during the next few years. Someone questioned whether the atomic bomb would materially shorten a war whose end was already recognized as certain, but this doubt was not repeated in the final report. All members agreed that international control was necessary but had different ideas about what should be controlled.

These rough notes were the raw materials out of which Rabinowitch, at Franck's request, began to write the report following the June 4 meeting. His first draft follows closely the minutes and summaries of that discussion. This draft, with the addition of a three-page summary, was submitted to members of the committee for comment. Four brief sets of suggestions were handed in, one unidentified, the others from Hughes, Seaborg, and Mulliken, who, though not a member of the committee, shared their interest in these questions. Other comments may have been made orally. None of the written ones asked for major changes. Some suggestions were accepted; some were not.

An uncut version of the Franck Report is printed for the first time in Appendix B. Much that it said about the almost limitless possibilities for destruction and the ineffectualness of monopoly or stock-piling of bombs in providing security had been said before, but because it was the first of the wartime statements by scientists to be published it acquired a reputation for originality which its authors never claimed. On the contrary, they insisted that it was the fruit of much long and painful thought by many people. They did offer tentative estimates of the effect of atomic bombs on the United States in terms of square miles and casualties; they went a little further in suggesting how a control organization might operate. But their chief addition, if not to earlier thinking, at least to earlier statements, lay in the following passage:

We believe that these considerations make the use of nuclear bombs for an early unannounced attack against Japan inadvisable. If the United States were to be the first to release this new means of indiscriminate destruction upon mankind, she would sacrifice public support throughout the world, precipitate the race for armaments, and prejudice the possibility of reaching an international agreement on the future control of such weapons.

Much more favorable conditions for the eventual achievement of such an agreement could be created if nuclear bombs were first revealed to the world by a demonstration in an appropriately selected uninhabited area.

The accuracy with which the framers of the Franck Report forecast the course of the postwar armaments race has been often and truly remarked. This is not to say that scientists are possessed of universal political wisdom, nor does it prove that the course the Franck committee advocated would not have produced its own train of equally difficult problems. Franck and his colleagues tried to evaluate these and concluded that the cause of peace would in the long run best be served by a demonstration of the bomb before dropping it as a last resort upon Japan.

Compton later raised a mild storm by stating that there was sharp division within the committee about use of the bomb and that only Franck and certain members had signed the report. The meeting notes give no hint of such difference, and Franck is certain that the report was signed either by all members or by him on behalf of the committee. Rabinowitch and Seaborg say that each individual signed.[58]

---

[58] *Atomic Quest*, p. 235. The copy in Hogness' files which was circulated for comment at the time has typed names of all the committee at the end. The Atomic Energy Commission historians did not find the original signed copy but believe that there was one (R. G. Hewlett to the author, July 2, 1963). Compton later decided he might have confused the period of the Franck Report with an early discussion (Compton to the author, September 30, 1958).

All this drafting, consulting, and revising was compressed into a few days. On Monday, June 11, the report was ready, and Franck himself left by train for Washington with it. There, on June 12, Franck joined Compton and Hilberry. Compton tried to arrange for Franck to see Stimson, but the Secretary was out of the city, and they had to be content with leaving the report in the office of Stimson's assistant, George L. Harrison. Compton later wrote:

At Franck's request, I accordingly transmitted the memorandum to Mr. Stimson with a covering note. In this note it was necessary for me to point out that the report, while it called attention to difficulties that might result from the use of the bomb, did not mention the probable net saving of many lives, nor that if the bomb were not used in the present war the world would have no adequate warning as to what was to be expected if war should break out again.[59]

Before the next panel meeting on June 15 Compton received Harrison's assurance that Stimson would see the report. But using the still untested atomic bomb against Japan was not, after all, the only route to an early peace being explored in the early summer of 1945, and that the busy Secretary of War ever had time to give the Franck Report his careful personal attention is a matter of some doubt. He later referred to it as among the suggestions forwarded to him by the scientists on the panel.

Back in Chicago, at the insistence of Szilard, a move was started to collect signatures in support of the Franck committee's recommendations and to solicit comments. The project did not get beyond the first few signatures because the report was declared classified and could not be circulated even in the laboratory. Nevertheless, its general tenor was no secret. Hilberry, who did not associate himself in any way with its recommendations, recalls numerous expressions of dissent when he and Franck returned from Washington, with feeling running high. Rabinowitch was frank to admit that the report could not claim unanimous backing.[60]

Of surviving comments two approved the report but suggested greater emphasis upon world-wide pooling of atomic explosives and placing them at the disposal of an international organization. Two dissented on the question of prior demonstration: Robert S. Stone,

---

[59] *Atomic Quest*, p. 236; interviews with Franck and Hilberry.
[60] Interview with Hilberry, June 5, 1957; editorial in *Bulletin of the Atomic Scientists*, I (May 1, 1946), 1.

director of the Met Lab health division, and Arthur J. Dempster, a senior physics consultant, neither of whom was to be active in the scientists' movement although Stone later became a sponsor of the Federation of American Scientists and Dempster spoke out sharply on occasion against restrictions on communication in science.

Stone agreed with the major portion of the report but did not concur in its appeal for a non-military demonstration.

The fact that we have developed this weapon without the knowledge of our allies other than the British convinces me that there will be a certain element of mistrust amongst the other allies no matter how we introduce it. Moreover it is inconceivable to me that the French and Russians are not already well aware of the possibilities even though they may not be as far along in the practical development as we are. Under these circumstances I feel that we would be losing nothing by using the weapon in our war against the Japanese. Any respect which the Russians have for us will not be increased if they later find that we had a valuable weapon which we did not use. In other words, I feel that if the weapon is sufficiently developed to be used effectively it should be used in our present war.

Stone thought it a good idea to announce to the United Nations that we had such a weapon and intended to use it against the Japanese, but, he concluded,

I feel quite strongly that we will be in a better position to secure international agreement on its suppression after its effectiveness has been demonstrated.

Dempster tied his comment to the parallel study of controls being made at the Met Lab under his chairmanship, which had reached conclusions differing from those of the Franck Report on the following points:

1. An international agreement controlling future activity should not be presented as an urgent immediate objective. It would be difficult to arrange at the present time because of French and British political rivalry, and the fact that the British have already made considerable progress in postwar developments. Russia will likely be suspicious for some time, as it was not included in the exchange of information. These powers may well try to force a disclosure of our developments through the Military staff Committee of the new Security Council of the International Organization.

2. A well publicized use against a military objective, such as the base at Truk, would be desirable. It would serve as a basis for an educational campaign designed to bring home to our people the new adjustments needed, and the danger of relapsing into an unjustified idea of security.

3. Any international agreement ultimately reached will likely be kept effective primarily by the general fear of prompt retaliation. This is the most effective control of new weapons.

It is significant that Dempster and his committee, early exponents of the nuclear deterrent and representing cautious opinion at the Met Lab, still did not exclude a future control agreement and that like the framers of the Franck Report they regarded the lifting of security and an educational campaign as essential to its achievement.[61]

6. The Panel Review, the Szilard Petition, and the Compton Poll

On Friday and Saturday, June 15 and 16, Compton from Chicago and E. O. Lawrence from Berkeley joined Fermi and Oppenheimer at Los Alamos for the panel meeting to complete their report for the Interim Committee on control measures.[62] Their recommendations on this subject were twofold: a billion-dollar-a-year government-sponsored research program, covering basic atomic science as well as military and peaceful uses; and authorization to the Manhattan District to carry on postwar research until a long-range program was adopted.

On the second day of the panel meeting Harrison, the Interim Committee's deputy chairman, reached Compton by phone. He asked that the panel consider the possibility of a demonstration of the bomb so that its views could be available to the Interim Committee before it considered the Franck Report.[63]

The harsh dilemma faced by the four panel members that week end remained vividly in Compton's mind more than ten years later:

We thought of the fighting men who were set for an invasion which would be so very costly in both American and Japanese lives. We were determined to find, if we could, some effective way of demonstrating the

---

[61] Comments attached to a copy of Franck Report in Hogness' files.

[62] With the aid of the Interim Committee log the dates of this panel meeting are now established by the authors of *The New World*, p. 367, as June 15 and 16 not June 9 and 10, as I erroneously assumed on the basis of Compton's description of it as on a weekend ten days after the Interim Committee meeting (see my article "Behind the Decision to Use the Atomic Bomb," *Bulletin of the Atomic Scientists*, XIV [October, 1958], 298).

[63] The Interim Committee log thus confirms Oppenheimer's recollection that this question was not on the original panel agenda but that a request to consider it was conveyed verbally, probably by Compton (interview with Oppenheimer, November 11, 1957). Compton (*Atomic Quest*, p. 239) had remembered the request as coming at the end of the meeting on June 1.

power of an atomic bomb without loss of life that would impress Japan's warlords. If only this could be done!

Ernest Lawrence was the last one of our group to give up hope for finding such a solution. The difficulties of making a purely technical demonstration that would carry its impact effectively into Japan's controlling councils were indeed great. We had to count on every possible effort to distort even obvious facts. Experience with the determination of Japan's fighting men made it evident that the war would not be stopped unless these men themselves were convinced of its futility....[64]

Others also remember Lawrence's obvious distress that week end though they did not know the cause. Fermi, whatever his emotional reaction to the decision, would have found it a challenge to devise alternatives. One thing that worried the panel members as they made their painful decision was the possibility that despite all seemingly foolproof calculations and trials of components the as yet untested device might "fizzle"—that is, explode feebly as a result of a stray neutron initiating the reaction prematurely—or that through some mechanical failure it might prove a dud. That this would be highly embarrassing was not the point. What mattered was that it would vitiate the shock effect on which British and American leaders counted to undermine Japanese will to resist. Nor could the scientists say "Wait a month for Alamogordo," for that test would involve component parts, not an assembled bomb. Oppenheimer later pointed out that the negligible signs of destruction on the desert after the test a month later confirmed the panel's opinion that a demonstration on wasteland would not have impressed the Japanese, but he also wondered, as he considered the matter in later years, if some demonstration capitalizing on the one phenomenon that the scientists underestimated—the psychological effect of the tremendous light—might not have been devised. But by the time of Trinity (the code name for the Alamogordo test) the whole machinery for using the bomb had been set in motion.[65]

The panel reported to Stimson as follows:

You have asked us to comment on the initial use of the new weapon. This use, in our opinion, should be such as to promote a satisfactory adjustment of our international relations. At the same time, we recognize our obligations to our nation to use the weapons to help save American lives in the Japanese War.

[64] Compton, Atomic Quest, pp. 239–40.
[65] USAEC, In the Matter of J. Robert Oppenheimer, p. 34; interview with Oppenheimer, November 11, 1957.

To accomplish these ends we recommend that before the weapons are used not only Britain, but also Russia, France and China be advised that we would welcome suggestions as to how we can cooperate in making this development contribute to improved international relations.

The opinions of our scientific colleagues on the initial use of these weapons are not unanimous; they range from the proposal of a purely technical demonstration to that of the military application best designed to induce surrender. Those who advocate a purely technical demonstration would wish to outlaw the use of atomic weapons, and have feared that if we use the weapons now our position in future negotiations will be prejudiced. Others emphasize the opportunity of saving American lives by immediate military use, and believe that such use will improve the international prospects, in that they are more concerned with the prevention of war than with the elimination of this special weapon. We find ourselves closer to these latter views; we can propose no technical demonstration likely to bring an end to the war; we can see no acceptable alternative to direct military use.

With regard to these general aspects of the use of atomic energy, it is clear that we, as scientific men, have no proprietary rights. It is true that we are among the few citizens who have had occasion to give thoughtful consideration to these problems during the past few years. We have, however, no claim to special competence in solving the political, social, and military problems which are presented by the advent of atomic power.[66]

Doubts once raised by the author on chronological grounds that the panel could have seen the Franck Report before reaching this conclusion are now proved unfounded by more accurate dating of the meeting, but doubts that they actually did see it or that careful examination of its argument entered into their report still remain. Oppenheimer has stated that, to the best of his recollection, although he may have known of the Franck Report he did not see it until it was printed after the war. Compton (in whose account in *Atomic Quest* the panel is said to have considered not only the Franck Report but two other expressions of opinion not yet formulated) later agreed that quite likely Oppenheimer was right about the report itself but that he, Compton, had tried to summarize it as accurately as possible. No doubt this appealed to everyone as entirely satisfactory. In the light of what has transpired the Franck Report strikes many people as a singularly moving and prescient statement; in the busy days of June, 1945, it was one of an endless succession of memoranda to be read if time permitted.

---

[66] Quoted in Feis, *Japan Subdued*, pp. 43–44; Stimson, "The Decision to Use the Atomic Bomb," p. 101.

The phraseology employed by the panel adds to doubts that they were working from the Franck Report itself—or at any rate from a meticulous reading of it. The third paragraph of the panel statement contrasts its viewpoint with that of advocates of a purely technical demonstration who wanted to outlaw atomic weapons. But the Franck Report did not talk about outlawing atomic weapons; it talked about controlling them, and by much the same means that Bush and Conant had been advocating and that Oppenheimer himself would do so much to fashion into a control scheme in the months ahead. The Franck committee and the panel did not disagree about using the bomb to administer a shock that would lead the Japanese war-lords to sue for peace. But the Franck committee hoped this could be done by a non-military demonstration and without loss of life; the panel did not believe that it could. Nor did the two groups dis-agree in hoping that knowledge of the unprecedented power of the bomb might shock the people of the world and their rulers into accepting some restrictions as the price of control. But again, they differed about whether a non-military demonstration could provide this shock.[67] What divided the seven scientists advising the War De-partment—three on the Interim Committee and the four panel members—from the Franck committee far more than any difference in the realm of ideas was their degree of closeness to the nerve center of decision. Those who bore responsibility tended to deal first with the most palpable peril—the continuance of the war; those without this burden could take the longer view that the real impact of the bomb and its immanent peril lay in the future.

Some bitterness against "administration scientists" (although it was leavened by personal affection and professional respect) might have been avoided if the panel's status had been more clearly defined. Stimson later described it as a channel through which suggestions were forwarded to him and to the President, showing that he thought of it as representative as well as advisory. Compton presented it in this light to the Chicago scientists. Oppenheimer, on the other hand, believes that the panel thought of itself as advising the Interim Com-mittee, and in practice this was the way it functioned. Only Comp-ton felt responsible for getting views other than his own to head-

---

[67] For a different interpretation of the panel report as representing cleavage between those who wanted to outlaw the bomb and those who wanted to outlaw war, see Robert Gilpin, *American Scientists and Nuclear Weapons Policy* (Princeton, N.J.: Prince-ton University Press, 1962), pp. 48-49.

quarters and tried honestly and tirelessly to do so, but—statements to the Met Lab people and his later reminiscences to the contrary— he did not ordinarily use the panel but dispatched opinions directly to Stimson's office or through Manhattan District officers.

Two high level, but seemingly perfunctory, reviews of the demonstration issue followed receipt of the reports of the Franck committee and the panel. A White House strategy meeting on June 18 concluded that plans for invasion and atomic bombing should proceed. An Interim Committee meeting on June 21 also confirmed the earlier recommendation for using the bomb. Panel members were not present, but in presenting the panel report of June 16 Harrison said that an urgent appeal from Chicago scientists for a technical demonstration had led him to request the panel review on this point.[68]

Those who have previously thought that the Franck Report had no impact whatsoever upon Interim Committee thinking will note the appositeness of this meeting to the withdrawal by Ralph Bard six days later of his concurrence in the third point of the June 1 recommendation of the Committee that the bomb be used without warning. On July 27 he wrote to Stimson urging that two or three days warning be given to the Japanese. He wished the United States to maintain its position as a great humanitarian nation; he believed the Japanese were searching for an opportunity to surrender on reasonable terms and that an excuse might be provided by a warning that included some information about the nature of atomic power. No, one, said Bard, could give positive assurance that this would succeed, but the stakes were enormous, and it was worth trying.[69]

Bard was influenced in part by the navy view that the fleet had pretty well won the Pacific war, making full-scale invasion unnecessary, but he also attributes his change of mind to the knowledge that many scientists wanted a prior demonstration. Bard resigned as undersecretary of the navy on July 1, and to make his dissent from the Interim Committee recommendation as emphatic as possible he obtained an interview with President Truman, who was about to leave for the Potsdam Conference, and repeated the views he had expressed

[68] Morison, *Turmoil and Tradition*, p. 631; *The New World*, pp. 363–69. For an account of the June 18 meeting and the cool reception accorded the idea of a "political" solution to the Japanese conflict, see John J. McCloy, *The Challenge to American Foreign Policy* (Cambridge, Mass.: Harvard University Press, 1953), pp. 40–44.
[69] Bard to Stimson, June 27, 1945 (copy from Bard's files); interview with Bard, June 10, 1957.

to Stimson. Truman assured him that questions of invasion and of warning the Japanese had received the most careful attention.

The decisions of the June 21 Interim Committee meeting were relevant also to that other campaign that certain scientists, notably Bohr, Bush, Conant, and Oppenheimer, had been waging, to persuade the administration to warn Russia of the bomb before it was dropped. On June 21 Bush and Conant pressed for favorable consideration of the panel's recommendation that Russia, China, and France not only be notified but be asked for advice about future co-operation. "After a lengthy discussion," reports *The New World,*

the committee concluded unanimously that considerable advantage lay in having the President advise the Russians at the coming Big Three meeting that the United States was working on the bomb and expected to use it against Japan. The President might say further that he hoped for future discussions to insure that the weapon become an aid to peace. Should the Russians press for more details, the President could say he was not yet ready to furnish them.[70]

Oppenheimer vividly remembers that after he and Bush had shared the tremendous experience of the Trinity test four weeks later Bush remarked as he left that Oppenheimer would be glad to know that the panel's recommendations would be implemented. Oppenheimer assumed this meant talks with Russia and was indeed relieved.[71] But if what the Interim Committee advised the President to say fell short of the communication envisaged by the panel, what actually occurred at Potsdam was a sheer travesty of it. "On July 24," relates Truman, "I casually mentioned to Stalin that we had a new weapon of unusual destructive force. The Russian premier showed no special interest. All he said was that he was glad to hear it and hoped we would make 'good use of it against the Japanese.' "[72]

The Franck committee had concentrated on political issues in begging for careful review of any decision on military use. "We were all deeply moved by moral considerations," says Rabinowitch, "but we did not think that in the necessarily a-moral climate in which wartime decisions have to be made these would be effective." Szilard felt that the moral argument ought to be forcefully stated and at the

[70] *The New World,* p. 369.
[71] Interview with Oppenheimer, November 11, 1957.
[72] Truman, *Year of Decisions,* p. 416.

highest level. He therefore drew up a petition to the President of the
United States urging careful consideration in the light of moral responsibilities. As with any similar Szilard production this petition went
through several versions, submitted to colleagues for suggestions. In its
first form the petition, according to Compton, found almost no support; according to Szilard it got fifty-five signatures.[73] A final version
was dated July 17, 1945. After several paragraphs of explanation, it respectfully petitioned the President:

> First, that you exercize your power as Commander-in-Chief to rule that
> the United States shall not resort to the use of atomic bombs in this war
> unless the terms which will be imposed upon Japan have been made public
> in detail and Japan, knowing these terms, has refused to surrender; second,
> that in such an event the question whether or not to use atomic bombs
> be decided by you in the light of the considerations presented in this peti-
> tion as well as all the other moral responsibilities which are involved.[74]

The petition received sixty-nine signatures. The three names, in
addition to Szilard's, mentioned by those who have seen the original
document demonstrate the wide appeal that the possibility of avoiding the use of the bomb had among scientists at this time. Ralph
Lapp has become a persistent campaigner against nuclear testing;
Eugene Wigner has in the main supported an expansion of nuclear
strength; while Walter Bartky, after chaperoning the expedition to
Spartanburg, remained entirely aloof from political issues.[75]

Franck and Rabinowitch recollect that they did not sign the Szilard
petition because they felt that the effectiveness of the Franck Report,
addressed to the Interim Committee, might be weakened by going
over its head to the President. A second petition, signed by eighteen
Met Lab scientists, read as follows:

> ...We respectfully petition that the use of atomic bombs, particularly
> against cities, be sanctioned by you as Chief Executive only under the
> following conditions:
>   1. Opportunity has been given to the Japanese to surrender on terms
> assuring them the possibility of peaceful development in their homeland.
>   2. Convincing warnings have been given that refusal to surrender will
> be followed by the use of a new weapon.

[73] Compton, *Atomic Quest*, p. 242; interview with Szilard, June 2, 1957; Knebel
and Bailey, "The Fight Over the A-Bomb," p. 22, give the date of the first petition as
July 3.
    [74] "A Petition to the President of the United States," July 17, 1945, copy in author's
files; printed in Morton Grodzins and Eugene Rabinowitch (eds.), *The Atomic Age*
(New York: Basic Books, Inc., 1963), pp. 28–29.
    [75] *The New World* (p. 399) and Knebel and Bailey, "The Fight Over the A-Bomb"
(p. 22), give the total as seventy.

3. Responsibility for the use of atomic bombs is shared with our allies.[76]

Szilard tried to circulate his petition at the Clinton Laboratories in Oak Ridge and at Los Alamos. The Oak Ridge story rests on fragmentary recollections. What must have been the early form of Szilard's document, categorically opposing the bomb's use on moral grounds, was discussed at a physics division meeting. Only two people signed it, at least one of whom later made formal retraction. But the question of use evoked a great deal of interest, and an alternative petition was drawn up asking that before the bomb was used a clear statement of intent be made to the Japanese government. Chemists as well as physicists joined in support. The petition had eighty-eight signatures, with many others ready to sign when circulation was stopped by military authorities on the grounds that it revealed the state of progress on the bomb.[77]

At Los Alamos only a few people knew about Szilard's petition. Between Clinton and the Met Lab there was some traveling back and forth by division and section leaders. Between these laboratories and Los Alamos there was much less communication, and this was reduced even further, some say, in the critical days before the Alamogordo test. Ralph Lapp was going to Los Alamos, however, and Szilard gave him a sealed envelope which Lapp was to give to another scientist to hold until Szilard could talk to Oppenheimer. The message got mixed up, and the envelope, containing the petition, was handed to Oppenheimer right away. Oppenheimer knew that military authorities would take action if he did not, and besides he was dubious about how far scientists ought to go in trying to influence political decisions. He said the petition could not be circulated.[78]

Edward Teller, who had shared Szilard's fear of a German bomb and backed his efforts to get work started in the United States, received a letter directly from Szilard asking support for the petition.

[76] As cited by Compton, *Atomic Quest*, p. 243; Compton thought this read as if those who framed it had been reading the minds of Truman and Stimson, but the Potsdam ultimatum of July 26 demanded unconditional surrender and did not say that a wholly novel weapon would be used. See also Knebel and Bailey, "The Fight Over the A-Bomb," p. 22.

[77] Interviews with Lyle B. Borst, February 20, 1962; Coryell, March 17, 1959; Rush, September 9, 1959. Recollections of the number of signatures vary from two or three dozen to several hundred. The figure sixty-eight is given by Knebel and Bailey, in "The Fight Over the A-Bomb" (p. 22); they quote the Clinton Labs petition as asking that "before the weapon be used without restriction in the present conflict, its powers should be adequately described and demonstrated, and the Japanese nation should be given the opportunity to consider the consequences of further refusal to surrender."

[78] Interview with Szilard, March 14, 1960; Ralph Lapp to the author, October 30, 1958.

Teller has later explained that he was already worried about how the bomb would be used and he now consulted Oppenheimer because, in addition to being the constituted authority, his brilliant gifts made him the natural leader. "Oppenheimer told me, in a polite and convincing way," writes Teller,

that he thought it improper for a scientist to use his prestige as a platform for political pronouncements. He conveyed to me in glowing terms the deep concern, thoroughness, and wisdom with which these questions were being handled in Washington. Our fate was in the hands of the best, the most conscientious men of our nation. And they had information which we did not possess. Oppenheimer's words lifted a great weight from my heart. I was happy to accept his word and his authority. I did not circulate Szilard's petition. Today I regret that I did not.[79]

As for the copy of the petition that he had circulated at the Met Lab, on July 17 or shortly thereafter, Szilard turned it over to Compton for transmission "through channels" to Washington. There was no evidence that it ever reached the President, who was by this time at Potsdam preparing to confer with Churchill and Stalin. Inquiry made by an Oak Ridge scientist of a White House staff member just after the war revealed no trace of it there. It has recently been mentioned as among papers turned over to Stimson's office by General Groves on August 1.[80]

The circulation of Szilard's petition naturally disturbed those who felt that the bomb ought to be used at the earliest possible moment. Some staff members, for instance those who had concurred in the conclusions of Dempster and his sub-committee on statutory controls, would doubtless have protested directly to Compton. He also received what he later described as "counterpetitions," from one of which he quoted as follows:

---

[79] From *The Legacy of Hiroshima*, by Edward Teller with Allen Brown (copyright © 1962 by Edward Teller and Allen Brown; reprinted by permission of Edward Teller and Doubleday & Co., Inc. [Garden City, N.Y.]), pp. 13–14.

[80] *The New World*, p. 399. In "My Trial as a War Criminal," one of the satirical fantasies in which Szilard occasionally indulged, he recalled the inconclusive fate of the petition. As part of his defense, ran Szilard's story, he had to fall back upon a petition he had circulated at the Met Lab during the war. "The prosecutor moved, however, that this document be stricken from the record on the ground that it was not transmitted by me to the President directly but was rather handed by me to the Head of the Project who forwarded it to the Manhattan District of the War Department, headed by General Groves. The prosecutor said that I, Szilard, should have known better than to agree to such a method of transmittal" (reprinted by permission of the *University of Chicago Law Review* [copyright © 1949 by The University of Chicago], XVII [Autumn, 1949], 82, copies in ASC XXV, 6, dated November 11, 1947).

Are not the men of the fighting forces a part of the nation? Are not they, who are risking their lives for the nation entitled to the weapons which have been designed? In short, are we to go on shedding American blood when we have available a means to speedy victory? No! If we can save even a handful of American lives, then let us use this weapon—now!
... These sentiments, we feel, represent more truly those of the majority of Americans and particularly those who have sons ... in the foxholes and warships in the Pacific.[81]

There is no doubt that the sentiment Compton described did exist, although no evidence has been found of any formal counterpetitions or of an organized countermovement. Among the collection of materials relating to scientists' views on the use of the bomb which Groves turned over to Stimson's office on August 1, only two letters urged using the bomb without warning.[82]

Compton was deeply troubled by the divided opinion among the scientists under his charge, reflecting as it did the painful conflict in his own mind about using the bomb. He asked Farrington Daniels, a chemist who had succeeded Stearns as director of the Met Lab on July 1, 1945, to take a poll among the scientists in the laboratory, and Daniels did so on July 12. Two and one-half years later Compton and Daniels published an account of this poll:

The scientists working in their laboratories at Chicago on July 12, 1945, were asked, one at a time, to vote in this poll by secret ballot without previous discussion. The poll was entirely voluntary and informal. It read as follows:
Which of the following five procedures comes closest to your choice as to the way in which any new weapons that we may develop should be used in the Japanese war:
1. Use them in the manner that is from the military point of view most effective in bringing about prompt Japanese surrender at minimum human cost to our armed forces.
2. Give a military demonstration in Japan to be followed by renewed opportunity for surrender before full use of the weapons is employed.
3. Give an experimental demonstration in this country, with representatives of Japan present; followed by a new opportunity for surrender before full use of the weapon is employed.
4. Withhold military use of the weapons, but make public experimental demonstration of their effectiveness.
5. Maintain as secret as possible all developments of our new weapons and refrain from using them in this war.

---

[81] Atomic Quest, p. 242; ellipses are Compton's.
[82] Knebel and Bailey, "The Fight Over the A-Bomb," p. 23.

After reading the questions, each of the scientists placed a number in an envelope expressing his opinion. The poll did not reach everyone, but all those who were approached voted, and the number comprised more than half of the scientists.

The scientists were physicists, chemists, biologists, and metallurgists who had received an academic degree. The results were as follows:

Procedure indicated above	1	2	3	4	5
Number voting	23	69	39	16	3
Per cent of votes	15	46	26	11	2

These five procedures were undoubtedly interpreted differently by different scientists, as they undoubtedly will be by present readers, but no definition or amplification of these procedures was made at the time of the poll.[83]

As the authors of this article were aware, complaints were made after the poll was taken that insufficient time was allowed for answering and that the questions were not clear. What was meant by "a military demonstration in Japan"? Did it mean full combat use? Or did it mean using the bomb in the way suggested by the petition Szilard was then circulating? The critics claimed that at least some of the 46 per cent who voted for the second alternative made the latter assumption.

The only interpretation of the results made in the 1948 article was the summary statement that "15 per cent favored full military use, 46 per cent favored its limited use, 26 per cent wanted an experimental demonstration before military use, and 13 per cent preferred to avoid any military use whatever." The rephrasing of the second alternative as "limited use" merely added to the confusion. No mention was made in the alternatives offered by Compton of a specific warning to the Japanese, upon which, fully as much as upon a demonstration, the scientists' recommendations had centered.

What Compton himself meant by the term "military demonstration" has never been fully clear. In the letter with which he accompanied the poll results in July, 1945, he referred to the second alternative of a military demonstration as "the strongly favored procedure," commenting that "this coincides with my own preference and is, as nearly as I can judge, the procedure that has found most favor in all informed groups where the subject has been discussed."[84] Did Comp-

---

[83] Arthur H. Compton and Farrington Daniels, "A Poll of Scientists at Chicago, July, 1945." *Bulletin of the Atomic Scientists*, IV (February, 1948), 44, 63.

[84] Quoted in Knebel and Bailey, "The Fight Over the A-Bomb," p. 23.

ton mean by this something other than the way the bomb was used at Hiroshima? Or did he not regard the dissident scientists, whose views he had tried so hard to see represented, as being fully "informed"?[85]

7. REACTION AT OTHER LABORATORIES

Why was there such intense concern at the Chicago laboratory about the future of atomic energy and the use of the bomb and so little elsewhere? The early completion of the Met Lab assignments and the consequent consideration as to how their work, no longer needed for the bomb, fitted into long-range plans and problems accounted for a good deal. Added to this was the seminal effect of James Franck and Leo Szilard. The young men at the Met Lab were stimulated by Szilard, and a substantial group of their elders felt that any idea that held James Franck's disinterested loyalty could not be entirely wrong.

Leaders in the effort to halt a nuclear arms race emerged in due course from other laboratories—Oppenheimer at Los Alamos, Urey at Columbia, a cluster of younger men at Oak Ridge—but these movements were not linked so closely as in Chicago to reservations about military use of the bomb.

At the SAM (Substitute Alloy Materials) Laboratory at Columbia Harold Urey says no such discussion took place. He himself was so convinced that no politician could afford to ignore a weapon that would end the war and save lives, whatever the long-range considerations might be, that he listened with some impatience to talk about not using the bomb when he was in Chicago in the spring of 1945. Urey joined Szilard and Bartky on the May 28 trip to see Byrnes at Spartanburg because he agreed that scientists should be more broadly

---

[85] Some years later Compton caused further dismay among former colleagues by describing the poll as providing almost unanimous support for the way the bomb was used. "There were a few," he wrote in 1956, "who preferred not to use the bomb at all, but 87 per cent voted for its military use, at least if after other means were tried this was found necessary to bring surrender" (Compton, *Atomic Quest*, p. 244). Compton went on to say: "My experience with this questionnaire has confirmed my faith in the reliability of democratic processes in judging matters of human concern. It is a striking fact that the same points of view were presented with closely the same degree of relative frequency by men active in widely different areas. The three groups to which I refer were: (1) the men in the Interim Committee, individuals concerned with human problems in their broadest terms and accustomed to accepting the responsibility for major decisions; (2) the scientists and other scholars whose professional activities were primarily of an intellectual type; (3) the mechanics in our shops who were working long hours in fabricating the bomb or in building instruments concerned with its development."

represented in atomic policy-making, but the possibility of keeping the bomb a secret from the Russians, about which Szilard was speculating, seemed to him nonsense.[86]

Irving Kaplan, a younger colleague of Urey's at SAM, tells much the same story. He spent a brief period at the Met Lab in 1943 and was astonished at the intensity with which the duPont and other issues were discussed. He had the same reaction when he heard talk at Oak Ridge in June, 1945, about a demonstration. He himself expected the bomb to be used and had no doubts then about the necessity of it. Both Kaplan and Urey participated actively in the scientists' movement after the war.[87]

Eugene Wigner, whose theoretical studies of chain reaction and work as codesigner of the Clinton pile took him to several sites, also observed with interest the marked effect of location upon concern with non-technical problems. John Simpson of the Met Lab spent some time late in 1944 and early 1945 at both Hanford and Oak Ridge and found that remarks about topics currently much discussed in Chicago produced no reaction. Interest never developed at Hanford. At Oak Ridge the lack of response is more surprising, for Clinton Labs was staffed in large measure by Met Lab people who knew about earlier agitation there and had contributed to the Jeffries Report. Several Clinton men recall their anxiety prior to the San Francisco conference in April, 1945, and their relief when a speech by Anthony Eden seemed to contain a hint that he knew about atomic energy.

Perhaps the restraint in talking to Simpson stemmed from caution. Clinton Labs scientists seem to have felt more oppressed than others by army restrictions and more cut off from knowledge of how work on the main objective was progressing. A few months later, as we have seen, they responded to the demonstration issue in a way that indicated some prior thought, and immediately after the war they plunged into political activity with tremendous vigor, explaining their views with a competence that made quite credible their claim that they had thought about the implications of the bomb for a long time. But so far as can be learned, the meeting in June or July, 1945, which rejected Szilard's petition and drew up its own was the only one of the kind held at Clinton Labs during the war.

When inquiries were made of Los Alamos scientists ten years later about wartime discussions of the implications of their work, the first

---

[86] Interview with Urey, July 23, 1958.
[87] Interview with Kaplan, April 3, 1962.

reaction was that until the very end of the war none at all had taken place. Gradually a few people dredged up memories of speculation about future developments in the privacy of Sunday mountain climbs or of some memorable exchange in a Technical Area hallway. A few remembered oblique talk in the company of Niels Bohr which had occasionally touched on something as specific as techniques of control. All agreed on the frantic pace of the final months before the Trinity test and on their obsession with security; and some suggested a half-conscious closing of the mind to the ultimate significance of their desperate effort to bring the war to an end. But the universal reaction of Los Alamos scientists has been amazement that they thought and said so little. So great was the absorption in the immediate task, they point out, that people of more than normal sensitivity to moral issues, who later became very active in the fight to control the bomb, accepted assignment in the Pacific without question.

This general pattern of compliant concentration was, in fact, broken on two occasions before the war ended. One of these was in 1944— probably in the spring—when Robert R. Wilson, the youthful leader of the cyclotron group who had come to Los Alamos via Berkeley and Princeton, called a meeting in X Building. Some twenty-five people, mostly from Wilson's group, came to what he describes as "the impact of the gadget" meeting. Wilson does not remember what was said, nor does he take any credit for this effort to stir up discussion. He is astonished now that not one person stopped and said, "I will not work on the bomb." Wilson was persuaded by Oppenheimer that such meetings were inappropriate until the job was finished.

Wilson was not involved in the next move—a meeting at the end of March, 1945. "This meeting," records a résumé of the following October, "was attended by about forty staff members. They discussed the economic future of scientists and the social consequences of nuclear energy. Because they could do nothing until secrecy was lifted they appointed a committee to revive discussion when something could be done."[88]

By this time achievement of a bomb before the war ended seemed almost certain, and anxiety as to what would be said about it at the forthcoming San Francisco conference was a major reason for this

---

[88] The committee members, drawn from different groups of physicists and chemists, were Victor Weisskopf, Joseph Keller, Kenneth Greisen, Paul Olum, Roger Sutton, and Samuel Weissman (untitled memorandum, October 24, 1945, ALAS II, 2).

meeting. No one was more concerned than Oppenheimer that knowledge of atomic weapons should play a part in international planning, but he did not think that an organization of scientists hampered by secrecy could do much about this, and his advice, that the important thing was to get on with the job, was conveyed through Philip Morrison and again put a stop to action.[89]

All technical workers on the Hill—the colloquial name for the Los Alamos mesa—were soon more frantically busy than ever preparing for the mid-July test, but recollections ascribe to the final six weeks a welling up of individual anxieties which might have added up to significant protest had any one person been ready to organize them. Indeed, when memories are pooled the picture of Los Alamos apathy about use of the bomb disappears. For a time, claims one physicist, you couldn't walk down the hall without being drawn into conversation. The participants in one of these encounters were Associate Director Robert Bacher and Volney Wilson, who as a young associate of Compton's in physics at Chicago had at first refused to work on S-1, choosing instead the defensive radar project at M.I.T. With further reports of German work Wilson had changed his mind in late 1941, but after the defeat of Germany his earlier doubts strongly revived. Outside Bacher's office the two men had a long talk in May or early June. Wilson proposed that they quit and not develop the bomb. Bacher said they couldn't stop now; it would be too easy for another Hitler to pick up where they left off; they must demonstrate to the world how powerful the new weapon was. Reluctantly convinced, says Wilson, "I proposed that we build a model city and invite all the leaders of the world including Stalin to see one bomb destroy this model city. I cannot recall his reply to this but I suspect he was much better informed than I and realized that we scientists had no real decision in the use of the bomb."[90]

Hans Bethe, head of T Division (theoretical physics), says the possibility of a demonstration was very much in the air—he went to see Oppenheimer about it just before some critical Washington meeting—but no one could controvert the possibility of failure or the other arguments that moved the Interim Committee and the panel.

Although Oppenheimer discouraged organized discussion and

[89] Seven ex–Los Alamos scientists and their wives gathered in Ithaca in 1959 and recorded their recollections of these events for the author. They tried to reconstruct another meeting between the Trinity test on July 16 and the end of the war, but it seems likely that the next one was on August 20 (see chapter ii).

[90] V. Wilson to the author, October 3, 1957.

stopped Szilard's petition, he was by no means unsympathetic or inaccessible to his worried associates. But having himself been impressed by Stimson's deep understanding of the international implications of the bomb and, after Trinity, reassured by Bush about talks with the Russians, he answered restive queries with assurances that these matters were being carefully considered and that quiet contacts were the best way to influence the administration.

8. THE FINAL DAYS

The decision which the Franck committee and the petitioners tried to modify has become one of the emotionally charged questions of our time. The circumstances under which it was carried to a conclusion are interesting enough in themselves—the tangled relationship between the Allies, conflicting intelligence regarding Japan's readiness for peace, a weapon still untried in combat and dependent upon the weather. But in addition, this decision, involving several areas of changing perspective, has become the focus of newly aroused interest in the process of decision-making in a democracy and in the role and responsibilities of the scientific profession, and it has seemed to call for a redefinition of international morality.

By the time the Interim Committee made its recommendations on June 1, plans were well advanced for the Alamogordo test; for over a year crews had been training to drop the bomb, and targets had been chosen. These and other preparations now entered their final stages; British assent to using the bomb, required by the Quebec agreement, was formally given on July 4. By July 6, when the President and Secretary of State Byrnes on one ship, and Secretary Stimson on another, sailed for Europe to confer with Churchill and Stalin, Stimson had in hand drafts of a warning to Japan and of a statement to be made by the President after the first bomb was dropped in Japan. As they crossed the Atlantic the bombing of Japanese cities, already causing fierce devastation, was intensified.

From July 15 to August 2 the three Allied leaders at Potsdam (after Labour's electoral victory Churchill was joined by Clement Attlee) received confusing reports of desperate conditions in Japan and of the peace overtures which the Japanese ambassador in Moscow had commenced on July 12. At the same time Japanese leaders continued to declare that unconditional surrender, if it involved renouncing the Emperor, was out of the question, confirming expectations of fanatic resistance. These reports, shared with something short of frankness among Allied representatives but largely known to the United States officials through intercepted messages, formed the background against which the issuance of a joint demand for Japanese surrender and the timing of a Russian declaration of war on Japan were considered. This latter step, agreed upon at Yalta the previous February but viewed with mixed feelings by Russia's allies, waited upon the conclusion of a Russian-Chinese agreement.[91]

But dominant in the minds of United States and British leaders was the coded message received by Stimson on the evening of July 16 announcing the successful test of the plutonium implosion bomb at Alamogordo that morning. Full reports from General Groves, brought by courier on the 21, included General Thomas Farrell's vivid account of the cloud, the light, the blast, the awesome sense in all who witnessed it of a new era in the history of mankind, and the news that the bomb's force, equivalent to 20,000 tons of TNT, had exceeded by 10 per cent the highest estimates. Two days later came confirmation that a second bomb would be ready for delivery in Japan soon after August 1, certainly before the tenth. This gave rise, as Churchill later phrased it, to a vision fair and bright of ending the war in one or two violent shocks in place of the nightmare of invasion. The news also had some noticeable effect, the extent of which is not quite clear, upon United States and British attitudes toward Russia's increased demands in Europe and toward the timing of her entry into the war.

Fortified meanwhile by Churchill against any temptation to fuller disclosure and discussion of the bomb's implications, Truman made his perfunctory statement about the new weapon to Stalin on July 24. The same day he ordered the War Department to instruct General Spaatz to drop a bomb in Japan as soon after August 3 as weather permitted, and this order was transmitted to Spaatz on the 25.

On the twenty-sixth a declaration was broadcast in the names of Truman, Churchill, and Chiang Kai-shek calling upon the Japanese to surrender and submit to occupation until "there has been established in accordance with the freely expressed will of the Japanese people a peacefully inclined and responsible government." Nothing was said about retaining the Emperor, though some United States officials, including Stimson, felt that assurance on this point would hasten compliance. The alternative to unconditional surrender, said

---

[91] See Feis, *Japan Subdued*, chap. vi, "The Calendar of Days at Potsdam."

the proclamation, was "prompt and utter destruction." This was the only reference to the atomic bomb. Two days later Premier Suzuki announced that the Japanese Government would ignore the surrender ultimatum and continue fighting.[92]

The Potsdam Conference broke up on August 2. Truman embarked the same day on the U.S.S. "Augusta" and, according to his memoirs, at some point early in the voyage confirmed the authorization to drop the bomb. The first one fell on Hiroshima on August 6. On the eighth Russia declared war on Japan, and a second atomic bomb was dropped over Nagasaki on the ninth. On the tenth Japan offered surrender under the Potsdam terms if the sovereignty of the Emperor was retained. The Allied governments agreed to this on the eleventh, and on August 14 the war ended.

Truman has taken full responsibility for introducing the atomic bomb as a weapon against Japan. But his decision was not so much a positive act as a choice not to halt the enormous, multifaceted effort which he had found well advanced three months earlier. To have called such a halt, contrary to the advice of his most trusted associates, would have required an almost inconceivable exercise of individual initiative. Truman and Stimson, the latter standing on the next level of responsibility, have both stated that they always expected the bomb to be used in the war in terms suggesting that although they recognized an alternative course they never seriously considered taking it. The days at Potsdam have often been considered as highly significant, but one must conclude that this decision had in all essentials been completed in the first three weeks of June.[93]

The bomb test in New Mexico came four days after Compton's poll in Chicago. Stimson's office, with Harrison in charge of atomic bomb matters, was far too busy forwarding details of the test to Stimson in Potsdam, confirming arrangements for delivery of bombs in the Pacific, and preparing to carry out decisions of the leaders at Pots-

---

[92] Feis, *Japan Subdued*, pp. 24–27, 94–101. The term "mokusatsu," which Suzuki used, means "to ignore" and was so translated at the time although Suzuki's statement was interpreted as a rejection of the ultimatum; see Feis and also Butow, *Japan's Decision to Surrender*, pp. 143–49.

[93] According to Stimson, "Once that decision had been made, the timing and method of the use of the bomb were wholly subordinated to the objective of victory; no effort was made, and none was seriously considered, to achieve surrender merely in order not to have to use the bomb." For this quotation and further amplification of the point, see Henry L. Stimson and McGeorge Bundy, *On Active Service in Peace and War* (New York: Harper & Bros., 1948), Vol. II, p. 629.

dam to worry about further reactions of Met Lab scientists to a decision that, so far as the Secretary was concerned, was already made, reviewed, and confirmed.

General Groves knew, of course, that a poll had been taken in Chicago. Someone in Washington—Harrison, perhaps, or his assistant, Lieutenant Gordon Arneson (who would later figure in international control negotiations)—was curious enough about the results to check with Compton, then at Oak Ridge. Compton later described how Colonel Nichols, Groves's deputy, had come to him saying that Washington wanted at once the results of the opinion polls on the use of the bomb.

> ... The votes and petitions were by now in my hands. I accordingly wrote out a message summarizing the results as objectively as I could and handed it to the Colonel. An hour later he came to me again. "Washington wants to know what you think."

Compton reviewed again the reasoning that had led him, with the rest of the panel, six weeks before at Los Alamos to concur in the use of the bomb. "My vote is with the majority," is the reply that he later quotes. "It seems to me that as the war stands the bomb should be used, but no more drastically than needed to bring surrender." And this was the message that Colonel Nichols relayed to Washington.[94]

Compton placed this incident on July 23. The poll results joined the Szilard petition in the pile of papers that Groves turned over to Stimson's office on August 1 as the Allied leaders at Potsdam were concluding their conference. Three days earlier the Japanese premier had rejected their ultimatum and unknowingly confirmed the decision to drop the bomb.

9. THE MET LAB LOOKS AHEAD

It was generally recognized during these agitations of June and July that the end of the war was near, but there was no overt knowledge among Met Lab scientists about progress on the bomb or what, if any, impression their representations about its use had made. Some claim that intelligent guesswork left few people uninformed about the test and its results. Others say they did not know about the test until after Hiroshima.

In any case the Met Lab scientists continued, and with increased interest, to discuss the problems out of which their concern about using the bomb had grown. A second Committee on Social and Po-

---

[94] Compton, *Atomic Quest*, pp. 246–47.

litical Implications (antedating perhaps the Franck committee by that name) had developed at some undetermined date out of the young men's March seminars. Its members—John Simpson and Arthur Jaffey, both physicists, Robert Maurer, a chemist, and J. J. Nickson, medical doctor in the biology section, who also served on the Franck committee—planned a new series of discussions in the early summer.

Maurer, thinking perhaps of the early spring as well as summer meetings, says that this committee played a central role in his own education and development of attitudes. "There was an enormous spread of understanding and sophistication of thought among the interested people at the Met Lab," he said later. "I fear that I was one of the less sophisticated individuals. I shall be everlastingly grateful to Szilard for his provocative intellectual leadership. . . . I remember also Dr. Daniels' sympathetic attempts to assist our committee to function."[95]

Farrington Daniels succeeded Joyce Stearns as laboratory director on July 1, and one of his first tasks was to devise a formula that would satisfy both the young scientists and the security officers. He later recalled how it was managed:

> . . . as soon as I took up the job, I was faced with the problem that the Military did not approve of holding a general meeting of the Laboratory scientists to discuss the social and political implications of the atomic bomb. It was an unfortunate, disagreeable task that I had to cancel the plans for these general discussion meetings. As a substitute, I got permission from the military authorities to hold a meeting of a committee to interview scientists, one at a time, concerning their views on the social and political implications and the possible courses of action. . . .
> Many members of the Met Lab came to express their views to this committee. . . . One interesting byproduct . . . was the opportunity for discussion among those who interviewed the committee. In the anteroom outside the committee room, the scientists would gather, waiting for their turn to appear before the committee and then they would again gather there and discuss things after they had interviewed the committee. So, in spite of the fact that there was no public meeting, there was, nevertheless, considerable discussion.[96]

Daniels, who was to smooth over many awkward situations for his politically minded charges in the coming year, sat in on these meetings, keenly interested as well as officially responsible. Stearns also continued his support, writing to Simpson on July 9 that he hoped

---

[95] Maurer to the author, August 5, 1958.
[96] Daniels to the author, July 23, 1957.

the panel discussions started by the younger members might grow into a significant institution at the Metallurgical Laboratory.[97]

The "panel discussions," held on Thursday evenings during July, were, in fact, interviews by the committee of individuals who wished to present their views with the understanding that new ideas would be passed along to the panel.[98] Most of the exchange was verbal, but a few memoranda were submitted: one to argue the case for a demonstration of the bomb in the United States with international observers present; and another to suggest that the current congressional debate on compulsory military training be postponed until legislators knew about the bomb.

A more comprehensive statement from Eugene Rabinowitch, dated July 12, 1945, besides revealing a stubborn hope that the bomb might not be used without prior warning, represents a kind of charter of the scientists' movement, albeit an unacknowledged one since it was immediately buried in classified files.[99] Outlining what scientists could do to prepare for the impact of nucleonics, Rabinowitch proposed by way of immediate action sufficient relaxation of secrecy to permit discussion with a wider group of policy-makers in Washington and perhaps even a campaign to tell the American people about the problem. The long-range program would stress education, beginning with the scientists themselves through exploration of such questions as removal of secrecy, their participation in world organization, and the relation between private and public research in nucleonics. Such discussion could take place under Manhattan Project auspices, but action would of necessity be partisan and Rabinowitch therefore recommended "an organization of those who have made up their mind about certain basic problems and decisions," to be extended to scientists at large as soon as the existence of the bomb was revealed. This "scientists action committee," by open propaganda or lobbying, should work for international control of nuclear power and other measures to avoid nuclear devastation and for "the most efficient organization of post-war research in nucleonics for the common good of mankind."

---

[97] Stearns to Simpson, July 9, 1945, in Simpson's files. Anxious to encourage the young men, Stearns forgot perhaps that Franck, Szilard, Rabinowitch, and Mulliken, who had chiefly sparked the discussion and action of the past months, were in their forties, fifties, and sixties.

[98] Undated announcement on "Social and Political Implications"; copy provided by Daniels.

[99] Rabinowitch's "Memo to the Committee on Panel Discussions, July 12, 1945," is printed in Appendix C.

Compton had fully supported Daniels in facilitating this exchange of views at the Met Lab, but he must have feared that rumors of the test on July 16 might precipitate unwarranted talk, for on the seventeenth he reminded the Met Lab scientific staff of the continuing need for close maintenance of security and of the channels that were open "for bringing effectively to the attention of the nation's leaders ideas that may develop within our project concerning [social and political] implications."[100]

The Committee on Social and Political Implications thought it was time that the Franck Report was made available to Met Lab scientists, but on July 23 Daniels had to report that since it contained secret information the best that could be done was to have Nickson, as a member of both committees, incorporate parts of the Franck Report into the fuller one which Daniels hoped would emerge from the panel discussions of the past weeks. This combined report, he assumed, would become a laboratory document distributed to all section chiefs and a report would also go to Compton for transmission to the scientific panel and to the Interim Committee.[101]

Since decreased attendance at the panel discussion of July 23 indicated that this technique had served its purpose, Daniels suggested a series of lectures, and on August 2 Norman Hilberry talked to the Met Lab scientific staff about the "Bush Plan for a National Research Foundation."

On August 6 came Hiroshima. The organization of research seemed suddenly academic and parochial, and a meeting hurriedly called for the seventh discussed what scientists should say about the bomb. The Franck Report could be discussed if not read, and Daniels himself summarized it for a meeting the following week. The report of the Committee on Social and Political Implications, which was still being formulated, now needed the added dimension of fears realized. There was no use in sending it to the panel or the Interim Committee, and it emerged a month later as a statement of views of the nascent "Atomic Scientists of Chicago."

10. CONCLUSION

"Any process started by men toward a special end," says Elting Morison, "tends, for reasons logical, biological, aesthetic or whatever they may be, to carry forward, if other things remain equal, to its climax.

---

[100] Compton to members of scientific staff of the Chicago Metallurgical Project, July 17, 1945 (copy in Simpson's file).
[101] Daniels to Simpson, Jaffey, Maurer and Nickson, July 23, 1945, in Simpson's file.

Each man fully engaged over four years of uncertainty and exertion in the actual making of the weapon was moved, without perhaps a full awareness, toward conclusion by the inertia developed in the human system."[102]

Scientists, by and large, were no less caught up in this process than statesmen or soldiers. But a few of those who worked on the bomb— a dozen or so influencing in turn several hundred—tried to counter the inertia. The blast on August 6 was the measure of their failure, in one sense complete but deserving at the same time some quali- fication.

In the final two years of the war scientists individually or col- lectively made three overlapping requests: that long-range planning in the field of atomic energy be undertaken; that Russia be told about the general nature of the atomic weapon; and that a demonstration be attempted to induce Japan to surrender before the bomb was used in combat.

The demand for long-range planning was technically answered by appointment of the Interim Committee in May, 1945, but this group of busy men, though well qualified for purposes of general political review, was not equipped to give this particular subject the kind of intensive consideration that scientists thought its revolutionary nature required. And the appointment was so long delayed that by the time the Committee began to work some of the problems it confronted had become very short range indeed.

The request for talks with Russia, like that for a planning com- mittee, had the support of scientists close to the government, and it, too, was nominally granted but suffered even greater political attrition as it went from panel to Interim Committee, then through Stimson to Truman, whose last minute announcement to Stalin defeated the purpose of the telling, which had been to build confidence and enlist co-operation. It must be added, however, that in view of what Russia had learned from espionage even Bohr's advice on this point a year earlier would have come too late.

The third recommendation from scientists was also part and parcel of the first. Those who urged a demonstration hoped—believed, in fact—that if policy-makers would only take a long look at the impact of the bomb they too would see the wisdom of foregoing its use until the issue had been publicized and the Japanese shown to be utterly

---

[102] Morison, *Turmoil and Tradition*, p. 620.

intractable. Again the ritual of acquiescence was maintained. The Franck Report reached the office of the Secretary of War; it inspired a review of the technical feasibility of a demonstration by four scientists whose technical competence and personal integrity no one doubted. But it cannot be said that scientists whose views differed from those of the panel had a chance to present them to the Interim Committee as Conant had recommended and Stimson had promised. Nor is there evidence that any group in Washington spent a fraction of the time and thought reviewing the argumentation of the Franck Report that its framers had put into formulating their astonishingly accurate prediction. What Oppenheimer later called the extraordinary lucidity of that report[103] made little impression at the time upon men who saw their first responsibility as the termination of war.

The Met Lab poll and the Szilard and Clinton Labs petitions, which indicated substantial backing for the Franck Report, were not completed in time to affect the decision, and Stimson and Truman saw them, if at all, only after final orders had been given.

Could the outcome conceivably have been different? This query is prompted by widespread—not unanimous—regret on the part of Manhattan Project scientists that they did not question at an earlier stage the use of the bomb, but one must conclude that the decision could have been altered only if scientists had been fully united. Had the seven scientists on the Interim Committee and the panel been convinced of the wisdom of a demonstration, they might have forced a more thorough examination of alternatives and of international repercussions. Possibly a majority might have done so. But without exception these seven men subscribed to the axiom that scientists were not qualified to make complex political decisions. Not one of them apparently found the Franck committee's recommendation practicable.

Or had those outside the immediate circle of government advisers been unanimous in demanding a demonstration, it is conceivable that their pressure might have been effective. But scientists were not so united. Some had fewer reservations than did panel members about using the bomb without warning. And among those who questioned it both loyalty and secrecy militated against the growth of any overt protest movement.

---

[103] Interview with Oppenheimer in *Le Savant et le pouvoir*, May 2–7, 1958.

The attitude of Manhattan Project scientists toward the decision remains ambivalent. Men who do not habitually speak uncharitably of colleagues still feel that dissenting views were not fairly represented. Others regret the decision, yet do not criticize it, knowing that responsibility might have tempered their viewpoint. And some feel that it was a political and military decision in which they had no reason to participate.

These differences among scientists over wartime policy were not insignificant, and a gulf, which Oppenheimer and Compton tried hard to bridge, did indeed develop between those who thought that scientists' influence upon policy could best be exerted through a small group of administrators and advisers and those who saw the usefulness of a broadly based organization explicitly recognizing political obligations. These divergent tendencies were not without effect, but what was far more evident as the war ended was unity in resolution to make science serve the cause of peace. To the story of how that resolution grew and expressed itself in action the remainder of this book is devoted.

PART II

Reaction
and Repercussions

CHAPTER 2

Reaction
August and September, 1945

B_{Y THE TIME} the bomb was dropped on Japan, many Project scientists outside Los Alamos had learned of the successful test at Alamogordo on July 16. Some knew or guessed that its use in the Pacific war would not be long postponed, and in the early days of August they listened to news reports with mixed emotions, composed in varying degrees of anticipation and dread. But apart from a handful of men involved in administration and delivery from Pacific bases, Project scientists, however crucial their jobs, were not told of specific military plans, and like the rest of the world, if not with the same complete bewilderment, they learned from press and radio on August 6 that a single bomb had all but obliterated a Japanese city.

1. AFTER HIROSHIMA

The immediate reaction varied from one part of the Project to another. At the Met Lab in Chicago those who had actively explored alternatives to military use received the news of Hiroshima as a shattering blow to their hope that the arguments of the Franck memorandum and Szilard's petition might swing the balance in Washington. "In the summer of 1945," wrote Eugene Rabinowitch five years later, "some of us walked the streets of Chicago vividly imagining the sky suddenly lit by a giant fireball, the steel skeletons

of skyscrapers bending into grotesque shapes and their masonry rain-
ing into the streets below, until a great cloud of dust rose and settled
over the crumbling city."[1] This sense of gloom and foreboding was
shared by those who had signed Szilard's petition or had cast their
vote for a non-military alternative in the Compton poll three weeks
earlier. Discussion of alternatives may have raised false hopes, but
it had also involved some appraisal of how its creators would feel
when the bomb was dropped, and so Met Lab people were in a sense
better prepared for Hiroshima than those who knew more about
technical progress.

At Los Alamos, as we have seen, there was no systematic exploration of implications and alternatives and hence little psychological
preparation. Toward completion of the bomb the whole laboratory
had worked with an absorption that left little time for reflection. The
test at Alamogordo on July 16 has been often and vividly reported.
But what seems like hyperbole to lay readers is gross understatement
to those who took part, for the experience there in the desert, which
the Spaniards had aptly called "Jornada del Muerto," lives with them
still as the most climactic of their lives. Perhaps only one who kept
the all-night vigil at the test site, William L. Laurence, the specially
briefed *New York Times* reporter, was as interested in the spectators
as in the explosion itself:

The big boom came about 100 seconds after the Great Flash—the first
cry of a new-born world. It brought the silent, motionless silhouettes to
life, gave them a voice.
A loud cry filled the air. The little groups that hitherto had stood rooted
to the earth like desert plants broke into a dance, the rhythm of primitive
man dancing at one of his fire festivals at the coming of spring.
They clapped their hands as they leaped from the ground—earth-bound
man symbolizing a new birth in freedom—the birth of a new force that
for the first time gives man means to free himself from the gravitational pull
of the earth that holds him down.
The dance of the primitive man lasted but a few seconds, during which
an evolutionary period of about 10,000 years had been telescoped. Primitive
man was metamorphosed into modern man—shaking hands, slapping each
other on the back, laughing like happy children.[2]

Later that day most of the men began the two-hundred-mile drive
back to the Los Alamos mesa. They were numb from strain and lack

---

[1] Editorial, "Five Years After," in *Bulletin of the Atomic Scientists* (January,
1951), 3.
[2] William L. Laurence, *New York Times*, September 26, 1945, pp. 1, 16.

of sleep, and for a few of them triumph was already tempered by exceedingly sober thoughts about the meaning of the day's success. In the next few days the whole community experienced a kind of cathartic shock. Unfaced issues suddenly loomed large. The scientists now talked of little else but the effect of the bomb upon the postwar world, seeing it chiefly in terms of the unprecedented power they had witnessed. In a matter of days, it is said, discussion reached a feverish pitch.[3]

In one sense the expected news of Hiroshima—though few on the mesa were informed about target or timing—was an anticlimax, for the blast, the wind, the light, and the power they had witnessed at Alamogordo had exhausted the capacity for astonishment. But there was another dimension that had yet to be fully grasped. With a natural impulse to mark in some way the climax to their efforts, a few people tried to assemble the kind of party with which occupants of the men's dormitories had repaid the quieter hospitality of their married friends. It is significant that people are vague about the date. (We were too exhausted after Alamogordo! Certainly no one celebrated Hiroshima!) Whenever the incident occurred, it was a memorable fiasco. People either stayed away or beat a hasty retreat. Oppenheimer found a level-headed young group leader being sick in the bushes and knew that the reaction had begun.

As the days passed the revulsion grew, bringing with it—even for those who believed that the end of the war justified the bombing—an intensely personal experience of the reality of evil. It was this, and not a feeling of guilt in the ordinary sense, that Oppenheimer meant by his much quoted, and often misunderstood, remark that scientists had known sin.

Still somewhat isolated on their mesa top, the chief link with "outside" for some weeks after the war ended was their chief, Robert Oppenheimer. "Oppie says"—the word began to spread—"that the atomic bomb is so terrible a weapon that war is now impossible," and by this hope they were sustained in the first days of peace as they pondered the moral and political issues that had occupied the Chicago scientists for so many months.

Oak Ridge, which was midway between Chicago and Los Alamos

---

[3] Reactions to Alamogordo were recorded somewhat after the event; an anonymous account written three months after and others by Frederick Reines and Willard Stout on the first anniversary are in ALAS II, 8; III, 2; see also anonymous memorandum, October 24, 1945, ALAS II, 2.

in physical isolation, occupied a kind of middle ground in its reactions on August 6. Although scientists at Clinton Labs had thought seriously about the demonstration issue, they had on the whole been far less concerned with atomic politics than those in Chicago; and they were less personally involved in the death and devastation at Hiroshima than those at Los Alamos. Few at Clinton knew officially about the Alamogordo test; most of them learned about it through delayed and *sub rosa* reports—one received a wine glass from a Los Alamos friend with a note saying, "Drink to us!" Oak Ridge had made enormous contributions to the bomb, and a common reaction on August 6 was irritated frustration at finding, as one senior biologist put it, that young second lieutenants, still wet behind the ears, knew more about what was happening than the scientists. Clinton Labs men later made the seemingly valid claim to having long had "a deep concern for the political problems which success would bring," and they were now assailed by a feeling of panic that they would be as cut off from the making of atomic policy in peacetime as they were from the climax to their vitally important war research.

This is not primarily a study of how the scientists who worked on the bomb felt about its use, nor an attempt to probe in depth this admittedly touchy and complex area of human motivation and rationalization. But certain reactions widely experienced by the scientific community created a climate of opinion and provided a mainspring of the action with which this book is chiefly concerned, and nonscientists have shown a justifiable curiosity about what these reactions were. I believe that most scientists who worked on the bomb reluctantly approved the use of the first bomb because it promised an early end to the war. But many who accepted Hiroshima were deeply shocked by the second bomb dropped on Nagasaki three days later. Eugene Rabinowitch recalls the horror with which Met Lab scientists received this news, and Samuel K. Allison, associate director of Los Alamos, denounced it publicly in a meeting with the press on September 1. What has since been learned about the interlocking of diplomatic maneuver, intelligence reports, preparations for delivery, and weather forecasts in those crowded three days has strengthened the feeling that Nagasaki should not have been bombed.

In September, 1945, Mrs. Margaret Smith Stahl, a sociologist and wife of a duPont engineer, gathered data on how Project scientists felt about the bomb and related problems. She sent questionnaires to four hundred fifty scientists—both pure and applied—whose names she chose at random from the members of the American Chemical Society and the American Physical Society. A total of 49.3 per cent responded (43.9 per cent of the chemists and 54.6 per cent of the physicists). Ninety-seven per cent thought that the United States government was right in sponsoring the development of the bomb, whereas only 66.5 per cent believed that we were justified in using it on Japanese cities—assuming that we could have won the war without it; an additional 20.8 per cent thought it should have been used only after prior warning.

The scientists were also asked this question: If you had been the one to decide whether to use the atomic bomb against Japan, which one of four things do you think you would have done? Fifty-three and nine-tenths per cent would have used it on one city at a time until the Japanese surrendered; 38.9 per cent would have demonstrated it to Japanese leaders in an uninhabited area, then given them a chance to surrender; 3.6 per cent would have refused to use it on cities at all; 1.8 per cent would have wiped out as many cities as possible before the enemy had a chance to surrender; another 1.8 per cent did not know what they would have done. And it is also significant that only 167 answers were received to this question as compared with 230 and 239 to the other two.[4]

With the passing years regret that the bomb was used seems to have grown rather than diminished, at least among those scientists who were either active in the postwar movement or on the fringes of it. Doubtless its use has seemed less justifiable as memories of the devastation and suffering attending each additional day of war have dimmed, but the regret began to grow as soon as word spread about the pressure that some of their colleagues had brought for a demonstration, and it has been further fed by observation of the accuracy with which events have borne out the predictions of the Franck Report.

In some measure the shock of Hiroshima was shared by all scientists.

---

[4] Margaret Smith Stahl, "Splits and Schisms, Nuclear and Social" (Ph.D. dissertation, University of Wisconsin, 1946). Mrs. Stahl was interested in differences between the attitudes of pure and applied scientists. Since this is not the focus of my study, I have not retained her breakdown into these categories. On most questions there was a difference of only 2 or 3 per cent in the replies of pure and applied. The exception was in answers to the last question quoted above: the alternative of dropping the bomb on an uninhabited area before demanding surrender was marked by 46.8 per cent of the pure scientists and by only 28.8 per cent of the applied. Mrs. Stahl believed that this data was supported by the evidence collected in more subjective fashion.

I. I. Rabi, director of the defensive radar developments at the M.I.T. Radiation Laboratory and a Manhattan Project consultant, described the contradictory emotions experienced by himself and his friends:

I would say that we are frankly pleased, terrified, and to an even greater extent embarrassed when we contemplate the results of our wartime efforts. Our terror comes from the realization—which is nowhere more strongly felt than among us—of the tremendous forces of destruction now existing in an all too practical form. By this, I do not mean to suggest that we who helped to create the new weapons are now overcome with a sense of guilt or regret. These instrumentalities were natural consequences of the scientific knowledge at our disposal, and as such were inevitable. They did help us to win a bitter war in which we were attacked in a most cowardly fashion.[5]

Scientists are by and large a rational lot. Their work provides the satisfaction of both immediate and long-range objectives, and their code permits a degree of indulgence in personal eccentricity that spares them as a group from more than the normal quota of neurotics. Instead of brooding about the tragedy of using science for destructive purposes, they tended to plunge into a whirl of educational and political activity. A few, like Rabi himself, were drawn into years of distracting service on government advisory committees.

But scientists are also for the most part humane and sensitive, and if rationality served them well, it spared very few of them, late or soon, from some feeling of direct responsibility. "Three months have passed since these bombs were dropped," wrote an anonymous Los Alamos scientist. "The initial horror has perhaps faded a little with time, but it cannot be forgotten."[6] A young scientist in another part of the Project described to a friend a reaction experienced in the autumn of 1946;

I wept as I read John Hersey's New Yorker account of what has happened during the past year to six who were lucky enough to survive Hiroshima. I am filled with shame to recall the whoopee spirit in the New York offices of Kellex when we came back from lunch to find others who had returned with the first extras announcing the bombing of Hiroshima. That evening we had a hastily arranged champagne dinner, some forty of us; I confess that the feeling of concern I had felt during the preceding three years on the project for what we were engaged in was lost that

---

[5] I. I. Rabi, "The Physicist Returns from the War," *Atlantic Monthly*, CLXXIV (October, 1945), 107–13.
[6] Anonymous "draft for pub.," ALAS II, 8.

evening in a feeling of relief at the relaxation of security, pride in our part in ending the war, and even pride in the effectiveness of the weapon. And at the same moment, the bomb's victims were living through undescribable horror (or rather, describable only in the simple, straightforward reportorial style used by Hersey). We didn't realize. I wonder if we do yet.[7]

Although the fact of the bomb was by far the most important element in scientists' immediate reaction to Hiroshima, they also found a welcome sense of release in the partial revelation of secrets. To an extent this relief was personal and even trivial—freer communication with relatives and friends, less caution required in daily contacts on city campuses, or in Oak Ridge and Los Alamos, anticipation of freedom from armed guards, travel restrictions, and censored mail. This feeling of emancipation was shared by their wives, many of whom had endured the inconveniences of improvised communities, grateful to have kept their families together during the war but still in many cases with only a vague notion of the purpose of their semi-incarceration. The army's compartmentation system did not include a category of information for wives, and their knowledge varied even more than the scientific staff's. One so favorably placed for applying scraps of information as Laura Fermi did not know until the very end that an atomic bomb was being made. A. H. Compton, on the other hand, felt unable to carry his administrative burden without the customary discussion with his wife and obtained clearance for her also, though it is doubtful that the authorities would have agreed to the practice on a wide scale![8] Wives of nuclear physicists who had kept abreast of their husband's prewar research and perhaps heard speculation that atomic energy might be harnessed into bombs drew their own conclusions as to why they were in Chicago, Los Alamos, or Oak Ridge, but this applied to only a small fraction of the thousands of Project employees. It is hard to see in retrospect why those who did not know were not more curious, but at Los Alamos at any rate, wives simply did not talk about these things. Nor did the inability to discuss the husband's work create, as one popular novelist has pictured it, unbearable domestic tension. Nevertheless, the partial relaxation of secrecy in everyday affairs was a great relief.

For the scientists themselves professional considerations outweighed

---

[7] A. Squires to J. Balderston, September 7, 1946, AORES IX, 2.

[8] Laura Fermi, Atoms in the Family (Chicago: University of Chicago Press, 1954), pp. 237 ff.; Arthur Holly Compton, Atomic Quest (New York: Oxford University Press, 1956), p. 10.

these personal ones. Work on secret projects had violated one of the most cherished articles of their unwritten creed, the open discussion of research. "The gossip of scientists who get together is the lifeblood of physics, [as] I think it must be in all other branches of science," Robert Oppenheimer was later to tell a Senate committee.[9] For themselves the resumption of this casual talk and communication would be one of the most valued increments of peace.

Since they assumed that this could not happen immediately, it was with some surprise that Manhattan Project scientists read summaries in the papers of Sunday, August 12, or scanned their own advance copies, of a report prepared at General Grove's request by Henry deWolfe Smyth. This now famous account of the origin and history of the Project, described the scientific principles behind the pile and the bomb and the separation of fissionable materials, and outlined the various methods employed. Few scientists on the Project had had so comprehensive a view that they did not learn a great deal of technical interest from the Smyth report.

Those who already felt grave concern about the dangers inherent in the scientific and technical triumph that Smyth described found satisfaction in his concluding section:

Because of the restrictions of military security there has been no chance for the Congress or the people to debate such questions. They have been seriously considered by all concerned and vigorously debated among the scientists, and the conclusions reached have been passed along to the highest authorities. These questions are not technical questions; they are political and social questions, and the answers given to them may affect all mankind for generations. In thinking about them the men on the project have been thinking as citizens of the United States vitally interested in the welfare of the human race. It has been their duty and that of the responsible high government officials who were informed to look beyond the limits of the present war and its weapons to the ultimate implications of these discoveries. This was a heavy responsibility. In a free country like ours, such questions should be debated by the people and decisions must be made by the people through their representatives. This is one reason for the release of this report. It is a semitechnical report which it is hoped men of science in this country can use to help their fellow citizens in reaching wise decisions. The people of the country must be informed if they are to discharge their responsibilities wisely.[10]

---

[9] U.S. Senate, Committee on Military Affairs, Subcommittee on War Mobilization, *Hearings on Science Legislation,* 79th Cong., 1st sess., October 8, 1945 to March 5, 1946, p. 298.

[10] Smyth, *Atomic Energy for Military Purposes* (Princeton, N.J.: Princeton University Press, 1945), p. 226.

Those who had pondered these questions hoped that Smyth was right about the awareness of the nation's leaders, but at any rate they now had official sanction for the educational program they were already planning.

Most scientists applauded the generous release of information, but the sudden and unexplained departure from the rigid wartime restrictions seemed extremely odd. It was fifteen years before they learned anything about the circumstances of the release. Smyth had finished his report early in the summer, but the decision on what to do with it was delayed until Stimson's return from Potsdam at the beginning of August. His experiences there had made him dubious about any step that would make things easier for the Russians, but back in Washington he found that General Groves, as well as Bush and Conant, was advocating that the official story be released as soon as the bomb was used in Japan as the only way to avoid false rumors and unfounded speculation both at home and abroad. Bush and Conant had long recommended liberal exchange of basic scientific data; Groves had a characteristically practical reason, namely, as he told General Marshall on August 6, that only by making clear at once what could and could not be discussed could the maximum secrecy be maintained.

British officials were skeptical about releasing so much information but left the decision to the United States. On August 9, the date of the Nagasaki bombing, Stimson though not ready himself to give an unqualified opinion, took Bush, Conant, and Groves to the White House to let the President hear their views. Their argument that "publication of the controlled study would prevent harm that might result from reckless and excited versions which were sure to circulate if the subject were shrouded in deep secrecy" convinced the President, and he authorized immediate release.[11]

Had the reason for this step been stated with a frankness matching the contents of the report some later ill feeling might have been avoided, for the extent of its revelations was a tempting stick with which to beat the erstwhile oppressor. Whenever scientists were accused in the coming months of wanting to give atomic secrets to the Russians, it was easy to retort that after the Smyth report there

---

[11] Herbert Feis, *Japan Subdued* (Princeton, N.J.: Princeton University Press, 1961), pp. 117–18; see also Richard G. Hewlett and Oscar E. Anderson, Jr., *The New World, 1939–1946* (University Park: Pennsylvania State University Press, 1962), pp. 400–401, 406–7 (hereinafter referred to as *The New World*).

was not much left to give. With evident satisfaction Szilard told the House Military Affairs Committee on October 18 that with the aid of the report other nations were about where we had been in the fall of 1942.[12] A humorous quip that perhaps Groves did not know how much he had released swelled into the rumor that the report had been issued by mistake and finally into the story, with which Drew Pearson brightened his October account of the scientists' feud with Groves, that when the General had tried to recall the report an adjutant had asked, "Did you ever try to pull an egg back into a chicken?" Again, at the height of the military-civilian control argument in the spring of 1946, the story that a high-school physics teacher, on the basis of the Smyth report, had accurately calculated the size of the bomb was used to demonstrate the incompetence of military management.[13]

Smyth's job of reporting the complicated developments received the highest praise; publication continued to be a controversial topic.[14] As the civilian Atomic Energy Commission took office in January, 1947, its chairman, David Lilienthal, called the Smyth report the worst breach of atomic security that had yet occurred; and Bernard Baruch was quoted as saying that the scientists had lambasted the army into its release. Commenting on these statements, Eugene Rabinowitch recalled how scientists had felt about the report in August, 1945:

The scientists were dumbfounded by the sudden publicity given to the industrial aspects of the atomic bomb project. Furthermore, they were not interested in it. The firms which have participated in the immense enterprize may have had an understandable desire to publicize their achievement, and the Manhattan District was anxious to show what it did with two billion dollars; but the scientists were and are indifferent to the revelation of technological aspects of the production of fissionable materials and manufacture of bombs. They greeted the Smyth report as a portent of resumption of free publication of the result of scientific research—a practice which is considered by a vast majority of scientists as indispensable, not merely for their careers ... but for the advancement of science as a whole and thus for the well-being of the nation.[15]

---

[12] U.S. House of Representatives, Committee on Military Affairs, *Atomic Energy, Hearing on H.R. 4280,* 79th Cong., 1st sess., October 9, 18, 1945, p. 87.

[13] "Washington Merry-Go-Round," October 17, 1945; Alfred Friendly, *Washington Post,* March 25, 1946.

[14] An inquiry from the Federation of American Scientists, suggesting that the record be set straight, went unanswered (Higinbotham to Conant, March 25, 1947, FAS XXI, 5).

[15] Editorial in *Bulletin of the Atomic Scientists,* III (February, 1947), 33, 68.

2. THE MET LAB

If more individual scientists were not stricken in the weeks following Hiroshima with an overwhelming sense of personal remorse it was in part because there developed a prompt, widespread, and intensely earnest collective preoccupation with two closely related subjects: the impact of the new weapon on world peace and the effect of continued secrecy upon international relations and upon the healthy growth of science and technology. The practical expression given to this preoccupation during August and September, 1945, was the organization of groups at Manhattan Project laboratories with the initial purpose of providing the American people and their leaders with the information needed for intelligent decisions.

At the Met Lab two cardinal documents of the scientists' movement, the Franck Report and Rabinowitch's July 12 memorandum on a scientists' organization, had already outlined principles and practice. There the news of Hiroshima did not precipitate, it merely lent new vigor to earlier discussions which the Committee on Social and Political Implications now extended by calling an open meeting of laboratory staff on Tuesday evening, August 7, to consider a statement about the bomb. Some twenty scientists joined the committee members, and Eugene Rabinowitch was made chairman of a committee to summarize the group's thinking.

At a second meeting on August 13, Farrington Daniels, as Met Lab director, reviewed the substance of the still secret Franck Report, including its suggestions for control of fissionable materials and its plea that the world be informed of the new weapon by some means other than military use. Daniels' summary stressed those points which would become the scientists' principal stock in trade in the coming campaign: the likelihood of speedy imitation by other nations, the dangers of an atomic arms race and the need for controls, the advantage enjoyed by an aggressor, and the inadequacy of any conceivable defense.[16]

With these ideas as the central theme Szilard prepared a draft statement for a meeting on August 15 and Rabinowitch another for August 21.[17] The arguments of the Franck Report, intended for the perusal of statesmen, were transformed into simpler phrases that might capture the attention of a less sophisticated audience.

---

[16] "Memorandum for Daniel's talk to employees," August 13, 1945, in Rabinowitch's files.

[17] Memorandums in ASC IV and XXVI.

The drafts took several weeks of rewriting. The claims to virtual unanimity suggest an easy consensus, and as far as fundamental ideas were concerned, this was true. But argument is a normal ingredient of scientists' conversation, and no one who observed them in those early days, haggling over shades of meaning and minor points of tactics, will be deceived by the formal results. The Szilard draft, for example, contained a section on birth control, which he was with difficulty persuaded to delete as being irrelevant to the main purpose. Contrary to the common impression, many of these men had for years been informed observers of the international scene and much given to private speculation upon it, but the prospect of making public statements made them extremely cautious.

Rabinowitch's contribution was the one selected as a basis for discussion. As considered on August 21 it was divided into three parts: (I) Responsibility of Science in the Postwar World; (II) Analysis of Unsatisfactory Solutions of the Atomic Power Problem; (III) Scattering of Cities, International Controls, and World Government. Section II listed certain slogans that might be used to mislead the public—do not reveal the secret; let's corner the raw materials; let's retain the leadership; a defense is sure to be found; if you smash our cities, we'll smash yours; let's scatter our cities and dig underground; let's prohibit atomic warware—and then proceeded to refute them. The third section proposed measures more likely to succeed: dispersion, international control of atomic energy, and world government.

The evolution of this document proclaims the care with which the scientists were preparing their case. The criticisms directed at Rabinowitch's draft on the twenty-first were reflected in a mimeographed version, dated August 31, with the title "Alternate Draft for Report of Committee on Social and Political Implications—to be considered at meeting of scientists, Tuesday, September 4, 1945." It contained the same basic arguments against the unsatisfactory solutions but in a less journalistic style. The section on valid solutions was greatly modified. Dispersal of cities and population was regarded less hopefully, and world government was omitted entirely; instead, people were urged to think seriously about means of achieving international control as the only alternative not leading to world suicide.

The emphasis upon world government did not, however, disappear without protest. A September 1 memorandum from Robert Maurer maintained that international control involved the relinquishment of "a little sovereignty" and was therefore unsatisfactory as a permanent solution. The conclusion of the final revision (the work of Bernard Weissbourd, J. J. Nickson, Austin Brues, and Eugene Rabinowitch) was a compromise: "Since world government is unlikely to be achieved within the short time available before the atomic armament race will lead to an acute danger of armed conflict, the establishment of international controls must be considered as a problem of immediate urgency."

At the same time Francis Friedman was preparing for more popular consumption a series of questions and answers based upon the false assumptions listed by Rabinowitch's original memorandum, and this provided the basis for much of the propaganda issuing from Chicago in the ensuing year.

A combination of circumstances and personalities was to make the Chicago group one of the most influential elements in the scientists' movement, and it is therefore worth noting what its initial policy statement did and did not say. Its general theme was that the introduction of a new dimension of power into international relations demanded some truly radical countermeasure and that the only one with a chance of success was international control. It stressed the responsibility of scientists to explain the significance of the bomb. It said a great deal about the futility of atomic secrecy, but it did not talk about freedom of science in general, an omission later mentioned by "non-atomic" scientists with a certain asperity and hints that Project scientists wanted to maintain their monopoly of atomic information. But Chicago attributed the omission solely to a wish to avoid the charge that scientists objected to secrecy because it interfered with their work. Its lead in this de-emphasis was followed by other Project site groups.

The statement noted that all scientists did not share in reservations about the bomb's use or feel responsible for its future employment, but the first press release of the Atomic Scientists of Chicago on October 4 claimed the support of 95 per cent of the scientists working on the atomic bomb project at Chicago. Cautious revision a week later to "over 90 per cent"—a figure no one challenged—still left the new organization with impressive support, but as John Simpson later remarked, "that five or ten per cent included people we respected, and that always bothered us."

But it was more than a meticulous desire to reconcile slight variants in opinion that led the Chicago scientists to postpone for two months the publication of their statement. "For some four to six weeks after Hiroshima," Szilard told an audience assembled by the editors of the *Nation* on December 3,

atomic scientists expressed no opinion on the political implications of the bomb, having been requested by the War Department to exercise the greatest possible reserve. Our response to this request does not mean that we were intimidated by the War Department. We kept silent because we all believed that Hiroshima was immediately followed by discussions between the United States, Great Britain, and Russia, as indeed it should have been, and we did not want to embarrass the President or the Secretary of State.[18]

We are never explicitly told through what channel this request reached the scientists, but as we shall see, the substance of it was well understood at all laboratories.

Because of this prohibition, what turned out to be the opening salvo in the scientists' campaign was fired not by the memo writers or the committees of worried young men but by a senior physicist and Manhattan Project administrator, Samuel K. Allison. The occasion of what came to be known as "Sam's butterfly speech" was a luncheon at the Shoreland Hotel on Chicago's South Side on Saturday, September 1, 1945, at which the University of Chicago announced to an audience of newsmen the formation of its new research institutes. Allison, as the newly appointed director of the Institute for Nuclear Studies, with such luminaries as Enrico Fermi and Harold C. Urey already enlisted as members, had come from Los Alamos (where he would continue as associate director until the new year) to be the principal speaker. Fermi, Urey, and some fifteen other present and future Chicago scientists were also there. To his army supervisors, Allison had proved a reliable administrator, a source of sound advice and a soothing influence on the young men when they got excited. Six weeks earlier his voice had sounded across the New Mexico desert in that memorable dawn, counting off the minutes to zero for his tense and anxious colleagues. At forty-four Allison was a tall, stocky figure with a reputation for slumbering through a lively party, then rousing himself suddenly to recite an hilarious tale of human foible or misadventure at the expense of himself or his friends. His usual air of imperturbable calm made doubly effective the occasions when he blurted out some piece of sound common sense in vigorous and quotable language. This was what he did at the Shoreland lunch

---

[18] Szilard, "We Turned the Switch," *Nation*, CLXI (December 22, 1945), 718–19.

on September 1, and his speech got black headlines in next day's *Chicago Tribune:* "Scientist Drops A-Bomb: Blasts Army Shackles."[19]

"We are determined to return to free research, as before the war," the *Tribune* quoted Allison as saying. After a semifacetious description of Los Alamos as virtual imprisonment in a luxurious concentration camp where freedom of speech and communion with fellow scientists were denied him, he warned that if the exchange of scientific information was prohibited by military regulation research workers in America would leave the field of atomic energy and devote themselves to studying the colors of butterfly wings.

The pedagogic calm of the meeting was shattered with the force of an atomic bomb, related the *Tribune* reporter. When Allison referred to the "tragedy" of the second bomb on Nagasaki, newsmen wanted to know whether scientists would work on the bomb if they had the decision to make over again. Only if we were as angry at the dictators as we were in 1942, said Allison. But Urey, who had seconded Allison's remarks about secrecy with characteristic vehemence, objected at this point; he did not wish to be associated with any statement that implied reservations about helping the government in time of need.

Repercussions were prompt. That evening long-distance calls from Colonel Kenneth D. Nichols at Oak Ridge, made at General Groves' request, invited Allison, Fermi, Urey, and Hogness to lunch next day, again at the Shoreland. In the early September heat Allison arrived without a coat and had to borrow the jacket that the hotel kept for University of Chicago professors. His explanation that lunch the previous day had been late and that sheer hunger had made him fractious did not placate Colonel Nichols who viewed the speech as the opening gun in a scientists' campaign against the army and as inaugurating a nation-wide speaking tour. Allison was astonished at this interpretation of his spontaneous outburst. Although not quite as isolated at Los Alamos as his words suggested, he had had no part in the Met Lab discussions of the past year; and besides, he was not cut out to be anybody's mouthpiece. As for the others, Allison recalls that Fermi "squirmed" and Urey "sort of flopped around," as Colonel Nichols made clear that he wished no more said about butterflies. A bill dealing with atomic energy was to be introduced when Congress reconvened and such talk might hurt its chance of passage.[20]

---

[19] *Chicago Tribune*, September 2, 1945, p. 5.
[20] Interviews with Hogness, January 18, 1960, and Allison, January 21, 1960.

Hogness' reaction was chiefly one of shock, for this was the first that he, and he thinks the others, too, had heard of an actual bill. Talk of War Department legislation was already causing uneasiness at Oak Ridge, and it would be surprising if similar rumors had not reached Allison at Los Alamos, Urey at Columbia, or Hogness at Chicago, or if Fermi, as a member of the scientific panel of the Interim Committee, did not have some inkling of what was afoot. Be that as it may, Nichols' statement indicated that the framing of legislation was proceeding apace without opportunity for general discussion among those who had a firsthand working knowledge of nuclear technology.

Nichols could tell them little about the still secret bill, but he assured them that Conant, Bush, and Oppenheimer approved of it. Far from allaying their suspicions, as Nichols expected, this merely provoked further protest. The men to whom Nichols spoke were on friendly terms with the scientist members of Interim Committee and panel. But scientists tend to recognize authority on an *ad hoc* basis, and the fact that men like Conant, Bush, and Oppenheimer had done a good job during the war, was not adequate reason for accepting their opinions about what should happen next. Science and technology have their pecking order, but it applies to fields rather than to individuals; to a remarkable degree a man is judged by the evidence with which he backs up his statements rather than by age or status. Even in the minds of the high-level group Nichols had assembled, there lurked a suspicion of "the brass."

Urey was especially incensed and, according to Hogness' recollection, went to Washington next day and "raised hell," although Urey himself, whose restless mind is more concerned with the present and future than the past, cannot now recall where he went or whom he saw at this point.[21] Certainly he is remembered by others as one of the few who effectively raised the alarm about continued military control of atomic energy and hasty legislation.

In any case, news of Allison's outburst spread quickly among his Project colleagues. Ten days later, Dorothy Thompson's syndicated column cited his remarks about the tragedy of the second bomb on Nagasaki. Atomic scientists, said Miss Thompson, were having to reach the American people through the back door of commentators like herself to warn that there is no monopoly of the basic scientific

---

[21] Interviews with Hogness, January 18, 1960, and Urey, October 17, 1961.

knowledge behind the bomb. The background of this remark is not clear, but on September 12, Waldo Cohn, a biochemist at Clinton Labs, wrote to Miss Thompson to express his satisfaction with what she had printed. With the exception of Allison, who volunteered his remarks, said Cohn, we see no qualified person being consulted. The men in Washington, military and civilian, are adminstrators and are not regarded by us as being equipped to testify in scientific matters. Far from being consulted, he continued, we are encouraged (to put it mildly) to leave formulation of policy to them, which as scientists and citizens we feel we have no right to do.[22] At Oak Ridge, too, it seems, the scientists were extremely sensitive about being "represented" by those whom they had not chosen and whose views they could neither check nor influence.

Leo Szilard, apparently not present at the Shoreland lunch, also viewed the situation with alarm. Like Urey, he could not recollect in detail what he did at this time, but he later identified as his an unsigned four-page memorandum of September 7, 1945, entitled "An Attempt to Define the Platform for Our Conversations with Members of the Senate and House of Representatives."[23] Much of the contents would reappear both in the platform of the atomic scientists and in atomic energy policy as finally adopted. Any domestic control system, said Szilard, should avoid creating vested interests that might make international agreements more difficult. Those who influenced the decisions of an atomic power commission should be connected with atomic energy work on a full-time basis. "Unpaid advisers whose attentions are largely occupied with subjects not connected with the field of atomic power are an evil and must be considered unacceptable." A permanent congressional committee might supervise the management of the atomic power commission; but "the scientists ought to be free, irrespective of any law or administrative order issued by the Atomic Power Commission to communicate to members of that Committee such information as they consider relevant."

Szilard feared that a new espionage act might be attached to domestic legislation on atomic secrecy. As already noted, his attitude about secrecy had provided one of the minor administrative headaches of the Manhattan Project. Szilard never denied his wartime

---

[22] Cohn to Thompson, September 12, 1945, copy in AORES III, 1.

[23] Copy in *Bulletin of the Atomic Scientists* files. Szilard assigned one copy to Charles Coryell at Clinton Labs and others to Met Lab associates John Simpson, H. H. Goldsmith, and David Hill. *The New World* (p. 422) incorrectly makes Simpson the author.

disregard of rules of compartmentation; in fact he later made rather a point of it in congressional testimony and in public speeches. In this private memorandum of September 7, he asked what would happen if an atomic armaments race developed and if scientists, under a reinforced espionage act, again had to choose "between obeying the rules and thereby slowing down the work, or violating the rules and thereby offending the law."

> I think most of us would, in such circumstances, choose to violate the law. Such violations . . . would, of course, not be prosecuted by the Atomic Power Commission. But it would create an intolerable situation in which the scientists involved could be intimidated and could not openly raise their voices in criticism . . . of the Atomic Power Commission without incurring the risk of being prosecuted for violation of the new espionage act.[24]

About the secrets relating directly to the atomic bomb, said Szilard, we must explain to congressmen that the first secret was given away when we dropped the bomb on Hiroshima and the second when the War Department released the Smyth report. There are still undisclosed secrets, Szilard admitted, but they affect further development of atomic bombs rather than the present stage. Congressmen should also be informed that the atomic bomb creates the additional danger of a preventive war arising from the race in the production of bombs, a danger which can be removed only if nations accept close supervision of many of their activities by foreign agents.

The relevance of what Szilard had to say to the bill on which War Department employees were then at work is very marked, but whether this resulted from actual or intuitive knowledge on Szilard's part is hard to say. Either would have been in character. It is virtually the only evidence that the atomic scientists were thinking concretely about domestic control at this time, confirming what all the participants now recollect, that international control and the related problem of secrecy completely dominated their thinking until early October when the terms of the May-Johnson bill became known.

Meanwhile in Chicago, an organization began to take form along the lines suggested by Rabinowitch in his memorandum of July 12. The three-part policy statement of nearly twenty single-spaced pages was somewhat long for enlisting members, and by September 14 an

---

[24] Concern about the penalty for inadvertent disclosure of information was felt throughout the Project; on September 14, 1945, Milton Burton at Clinton Labs wrote to Congressman Hatton W. Sumners of Texas objecting to the death penalty for disclosure of atomic secrets; ASC IX, 8.

organization committee was circulating a more concise proposal of action for signatures. The "General Purpose" of what shortly became the Atomic Scientists of Chicago was conceived as follows:

1. To explore, clarify and consolidate the opinion of the scientists on the problems of the role and responsibility of science, particularly as far as the implications of atomic power are concerned.
2. To present this opinion before the National Administration and to influence the decisions which this country will have to make in the field of atomic power research and applications and international problems resulting from it.
3. To educate public opinion to the full understanding of the scientific, technological and political implications of the new scientific development, particularly those resulting from atomic power.

Two "Immediate Objectives" were proposed:

1. To support the immediate establishment of international controls over atomic power developments, and to work toward a permanent solution of the atomic problem on the basis of a more unified world community.
2. To study and make recommendations as to the national policy on atomic power research and development, the relation between free and secret research, the respective roles of government, universities and industries in the atomic field and similar problems. These recommendations must be correlated with the solution of the main problem under 1.

And finally five "Modes of Action" were offered:

1. Study and discussion within the organization.
2. Preparation of reports to the people and Congress, releases to the press and other publications.
3. Individual contacts with responsible persons who are active in civic affairs. [The penultimate draft had read: Establishment of a "lobby."]
4. Coordination of efforts with similar organizations in this country, Great Britain, Canada and other countries.
5. Organization and encouragement of discussion groups in colleges, universities, etc.

A general meeting on September 25 considered the draft of a constitution and elected a temporary executive committee. Of its seven members, Leo Szilard, J. J. Nickson, Glenn Seaborg, and Eugene Rabinowitch had been on the Franck committee, and John Simpson had led the continuing Committee on Social and Political Implications; other members were Austin M. Brues, a medical biologist, and a young physicist, David Hill.

An important factor in the early and continuing strength of the Atomic Scientists of Chicago was the proximity and support of the

University of Chicago, where parts of the Metallurgical Laboratory continued for some months to occupy their wartime quarters in Eckhart, Ryerson, New Chem, and at "Site B" across the Midway. During the fall and winter of 1945, a number of ASC members returned to posts in the university or took up new appointments there; after 1946 the government laboratories were gradually moved to the new Argonne establishment southwest of Chicago, but until 1947 the association between Met Lab and university personnel remained close.

Chancellor Robert M. Hutchins felt both pride and responsibility for the University's share in the development of atomic energy, and he, as well as members of the political and social science faculties, entered promptly into discussions with the scientists of problems related to the bomb. On September 9, sixty-four university faculty members and Met Lab scientists sent a petition to President Truman, asking that the United States share the secret of the bomb with the United Nations as a gesture of confidence of which time would show the wisdom, magnanimity and daring. The signers included theologians, political scientists, doctors, as well as scientsts.[25]

Hutchins took steps to extend the formulation of opinion beyond the campus by calling a conference on atomic energy at the University of Chicago on September 19 and 20, 1945—the first of many such meetings of troubled scholars and men of affairs. This one was confidential, though no classified material was discussed. Of the fifty conferees over half were laymen, most of them exposed for the first time to atomic energy problems. Distinguished economists and political scientists came from Princeton, Yale, and Columbia. William Benton and Beardsley Ruml offered advice on public relations. Secretary of Commerce Henry A. Wallace and Philip Hauser, director of the Census, unofficially represented government. David Lilienthal, head of TVA, and Chester Barnard, president of the New Jersey Bell Telephone Company, would later help draw up the State Department plan for international control. Here, in all probability, Urey, Szilard, and E. U. Condon shared their fears about the domestic atomic energy program that the War Department was framing.

Chicago scientists took an active part. Szilard was now able to recapitulate the international considerations that he had tried to impress upon government officials the previous spring. And James

---

[25] *New York Times*, September 10, 1945, p. 5. The *New York Times* pointed out that the names of Hutchins, Allison, and A. H. Compton were missing, but neither Allison nor Compton were then living in Chicago.

Franck, a willing and inspiring conversationalist but one whose remarks did not often receive public notice, dealt with that topic which scientists considered central to an understanding of atomic energy problems:

Let us now discuss the damage which the perpetuation of full secrecy will create. It is said and will be said again and again that the great success achieved during the war is the best proof that scientists need to be guided by a rigid control; that they have to be prevented from being led astray by their so-called scientific curiosity; and that no patience should be wasted on the whims of impractical dreamers and prima donnas. While this looks funny to us, it has been said in earnest, in only slightly more polite words, by one of the best known science reporters in one of our very best newspapers. The high-ranking officers of the Army, who officially directed our work, were, of course, much too polite to tell us their opinion *expressis verbis*, and they learned in the years of cooperation a good deal about the ways and methods by which scientific progress is achieved. But so far as secrecy is concerned, they were unrelenting and, in all honesty, we have to admit that they had to be. Nevertheless, let there be no doubt that a stiff price had to be paid for secrecy, not only because of the necessity of building the factories in deserts, but also because of the wasting of talent and scientific manpower, and the loss of precious time by the compartmentalizing which was regarded as necessary. The flow of essential information from one site to another was slow, and, indeed, to a great extent, prevented. One obtained only that information which was regarded as absolutely necessary for his special task, and the decision of what was necessary was, let us put it mildly, not always a good one. If the success achieved by the scientists proves anything, it proves that good swimmers are even able to swim in a lake of molasses. But one cannot expect high efficiency and speed records under such conditions.... If the same kind of secrecy is to remain under Army regulations, enforced by the permanent threat of the espionage law, if nuclear physics and nuclear chemistry are to remain secret sciences in their entirety, without competition, without the responsibility of attracting students by free and open teaching, and without scientific publications, the progress in nucleonics will soon be reduced to zero. Even financial support from private and government sources will not change this picture.[26]

Statements were read from P. W. Bridgman and Albert Einstein, who could not be present. A Washington meeting prevented Fermi's attendance, but from Los Alamos, where he would remain until January, he sent his comments to Hutchins. Since Fermi's great affability in sharing his non-scientific views in private conversation, especially with younger associates, was matched by an extreme reserve

---

[26] Excerpt from a speech by James Franck at the University of Chicago Conference on Atomic Energy, September 19–20, 1945 (proceedings and speeches of the conference in ASC XXVIII, Vol. XV).

in stating them publicly, it is instructive to see what they were at this point. Fermi wrote:

There is general agreement, I believe, on the following points:

That the new weapon has such destructiveness that in case of a war between two powers both armed with atomic bombs, both belligerents, even the victor, would have their cities destroyed.

That the atomic bomb gives an unprecedented advantage to a sudden attacker.

That the balance between defensive and offensive is strongly shifted in favor of the second. Perhaps the only effective defensive measure is a very extensive decentralization of our urban and production centers.

I believe that also the following points are true although the agreement as to them is perhaps less general at least in the non-scientific public:

That secrecy on the industrial aspects of the development would slow up a potential competing nation by only a few years.

That secrecy on the scientific phases of the development not only would be of little effect but soon would hamper the progress of nuclear physics in this country to such an extent as to even make it exceedingly difficult to grasp the importance of new discoveries made elsewhere in the field.

From these points one conclusion emerges. That it is imperative that this country not only should have but should put in operation in a very limited time a policy to face the new dangers. Inaction, hope that things may reach of themselves a satisfactory settlement or engaging in a half-hearted race of armaments would be in my opinion fatal mistakes.

The possibility of an honest international agreement should be explored energetically and hopefully. That such agreement may prove possible is, I know, the most fervent hope of the men who have contributed to the development. In their optimistic moments they express the view that perhaps the new dangers may lead to an understanding between nations much greater than has been thought possible until now.

One of the main reasons why I regret not to be able to attend the conference is that I lose the opportunity to hear the views of people more experienced than I am in international affairs on the practicability of an international agreement supplemented by effective control measures.

A few remarks as to the peaceful possibilities of atomic energy. There is little doubt that the applications both to industry and to sciences other than physics will develop rapidly. One of the great advantages of an international agreement would be to permit the free growth of such application outside of the shadow of the war use of the new discoveries.

Please accept the expression of my regret for not being able to come to the conference.[27]

Szilard, Franck, and Fermi had had years in which to formulate their ideas. It is more remarkable that six weeks after Hiroshima the

---

[27] Fermi to Hutchins, September 14, 1945, ASC XXVIII, Vol. XV.

political and social scientists, chiefly from Yale's Institute of International Studies and the University of Chicago, were ready with papers on "Strategic Consequences of the Atomic Bomb," "Control through Existing Types of International Organization," "Control of the Atomic Bomb by Mutual Inspection," "Dispersal of Population and Industry," and "Controlling Atomic Power by Treaty."

These papers must have broadened somewhat the views of the scientists. They, in turn, believed that through this conference the thinking of a number of important people was "jogged into the right tracks,"[28] and indeed several of the non-scientists present were shortly asked to testify at congressional hearings on atomic energy and science legislation.

University sponsorship of interdisciplinary discussion continued, and research projects were undertaken by the Office of Enquiry into the Social Aspects of Atomic Energy, established by sociologist Edward Shils and Dean Robert Redfield of the Division of Social Sciences. A factor of no small significance in the success and influence of the Atomic Scientists of Chicago was the $10,000 that Chancellor Hutchins drew from special educational funds to support its initial efforts and those of a Washington office.

3. CLINTON LABORATORIES

The impulse of Project scientists to organize in order to educate themselves and others in the implications of atomic energy was rapidly reinforced by uneasiness about channels of communication with those who were formulating national policy. About the past or future activities of the body on which scientists were supposed to be represented, the Interim Committee and its scientific panel, scientists in general received no news, and the fear spread that they might be left without any means of voicing their opinions except such as was allowed them by the army. How adequate this would be was not entirely clear. It became evident in August and early September that written communication between the sites was still subject to censorship, and a directive issued by Colonel Nichols just after Hiroshima reminded Oak Ridge scientists that "the official statements and re-

---

[28] John Simpson, "Federation of Scientific Organizations Proceedings (mimeographed), November 16, 1945, p. 146. Lilienthal has recently published his notes on the Chicago conference with the comment that it is remarkable to see the extent to which the issues raised there have remained lively, unresolved, and basic to American policy (David E. Lilienthal, *Journals of David E. Lilienthal*, Vol. II: *The Atomic Energy Years, 1945–1950* [New York: Harper & Row, 1964], Appendix A, pp. 637–45).

leases comprise permissible limits of disclosure of information at this time. Independent publications, addresses or advertising by individuals or groups cannot be released without prior clearance."[29]

This fear of Army interference was a dominant element in the organizing of scientists at Oak Ridge, where the whole character of the wartime operation differed very much from the university oriented one at Chicago. Some scientists at Oak Ridge were concerned with research on the various methods of providing fissionable materials for a bomb, others with pilot production plants. K-25 was the code name for the gaseous diffusion plant operated by the Carbide and Carbon Chemicals Company, a subsidiary of the Union Carbide and Carbon Corporation; Y-12 was an electro-magnetic plant run by Tennessee Eastman; and X-10 referred to the Clinton Laboratories, working on plutonium research. On July 1, 1945, the Monsanto Chemical Company took over the management of the Clinton Labs from the University of Chicago. The personnel was so successfully segregated that as late as mid-November a leader in the Clinton Labs scientists' organization did not know personally any member of the organizations at the other plants, and three separate groups sprang up in the late summer of 1945. Those at K-25 and Y-12, predominantly engineers, combined in December, 1945. Amalgamation with the organization at Clinton Labs was discussed at the same time but did not take place until June, 1946.

The group at Clinton Labs, which became the Association of Oak Ridge Scientists, or AORS, was the one that most effectively made contact with people at other Project laboratories with whom its members shared a common academic background. Many had come from the Chicago Met Lab. Of all the site organizations, the Clinton Labs men showed the strongest disposition to take prompt and direct political action. The dip in morale that was noted among them as the war neared its end and the sense of being cut off from knowledge of how the Project was going came to a head in a fit of G.I. gripes when the management insisted on business-as-usual on the day of the Japanese armistice. Ill disposed to work, a large part of the Physics department congregated in the library, and a bull session developed into an exchange of fears and hopes about the future of atomic energy more open than any that had hitherto taken place. Similar sessions

---

[29] Meeting notes, September 22, 25, 1945, AORES I, 5; II, 2; Nichols to Rush, n.d. (in pencil: "immediately after Hiroshima"), in Rush's files.

were held in the next few weeks with a gradual increase in numbers. The participants viewed with increasing alarm the apparent belief of the public that the United States had a secret that would guarantee its safety. The conviction grew that they must dispel this illusion.

The direction of their thinking is well illustrated in a letter of August 21, 1945, from Joseph H. Rush to Senator Elbert Thomas, chairman of the Senate Military Affairs Committee. This letter, one of many that Rush was to write in the next two years on behalf of AORS or the Federation of American Scientists, seems to have been the first postwar attempt by scientists at political contact and contains the earliest reference to a War Department atomic energy bill. A United Press story on August 20 had quoted Senator Thomas as speaking of the discovery of a secret belonging to the American people that should be used for their benefit. It was necessary to understand, said Rush, that this discovery was one that others likewise could make. It remained to be seen what the President would recommend, but he found it disquieting that the measure was being prepared in the War Department. He was not against proper safeguards, but these should not be extended to such lengths as to stifle free research. "I hope," Rush went on,

that my concern is unnecessary; but the military is by nature conservative and even short-sighted, and it is of the utmost importance that the Congress and the public at large should realize that we have but reached a new phase in a field of inquiry of which the atomic bomb is only a crude pioneering expression. Such an agency will not be confined to national boundaries.

You will understand, of course, that I have expressed these views as an interested scientist and citizen, and without relation to my employment in the Project.[30]

No minutes were kept of the earliest discussions at Clinton Labs, but both Rush and Paul C. Tompkins jotted down notes about them within the next few weeks. When "most of the physics department" held an informal meeting on August 31 and appointed Rush, R. Scalletar, and D. Saxon to draft proposals for action, complaints about buses, cafeteria service, working hours, and salaries were still in evidence, but in a series of daily meetings the following week these trivial issues were submerged in concern with developments relating to atomic energy. Eight people met as an informal steering committee to draw up a statement summarizing all this talk. They agreed that

---

[30] Rush to Senator Thomas, August 21, 1945, in Rush's files.

action should be taken, and a larger group assembled on September 8, divided into committees: executive, planning, information and records, contacts, and editorial.[31]

By September 14 a statement of intent was being circulated among the Clinton Labs scientific personnel for signatures. The new organization proposed to publicize the conviction that there could be no monopoly of the atomic bomb and the conclusion that the security of the United States required international control under adequate safeguards. Action would take the form of individual and group communication with public officials, testimony at congressional hearings, and getting views before the public through the various news media and through contacts with national and civic leaders.[32]

It is no doubt true that certain ideas and the determination to organize in support of them arose independently at the various sites, but copies of the Chicago draft of August 31 reached Oak Ridge, as did a copy of Szilard's September 7 memorandum, cautiously identified only as "to group from Coryell—memo received from outside." Probably this happened before the two statements of purpose, both dated September 14, were circulated at Chicago and Clinton. AORS did not mention self-education. Otherwise the two statements were very similar. Like Chicago, AORS avoided the word "lobby," but it clearly intended to apply pressure as needed.

Also on September 14 Los Alamos was drawn in when Robert Wilson received through the Project intelligence officer (it is not clear whether his intervention was by design or accident) a message from H. H. Goldsmith in Chicago saying that "a few of us" would be down at Clinton September 17 through 19 and hoped that someone from Los Alamos could discuss "the programs concerned with social implications of our respective groups and their possible coordination."[33]

This first intersite meeting on September 17, fitted in between official conferences, was briefly noted by Paul Tompkins: "met fellows from Chicago and Los Alamos and found them organizing for the same purpose. They had also drawn up statements expressing identical views. These were exchanged. Copies of all were duplicated for distribution where they would do the most good." Behind this laconic record was a mounting excitement. When he returned to Los Alamos Vernon Cannon reported:

---

[31] "Oak Ridge History," in Rush's files.
[32] *Ibid.*; AORS statement of intent and related material in AORES I, 6.
[33] Message conveyed to R. Wilson, September 14, 1945, ALAS IV, 1.

I was literally pounced upon by people hungry for news of political activity at Los Alamos—the size of the Association—is Oppenheimer a member—why not [he joined as soon as he resigned as director]—Teller, Bethe—the restrictions on publicity—and hundreds of other questions. The Clinton group is exceedingly anxious for close contact with the group here, for amalgamation, if it seems a wise move, and for advice from this group which they feel is in a stronger position than their own because of its larger size, its better known personnel, its direct contact with the bomb research, and its support by Oppenheimer in whom they have considerable confidence.[34]

Clinton Labs chemist Charles Coryell, writing to Los Alamos friends, said he had been "shocked" by the similarity of thoughts and action taken by the three segregated groups. "We may be blind to certain holes in our plans and flaws in our arguments," he said, "because we found it too easy to achieve essentially unanimous consensus."[35]

Collaboration, however, got off to a slightly rocky start. While the guests from Chicago and Los Alamos were still there, the Clinton Labs group wrote a letter to Senator Arthur H. Vandenberg of Michigan commending his resolution setting up a joint committee on atomic energy. It was signed by a hundred and ten people in chemistry, physics, and biology and health physics and entrusted to Hy Goldsmith of Chicago, who was en route to Washington, with instructions to mail it there or, if he wished an excuse for an interview, to deliver it in person to Vandenberg. But in an impromptu conference on tactics Goldsmith and Szilard decided the move was unwise and Goldsmith pocketed the letter, casually informing the men at Clinton a week or so later. Not at all pleased, they sent it to Vandenberg anyway, though by the time he received it his resolution had already passed the Senate.[36]

Meanwhile the site statements exchanged at Oak Ridge received their first public notice. On Friday morning, September 21, Clinton Labs biologist Paul Henshaw, in Washington on professional business, called on Raymond Swing, Mutual's star commentator, whose weekly broadcasts on atomic energy had impressed the scientists with his understanding of its implications. When Swing saw the Clinton, Met Lab, and Los Alamos statements he wanted to use them that very

---

[34] Tompkins' "Outline of Development of AORSCL," AORES II, 2; ALAS Log, October 3, 1945, and Cannon's penciled notes in ALAS II, 2.

[35] Coryell to N. and G. Sugarman, September 21, 1945, AORES III, 9.

[36] Rush to Vandenberg, September 18, 1945, and related material in AORES III, 3.

evening, but Henshaw felt bound by the intersite decision to hold up publication until the administration had announced a policy. Phoning Oak Ridge for advice, he was told by his AORS associates that Swing might use the statements provided that neither laboratory nor individual names were mentioned. The statement of intent, Henshaw learned, was being circulated to test army reaction, but so far there had been none.[37] Swing used the site statements in the specified way, giving the scientists' groups their first major publicity; henceforth, he became one of their most vocal supporters.

The following day, Henshaw called on Senator Tom Connally, chairman of the Foreign Relations Committee, to challenge a statement attributed to Connally that every offense produced a defense and that civilization could survive atomic war as it had survived floods, plagues, and other catastrophes. Connally also wanted copies of the site statements to use at the next meeting of his committee. Again Henshaw consulted his friends at Clinton Labs, but they decided not to risk a leak to the press through Connally's committee and drafted a special letter to him instead.[38]

These first collective acts by Clinton Labs had been preceded by numerous individual overtures fortuitously determined by inspiration or personal acquaintance. When Coryell, known as a man of boundless energy, was urged by his Los Alamos correspondents, Nathan and Goldie Sugarman, to apply that energy to problems produced by the bomb he explained that this was not a new idea at Oak Ridge and that already (on September 21) vacation trips to the east coast had been put to good use. With an organization to back them these contacts increased, their importance underlined by realization that after the first frenzied interest press and public were devoting little attention to atomic energy. The newspapers were occupied with the myriad aspects of transition from war to peace. The movement of occupation forces, the signing of the peace with Japan, the return of servicemen, the now shortened but hope-killing casualty lists, and the horrors of Bataan competed for public attention with the Labor Day traffic jam of the first peacetime holiday, an elevator strike in New York, the threat of a long distance phone tie-up, and the return of tails to men's shirts and whipping cream to the dinner table.

[37] Tompkins' "Outline," AORES II, 2.

[38] Interview with Henshaw, December 27, 1962; Tompkins, "Outline," AORES II, 2; Cohn to Hy [Goldsmith], n.d., *Bulletin of the Atomic Scientists* files.

Congress reconvened ahead of schedule to cope with peacetime problems: the relaxation of controls, agricultural commodity price supports, and above all, tax reduction. On September 6, the Senate received the Vandenberg proposal for a joint committee on atomic energy and from Brien McMahon, the junior senator from Connecticut, a very unripe resolution providing that the UN Security Council be licensed to conduct nuclear research; but Congress was far more interested in the appointment of a committee to investigate Pearl Harbor. When the foreign ministers conference opened in London on September 10, the *New York Times* forecast that the atomic bomb would overshadow all its meetings, but little explicit evidence of this seeped into subsequent reports. Early in September the *Times* published William L. Laurence's description of the bomb's damage in Japan and of the bombing flight over Nagasaki. Secretary of the Interior Harold L. Ickes announced that Alamogordo would be a national monument, and the bomb site there was opened to newsmen with Geiger counters so they could see how little radiation remained and could evaluate reports from Hiroshima and Nagasaki of great residual amounts.

But such items were hardly evidence of major policy formulation. On September 12, the *New York Times'* military commentator, Hanson W. Baldwin, pointed out that five weeks had passed since Hiroshima and nothing had been done about the atomic bomb. The great surge of awe and interest had slackened, he said, and by failing to enlist atomic fission in winning the peace, the United States was losing her moral leadership. A *Times* editorial on September 19 referred to the issue of keeping the secret of the bomb that had arisen between physicists and statesmen, but its columns had failed to reflect any such discussion.

Two days after Raymond Swing's broadcast about the site organizations two Clinton Labs chemists, Spofford G. English and Harrison Brown, began three days of exploration in New York City on behalf of the newly formed contacts committee. English eventually became an assistant general manager of the Atomic Energy Commission and Brown, writing and speaking widely on the impact of science, an internationally known geochemist at California Institute of Technology. In 1945, they were two obscure but earnest young scientists.

Their interviews, however, produced immediate results, and the trail they laid can be picked up at numerous points in the future. Brown in company with Eugene Wigner saw Mrs. Roosevelt, who "was very nice," grasped their ideas at once, and offered introductions in Washington. Her column on September 25 reflected their visit. She was disturbed, she said, by talk in the press of keeping the secret of the bomb. The sovereignty we would have to renounce to achieve international control would be a small price to pay for the avoidance of a nuclear arms race.[39]

Making the rounds of editorial offices English and Brown left copies of site statements at McGraw-Hill, with Bruce Bliven of the *New Republic*, and with William L. Shirer. They called on Norman Cousins of the *Saturday Review of Literature*, whose August 18 editorial, "Modern Man Is Obsolete," had shown so prompt an understanding of the bomb's challenge, and he put them in touch with thirty or forty internationally minded public figures who eventually helped with articles, advice, and fund raising.[40] On the third day of their New York tour they dropped in at the office of the *New York Herald Tribune* to ask advice about press contacts and to their surprise were offered a front-page story on September 26 if they would release the AORS statement and indicate the extent of support behind it. They immediately phoned Oak Ridge for instructions, creating a minor crisis in the new organization. To understand why, we must review the agitated discussions of policy and procedure that had been taking place almost daily among the Clinton Labs scientists.

Their chief concern was the extent to which the army would tolerate independent action. In retrospect this anxiety seems slightly neurotic, but it had been fostered by a few official pronouncements and by a flock of rumors. On September 12, Colonel Nichols, in charge of the Manhattan Engineer District office at Oak Ridge, had again written to Clinton Labs employees to say that although slightly more latitude was being given individuals and organizations to issue statements, within the limits of information officially released, it was still necessary to submit such statements in writing; facilities had been set up at Oak Ridge for handling requests expeditiously.[41] This was mildly reassuring, but the Clinton Labs men had got wind of a more stringent directive issued by the Carbide and Carbon Chemicals Corporation of Oak Ridge, and signed by an officer of the Army, to employees at the K-25 gaseous diffusion plant prohibiting discussion

---

[39] *Washington Daily News*, September 25, 1945.
[40] Vernon Cannon's penciled notes in ALAS II, 2.
[41] Form letter from Colonel Nichols in Rush's and Henshaw's files.

or speculation on (a) international agreements, beyond presidential releases; (b) postwar usage of the principle; (c) postwar use of present facilities; (d) medical speculation; and (e) relative importance of various methods, plans, their relative functions or efficiency.[42]

On September 19, Rush, Coryell, Cohn, and Weinberg met with A. H. Compton, M. D. Whitaker, the director of Clinton Labs, and his assistant, R. L. Doan, to discuss "the directive forbidding discussion of political and social implications." The scientists explained what they were doing to organize and make outside contacts. Compton, as director of the plutonium project, assured them of his support. So long as they did not violate security regulations, he thought they were within their constitutional rights. The questions they proposed could best be handled by the general scientific group rather than by those involved in administration like himself.[43]

In the 1930's, when these younger colleagues were learning elementary physics and chemistry, Compton had been one of a handful of American scientists ready to demonstrate their awareness of social problems by joining the Association of Scientific Workers. But now his administrative responsibilities induced in him a cautious ambivalence. He was not at liberty to tell them all he knew of official intentions; he assured them that their views were fully shared by the three scientists on the Interim Committee, Bush, K. T. Compton, and Conant, and by the panel, of which he was a member, an assurance that they interpreted as a kind of betrayal when they learned within the next few weeks that these men were endorsing a bill which made possible continued military control. But when the Clinton men asked him about the ban on political and social discussions, Compton did not equivocate. He offered them, in fact, a direct line to the Interim Committee for any opinions they wished to express.

(What Whitaker and Doan said was not recorded. Probably, one AORS member now reflects, Whitaker protected them more often than they realized. Some early AORS meetings took place on company time; section chiefs were among the most generous contributors to the first appeal for funds; and when a scientist in the newly formed organization at the Carbide laboratory in New York reported pressure

---

[42] As quoted by Frank Kingdon over WMCA, October 16, 1945; text of broadcast in AORES XIV, 2.

[43] "Notes for an Oak Ridge History," in Rush's files; Tompkins "Outline," AORES II, 2; an anonymous "Rough Historical Note," AORES I, 5. Since no such directive appears in the AORS records, I assume it is the Carbide letter they discussed.

not to make statements, Rush replied that management at Clinton had indicated only that it did not wish to be involved one way or the other. However, a few weeks later the Association of Oak Ridge Scientists was asked to drop Clinton Labs from its name.[44])

The substance of the September 19 conference was relayed to a meeting of Sections C II, III, IV, and VI on the twenty-second. Anxiety about communication with Washington and with other sites was reflected in the discussion—Clinton Labs now learned that personal mail in and out of Los Alamos had been censored for two years; the letter to Coryell from Los Alamos suggesting action had taken eleven days to reach him; a copy of AORS' statement of intent had been removed from an envelope addressed to Los Alamos; the use of personal messengers between sites was recommended.[45]

This meeting had convened at 8:30 A.M. Evidently word had not yet reached Oak Ridge of remarks made by General Groves the previous day in New York City, where he had received a scroll from Mayor Fiorello La Guardia at City Hall, then been tendered a luncheon at the Waldorf by the International Business Machines Corporation, followed by a press conference. The gist of Groves's remarks at these several events, as reported in the press, was that "if this nation controlled the atomic bomb for a few years until other nations are prepared to share it, we will go a long way toward preserving universal peace." News accounts made much of Groves's disagreement with the scientists' estimates that other nations could have an atomic bomb in two to five years. "The more they talk," Groves was quoted as saying, "the shorter the time seems to get, but they are thinking of science and theory and not of building and operating a plant."[46]

The scientists at Clinton Labs (and also at Los Alamos) were exasperated that while they were asked to keep silent Groves used his official position to discredit their opinions. And so on September 22, presumably after the morning meeting, a protest was drawn up to the Interim Committee to be forwarded by Compton in accordance with his recent offer. Expressing alarm at the false sense of security encouraged by Groves's statement, the letter denied that other nations would be unable to marshal the resources of men and industry sufficient to duplicate the bomb.

---

[44] Bonner to Rush, October 9, 1945; Rush to Bonner, October 19, 24, 1945, AORES II, 8; memorandum, November 28, 1945, AORES I, 5.

[45] Meeting notes, September 22, 1945, AORES I, 5; Cohn to [Goldsmith], ca. September 24, 1945, *Bulletin of the Atomic Scientists* files.

[46] *New York Times*, September 22, 1945, p. 3.

Up to this time, security regulations and interpretations based on them have largely prevented us from making our convictions known to the public. Fully aware of our responsibilities, we have conscientiously complied with all rules imposed on us, as shown by the very successful maintenance of secrecy thus far.

The statement by General Groves, in view of his official position, tends to discount in advance the opinion of the scientific workers of the Project, the only large group of the population having intimate knowledge of its details and implications. Together with the Army policy of abridging free expression even in matters not connected with technical problems, it interferes, we believe, with the development of an intelligent public opinion and policy based upon the pertinent facts in a situation of transcendent importance for the future of this country.

We respectfully request, therefore, that the Interim Committee take steps to make clear to the public that General Groves did express only his personal opinion and that he did not represent the project in his official capacity.

We request furthermore that we be granted full and explicit recognition of our right as citizens of the United States to express in public and without censorship our opinions in all matters that do not involve disclosure of technical information.

In view of the urgency of the situation due to impending Congressional action, we are in conscience bound to ask for an immediate reply to our request. We feel sure that it will be recognized that our only motivation is our regard for the welfare and security of our nation.[47]

Warren Johnson, chemistry section chief at Clinton, was going to Chicago and took this letter along for additional signatures. On the evening of September 24, he phoned that a wire was on its way to Oak Ridge with one hundred names, but by 10 A.M. the following day, when the meeting convened to consider the release to the *Herald Tribune*, the wire had not come, and the release was discussed against a background of increased uneasiness about freedom of communication. Neither Oak Ridge nor Chicago records reveal the fate of the lost signatures; with or without them, Compton forwarded the protest to the Interim Committee, but circumstances did not favor a prompt reply. On the very day Groves spoke, Secretary Stimson turned over control of the War Department to his successor Robert P. Patterson. Many matters must have appeared more urgent to the new secretary than the captious complaints of a few scientists about General Groves. On October 2, George L. Harrison, deputy chairman of the Interim Comittee, wrote Compton that he would bring the Clinton Labs' letter to Patterson's attention. As for the In-

---

[47] Copies in ASC XXVIII, Vol. XIV, and in AORES III, 10.

terim Committee, wrote Harrison, it was and would remain fairly inactive until it got a report from its scientific panel, but as an advisory committee, it had never been empowered to grant or to deny the right to express opinions.[48] As we shall shortly see, the Los Alamos scientists were also under some misapprehension about the function of this committee and what they might expect from it.

This incident helps to explain why those who attended the meeting on September 25 were so exercized about the timing of their first public statement, into which they felt prematurely pushed by the call from Brown and English. From Chicago Johnson reported rumors that an official pronouncement on atomic energy—presumably a presidential message—might be made on Friday, three days hence, and the Chicago group wanted to wait and make a joint statement. There was another complication: the proof of strong support requested by the *Herald Tribune* was not yet ready because the signatures collected during the past ten days had not been carefully analyzed. How far should they lay their cards on the table? Should they concentrate on the issue of secrecy and postpone the question of international control? Comments on all these points produced ten typed pages of notes and must have absorbed the remainder of the working morning. When they finished an hour and a half was left before Brown and English expected an answer. A committee of three, J. H. Rush, R. N. Lyon, and W. E. Cohn, was delegated to frame a release, and E. G. Bohlmann was to complete the analysis of signatures that he had begun while the meeting was in progress. Statement and figures would be phoned to New York and Brown and English left to judge the wisdom of releasing them.

Brown and English decided in favor of the release in the *Herald Tribune* and made it the following day, September 26, on behalf of the Association of Oak Ridge Scientists at Clinton Laboratories, comprising 96 per cent of the civilian physicists, chemists, engineers, and biologists at the main research and development laboratory at Oak Ridge, all having one to three years of experience in the development of the bomb and plants for its production. We feel it our responsibility, they said, to point out certain facts about the atomic bomb to the American people: we can expect no enduring monopoly; other scientists know the fundamental principles and would not be handicapped, as we were, by the uncertainty that a bomb was feasible.

---

[48] Harrison to Compton, October 2, 1945, copy in AORES III, 10.

The Smyth report has revealed that several different processes have been successfully employed, and other independent attempts can now be made with the knowledge that the goal is achievable.

We believe that there is only one way open to us as a nation. Every effort must be made immediately to arrange for the control of this weapon by a world authority which can exercise complete and effective control of the production of the essential materials and of their use in every country.[49]

Other papers noted the new organization and its statement the following day.

The effort to estimate accurately the strength of support behind this public statement raised some delicate questions of internal policy at the meeting on September 25: Had action up to this point fairly represented opinion at Oak Ridge? Had the statement of intent been adequately circulated? Should membership depend upon academic training, laboratory status, or simply upon being interested and informed? A member of the health physics division said his group had been busy and had had no part in action taken to date.

It was explained then and later that the movers of the organization had no intention of acting undemocratically, but being "scared to death" of army interference had feared to nullify their efforts by spreading their discussions too widely. Bohlmann's compilation of signatures to the September 14 statement indicated a fairly solid front:[50]

	Number	Per Cent
Contacted	170	93.4
Signed	162	95.3
No	4	2.4
Undecided	4	2.4
On vacation	12	
Total (chemistry, physics, engineering, medicine)	182	

In any case, the suggestion that their procedure had been high-handed was taken to heart, and when on October 4 the Association of Oak Ridge Scientists at Clinton Labs was formalized, the executive committee represented the sections of the laboratory on the basis of numerical strength. The single representative from biology, Paul Henshaw, became chairman of the committee and hence of the organization. The other officers, all from chemistry, were E. G. Bohl-

---

[49] Text in FAS VII, 2; New York Herald Tribune, September 26, 1945.
[50] Notes in AORES I, 5.

mann, recording secretary, Waldo Cohn, corresponding secretary, and J. G. Stangby, treasurer. The other chemists were Harrison Brown, Spofford G. English, and R. P. Metcalf. K. Z. Morgan represented health physics; L. B. Borst and J. H. Rush, physics; and R. N. Lyon and M. D. Peterson, the technical division. This committee met two and three times a week for the next few critical months, with lunchtime sessions resumed in the evening and lasting late. Its members served on at least one of six other main committees and on subcommittees as well.

By October 2, a new statement of purpose was ready for circulation, and those who signed constituted the membership of the Association of Oak Ridge Scientists at Clinton Laboratories. The earlier statement was broadened to include the responsibility to define and outline adequate safeguards in connection with international control and by the addition of a third objective: "To promote in the future the attainment and use of scientific and technological advances in the best interests of humanity."[51]

The question of emphasis upon relaxation of secrecy or international control, debated inconclusively in that long meeting on the twenty-fifth, had been decided in favor of international control. The reasoning behind this decision was explained by Rush to Francis T. Bonner of the SAM Laboratory at Columbia, who had seen the *Herald Tribune* story and, after asking for further information about the Oak Ridge organization, inquired why they had not come out for relaxation of security regulations. Rush explained:

We feel that if we demand relaxation of restrictions in advance of decisions of broad political policy, we shall be liable to the accusation that we are acting merely as a pressure group to obtain narrow professional objectives. Quite aside from that question of tactics, I am certain that many of us would be unwilling to see a policy of relaxation of secrecy instituted in advance of political decisions consistent with such a policy. We are therefore concentrating on the central issues expressed in our Statement of Intent, feeling sure that intelligent action on them will resolve the internal questions as well.[52]

When the organizers of AORS were debating the timing of their public announcement and the weight of opinion behind it, the ques-

---

[51] Tompkins' "Outline," AORES II, 2; "Plan for Formal Organization of AORSCL," in Rush's files.
[52] Rush to Bonner, September 29, 1945, AORES II, 8.

tion arose of including people at Y-12 and K-25, where it was rumored there were stirrings of interest, but no one was well informed about the character and strength of sentiment there. AORS men regarded themselves as an action group and foresaw that the difficulties of reaching agreement and implementing it promptly would multiply with numbers and diversity. This continued to be their attitude for some months even after scientists and engineers at K-25 and Y-12 gave proof of genuine concern. Whether the aloofness of AORS stemmed to any degree from a belief that more than a physical gulf existed between scientists and engineers was never, of course, explicitly stated.

In retrospect, a marked difference between the two groups is apparent, and it was diametrically opposite to what one would, offhand, expect. The scientists, many of them absorbed professionally in highly abstruse theory, swung into action as political tacticians; the engineers, or at least those who took any part in the movement at all, concentrated on longer range solutions and became enthusiastic students of world organization.

Four people, meeting in a dormitory lounge on September 13 to discuss world government provided, in fact, the nucleus of the organization at Y-12 that later called itself the Atomic Production Scientists of Oak Ridge, nick-named APSOR. They agreed that the bomb could not be kept secret and that some form of international control of it was necessary. Meeting five more times in the next three weeks with a gradual increase in numbers, they decided to postpone the study of world government and to organize a group like that at Clinton Labs, about which they learned late in September. APSOR's statement of intent declared its objective to be "the advancement of research and development in the field of atomic energy and nuclear physics with a maximum benefit to humanity" and assumed responsibility for advising the public and Congress on all matters relating to scientific and technological problems. Control of the bomb must be based upon the facts of "no secret" and "no defense."[53]

The beginnings of the third group at the K-25 plant have left no trace in the files. It organized early in November as the Atomic Engineers of Oak Ridge and in late December, 1945, merged with

---

[53] Wm. R. Kittredge, "World Government Groups at Oak Ridge," AORES VII, 2. Notes of meetings in September, 1945, list as present J. Balderston, D. Gruen, W. McLean, and D. Wehmeyer and later T. Rockwell and R. Benner, AORES II, 4.

APSOR to form the Oak Ridge Engineers and Scientists. The contributions of these groups will be described in a later chapter.

Close on the heels of the September 26 release from Clinton Labs came nation-wide publicity for Oak Ridge in Daniel Lang's *New Yorker* article, "The Atomic City."[54] Lang was much impressed by the vast installation in the Tennessee hills and by the thirty-five miles of circuitous driving required to view the sprawling community of plants, houses, and shops scattered across Roane and Anderson counties. It was amusing for Oak Ridge readers to see all this described in the *New Yorker*'s sophisticated prose and mildly satisfying also to have their accomplishments publicly recognized. But a few passages annoyed and disturbed the scientists at Clinton Labs, notably one referring to an encounter with an Oak Ridge physicist:

> The physicist gave what seemed a slightly demented giggle. "I still don't see how my job ties up with the bomb," he said, "and I certainly don't know any more than you do just from reading the papers. I wouldn't know what to say even if I did open my mouth, but I'm going around not talking!"

This was not the image to inspire public confidence in the scientists' claim to special knowledge and awareness. Spofford English exploded to E. B. White of the *New Yorker* in a postscript to an otherwise dignified letter on behalf of the contacts committee. Where in hell, English wanted to know, did Lang get hold of the giggling physicist who knew only what he read in the papers. In three years at Oak Ridge, English said, he had never met such a person.[55]

Lang had indeed visited Oak Ridge during that period of agitated daily meetings on tactics and policy, but when Clinton Labs men tried to see him, English reported to White, they were told that he was not interested in taking sides. This reply did not, in point of fact, originate with Lang, who knew nothing of the ferment at Clinton Labs and regarded the giggling physicist as a "loner" obliquely expressing his indignation at secrecy and compartmentation. Lang's eventual sympathetic interpretation of the scientists' movement was based on later acquaintance with the federation in Washington.[56]

---

[54] Lang, "The Atomic City, Oak Ridge, September 20," *New Yorker*, XXI (September 29, 1945), 48–55. This and Lang's other articles on the early atomic age are reprinted in Daniel Lang, *From Hiroshima to the Moon* (New York: Simon & Schuster, 1959).

[55] S. G. English to E. B. White, October 26, 1945, AORES III, 7.

[56] Interview with Lang, October 21, 1964.

4. LOS ALAMOS

Last of the "big three" to issue a public statement were scientists at the Los Alamos Laboratory, although they had preceded the Met Lab and Clinton by several weeks in completing the formalities of organization. The meeting of March, 1945, had postponed the question of organization, or even a definition of its purpose, until more open discussion was possible, but a few days after the war ended activity was resumed when a small group met on August 20 (Roger Sutton, William Woodward, Morris Perlman, Robert Christy, and William Higinbotham) and resolved the earlier argument over objectives by agreeing to give priority to political problems and drafted a proposal for general circulation.[57]

Meeting later the same day some sixty people confirmed the decision to ignore "the economic stability of scientists" and agreed to organize for political discussion, leaving the question of affiliation with other groups until later. This anxiety about professional security cropped up briefly at all the sites, affecting particularly those whose school and college years had been shadowed by the depression and who now realized that they had spent their formative research period in a field with an uncertain future. Slightly older men with assured positions had no such concern, and at Los Alamos the influential voice of Hans Bethe helped turn the tide against union-like activity by persuading his young friends that one worry they would not have in the coming years was jobs.

Plans for a meeting of all interested people on the hill were entrusted to Sutton, Woodward, Christy, and Higinbotham of the sponsoring committee plus Paul Olum and Robert Wilson, whose interest dated back to the first X Division meeting in 1944. The new committee dealt with a residue of dissent from those who wanted to discuss the "democratization of the laboratory," and before an organization meeting was held on August 30 "it was clear to everyone that the international control of atomic energy . . . should be the only issue with which the organization was concerned."[58]

Even now Los Alamos people knew little or nothing about the Franck Report's analysis of the bomb's impact upon world relations. The international bent that so promptly imbued their thinking, in-

---

[57] Notes in ALAS Log, ALAS II, 2.

[58] Untitled memorandum, October 24, 1945, ALAS II, 2; memorandum from D. Frisch and H. Richards, ALAS Log, ALAS II, 2; memorandum October 24, 1945, ALAS II, 2.

sofar as it had an outside source, stemmed rather from the influence of Niels Bohr, or of Bohr through Oppenheimer.

Copies of Bohr's August 11 statement on "Science and Civilization" in the *Times* of London were circulated at Los Alamos. Repeating what he had said earlier to Churchill and Roosevelt about the new complications in the task of maintaining peace, Bohr now offered the scientists of the world a direct challenge:

Not only do the bonds created through scientific intercourse form some of the firmest ties between individuals from different nations, but the whole scientific community will surely join in a vigorous effort to induce in wider circles an adequate appreciation of what is at stake and to appeal to humanity at large to heed the warning which has been sounded.

If the scientists at Los Alamos needed any encouragement to think about atomic energy in international terms—which most of them, with their attachment to the non-parochial traditions of science, did not—it was Oppenheimer who provided it, giving form, as well as inspiration, to the hope that now spread across the mesa that the evil sprung from conflict could be made to serve the cause of peace. At first, as we shall see, he was to counsel an unpopular degree of restraint in action and to take an unpopular stand on domestic legislation, but let this not obscure the fact that, as far as Los Alamos was concerned, it was he as much as any one person who set the goal of internationalism.

But stronger than any single influence upon scientists at Los Alamos was the bomb itself. All too vividly did their imaginations transfer the vast destructive power that they had unleashed upon the empty desert to the two crowded cities in Japan and to the conduct of future wars. This theme of the bomb's awful effectiveness was embellished by firsthand accounts of those who had gone with the bombs to the Pacific, among them Captain William S. Parsons, who had assembled the first bomb in the air as the plane neared Hiroshima, and Philip Morrison, who went to Tinian with the Nagasaki bomb and took an observation flight over the island of Honshu before coming back to Los Alamos. Morrison, the most articulate of the group, combined a rare sensitivity of spirit with a wide-ranging mind and a gift of language that he later employed with considerable skill at congressional hearings. The substance of what he told his colleagues on his return to Los Alamos he later described to a radio audience in the following words:

We flew down the Inland Sea, past Osaka, Kobe, Nagoya, and a score of smaller cities. All of them looked the same from the air. The green and gray of the untouched Japanese city—with its gardens and its universal gray tile roofs—was in every town just a narrow fringe to a great rust-red circle, where the wreckage had incinerated under fire-bombs. Our B-29's by the hundreds had ruined the cities of Japan. We circled finally low over Hiroshima and stared in disbelief. There below was the flat level ground of what had been a city, scorched red in the same tell-tale scar. But no hundreds of planes had visited this town during a long night. One bomber, and one bomb, had, in the time it takes a rifle bullet to cross the city, turned a city of three hundred thousand into a burning pyre. That was the new thing.[59]

By the time Morrison brought back these confirmatory details, the Los Alamos organization was well under way. On August 23, the committee of six, augmented by Victor Weisskopf, Morris Perlman, and Louis Slotin,[60] had invited all staff members to a meeting on Thursday, August 30 at 7:45 P.M. in Theater No. 2, the largest meeting place on the hill.[61]

Approximately five hundred people came. They approved a motion to form an organization called the Association of Los Alamos Scientists—the contraction to ALAS, though stressed on the first syllable, did not, of course, pass without comment—its object "to promote the attainment and use of scientific and technological advances in the best interests of humanity." The membership was to be limited for the present to white badge workers, that is, laboratory staff with college degrees, but would be extended as soon as possible.[62]

Several alternative statements about the significance of atomic energy, intended for public release, were considered at the August 30 meeting, and one was selected as a basis for reworking by a drafting committee. The authorship of the final draft was not stated, but Hans Bethe, Robert Christy, David Hawkins, and George Placzek had had a hand in earlier stages and had had the help of Frank Oppenheimer, Robert Williams, J. R. Zacharias, Richard Feynman, S. K. Allison, and Edward Teller.[63]

---

[59] ALAS series for station KOB (Albuquerque), No. 3, FAS XXII, 2.

[60] Slotin was a brilliant young Canadian physicist who died May 30, 1946, after a radiation accident at Los Alamos. His death was the subject of a novel by Dexter Masters, *The Accident* (New York: Alfred A. Knopf, 1955), which provides in some respects the most successful evocation of Los Alamos atmosphere and personalities.

[61] Copy in ALAS II, 16.

[62] Report in ALAS II, 2.

[63] Drafts may be found in ALAS II, 4, and III, 2.

Shortly after this meeting, statements were exchanged with Chicago, where the framing was well advanced by August 31.[64] The Los
Alamos statement dealt with the same topics as those from other
sites—the use of the bomb in a future war, the possibility of defense,
the duration of our monopoly, an atomic arms race, the feasibility of
international control, and the prospects of peacetime application.
The answers provided were much the same, too, but the borrowing
of well-turned phrases does not necessarily disprove claims to independent thinking.

"The Document," as it was referred to in ALAS records, had a
stormy career, the incidents of which reveal among the ALAS scientists a disputatious temper and a disposition to buck the authorities that was far more credibly in character than the appearance of
docility that their group presented to the outside. But during the next
few weeks when the scientists at Clinton Labs and Chicago were testing the length of their rope as far as speech and action were concerned, no hint of the ruckus over the Document at Los Alamos
leaked into their records.

After reworking by the drafting committee, the ALAS statement
was sent to Oppenheimer with the signatures, he was told, of "virtually all civilian staff members." It was intended for the public press,
subject to the approval of the Interim Committee, to which Oppenheimer was urged to transmit it without delay.[65] This he did. It was
received in the War Department on Monday, September 10, and on
the fourteenth George Harrison called Oppenheimer at Los Alamos
to say that he had shown it to Stimson; more copies were wanted in
Washington, but it was thought inadvisable to release the statement
from Los Alamos.

The following day, Oppenheimer discussed this reply at length with
several members of ALAS; he was disturbed by the delay but insisted
there must be a good reason and assured them that he would find out
what it was; he did, in fact, write at once to Harrison urging that release be approved. On Tuesday, September 18, Oppenheimer left for
Washington; he phoned Los Alamos on Thursday to say, as Higinbotham colloquially reported, that "the situation looked real good"
in Washington and that the administration wanted to do the right

---

[64] Simpson's files contain three drafts marked "considered at a meeting at Los Alamos,
Aug. 30th"; Goldsmith sent the ASC draft of August 31 and other drafts to Wilson at
Los Alamos on September 5 (Simpson's files; ASC XXVI, VIII; ALAS IV, 1).

[65] Weisskopf ("for the Committee") to Oppenheimer, September 7, 1945, ALAS
III, 2. Unless otherwise noted, what follows is based on notes by Higinbotham in reporting on the Document to an ALAS meeting, September 28; ALAS II, 2.

thing. There were no developments on the Document, but it was being passed around and proving very helpful.

The temporary executive committee had discussed the situation on the eighteenth, as did the new one when it held its first meeting on Friday the twenty-first and elected Higinbotham as chairman. The other members were David Frisch, Joseph Keller, David Lipkin, John Manley, Captain Lloyd Roth, Victor Weisskopf, Robert Wilson, and William Woodward. They agreed that ALAS should "hold tight" in trying to publish the statement, and to avoid any misunderstanding, Weisskopf wrote to Oppenheimer on Sunday asking his opinion about the following lines of action: the issuing of a "group statement, political only," letter-writing to newspapers and congressmen, and influencing radio commentators. Finally, he asked Oppenheimer: If you were a member of the Interim Committee, would you concur in their conclusion?

Oppenheimer's reply came back on the twenty-sixth. He regarded a group statement as strongly inadvisable; he saw no objection to letter-writing or contact with commentators if done discreetly and not in the form of mass action; but he concurred with the decision not to release the ALAS statement. It had, in fact, been classed by the War Department as a state paper and ALAS had, therefore, lost control over it. However, it had aroused a lot of very helpful discussion in the Cabinet (presumably the meeting on September 21 devoted to atomic energy).

Meanwhile news reached Los Alamos of Swing's September 21 broadcast about the statements prepared at certain unidentified laboratories—Swing was not heard on New Mexico stations—and on the twenty-fifth, the *New York Times* arrived with reports on Groves's September 21 speeches in New York. His remarks found as little favor with the scientists at Los Alamos as with those at Oak Ridge.

The rebuke Groves received from Los Alamos was all the more telling because its author, John Manley, was a quiet, dependable senior physicist who had brought his group from the Met Lab to Los Alamos early in 1943, and had helped Oppenheimer plan the laboratory and been one of his most trusted assistants. As Groves knew, Manley was no hothead nor prone to verbal fireworks. Manley had already written to Groves on August 30 to say that scientists at Los Alamos and Chicago were much disturbed at being enjoined from speaking out and at the same time kept in ignorance of how future policy was shaping up. Manley was afraid of a wholesale exodus.[66]

---

[66] *The New World*, p. 421.

On September 26 he again wrote to Groves expressing his concern lest the speech at the IBM luncheon should have unfortunate repercussions.

A number of us here are trying very hard to keep our more impatient colleagues from doing anything which might embarrass the Administration. This is reflected in the fact that our statement has been submitted through proper channels and we have avoided any group release to the press. We are following this policy in spite of strong feelings in many quarters for contrary action. Your statement is readily interpreted as an attempt to discredit any statements by scientists and therefore increases many fold the difficulty of holding to our present course.

You surely realize that you speak as a representative of the whole Project and therefore, there is little equality in a situation in which you speak quite freely, even to the point of minimizing the statements of scientists who are still your associates while the scientists as a group voluntarily refrain from making public statements.

I hope that we may continue our present policy, but I see grave danger that statements such as yours can split opinion into three factions—the Administration, yourself as an Army Officer, and the scientists. The situation is one in which we should all be together—not in opinion, but in using the utmost care that the expression of opinion by any group does not antagonize any other.

Did it really add anything to the expression of your opinion to say, "and the more they talk the shorter the time seems to get"?[67]

The day after Manley wrote to Groves, Norris E. Bradbury, acting director in Oppenheimer's absence and shortly to succeed him, wired Oppenheimer in Washington that he was being strongly pressed by senior and junior staff members at Los Alamos to send a protest to the Interim Committee that Groves or others spoke as individuals and did not necessarily represent administrative opinion.[68] Oppenheimer replied to Bradbury's wire with a long teletype message:

TO: COMM. N. E. BRADBURY

FROM: J. R. OPPENHEIMER

I have several points to make in answer to your telegram.

First, I personally would have no objection to your sending the message suggested to the Interim Committee, provided the phrase that "that Committee has requested that public statement not be made" be deleted since this does not correspond to the facts. However, the Interim Committee is largely defunct and I doubt whether the desired answer will be forthcoming

---

[67] Manley to Groves, September 26, 1945, copy in ALAS II, 2.
[68] Copy of wire Bradbury to Oppenheimer, September 27, 1945, ALAS II, 2.

[this last phrase underlined in pencil]. General Groves and I can both assure you that he spoke in New York, as at other times, as an individual and I can assure you that the quoted newspaper accounts do not appear to correspond with the views of any of the members of the Interim Committee, nor, I believe, to official War Department views. Answering Higinbotham, I have a reply from Mr. Harrison on the famous memo. Mr. Harrison points out that since this document was presented to the President who has regarded it as an expression of scientists' views, it is not appropriate for anyone other than the President to release it for publication. It is my feeling, and the general feeling of all with whom I have talked, that public discussion of the issues involved is very much to be desired, but that it should follow rather than precede the President's statement of national policy which will be conveyed in his message to Congress. We do not anticipate further great delays in this message.

The view that individual statements are more desirable than group statements is not an order or an official request at all, but corresponds to my own belief and that of others with whom I have talked, that group statements tend to be rather ineffective in affecting American public opinion. This is a matter for you to judge. You are under no obligation to accept my advice.

Finally, for such use as Bradbury wishes to make of it, I have the following information: I have been in consultation not only with Dr. Bush, General Groves and Mr. Harrison but with the acting Secretary of State and the new Secretary of War. I believe that such differences as now exist do not have to do with any general formulae about the handling of atomic energy, but only affect the concrete, practical steps which must be taken to realize any effective international accord. I have not found anyone who does not understand the content and gravity of the arguments that were advanced in the Los Alamos memo, or who fails to agree in a general way with the conclusions.

I have read this teletype to General Groves, who states emphatically that the quoted newspaper accounts do not correspond with his views.[69]

Undoubtedly, Higinbotham had seen Oppenheimer's teletype when he made his report on the history of the Document to the members of ALAS assembled in Theater No. 2 on the evening of September 28. If he followed his prepared notes, he said by way of summary something like this:

The old and new committees have been ... discussing the situation with themselves and with each other almost continuously.... As everyone knows, there is a terrible lot at stake. It is obvious that the administration bill will be at least as good as any that may be proposed and it is certainly a lot better than most. In any event, the suppression of our document is

---

[69] Copy of teletype Oppenheimer to Bradbury, September 28, 1945, ALAS II, 2.

a matter of political expediency, the reasons for which we are not in a position to know or evaluate. We have one representative who does know what is going on and knows personally the people involved, that is, Oppie. The committee will vouch for his attitude and everyone knows his ability. The intensity of his feeling on this subject is clearly indicated above. The administration has pulled a boner in allowing Groves to talk; it has made a mistake in giving our doc[ument] to the President without asking.... We still believe and urge you to go along with Oppie and the administration. The job of educating the people and keeping them alive to the problems is the big job. Our statement if issued now could hardly be a scratch on the larger job but would be a break with the administration.... If it should turn out that the administration has broken faith then it will be our duty to go the works.... We recommend that nothing be done with present statement—should go on with all other activities and be ready to propose new statement.

Higinbotham's concluding note was to himself: "If necessary consult committee on vote of confidence and resignation." But things went better than he expected. As he would be first to admit, Higinbotham was not one of Los Alamos' leading scientists. An excellent electronics man, but without a doctor's degree, his fame on the hill rested chiefly on a friendly manner that led everyone to call him Willy, a lively way with an accordion, and skill as a square dance caller. But those who had thought of Higinbotham as a somewhat frivolous character had reckoned without his heritage from Presbyterian preachers and educators; he pitched into the organizing of ALAS with a seriousness that had not been evident at Saturday night square dances. His appeal for moderation was successful. The meeting agreed not to make a release until the President made his statement, and a motion was carried without debate "that Willy tell Oppie that we are strongly behind him." Edward Teller led a discussion on the implications of atomic power and the scientists' place in influencing public opinion. He urged that careful research and consideration precede the making of so-called scientific statements and that facts only, without political conclusions, be presented by scientists.[70]

By October 3 when the President's atomic energy message provided the awaited signal for public discussion the frenzied impatience at Los Alamos seems to have abated. It was decided to release a statement in ten days' time unless strong reason to the contrary was presented by Oppie. Several drafts converted the form, but not the substance, of the earlier document into something quite different. ALAS

---

[70] Meeting notes, September 28, 1942 [sic], ALAS II, 4; ALAS Log II, 2.

members were told that their first statement was to be regarded as a dead duck and would doubtless rest in government archives for a long time to come; the new document was "more modern" and would be released on October 14.[71]

Whether from prudence or pride a certain reserve was maintained between the sites. Unsigned notes preserved among Clinton Labs papers record a call from an unnamed person at Y (the Project code name for Los Alamos) on the day of Higinbotham's report: ALAS agreed with the AORS position as outlined in the release of September 26 but was not ready with a follow-up although its members had full freedom to participate.[72] Two months later Higinbotham was emphatic in telling the organizers of the Federation of American Scientists that Los Alamos had had no trouble with its political statements and policies, that the civilian laboratory directors had been encouraging, and the security department co-operative. "None of the documents which were mailed out got sent back, and we have had very little trouble in getting anything cleared."[73] Higinbotham omitted a great deal, but it was true that the negotiations over the Document left no real scars, illustrating the capacity of scientists on most occasions—for there have been notable exceptions—to operate with honest differences of opinion and to speak plainly without rancor. This is, indeed, one of the strengths that they might as a group bring to the consideration of non-scientific problems.

In other respects, the organization of ALAS proceeded smoothly. So that no one could challenge the competence of its members to speak as scientists, the qualification for full membership was made a college degree plus at least two years of graduate study. An associate classification for those with briefer academic training included most of the young scientists and engineers in the army's Special Engineer Detachment, known as SED's, and some WAC's. On September 22, the ALAS membership included 321 civilians and 227 military personnel. Among the latter were senior scientists assigned by the army or navy to the regular laboratory staff, and the propriety of their participating in ALAS was soon questioned. The decision was up to the individual, said General Groves, but he believed that an officer or an enlisted man should avoid allying himself with organizations

---

[71] Meeting notes, October 5, 1945, ALAS II, 4; drafts of a new statement in ALAS II, 4; III, 2.

[72] Notes on a call from Y, September 28, 1945, in Rush's files.

[73] "Federation of Scientific Organization Proceedings" (mimeographed), November 17–18, 1945, p. 47.

expressing opinions that as an individual military man he could not properly express. Roth resigned from the executive committee and was replaced by Woodward.[74]

5. THE WORD SPREADS

The Los Alamos representatives who talked about amalgamation at Oak Ridge on September 17 already had in mind a broader organization than the combined Manhattan Project groups—one to which scientists could belong when they left the Project, as many at Los Alamos were already planning to do. William Woodward of ALAS had started an exploratory correspondence with individuals at some sixty-five laboratories, explaining the aims of ALAS and asking whether they would support an organization to pursue them.

Among the early replies were two from the Radiation Laboratory in Cambridge, which, with its large complement of M.I.T. and Harvard faculty, was the most influential wartime aggregation of scientists outside the Manhattan Project. A sizable number of Rad Lab people had been lured to Los Alamos in 1943 or 1944, and as was the case with Oak Ridge and Chicago, the two places were linked by personal and professional friendships. One of the answers from the Radiation Lab came from its director, Lee A. DuBridge. Explaining that news had reached them of the concern about education and control and that Rad Lab people were greatly interested, DuBridge continued:

> We have decided that it would be best for the present to leave to the scientists connected with the Manhattan Project the leadership in starting such a movement. We would then swing in behind it in any way possible, and, in addition, would assist in public dissemination of views if the connection of the scientists with the Manhattan Project makes it awkward for them to do so.
>
> We have formed a small physics club here, whose primary purpose it is to discuss important problems in physics. The club is limited to fifty members for the present, and I am Chairman and Dr. Ernest C. Pollard is Secretary-Treasurer. This club is already serving as a forum for discussing problems such as the ones in which you are interested.... Unfortunately our group will be largely dispersed during the next three months, but we could possibly retain a skeleton organization, keeping in touch with each other by mail. At any rate, I shall bring your communication to the attention of this group so that they can be thinking about the matter.

---

[74] Entry for September 22, 1945, ALAS Log, ALAS II, 2; Colonel Tyler to Keller, September 17, 1945, ALAS II, 7.

We all wish you the greatest possible success in your endeavors, and you may be assured of the support of all physicists, at least in the Cambridge area.[75]

The other reply was from Ernest Pollard. "It seems now necessary for such an organization to exist," he said. "It shows, however, that the times are critical when scientists have to announce their devotion to humanity. The search for truth can hardly be anything else." Pollard continued:

We at the Radiation Laboratory are not so far along as you in this kind of organization. This is certainly because radar, while it has been used as a very destructive weapon, still has with it a great deal of peacetime value and has saved many lives by direct intervention. While I am of the opinion that atomic energy has already saved many lives by stopping the war, it is still not so apparent that it has been used humanely. Therefore, I can see that you would be ahead of us in your social and political thinking to insure that it is used humanely in the future.[76]

Some would say that devices like the proximity fuse and radar had been far more important in turning the tide and hence in winning the war than the atomic bomb, but decisive as they were, the effect had been cumulative and produced in those who fashioned them no sudden traumatic reaction. Nor did it bring them either the public notice they deserved or the specious fame that came abruptly to those in the Manhattan Project. A Radiation Laboratory release, containing as full a description of its work as security permitted, was ready just as Hiroshima was bombed and went virtually unnoticed. The impression developed that the submerging of their own contribution by the flood of interest in atomic energy and atomic scientists left Rad Lab people feeling slightly resentful, but they do not now admit to this. Wry remarks on the irony of the timing, says J. R. Zacharias, were "just teasing."

The situation at the Radiation Lab also differed from the atomic research centers in that relations with military collaborators there had developed with fewer misunderstandings and tensions. The prompt success of Rad Lab products had impressed the military men, and the scientists, in turn, had developed a strong feeling for the importance of tactical secrecy in the course of applying their devices.[77] It is true that the opposition in Cambridge to some of the restrictive

[75] DuBridge to Woodward, October 1, 1945, ALAS IV, 6.
[76] Pollard to Woodward, October 1, 1945, ALAS IV, 1.
[77] Interview with E. M. Purcell, December 21, 1961.

provisions of the May-Johnson bill was vigorously expressed, and an ex-Radiation Lab member, Louis Ridenour of the Physics Department at the University of Pennsylvania, became a leader in the fight for declassification and the free dissemination of scientific information. But the statements from Cambridge advocating international control of the bomb or freedom of research had fewer overtones of a crusade than those from Oak Ridge, Los Alamos, or Chicago.

Of the scientists' organizations that had coalesced by the end of September, 1945, one more remains to be mentioned—a group composed chiefly of people at the Manhattan Project's SAM Laboratory at Columbia University. After the departure of Fermi, Szilard, and their associates for the Met Lab early in 1942, Urey continued to direct work on isotope separation in a research unit operated for the Manhattan Project by the Carbide and Carbon Corporation. The staff had gradually been reduced by transfers to other Project labs and was facing rapid dissolution in the autumn of 1945 as Urey and others took up academic appointments elsewhere. Nevertheless, with the support of small groups of employees of the Kellex Corporation and other Project contractors in the New York area, a temporarily effective organization was formed, which called itself the Association of Manhattan Project Scientists, New York area; early in 1946, it merged with the larger Association of New York Scientists.

Like the other Project groups, the one at SAM claimed an independent origin in the troubled exchange of ideas about the impact of the atomic bomb before statements from other sites began to arrive. A few interested people sounded out others and, encouraged by the announcement about the Clinton Labs group, a preliminary meeting was held on September 28.[78]

A statement of intent, patterned after those at the other sites, was circulated to see what support it would get. The response was tremendous, C. D. Swartz later told the representatives of scientific organizations in Washington. "There were perhaps one per cent of the people in the laboratory whom we contacted," he said, "who felt that scientists really should not organize to state their views at this time, and that was all the opposition that we got." Among the 99 per cent, Swartz admitted, there had been some disagreement. Should they confine themselves to statements of scientific fact and to correcting errors or go ahead and make statements about the social and political

[78] Bonner to Rush, October 9, 1945, AORES II, 8.

implications of atomic energy? The "higher ups" in the laboratory urged great caution at the beginning lest scientific prestige be endangered by straying beyond the bounds of scientific fact. Relations with the army and management had also troubled the organizers at SAM. They had agreed to submit press releases for approval, but Groves's public statements, expressing views opposite to theirs, raised the question of what they should do in the future. Several men had been called in by a Carbide vice-president, who assumed they were starting a "white collar" union and made it clear that they were not to use the name of the company or make statements that would bring it publicity.[79]

Undeterred, the SAM group, with an initial membership of two hundred held an organization meeting on October 10, adopted a constitution, and elected an executive committee with Richard D. Present as chairman. When the meeting convened at 6:30 P.M., the chairman provoked a ripple of laughter by saying they had to be out of the building by 10:30, but they barely made the deadline. The definition of views on domestic and international control dominated two other October meetings, and it was mid-November before permanent committees were appointed. Meantime the executive committee had sought advice from radio commentators Raymond Swing and Johannes Steel and had been in touch with the Federal Council of Churches, the League of Women Voters, the Lawyers Guild, and similar organizations.[80]

One major Manhattan Project installation is notably absent from this account—the huge plutonium production plant at Hanford, Washington, run by the duPont Company. One or two meetings were held there after the war and for a time the nucleus of an organization was believed to exist, but it developed into a branch of the American Chemical Society, not of the Federation of American Scientists.[81]

But wherever scientists were at work in the late summer of 1945 at least a few people discussed their responsibility for the destructive-

---

[79] Swartz's report of AMPS in "Federation of Scientific Organizations Proceedings" (mimeographed), November 17–18, 1945, pp. 26–33; Bonner to Rush, October 9, 1945, AORES II, 8.

[80] The name of the organization was changed from Association of Manhattan Project to Association of Manhattan District Scientists as being more familiar to the public. R. D. Present to K. Way, October 11, 1945, ASC XVI, 9; AMPS Newsletter, November 2, 1945, FAS VI, 1.

[81] Stahl, "Splits and Schisms," p. 258.

ness of war and what could be done about it. Although this book deals chiefly with the response of Manhattan Project scientists and cannot include everything that American scientists said about the bomb, neither can it ignore the prompt reaction of one organization that had already admitted the responsibility that the Project scientists suddenly took so much to heart.

The American Association of Scientific Workers, formed in 1938, was an offshoot of the older and stronger British AScW, itself a product of the social-relations-in-science movement of the 1920's, which had attracted many prominent British scientists with liberal or left-wing views who were concerned in a period of economic depression with salaries, hours, and conditions of laboratory work.[82] In the United States the social-relations-in-science movement was never so powerful an intellectual force; it enlisted fewer prominent people and provoked less lively discussion of issues. A few members of the new site organizations of 1945 had belonged to the AAScW before the war, chiefly people of moderate political views whose conscience had been sharpened by the depression, but they were not the chief instigators of the Project site groups nor did they press the claims of the American Association of Scientific Workers to speak for science at this juncture. What the needs of the moment seemed to require was a new organization enlisting the widest possible support for an attack upon problems directly related to atomic energy.

Although the local branches of the AAScW had suffered from the absorption in war research, its central leadership, under Kirtley F. Mather, professor of geology at Harvard, was still active and in the early summer of 1945 prepared an analysis of the Bush report on federal support of science and drew up a statement on the control of atomic energy. The latter statement was sent to President Truman and made public on August 14 when the Manhattan Project groups, still dazed by the impact of Hiroshima and Nagasaki, were both unable and unwilling to speak. The leaders of the AAScW, occupying a less delicate position in relation to secrecy, did not have to worry about violating regulations or inviting more stringent ones when they wrote about the hopes and fears aroused by the bomb and the responsibility of the entire citizenry; but they were no less mesmerized by the magnificence of the technical accomplishment than their brethren on the Project as they noted "this splendid achievement of science in the service of mankind" and expressed "the hope that

---

[82] Neal Wood, *Communism and British Intellectuals* (New York: Columbia University Press, 1959).

further developments will follow as rapidly as possible, with all appropriate safeguards."

The AAScW offered the following proposals for consideration: Control of bombs and other applications should be vested in the UN Security Council; governments presently owning and controlling plants and processes should retain them but should release information on scientific discoveries and developments at the earliest possible time as specified by the Security Council; materials for fundamental research and development should be made available to qualified institutions; the United States and other UN governments should encourage research; results of future research should be freely published; the use of patents should be available to industry to stimulate production of peacetime goods; and these steps should be integrated with the recent proposals of Vannevar Bush for federal support of science.[83]

Although these proposals were offered for discussion, not as a final plan, they provided an object lesson for Manhattan Project scientists—if, with their knowledge of the complexities of atomic processes, one was needed—in the perils of combining general principles with specific recommendations about control, ownership, patents, and the like. The site groups and the federation that grew out of them would try their utmost to confine public statements to generalities relating to science, to reach conclusions on specific points only after careful study, and not to jeopardize their authority as scientists by speaking on topics to which their technical knowledge or insights were not clearly relevant. As succeeding chapters will show, it was a counsel of perfection more easily offered than followed.

In early September, 1945, the site groups were moving very cautiously. By chance the receipt of Woodward's exploratory letters from Los Alamos at laboratories across the country coincided with Raymond Swing's broadcast on September 21 noting the existence of the embryonic organizations and quoting their statements. The Clinton Labs release followed five days later. Scientists in Cambridge, New York, Philadelphia, Maryland, and California, as well as those who had worked on the bomb, had begun seriously to look at the world in the light of Hiroshima when the issue of domestic control of atomic energy galvanized them into action.

---

[83] Supplement (September, 1945) to the Newsletter of the American Association of Scientific Workers, No. 12, September–October, 1945. The statement on atomic energy was signed by Kirtley F. Mather, Bart J. Bok, Henry Borsook, Karl F. Lark-Horovitz, Harry Grundfest, and Melba Phillips.

CHAPTER 3

The May-Johnson Bill

U P TO THE END of September, 1945, two topics dominated discussions among scientists of the Manhattan Project: the imperative need for international control of atomic energy and the deleterious effect of secrecy upon international confidence and the growth of science. Problems of domestic control were not explicitly considered except in Szilard's September 7 memorandum.

Suddenly the situation changed. On October 3, President Truman sent to Congress his message on atomic energy, and on October 4 a War Department bill to establish an atomic energy commission was introduced in House and Senate. Domestic control became, for the time being, the great preoccupation of the atomic scientists; it precipitated the unification of the site organizations into the Federation of Atomic Scientists and its almost immediate expansion into the Federation of American Scientists.

1. THE OPPOSITION FORMS

The President's message was reassuring. Drafted, as scientists learned only years later, by Herbert Marks, a young lawyer on the staff of Undersecretary of State Dean Acheson, the message emphasized the dangers and the potential benefits in the release of atomic energy

128

and asked for prompt action to guard against the hazards of misuse. It called for government control of materials and processing, with a minimum of interference in existing patterns of research and industry. The President invited Congress to share in outlining principles and policy.[1]

What the President had to say about international affairs reflected, scientists were told, the views of Stimson and was in gratifying accord with their own thinking. The President described atomic energy as "a new force too revolutionary to consider within the framework of old ideas"; he spoke of eventual renunciation of military use and of directing all future scientific endeavor toward peaceful and humanitarian ends. International discussions could not wait until the United Nations began to function, and therefore the President proposed consultations with our wartime associates, Britain and Canada, "in an effort to effect agreement on the conditions under which cooperation might replace rivalry in the field of atomic power."

This was the official statement of policy for which Manhattan Project scientists had been advised to wait. The Clinton Labs group at Oak Ridge had jumped the gun on September 26 in response to the unexpected interest of the *Herald Tribune*. Los Alamos, after the miscarriage of its first pronouncement, was engaged in preparing a substitute. The Met Lab scientists were impatiently waiting for a chance to speak, and their first press release on October 4 announced that the Atomic Scientists of Chicago supported wholeheartedly the President's statement.[2]

Satisfaction was shortlived. For when they had grasped the tenor of the bill that Senator Edwin C. Johnson of Colorado introduced on October 4 as S. 1463 and Representative Andrew J. May of Kentucky as H.R. 4280, many scientists did not like it. The bill provided that all sources of nuclear energy and all activities connected with research, production, and release of such energy be controlled in the interest of the nation and world peace (the latter phrase was inserted at State Department insistence) by a part-time commission of nine appointed by the President with the consent of the Senate but removable by the President without stated cause other than national interest. A full-time administrator and deputy administrator ap-

---

[1] Text in Harry S Truman, *Year of Decisions* (Garden City, N.Y.: Doubleday & Co., 1955), pp. 530–33; Richard G. Hewlett and Oscar E. Anderson, Jr., *The New World, 1939–1946* (University Park: Pennsylvania State University Press, 1962), pp. 425–27 (referred to hereinafter as *The New World*).
[2] Copy of release, October 4, 1945, ASC I, 15.

pointed by the commission would be its executive agents. Members of the armed forces might fill these posts or serve on the commission.

Government ownership of nuclear materials and plants was not mandatory. At the same time the commission was given custody of all ores, plants, stocks, processes, technical information and its sources, contracts, leases, patents and patent applications, and other rights of any kind judged to be relevant. This custody could be exercised through the commission's broad licensing and contractual powers, which it was cautioned to use equitably and so as to discourage monopoly and restraint of trade. It had broad powers of confiscation though it was advised to make generous payment and to reimburse states and municipalities for tax exemptions.

The commission was given plenary power over research whenever nuclear fission or transmutation of atomic species was involved on any scale whatever, but it was instructed to interfere as little as possible with small-scale research, especially in non-profit laboratories, and to utilize and encourage research facilities in colleges, universities, and hospitals.

The commission could bar at source any information it wished to keep secret. Violations of its security regulations might incur a fine of $100,000, ten years in jail, or both; willful transmission of information with intent to jeopardize the interests of the United States risked a maximum penalty of $300,000 fine and thirty years in jail. (Scientists, whose salaries had not yet begun to reflect their new prestige, enjoyed the reply attributed to E. U. Condon when General Kenneth C. Royall, coauthor of the bill, asked him if he thought a $300,000 cash fine was enough, "Hell no! Make it a million.")

The fate of the bill was to hinge as much upon its omissions as upon its positive provisions. To the scientists its negative shortcomings were most marked in the field of foreign policy, for it failed to balance emphasis upon military applications and possible military membership on the commission with any reference to the sharing of information with other countries upon which international control would necessarily be based. Its only statements about exchange of information were restrictive.

Some government officials, concerned primarily not with science but with administration, observed the lack of any specific statement on the nature and extent of government control, which meant that it might be excessively broad or excessively narrow. And the bill insulated the commission and administrator from normal administrative

and congressional checks in regard to appointments, dismissals, budget-
ary review, and the like. Its security clauses were offensive to lawyers
as well as scientists.

As we shall see, these legal and administrative objections to the
May-Johnson bill became known to scientists only in piecemeal fashion
as their own unpremeditated campaign against the bill developed.
Had the strength of their resources in terms of allies been immediately
apparent, they would perhaps have reacted with less panic and also
with less effectiveness.

But as public interest in atomic energy, which had flagged when
the first astonishment subsided, revived in the days following the
President's message and the introduction of the bill, scientists found
more cause for alarm than for reassurance. As represented in the press,
the chief concern of Congress and of Washington officialdom was
whether to keep the bomb a secret from other nations, a topic that
had been extensively explored at a cabinet meeting two weeks earlier.

The occasion was one of some poignancy, for it fell on September
21, the seventy-eighth birthday of Stimson, the retiring secretary of
war, who had been persuaded by the President to stay in Washington
an extra day to present to the cabinet the views that he had submitted
to Truman in a memorandum on September 11. Most Manhattan
Project scientists would have been both pleased and dismayed—
pleased by Stimson's earnest championship of international control,
dismayed by the ignorance or negativism of the majority of the cabinet.
It did not matter so much, declared Stimson, whether the Russians
got the bomb in a few years or many, but it mattered greatly that when
they did get it they should be in a frame of mind to co-operate, not
to oppose. A generous offer now—not with a weapon on the hip but
with a plan to control the bomb and to share the benefits of atomic
energy—might induce such a co-operative mood. We should not offer
to turn over the bomb, but we might offer to stop all work on military
applications if Britain and Russia would do likewise. Although not
highly optimistic, Stimson thought any other course would lead to
mutual destruction and so was willing to gamble on Russian good
faith. He recommended a direct approach because the United Nations
was not yet prepared to undertake such a difficult assignment.

Unfortunately, this was Stimson's last official word. Secretary of
State Byrnes was in London, but he had made clear his disapproval
of international control. Of the rest of the cabinet only Henry Wallace

declared himself as "completely, everlastingly and wholeheartedly" in favor of Stimson's proposal. Undersecretary of State Dean Acheson, and Stimson's successor, Robert P. Patterson, expressed more guarded agreement. Secretary of the Treasury Fred M. Vinson and Attorney General Thomas C. Clark were opposed to sharing any secrets, as, less dogmatically, was Secretary of the Navy James V. Forrestal, who commented that trust had to be more than a one-way street. Several members of the cabinet, Stimson's biographer points out, were entirely "green" as far as atomic energy was concerned, and many comments were beside the point.[3]

But this is a recently reconstructed story. What the press reports of the cabinet meeting emphasized at the time and what caught the congressional ear was not Stimson's temperate appeal but Wallace's proposal that atomic secrets be shared at once as a gesture of international confidence.[4] The uneasiness that this suggestion engendered on Capitol Hill was not allayed by the President's invitation to Congress to share in formulating atomic policy; uneasiness increased, in fact, with the realization that the War Department bill, which the White House was backing, left in executive hands the power to communicate atomic "secrets" to foreign governments. The trend of congressional thinking showed up in a North American Newspaper Alliance poll in which 90 per cent of those who replied were opposed to giving up secrets of the bomb.[5] On October 8 Truman held an impromptu press conference at a Tennessee fishing lodge to announce that the United States would not share technical knowledge of the bomb even with its former allies. At the first opportunity, therefore, congressmen directed their interrogation of scientists to the nature and importance of atomic secrecy.

The scientists for their part were greatly alarmed by what the press revealed about congressional attitudes, first by the widely held belief that there was a durable secret, and second by a tendency to present the issue as a simple choice between absolute secrecy and telling everything. Comment frequently ignored the alternative offered by Stimson—and the course behind which a majority of Manhattan Project scientists were preparing to unite—namely, a declaration of readiness to turn over the technical details of bomb production to a world authority under adequate controls. Scientists were already en-

[3] Elting E. Morison, *Turmoil and Tradition* (Boston: Houghton Mifflin Co., 1960), pp. 641–42; Truman, *Year of Decisions*, pp. 525–27.
[4] *New York Times*, September 22, 1945, pp. 1, 3.
[5] *New York Times*, October 1, 1945, p. 5.

countering a difficulty that would continue to plague them for some time to come, that no matter how often or how carefully they explained the distinction between theoretical knowledge and manufacturing techniques or stressed the qualifying phrase "under adequate controls," they were likely to be accused of wanting to give away the bomb.

The first opportunity for scientists to lay their views officially before Congress came during hearings on national science foundation bills before a subcommittee of the Senate Military Affairs Committee with Senator Kilgore as chairman. On October 8 and 9 Irving Langmuir of the General Electric laboratory and the Harvard astronomer, Harlow Shapley, emphasized the importance of freedom of research for the continuing growth of science and explained that scientists feared tremendous repercussions because of the military usefulness of atomic energy. Thus introduced, the subject of secrecy continued to be the focus of attention as Congress turned to consideration of the May-Johnson bill.[6]

In the Senate the Johnson bill was the victim of a triangular jurisdictional dispute. Majority Leader Alben W. Barkley's efforts to place it in the hands of the Military Affairs Committee were opposed by Senator Connally, who saw in this move a threat to the power of his Foreign Relations Committee. In addition Senator Vandenberg's resolution setting up a joint committee to deal with atomic energy legislation had gathered enough support to pass the Senate and now awaited House action. The stalemate, which was already developing before the introduction of the Johnson bill on October 4, continued until Friday, October 12, when committee approval of Senator Brien McMahon's resolution, calling for a special Senate committee to conduct atomic energy hearings, pointed to a way out of the impasse.[7]

In the House the same bill, introduced by Representative May, made excellent progress, an initial success that was to prove in the end its undoing, for the speed with which Chairman May pushed the bill through the House Military Affairs Committee became the focus of the immediate outcry that scientists and their supporters raised against it. The first hearings were held without fanfare on Tuesday, October 9. There were four witnesses: Secretary of War Patterson, General Groves, Vannevar Bush, and James B. Conant.

To those familiar with scientists' deep concern about the impact

---

[6] U.S. Senate, Committee on Military Affairs, Subcommittee on War Mobilization, *Hearings on Science Legislation*, 79th Cong., 1st sess., October 8, 1945–March 5, 1946.

[7] *New York Times*, October 5, 1945, p. 4; October 13, 1945, p. 5.

of atomic energy, no remarkable statements were made that day although a few of the facts and forecasts elicited from Bush and Conant in support of the wide powers granted to the commission, such as Bush's admission that uncontrolled experiments in some attic might sterilize the passers-by, startled less knowing members of the audience. Secretary Patterson showed a clear appreciation of the importance of the developments under discussion, and General Groves avoided provocative statements as he stressed his desire to relinquish his broad wartime powers as quickly as possible and to place the fast-moving and unpredictable Project under congressional control. His statement about the various levels of secret information was one to which few scientists could have taken exception.[8]

The paper most widely read by Manhattan Project scientists in their scattered locations was the New York Times, and its columns have therefore been used to reconstruct what they knew about the course of events relating to atomic energy. What the Times picked out about these hearings next day was their extraordinary speed. The front-page full-column report was headed: "Atom Control is Speeded by House Military Group—Committee Plans Bill This Week after Five Hour Hearing—U.S. Lead Put at 5 to 20 Years—Experts Study Bomb Defense."[9] This news—and the realization that the testimony of Conant and Bush was regarded in Washington as adequately representing the voice of science—came as a distinct blow to those scientists who had counted on congressional hearings as a forum for public debate. They proceeded to impute to Chairman May a malevolent intent of shutting them out. Actually May, as agent rather than author in the business, had considerable incentive to proceed with dispatch. Not only did he receive reminders of urgency from the White House, but the letter from Secretary Patterson to Speaker Sam Rayburn that had accompanied the bill when it came from the War Department on October 3 had seemed a guarantee of influential backing. Wrote Patterson:

The bill was prepared by the Interim Committee appointed by the Secretary of War with the approval of the President. The Committee devoted months of study to the question of how best to secure for the nation adequate control over this unprecedented development. It consulted with other interested Government departments and had the benefit of the

[8] U.S. House of Representatives, Committee on Military Affairs, Atomic Energy, Hearings on H.R. 4280, 79th Cong., 1st sess., October 9, 18, 1945.
[9] New York Times, October 10, 1945, pp. 1, 4.

views of the leading physicists and the representatives of those industries must [sic] closely connected with the development of the atomic bomb. As now submitted, therefore, the bill embodies the consensus of the Committee, the interested departments, and the scientists and representatives of industries most directly associated in the program.[10]

Whether or not they saw this letter at the time, it was clear to opponents of the bill that they had to combat the impression that responsible scientists were united behind it. Their efforts to do so were hampered by lack of reliable information about the sponsorship of the measure; and the same vagueness about the function of the Interim Committee panel that had led to charges of misrepresentation of views on the use of the bomb again gave rise to hard feelings as the limits of the panel's connection with the May-Johnson bill were revealed. As at other points in this story, habitual administrative reserve, to which scientists on the whole were unaccustomed, together with the secrecy attaching to atomic energy, fostered misunderstanding.

But in regard to the origin of the May-Johnson bill there is no need to keep the reader in the same state of half knowledge in which scientists then labored and in which they remained for some years thereafter. Domestic atomic energy legislation fell within the provenance of the War Department's Interim Committee, which delegated the drafting to two Harvard Law School graduates, General Kenneth C. Royall and a civilian on the War Department staff, William L. Marbury. They had available studies to which scientists had contributed—memorandums of July and September, 1944, containing recommendations of Bush and Conant; the Tolman and Jeffries reports of late 1944; the July, 1945, report that Norman Hilberry had made on the basis of the Met Lab Committee studies. The scientific panel of the Interim Committee was at work on a report on long-term research applications, but this was not finished until after the bill was in final form.

The Interim Committee, its numbers reduced by the absence of Stimson and Byrnes in Potsdam and the resignation of Bard, and with no panel members present, was presented with the first draft on July 19.[11] In general viewpoint the bill resembled the ideas that Bush and Conant had put on record in September, 1944; it provided a part-time

---

[10] U.S. House of Representatives, *Reports*, Misc. V, Report No. 1186, 79th Cong., 1st sess., November 5, 1945, pp. 1–3.

[11] Those with a special interest in suggested modifications or in the views of particular people are advised to consult *The New World*, pp. 412–14, and other sections of chapter xii in that book, on which the above account is based.

commission of nine that, in line with Bush's desire to protect scientific research from political interference, was a semiautonomous body with a great deal of power. But the bill's authors had, one is tempted to say, outbushed Bush. Using year-old memorandums, they had not kept abreast of changes in the thinking of Bush and Conant, and at the July 19 meeting Bush's criticisms were emphatic. He had decided that the commission should be entirely civilian; its operations need not be exempt from civil service requirements or from the usual auditing; and its powers over private property and in the field of security were excessive. With support from Conant and K. T. Compton he argued that the commission's control of research was too broad and too tight, invading, in Bush's view, the territory that should properly belong to a science foundation, for which he had just outlined a proposal. General Groves agreed that military members on the commission were unnecessary if the armed services were represented by a military advisory board.

Those familiar with the shape of the conflict over domestic legislation that followed will recognize how much misunderstanding within the scientific community might have been avoided had the scientist members of the Interim Committee found it possible to reveal the nature and extent of their objections to the bill. In the subsequent redrafting some of Bush's recommendations were included, but he remained so dissatisfied with its general tone (another point in common with its later critics) that on August 7 he requested a complete review. But Bush was occupied with many other angles of research demobilization. Other officials were soon diverted from the contents of the bill to the mechanics of introducing it to a possibly refractory Congress, and the review did not take place.

If the three scientists on the Interim Committee were uncomfortable at Patterson's sweeping assurances to Chairman May of scientific backing for the bill, they did not say so when they testified on science legislation a few days later; nor did word of their displeasure leak out, and the scientists who disliked the May-Johnson bill were left to assume that they were battling not only the army but the members of their own profession who had most influence upon policy.

Within ten days of its introduction, a significant portion of the American scientific community was in full cry against the May-Johnson bill. John Manley's August 30 letter to Groves, Allison's Shoreland speech of September 1, and the tone of early Clinton Labs discussions indicate that combustible material existed. It might have exploded spontaneously, but Leo Szilard, leaving nothing to chance, provided the match.

By his own account Szilard was in Washington early in October and happened to pick up a copy of the bill.[12] But Szilard never waited for things to happen, and so one looks for the story behind this coincidence. One discovers that E. U. Condon, associate director of the Westinghouse laboratory, was also in Washington in late September or early October in connection with the directorship of the Bureau of Standards, about which Secretary of Commerce Wallace had approached him at the University of Chicago conference on September 19 and 20, at which Szilard, too, had been present. Shortly thereafter Szilard and Condon, sponsored in some instances by Wallace, made a series of calls in Washington upon people likely to be interested in atomic energy legislation. The most productive of these visits was to James R. Newman, a lawyer whose Columbia University training had included a good deal of science and who had recently become head of the science section in the Office of War Mobilization and Reconversion (OWMR). Wallace had phoned Newman to ask if he might send over two scientists who had complaints about the May-Johnson bill.[13]

Szilard and Condon were both men of definite convictions and not shy about expressing them. They also shared a dislike of the security regulations of the Manhattan Project. Szilard had bucked them all through the war; Condon had made one major gesture of protest by resigning after a few weeks as associate director of Los Alamos because he was horrified at the prospect of science so tightly shackled by security. He had remained with the Project, however, as a consultant to the research group in Berkeley.[14] In other ways the two men complemented one another well. "I bring him along," confided Szilard to Newman in a conspiratorial tone, "because he looks like an honest farm boy." Szilard also found Condon a desirable ally vis-à-vis their fellow physicists, among whom Condon, at this time

[12] Szilard, "We Turned the Switch," *Nation*, CLXI (December 22, 1945), 718–19.
[13] Interview with Newman, December 29, 1961.
[14] Leslie R. Groves, *Now It Can Be Told* (New York: Harper & Bros., 1962), Appendix VII, reproduces Condon's letter of explanation to Oppenheimer in April, 1943. Condon attributes the start of his long troubles with Groves to his having questioned the adequacy of Groves's arrangements for the Los Alamos water supply, a point that those who lived through later shortages will not fail to appreciate (interview with Condon, July 29, 1962).

vice-president of the American Physical Society, was better known than Szilard and widely liked.

Possibly none of the three men had yet seen the completed bill when the meeting with Newman took place, but Newman had previously been special assistant to Patterson at the War Department, knew the people engaged in the drafting, and is sure that he was aware of its general character well before it was introduced on October 4. The complaints of the two scientists, whether based on more or less knowledge than Newman's, fortified his reservations about the bill, and from this interview there developed a liaison of great significance. Henceforth Newman, who knew much more about science than the scientists did about politics and administration, became political tutor, first to Szilard and Condon, then to younger men who followed them to Washington. The connection acquired added importance when on October 18 the President authorized the Office of War Mobilization and Reconversion to take charge of atomic energy legislation for the administration, and Newman, as chief of its science section, became a *de facto* science adviser to the President, who had reacted somewhat unfavorably to Bush's more austere attempts to induct him into the technical mysteries of the new age.

Whatever the date of Szilard's first sight of the May-Johnson bill, he was back in Chicago with copies of it on October 9. One of these he gave to Edward Levi of the University of Chicago law faculty with the request that it be given careful and immediate study. That evening the Atomic Scientists of Chicago held a general meeting. Condon, who had also arrived from Washington, analyzed the bill, and A. H. Compton (since July 1 chancellor of Washington University in St. Louis but continuing for the time being as director of the plutonium research units still operated by the University of Chicago) spoke on "The Scientist and the Government; the Scientific Panel and the Interim Committee." Compton's explanation of the reasoning that had led the panel to approve the decision to drop the bomb on Japan was greeted by expressions of doubt that Met Lab views on the subject had been adequately represented.[15]

This excursion into recent history contributed to the rebellion that was rapidly building up over the May-Johnson bill, but action was delayed by a typical two-day hassle. When the news arrived that May

---

[15] Meeting notice, etc., in ASC XXVI, Vol. IV; report of meeting in *Bulletin of Atomic Scientists*, I (December 10, 1945); Donald Hughes to the author, October 1, 1957.

had closed the one-day hearing on the ninth, Szilard and other members of the executive committee were already at work on the ASC's second press release calling for a joint bipartisan committee to hold extensive hearings (as provided in Vandenberg's concurrent resolution). As originally written the release suggested that Congress provide continuity by authorizing the Manhattan Project to carry on until June 30, 1946, but Met Lab authorities did not like such specific recommendations of policy. Farrington Daniels, the laboratory director, suggested they be omitted, but Szilard threatened to resign from the executive committee if the point about a bipartisan committee was dropped, as he had already sent the release to the *New York Times* and the *Washington Post*, where he had been assured it would appear in full. The final decision was to drop the recommendation to continue the Manhattan Project but to retain the demand for a bipartisan committee, and this was the form in which the release went out for October 11.[16]

The *Washington Post* quoted the ASC statement, citing also a protest from Clinton Labs, under the headline "Experts Fight Hasty Action on Atomic Bill."[17] The *New York Times* did not use the release on the eleventh, but a day later carried the following item:

Atomic Scientists at the University of Chicago were reported in a state of near revolt today against continued surveillance by Army security police who were accused of instituting a "rule of fear" to halt the scientists in their efforts to warn the public about the future perils from the atomic bomb.
The disclosure that the physicists were contemplating a formal protest to President Truman to force the Army to discontinue its censorship gag came in the wake of verified reports that military police at the University were questioning writers sent to interview the scientists.[18]

New York's *P M* quoted "a top-flight physicist" in Chicago as saying that the scientists were being muzzled so that War Department legislation could be railroaded through and army and navy men placed in charge of atomic energy.[19] Szilard may have been restrained from telling Congress what to do, but he had managed to create quite a stir.

A visitor from Los Alamos, former Met Lab physicist Herbert

---

[16] Executive committee minutes, ASC VI, 12; release in *Bulletin of Atomic Scientists* files.
[17] *Washington Post*, October 11, 1945, p. 6.
[18] *New York Times*, October 12, 1945, p. 5.
[19] *P M* (New York), October 12, 1945.

Anderson, was infected by the excitement in Chicago and sent off a furious letter on October 12 to ALAS chairman W. A. Higinbotham. "Have you read the Johnson bill?" Anderson began. "This is the bill we had been waiting so anxiously all these weeks, the bill which, it had been assured us, was a 'good' bill whose early passage would assure rapid progress in the field of atomic power. We had been asked by our representatives in Washington to withhold comment lest this cause undue controversy and delay the acceptance of the measure."

The great power given to the commission was not necessarily bad, said Anderson, but at the Met Lab the wording of the bill was being interpreted to mean that the administrator would be an army man, his deputy a navy man, and that the other members, since they would be part time with their chief obligations elsewhere, would probably leave much of the responsibility in the hands of the administrators. "If the atom bomb," Anderson continued, "is the world shaking force we believe it to be—if it is to give us everlasting peace or worldwide devastation, we cannot permit it to rest in the hands of a body so flippantly conceived."

Declaring that the security provisions of the bill were frightening, Anderson continued, "It will always be a difficult burden to remember what the Commission will punish and what it will not. No matter how liberal the interpretation of its powers may be, the mere existence of the power will tend to drive scientists from the field of atomic transformation." Moreover, he asked, why should the scientists, who imposed secrecy upon themselves before the government and the army were even aware of the dangers and who kept faith throughout the war, now be subjected to restrictions beyond those that already existed in the Espionage Act.

"I must confess," he concluded, "my confidence in our leaders Oppenheimer, Lawrence, Compton, and Fermi, all members of the Scientific Panel advising the Interim Committee and who enjoined us to have faith in them and not influence this legislation, is shaken. I believe that these worthy men were duped—that they never had a chance to see this bill. Let us beware of any breach of our rights as men and citizens."[20]

Anderson's letter reached Los Alamos as his colleagues there were trying to sort out their reactions. If recollections serve, a copy of the bill was brought from Washington by Oppenheimer just after it was introduced and was discussed by him at an ALAS executive com-

---

[20] Anderson to Higinbotham, October 11, 1945, copy in ASC XXVIII, Vol. XIV.

mittee meeting on Sunday evening, October 7. The immediate reaction was unfavorable, but Oppenheimer's arguments on its behalf were so persuasive that in the end all but one of those present voted to endorse it.[21]

Other members of ALAS were given opportunity to form opinions about the bill at a meeting hastily called for Friday evening, October 12, when it was analyzed by Robert Williams, who suggested careful scrutiny of certain provisions: the part-time commission, the powers of the administrator, and the stiff penalties for revealing information. General discussion was postponed for a week, and all members were urged to read the bill.[22]

Several sets of comments and proposed changes show that the injunction was heeded and that the bill was not accepted uncritically at Los Alamos.[23] Replying to Anderson on October 16 Higinbotham said Los Alamos people were discussing the bill for all they were worth, but until unanimity was reached there would be no public statement, as it was important that scientists should not publicly disagree. Another bill, said Higinbotham, might be much worse—a negative argument that won some converts at first but failed to carry weight in the long run. Despite these clear signs of uncertainty word soon leaked out to other sites that Los Alamos supported the May-Johnson bill; the news caused consternation but apparently not any second thoughts about the possible virtues of the bill.

If Szilard's writ did not run at Los Alamos, at Oak Ridge his influence was again evident. The AORS executive committee, meeting on October 8 (it met again on the ninth and tenth), considered the text of a telegram that Szilard recommended sending to Majority Leader Barkley, Speaker Rayburn, and John W. Snyder of OWMR.[24] The executive committee improved upon Szilard's suggestion by wiring also to Senator McMahon and Senator Kenneth McKellar of Tennessee, asking them to continue their efforts to form a committee to study atomic energy. Telegrams went to Representatives May, Leslie C. Arends, and Clare Boothe Luce of the House Military Affairs Committee, recognizing the pressure for legislation but urging careful consideration of all aspects of atomic energy.[25]

---

[21] Interviews with Sugarman, October 8, 1959, and Higinbotham, October 18, 1961.
[22] Meeting notes, October 12, 1945, ALAS II, 4.
[23] ALAS V, 11.
[24] AORS executive committee minutes, AORES I, 6.
[25] AORS Daily Bulletin, October 18, 1945, AORES XX, 1.

As Szilard had intended, these steps were publicized in the press for other legislators to note. One of the first members of Congress to respond to the overtures of the scientists was Representative Helen Gahagan Douglas of California. On October 12 she protested the extraordinary speed of the Military Affairs Committee one-day hearing. Citing requests to testify from the Chicago and Clinton Labs groups (formal requests are not found in the files), she said that these scientists had been forbidden to speak although "they alone can tell us what is fully in store."[26]

When queried on this point by reporters Chairman May said that his committee had heard everyone who asked to testify and closed its hearings because there were no more witnesses; he followed this up next day with the statement that no further hearings would be held. Again stressing his committee's vigilance in searching for information, he quoted from a telegram received by Secretary Patterson two days earlier from panel members Oppenheimer, Fermi, and Lawrence urging prompt passage of the bill.[27] May later placed the full telegram in the committee records and with it a long covering letter of October 12 from Patterson, giving the ample qualifications of the signers, whose function it had been, he said, to advise the Interim Committee on "matters relating to atomic energy, including specifically, legislation for postwar domestic control over this field. . . . Because of the importance of their work on the bomb project," said Patterson, "it occurred to me that you and your committee would surely be interested in having the views of these three scientists."

The telegram, which had been sent to Patterson from Santa Fe on October 11, read as follows:

We would most strongly urge the passage of the legislation now before Congress for the creation of an atomic energy commission. We know from our close association with the actual work in this field that delay will cost us heavily in efficiency, in accomplishment, and in spirit. We believe that with wisdom operations can be carried on within the framework of the proposed legislation safely, effectively, and in the best interests of this Nation. We believe that the broad powers granted the Commission by the legislation are justified by the importance and the perils of the subject. We think it necessary for the American people to understand in full the implications of the new technical situation, but we believe that the proposed legislation will make it possible for their desires and decisions to be responsibly and fully implemented. We assure you that in our opinion

---

26 New York Times, October 13, 1945, p. 5.
27 New York Times, October 13, 1945, p. 5; October 14, 1945, p. 4.

the legislation as presented represents the fruits of well-informed and experienced consideration.

J. R. Oppenheimer
Enrico Fermi
E. O. Lawrence[28]

Again it was many years before the background of the panel telegram was made public. Acting on suggestions from both Conant and Patterson that a panel meeting might help to quell the rising storm, Harrison, as chairman of the Interim Committee, telephoned Oppenheimer at Los Alamos on October 11. Oppenheimer thought that a joint expression of support for the bill might serve the purpose until the following week when a panel meeting could be held while he was in Washington to testify on science legislation.[29]

The panel's powerful dissuasion from further discussion seemed doubly unfortunate to opponents of the May-Johnson bill because it came in the midst of accumulating evidence that what they conceived to be cardinal points of atomic age politics were not well understood. A few days earlier the press had reported that a scientist at a private laboratory, the Crosby Research Foundation in Hollywood, knew of a defense against the atomic bomb. Eight Chicago scientists branded this claim as preposterous; they offered to pay their own expenses to go and question the Crosby scientist and to work in the laboratory while he attempted to "explode" them. This is the kind of nonsense, they said, that does a lot of harm at a time when people must think more clearly than ever before. Members of the Los Alamos association also protested to Crosby, who replied that he had planned a retraction but that the Chicago statement made him so angry he was not going to bother.[30]

On October 12 the House Naval Affairs Committee reported a possible defense by exploding the bombs far out over the ocean. Again the Met Lab scientists spoke up, deploring the spread of false optimism and declaring that reports that conveyed the impression that the armed forces had things under control could do incalculable harm.[31]

---

[28] U.S. House of Representatives, Committee on Military Affairs, *Atomic Energy, Hearings on H.R. 4280*, 79th Cong., 1st sess., October 9, 18, 1945, pp. 106–7.

[29] *The New World*, p. 432.

[30] Statement, n.d., ASC IX, 2; Associated Press dispatch in ALAS IV, 3; ALAS meeting notes, October 12, 1945, ALAS II, 4.

[31] *New York Times*, October 12, 1945, pp. 1, 5; October 14, 1945, p. 4.

2. SCIENTISTS IN WASHINGTON

With congressmen talking about "a secret" and the press uncritically reporting techniques of defense to an unwary public, it seemed essential to play for time. This the dissenting scientists prepared to do in the week that began on Sunday, October 14. Raymond Swing later christened it "science week in Washington." By the end of it, hearings had been briefly reopened, names of hitherto unknown scientists had hit the front pages of leading newspapers, the young men themselves had had some elementary lessons in Washington politics, and substitutes for the May-Johnson bill were being seriously considered. For "the scientists' movement" it was a most critical week, and it has some broader implications for those who like to observe how policy is made. Altogether it seems to merit a day-by-day account.

Sunday, October 14, 1945

The week opened with the publication of the first statement from the Association of Los Alamos Scientists—the successor to the ill-fated "Document" now reposing safely among the state papers. The *New York Times* put it on the front page with the headline "400 Experts Decry Lone Atom Policy." ALAS presented the case for international control, stressing the likelihood of speedy imitation by other nations and of vastly greater bombs, the difficulties of defense, and the special vulnerability of the industrialized United States. It expressed the opinion that control was technically feasible but that its achievement was primarily a political, not a technical, problem. In conclusion, it prophesied that "a world in which nuclear weapons are owned by many nations and their use held back only by fear of retaliation will be a world of fear, suspicion, and inevitable final explosion."[32]

The ALAS statement made no reference to domestic legislation, but elsewhere in the Sunday *Times* more attention was paid to atomic energy than had been the case for several weeks; the testimony of Langmuir, Shapley, Groves, and the other witnesses before congressional committees was adequately reviewed, and May's reference to the panel telegram was reported. But only in Waldemar Kaempffert's science column was any real point made of the substantial opposition that had developed among scientists in the past ten days to the May-Johnson bill.

---

[32] *New York Times*, October 14, 1945, pp. 1, 4; text of ALAS release in FAS XVII, 7.

In Washington Condon and Szilard, returned from their Met Lab visit, acquired two young assistants, Lyle Borst and Harrison Davies from Clinton Labs, and the four of them prepared to do their utmost to stop the May-Johnson bill.

Monday, October 15, 1945

On Monday this opposition gathered welcome recruits when the Cambridge scientists sent a letter to the War Department strongly criticizing certain sections of the bill. Their views were not communicated to the press, but people at other laboratories quickly learned of them through the exchange of duplicated material that was now becoming common. Continuing their earlier correspondence about organization, Ernest Pollard filled in the background for William Woodward at Los Alamos. Alerted by the President's Message someone had dug the bill out of the *Congressional Record*.

Everyone who read this immediately became vigorously alarmed since it appeared that autocratic powers were being given over research in the whole of nuclear physics and we feared that security restrictions would be so severe as to close down all nuclear research except in what, pardon us, we call monasteries.

In the space of an hour or two, a group of seventy people met and appointed a working committee and a drafting committee, one to study the bill and get interviews with the equivalent of leaders and the other to draft an open letter to the President which would be signed by all who wish to sign it.

This "reasonably worded statement," of which Pollard enclosed a copy, was signed by two hundred ninety people at the Radiation Lab plus some at M.I.T. proper, Harvard, and Columbia.[33]

Pollard omitted the fact that the statement had been stopped short of the White House by the War Department in the hope that M.I.T. and Harvard presidents Compton and Conant, both members of the Interim Committee, could mollify their contentious staff members. Pollard's letter did, however, summarize the results of the working committee's week-end conferences with Compton, Conant, and Shapley and by phone with Oppenheimer and Urey. The committee had convinced Conant that if the intent was to permit freedom of nuclear research the bill in its present form did not say so. Clarifications prepared by the committee had been sent by teletype to Harrison and a copy was enclosed for Woodward. Pollard concluded:

---

[33] A copy also reached Chicago; see ASC XXII, 6.

Some of us are not entirely free of suspicion that others wish the intent of the bill to be drastic in action. If this should be so, and we shall gauge this by the failure to include our clarifications, then we intend to make the loudest possible outcry against the passage of the Johnson bill. I would very much appreciate hearing from you as to whether you feel as we on this subject and whether you think that we on the working committee have, in fact, carried the ball for a gain.[34]

Accompanying the clarifications forwarded to Harrison on Monday, October 15, was an explanation from the Radiation Lab's director, Lee DuBridge:

A group of some 300 physicists in this area who have studied the present wording of the Johnson bill have been greatly worried that the intent of the bill is to restrict and control all nuclear research to the detriment of advancement in this field. A committee, representing this group, have met with Dr. J. B. Conant and were assured that this was not so. Dr. Conant agreed that the impression given by reading the bill could lead to great unrest among physicists because of uncertainty as to the intent. He was perturbed that this substantial fraction of the country's physicists had interpreted the bill to mean that it was the purpose of the War Department (in sponsoring the bill) to strictly control under license all nuclear research whether on a scale involving large energy or not.

The committee proposed for Dr. Conant's comment, certain changes of wording and a single addition directed toward a clarification of the bill with regard to the extent of control over basic research. The following items in this message are the specific modifications which this group believes would clarify the bill with regard to the control of research without endangering other powers of the Commission. It is the belief of the committee that if the recommended clarifications are introduced in these or equivalent words that you will have the uniform support of all physicists for the bill.[35]

Most of the changes involved the inclusion of qualifying phrases that would exclude small-scale use of nuclear energy from the plenary control of the commission. To make doubly sure on this point, a new section was proposed:

Nothing in this Act shall be construed in such a way as to allow interference by the Commission with the right of private agencies or persons to conduct basic research and to disclose the results of such research in nuclear physics, or in chemistry, biology, medicine and other fields using the products or methods of nuclear physics, provided the sources, mechanisms or materials employed in such research are not of such size as to be deemed by the commission to constitute a national hazard.

[34] Pollard to Woodward, October 16, 1945, ALAS IV, 1.
[35] Copy of recommended changes, with covering letter from DuBridge to Harrison, October 15, 1945, Camb.

It was also suggested that the powers of the administrator be restricted in favor of the commission.

From Oak Ridge on Monday, Paul Henshaw, the chairman of AORS, reinforced the earlier spate of telegrams with wires to four representatives urging further hearings and with still more wires to Senators McMahon, Barkley, and McKellar supporting the establishment of a special committee to explore broad issues before considering specific bills, as provided in McMahon's still pending resolution.

Determined to see that their own background knowledge was adequate, the AORS information and records committee that same Monday outlined its program: compilation of all published material on atomic energy; collection of information on legislation before Congress, including the *Congressional Record* and opinions expressed by congressmen; the dissemination of useful information to the AORS membership by means of bulletin boards (a daily bulletin of one or two typewritten sheets was begun next day and continued through November 21); the compilation of lists of other interested organizations and their members; and maintenance of a record of correspondence and copies of all documents received or sent out by AORS members.[36] It was, of course, an impossible program to maintain in the odd hours that could be given to it, but the volume of the committee's records is a monument to a not inconsiderable success.

In Chicago on October 15 there took place a free-for-all discussion of the May-Johnson bill and related topics. Four executive committee members, Rabinowitch, Nickson, Seaborg, and Simpson, were joined by H. H. Goldsmith, Farrington Daniels, Bernard Weissbourd, Harold Urey, who was commuting these days between New York, Washington and Chicago, and Nathan Sugarman from Los Alamos.[37] Daniels had received a phone call from A. H. Compton in Washington asking that one member of the Chicago group come for a luncheon meeting with representatives of the War Department on the seventeenth. The Met Lab would pay the expenses of one man only; Nickson was Daniels' choice although he wanted the appointment to come from the ASC. There was no objection to this. Nickson's experiences on the Franck committee and in the summer discussions made him a satisfactory delegate. Szilard was in Washington, and it was eventually decided that after the ASC general meeting on Tuesday evening John Simpson should go too.

---

[36] Meeting notes in AORES I, 6; XX, 1.
[37] Meeting notes, October 15, 1945, ASC VI, 12.

At this point Urey's arrival turned attention to the bill itself. He had phoned several prominent scientists across the country and had found vehement opposition to its present form. Langmuir was "high in the air" about it; DuBridge was "up in arms." Ernest Lawrence had not read the bill when Urey phoned him a week earlier, but after doing so he had called back to say that it was a "bad" bill. (The notes do not record any comment on the telegram signed by Lawrence four days before, but probably the Sunday *Times* containing May's quotations from it had not arrived in Chicago when this group met on Monday.) Oppenheimer and Fermi, said Urey, were also wavering. Compton's projected conference indicated that he, too, saw room for compromise.

Either the secretary on this occasion was inept, or more likely, the participants were all trying to talk at once, interrupting and contradicting as those of common experience and aims can do. These people, whose public pronouncements had sounded so confident and united, were displaying among themselves a becoming uncertainty—raising questions and offering partial answers—about how to deal with what they now conceived to be a crisis for American science. Was the May-Johnson bill really going to be pushed through without further discussion? Should they try to amend it? Was there time for a careful investigation of alternatives or for a campaign to educate the voters? Who would make good commission members—Tolman, Oppenheimer, Urey, Lawrence? Weissbourd suggested David Lilienthal.

The question most avidly discussed was why the four members of the scientific panel had supported a bill that left an opening for the authoritarian exercise of power and for the hamstringing of scientific research. This was difficult for those who admired them to understand. The best justification offered was a belief that it was safer to trust the commission and the administrator to use their powers wisely than to risk the chance that Congress, subjected to multiple pressures during a long debate, might produce something very much worse. This argument had already been employed at Los Alamos; it was not good tactics to make much of it in public.

Urey, with customary directness, expressed himself more positively than the younger men, but he took a moderate stand. This group, he said, could draft modifications to the bill. If it could go through with enough relaxation of secrecy so that people could work, then it would be time to see what could be done about the international situation. Only by remaining strong could the United States offer an olive branch. Within a few days, on a trip to Washington and as an unofficial representative of the ASC, Urey was to change his mind about modifying the bill.

A crucial point missed by the recorder at this meeting was noted a few days later in Oak Ridge, namely, that the Atomic Scientists of Chicago had obtained from colleagues at the University of Chicago Law School a twelve-page criticism of the May-Johnson bill, which Nickson took to Washington for discussion with Compton and the AORS representatives.[38]

In Washington on Monday Condon, Szilard, Borst, and Davies were operating from informal headquarters at the Wardman Park Hotel. Thanks to Borst's jottings in a diary, we know that they talked to Robert K. Lamb, legislative representative of the CIO and received a briefing from him on what to expect in regard to the bill. It looked then as if the House Military Affairs Committee would meet on Tuesday and vote the bill out on Wednesday, with a House vote perhaps on Thursday. There was not much time to lose. They discussed tactics in general—which other committees might enter the picture and which individuals pulled which strings in Congress. The quickest way to make opposition felt, advised James Newman, with whom the scientists were also in close touch, was to loose a flood of telegrams demanding further hearings; he recommended wires to Chairman May, with copies to his own boss, John Snyder, in care of the White House so there would be an independent check on the number received.

"The best quantitative measure of what we accomplished," recalls Lyle Borst, "was Szilard's phone bill at the Wardman Park." The phone was indeed exactly suited to Szilard's *modus operandi*, suggesting urgency, complicity, and a gentleman's disregard of petty expense. That evening he called everyone he could think of. Borst's diary listed Urey, Shapley, Frederick Seitz, Eugene Wigner, Beardsley Ruml, Dean George B. Pegram at Columbia, I. I. Rabi, Selig Hecht, and Oppenheimer.[39]

Two items of news originated on Monday that in due course cheered the Wardman Park cabal. Talking to reporters, Representative May showed the first signs of wavering in his determination not to hold more hearings. May's change of heart, the *New York Times* would report next day, seemed to be the result of protests from

---

[38] AORS Daily Bulletin, October 18, 1945, AORES XX, 1.
[39] Interview with Borst, February 20, 1962.

scientists and of a wire from CIO president Philip Murray to Speaker Rayburn accusing House leaders of railroading legislation.[40]

And on Monday also, OWMR director John Snyder sent to the White House a memorandum that his assistant, James Newman, had begun to prepare some two weeks earlier, recommending six modifications in the May-Johnson bill: less emphasis should be given to weapons, and mention of peaceful applications, now absent, should be included; the commission should be less independent of the executive and its operations more closely integrated with government policy; it should sponsor research in social and political implications as well as in the science and technology of atomic energy; the part-time commission should be replaced by a full-time board representing special fields, including two from the armed services and one from the physical sciences; the administrator should be a civilian; the commission should have greater control over materials, plants, and patents, but it should not be allowed to dismiss employees without legal proceedings.[41]

The impression was still current that the May-Johnson bill had White House support, but it was after receipt of this memorandum that Truman gave OWMR the responsibility for co-ordinating administration views on atomic energy legislation.

Tuesday, October 16, 1945

By Tuesday the group of scientists in Washington had expanded with the arrival of Herbert Anderson and Robert Wilson of Los Alamos, Nickson from Chicago, and two more Clinton Labs men, Howard J. Curtis and Waldo Cohn, the latter there briefly at the start of a "vacation" devoted largely to interviews and a radio appearance in New York on behalf of the atomic scientists. Borst, Davies, Szilard, and Anderson talked with Representatives Jerry Voorhis and George E. Outland of California and found them much interested in the scientists' point of view. Szilard, Borst noted, evaded a discussion of the Oppenheimer-Fermi-Lawrence telegram.

Others of the group spent much of Tuesday—all day and all night, according to Curtis—with Barry Commoner, Charles Kramer, and Herbert Schimmel, assistants to three senators "on our side." (The

---

[40] *New York Times*, October 16, 1945, p. 3.

[41] Memorandum Snyder to Truman, October 15, 1945, copy in files of Byron Miller. Miller, in an interview January 20, 1960, says that when he joined Snyder's staff about October 1 Newman had already drafted such a memorandum.

scientists were to see a good deal of these and other legislative aides in the next few weeks. Schimmel, a Ph.D. in physics, was chief investigator for the Senate Military Affairs Committee and its subcommittee on war mobilization which was conducting hearings on science legislation under the chairmanship of Senator Kilgore; Commoner, a biologist and a lieutenant in the navy, was assigned to the Kilgore committee with the task of obtaining the views of the scientific community regarding science legslation.) These three men seemed very knowing about the ways of Capitol Hill, and their advice that the site organizations ought to take a united stand on domestic legislation was seriously considered by the unofficial site representatives during the next few days.[42]

On Tuesday afternoon the scientists learned that their immediate objective had been achieved. Chairman May (acting on instructions from Patterson) had agreed to reopen hearings on the May-Johnson bill on Thursday morning.

In Chicago that evening the weekly general meeting elected John Simpson chairman of the ASC, then heard a Manhattan Project security officer talk about the importance of concealing information and Dean Robert Redfield of the Social Sciences advise them on how to spread it. The services of the first speaker were certainly unsolicited. The second was there in response to an appeal from Katherine Way, the ASC's chairman of publicity, for help in making contacts with the press and radio and in setting up conferences with leaders in business, labor, and education.[43]

From Los Alamos on this Tuesday Higinbotham wrote to Oppenheimer in Washington where Oppenheimer and Robert Wilson were to testify on Wednesday on science legislation. It was a formal letter, tactfully pointing out that ALAS had in the past experienced some difficulty because of a lack of sufficiently good contact with him. "The Interim Committee," Higinbotham reminded Oppenheimer, "gave us no answer at all, which many interpreted as neglecting us." We intend, he said, to get closer collaboration with Oak Ridge and Chicago and to put a stop to precipitous action. However, there would be many cases where some action should be taken. ALAS would probably reply to news articles from time to time; if Oppenheimer wished them to notify him in all important cases, they would be glad to do

---

[42] Curtis reporting to the ASC executive committee, October 20, 1945, ASC VI, 12.
[43] Meeting notes, October 16, 1945, ASC XXVI, Vol. IV; Way to Redfield, October 18, 1945, ASC XIX, 9.

so. The Johnson bill was being carefully studied, and suggestions would be forwarded as soon as majority acceptance was obtained.[44]

Press and radio were taking note. In the "Washington Merry-Go-Round" Drew Pearson began a series of comments about the scientists' feud with the Army, quoting the Carbide Corporation's directive forbidding talk about the implications of atomic energy, which the Clinton Labs men had already discussed with Compton. General Groves, Pearson said, was the principal target of the scientists' opposition to the May-Johnson bill. Neither May nor Johnson had studied the bill before they introduced it; in fact, it had been shrouded in such secrecy that the War Department had at first referred to it by number, then got cold feet and let out more information.[45]

It was on this Tuesday evening that Frank Kingdon, the WMCA commentator, also focused the attention of a large radio audience on the scientists' protests. We are enforcing, said Kingdon, "the most dangerous censorship which has ever been clamped on freedom of thought and speech in this country whether in peace or war. This is so full of menace that I cannot understand why every university faculty and learned society in the country has not called an emergency meeting to protest it."[46]

Wednesday, October 17, 1945

On Wednesday, three scientists—Robert Oppenheimer, Howard J. Curtis, and Robert R. Wilson—testified at the hearings on science foundation bills. An audience of two hundred crowded into the Senate hearing room, and the testimony, reported the *New York Times*, turned into a round-table discussion of ways to control atomic energy. This was no accident. That the scientists obtained a platform denied them in the House committee hearings is credited to the senatorial assistants Schimmel and Commoner, who had enlisted Chairman Kilgore's co-operation in permitting questions and answers to veer in the direction of atomic energy problems.[47]

Oppenheimer was the first witness. His prepared statement offered general reasons for establishing a science foundation, but he asked to preface it by commenting on ways in which atomic energy complicated the problem of fundamental research. The government, he

---

[44] Higinbotham to Oppenheimer, October 16, 1945, copy in ALAS II, 2.
[45] "Washington Merry-Go-Round," October 16, 17, 1945.
[46] Kingdon broadcast, October 16, 1945, text in AORES XIV, 2.
[47] Interview with Curtis, October 18, 1961; Commoner to author, April 19, 1962.

believed, would inevitably control major nuclear research facilities, and military application of atomic energy would mean keeping some things secret. Yet the necessity for secrecy was to him a matter for the deepest concern. "One is not in a position to freeze the state of atomic energy as it is today," he told the senators. "One will so freeze it if one prevents the free discussion, free publication, free criticism of the scientific elements in the atomic energy program."[48]

Oppenheimer then read a statement from Enrico Fermi, prepared at Kilgore's request and largely concerned with the same subject. Too strict organization of science, said Fermi, stifles initiative and imagination, especially of young men who now tended as a result of their wartime experiences to expect to be handed problems. Extensive limitation on scientific intercourse, he went on, affects the development itself unfavorably, not through the conscious rebellion of scientists, but through the absence of the stimulus that comes from the interaction between colleagues of different backgrounds and different points of view.

After some discussion of international exchange of personnel and fellowships, Senator J. William Fulbright of Arkansas asked Oppenheimer whether his own statement and Fermi's were directed to the bill under discussion or to the May-Johnson bill, to which they seemed more directly related. Fermi's statement, replied Oppenheimer, might have been influenced by the May-Johnson bill and his reluctance to see wartime secrecy carried over into peacetime research. His own was written "considerably before" he read the bill. "The Johnson bill, I don't know much about," he continued, "but what I do know about it is that you could do almost anything under that bill, and a wise commission could operate with complete freedom under that bill. Whether it will or not, I don't know."[49]

This repudiation of panel responsibility did not go unremarked by scientists in the audience, assured as they had been that the panel represented them in policy-making. The discussion proceeded, however, without comment. Oppenheimer assumed that the commission would not care to exercize its powers to the full, a restraint, Senator Fulbright noted, that was not characteristic of most commissions. But Oppenheimer, again disclaiming full knowledge of the bill's back-

---

[48] U.S. Senate, Committee on Military Affairs, Subcommittee on War Mobilization, *Hearings on Science Legislation*, 79th Cong., 1st sess., October 8, 1945–March 5, 1946, p. 298.
[49] *Ibid.*, p. 308.

ground, emphasized the predicament of its authors. They were aware, he said,

that they did not know what developments would be of fundamental military importance and of fundamental national importance. They could not write down a set of problems which they wanted to control and another set which they didn't, because no one, neither the scientists nor those who gaze in a crystal ball, could make this demarcation into a field which was important and another field which wasn't, and it is this background which made them write the bill so broadly.[50]

This was as reasonable a defense of the bill as anyone had yet offered. It could be construed, Oppenheimer admitted, so as to stop science in its tracks, but the atomic bomb—"the two billion dollar straw that will break the camel's back"—constituted far more than a legislative matter. The bill itself was not the problem, he said; it simply indicated that the problem existed. The distinguished senators were no doubt accustomed to having two sides of a question presented, but perhaps not so ably by the same witness. Oppenheimer was quite right; there was something to be said on both sides, but it is not surprising that one paper next day spoke of his "oblique attack" on the May-Johnson bill.[51]

Curtis was the next witness. Tall, blond, with an easy manner, and looking younger than his thirty-eight years, he might have been doctor, lawyer, or business executive, and it must have reassured his audience to be told that he represented the rank and file of the Project scientists. Until early 1943, Curtis explained, he had been a professor of physiology at Columbia; he had then joined the Manhattan Project as both physicist and biologist and was now in charge of the biological research section at Clinton Laboratories. His statement, prepared co-operatively before he left Oak Ridge, directed attention almost exclusively to atomic energy—the effect of the bomb upon peacetime research and the imperative need for international control. It was an adequate statement of the AORS position, a bit repetitious and, after Oppenheimer's felicitous handling of language, pedestrian. In reply to questions Curtis said the Clinton group felt that a science foundation should be built around a peaceful economy. If we are preparing for war we should maintain large secret laboratories; if for peace, our science should be based upon the free dissemination of scientific information.

---

[50] *Ibid.*, p. 309.
[51] *PM* (New York), October 18, 1945.

Asked to comment on the AORS statement, Oppenheimer expressed general agreement, but Curtis had spoken of turning bombs over to an international organization to maintain peace, and he wished to make clear that the atomic bomb was not a police weapon; it could not be used, for example, on a Louisiana town that was not governing itself properly. Second, Curtis had said that international problems were primary and that no domestic legislation should be passed until they were solved. He agreed absolutely with the first part of the statement, as, he thought, did all at Los Alamos. So did the War Department. But the May-Johnson bill did not constitute a solution to domestic problems; it merely constituted a framework within which the solutions might be elaborated. An international organization could not be created by pushing a button but must be based upon a slow growth of confidence. The Johnson bill, or its successor, must not be postponed until there was an international organization.

Oppenheimer also differed with the AORS statement in regard to the effect of atomic secrecy upon scientific research, for there existed, he thought, "an amount of lore and technical discovery" connected with the actual manufacture of bombs that could be kept secret without interfering in a major way with the pursuit of science, although it might, he agreed, interfere with the establishment of international confidence.

Finally, said Oppenheimer, scientists could not help by underestimating the difficulties, and the AORS statement, he thought, gave an impression of political naïveté that he would not want to see given, even if it corresponded to the facts. Coming from one who assumed so much about the commission's wise use of its powers, the choice of the word naïve was perhaps not a happy one, but in his own testimony, as in his administration of Los Alamos, Oppenheimer had been extremely careful to distinguish, insofar as this was possible, between scientific and political problems. The qualifications that he insisted on making in the AORS statement reflected the greater maturity of his thinking in the area being discussed; and although his public correction of his young colleagues at their maiden appearance before Congress seemed a little rough, it is the kind of straight talk that scientists are used to. In the scientists' movement in the coming months, with the ambiguous role of the panel no longer confusing the picture, Oppenheimer's position was that of a very helpful elder statesman.

The testimony of Robert Wilson, who had just accepted a professorship in physics at Harvard but identified himself as a member of the executive committee of the Association of Los Alamos Scientists, concluded the morning's hearings. Wilson, at thirty-one, was a brilliant experimentalist with an amiable manner, a deceptive boyishness, and an idealistic view of the broader implications of science tempered by common sense. He was to be one of the mainstays of the scientists' movement after some of the early enthusiasts had lost their initial fervor.

No one had warned Wilson that it was in order to talk about atomic energy, and he was puzzled by his colleagues' annoyance that his prepared statement dealt exclusively with fundamental and programmatic research. But Wilson managed some effective off-the-cuff remarks about the inconclusive wartime discussions at Los Alamos and about the enormous impact on their thinking of the test in the Jornada del Muerto. At Los Alamos, said Wilson, we have been preoccupied with the international aspects of the problem and have not concerned ourselves much with domestic legislation, though our views are very similar to those expressed here today. Which views, he did not say.

Senator Fulbright wanted to know how many had been involved in the discussions at Los Alamos. In the days before the bomb exploded, replied Wilson, about fifty; afterward everyone discussed these problems. At the first organization meeting there were five hundred to seven hundred present; the usual weekly meetings had four hundred or five hundred. The greatest difficulty, commented Oppenheimer, was deciding who counted as a scientist; otherwise one would say "everybody."

Wednesday was the day originally scheduled for Compton's lunch for scientists and War Department representatives, but plans were changed; instead the men from Los Alamos, Chicago, and Oak Ridge got together to talk about an intersite organization, laying the ground for their first joint meeting in Chicago the following week. After lunch Curtis, Wilson, Davies, Nickson, and Borst had a talk with Senator Fulbright. His point of view was "for us," Curtis later told the Chicago executive committee, but he warned that the Washington game was tough; he thought the bill would go through because most of Congress did not know what it was about, and when Congress does not know anything about a bill, they just pass it. Fulbright was pessimistic about educating Congress.[52]

---

[52] Curtis report to the ASC, October 20, 1945, ASC VI, 12.

None of the scientists' reports of these busy days mentioned what use they made of the legal criticism of the May-Johnson bill that Nickson had brought from Chicago, but it was effectively employed on Wednesday in at least two directions. Secretary of Commerce Wallace sent a memorandum to President Truman saying that in view of the President's favorable reply to a memorandum of two days before he ventured to pass along the reaction of leading scientists to the May-Johnson bill. He listed eight points to which they raised objections.[53] And a group of scientists who refused to release their names made available to a *PM* reporter the analysis of the bill on which their opposition was based.[54] Although not identified as such, this was the analysis prepared by Professor Edward Levi of the Chicago Law School at Szilard's request. Levi's criticism centered around the wide powers given to commission and administrator, which made them in some areas independent of the law. It noted the commission's power to apply its own secrecy rules retroactively to wartime employees, to make and modify contracts, to acquire property and mineral rights by forced sale, and to control all nuclear research. The bill allowed the commission to operate outside the normal channels of the Civil Service and of the government auditing machinery; it granted the commission wide powers of dismissal of its own employees and allowed the President arbitrarily to dismiss commission members. The lawyers had found even more undesirable items in the bill than the scientists. The Levi critique concluded:

> The most serious problem raised by the bill appears to be the possibility that a Commission or Administrator might determine that rigorous control and direction of atomic research is required not for the purpose of military security alone, but because greater development might then be expected. This would constitute a judgment as to how research can be best carried out. Moreover there is some question whether under conditions of broad censorship which may go beyond military requirements, independent and original research is possible.[55]

Wednesday evening there was a dinner for scientists and senators, the first of a series arranged by Watson Davis, director of Science Service. The young men who had interviewed Fulbright were there;

---

[53] Wallace to Truman, October 17, 1945, copy in Byron Miller's files.

[54] *P M* (New York), October 18, 1945.

[55] Analysis of S.1463: Proposed Atomic Energy Act of 1945, by Edward H. Levi (copy in FAS XI, 5). During the war Levi had served in the antitrust division of the Justice Department; in 1950 he became dean of the University of Chicago Law School and in 1962 provost of the university.

so were Oppenheimer, Fermi, Urey, Szilard, Condon, and Shapley, who as master of ceremonies put across very ably, his colleagues thought, the idea of "educating" senators. On hand to be educated were Senators Kilgore, McMahon, Alexander Smith of New Jersey, Charles W. Tobey of New Hampshire, Glen Taylor of Idaho, James E. Murray of Montana, and Hugh Mitchell of Washington. Secretary of Commerce Wallace and James Newman represented the administration.

Lyle Borst remembers the occasion as a decisive one. Senator Tobey, the ranking Republican and clearly a man of influence, rose, looked around the table, and said pointedly, "It looks as if we have a nonpartisan issue." "Everyone took their cue from him," Borst recalls, "and that was the way it remained." The consensus of opinion seemed to be that everything now depended upon the President, that he was trying hard to make up his mind about the May-Johnson bill and wanted to do the right thing. Immediate publicity was indicated, and Herbert Schimmel offered to arrange a press conference for the next day. The senators who attended the dinner took such favorable reports of it to Majority Leader Barkley that he, too, expressed interest in talking to some scientists.[56]

A. H. Compton's name does not figure in the casual reporting of this dinner, but along with Fermi and Oppenheimer he was in town to testify, mediate, and attend the panel meeting requested by Harrison the previous week. In the course of this meeting, held earlier on Wednesday at the Pentagon, panel members had been frank to admit their own reservations, especially about the security provisions of the bill, and they had discussed the accumulating evidence of widespread dissatisfaction as well as such important individual opinion as that of K. T. Compton, a member of the Interim Committee, who had been converted to the views of the Cambridge majority in the course of his mediation efforts the previous week end.[57]

But the panel was ready only to qualify, not to recall, its approval of the bill, and tense hotel room negotiation between panel and May-Johnson opponents took place, probably on Wednesday evening after the dinner, for Oppenheimer had volunteered to see Szilard, Urey, and Anderson before they testified on Thursday in the hope of avoid-

---

[56] Curtis report to the ASC, October 20, 1945, ASC VI, 12; interview with Borst, February 20, 1962; FAS Newsletter, November 5, 1945, FAS XV, 8.

[57] The New World, pp. 432–33. I have found no specific reference to the presence of another panel member, E. O. Lawrence, in Washington during this week.

ing "a public wrangle." Recollections include a preliminary gathering at the Wardman Park, where Szilard, Condon, Urey, and their allies, including James Newman, discussed defeat rather than modification of the bill, then a departure of the leaders for the Statler Hotel, where a heated and entirely unproductive parley took place with panel members and Lee DuBridge. When this was clearly getting nowhere Szilard and his associates went back to the Wardman Park, and although it was late, they set to work at once outlining the directions that a new bill ought to take.[58]

A day or two in Washington had helped people to decide where they stood. DuBridge was convinced that the criticisms he had voiced so strongly on Monday on behalf of the Cambridge scientists could be met, whereas Urey, who in Chicago on Monday had counselled moderation and talked of revision, was now in favor of a fresh start.

Thursday, October 18, 1945

The important event of Thursday, October 18, was the reopening of the House Military Affairs Committee hearings on H.R. 4280. These hearings have been continued, announced Chairman May, to permit "a group of interested people, known as scientists," to present their views. The press had indicated that the committee was trying to rush things, but he wished to say that up to this moment no request had been made for a hearing on behalf of scientists except somewhat indirectly through General Royall of the War Department, who, though he did not ask for further hearings rather encouraged the idea. The committee would now give patient consideration to those representing scientific work in the United States.[59]

Some patience was required before the day's testimony was over, for the scientists had an odd way of making proposals, offering alternatives, and then proving reluctant to be pinned down as to which course was incontrovertibly the best.

The first witness was Leo Szilard. "When I came down to Washington," he said, "I understood that the committee had closed its hearings. Day before yesterday, late in the afternoon, I was notified that I was to appear as a witness. Subsequently I dictated my statement to a stenographer while she was operating a switchboard. In these circumstances I hope to have your indulgence if the statement is not

[58] Interview with Wilson, June 2, 1959.
[59] U.S. House of Representatives, Military Affairs Committee, *Atomic Energy, Hearings on H.R. 4280*, 79th Cong., 1st sess., October 18, 1945, pp. 71 ff.

as clear as it might otherwise have been." With this characteristic preamble Szilard explained that during the past few days he and his colleagues had discussed the problems that atomic energy presented, the functions required to solve them, and the machinery needed to perform the functions. You cannot have an intelligent discussion of machinery, said Szilard, if some people think its function is to build power plants in remote places and others think it is "to provide us with atomic bombs so that we can blast the hell out of Russia before Russia blasts the hell out of us."

Szilard proceeded to outline a tripartite organization, dealing with research, industrial developments, and military applications that would be directed by a policy-making body representing the three divisions and the Departments of State, War, Interior, and Commerce—the areas in which the impact of atomic energy would be most clearly felt. Szilard's description of this machinery is not easy to follow even in print and the listening congressmen had to ask a good many questions. Szilard seized the opportunity to air some of his pet peeves— the too free revelations of the Smyth report, compartmentation in the Manhattan Project, and his lack of confidence in its wartime direction.

Suppose one person or several should be struck down, would it destroy the know-how of the bomb? "No," replied Szilard. "I believe if some of those persons who believe they know everything were struck down it would promote rather than retard the development of atomic power." What about reports that a defense against the bomb was possible? Szilard showed off again: If anyone perfected a device for detonating a bomb at three miles distance, he would undertake in about one month to perfect a defense against the defense.

But Szilard did not have things all his own way. Representative Thomason, evidently briefed in advance, quizzed Szilard about his stubborn refusal to sign over patent rights relating to atomic energy to the government as agreed in the terms of his employment with the Project. Szilard explained with some asperity that such a signature involved taking an oath, and this he would not do without the advice of a patent attorney; he was waiting for the government to clear someone to advise him.

But despite Szilard's difficulty in providing answers brief enough to satisfy Chairman May and accurate enough to satisfy himself the interrogation showed him to be free from doctrinaire political views and to have, on some points, an unexpectedly practical approach. He also asserted a great respect for "secrets." He recommended that research be sponsored by the government rather than by universities or industry, not because of a particular political philosophy, but for reasons relating to long-term or short-term objectives for atomic power; these he would like to discuss in executive session.

There should be competition, said Szilard, among some five or six government laboratories scattered across the country. Although tasks would be assigned, each laboratory would be permitted to spend some portion of its budget, say 40 per cent, on other objectives. This he recommended because wartime experience had shown that the method selected and assigned by the central authorities had sometimes turned out to be unworkable whereas that developed by a local group had worked. Although Szilard believed that the commission should have power and resources to carry on research, he did not approve of its having power to prevent others from doing so.

Asked whether his objection to the present bill rested on his fear of the perpetuation of military control, Szilard replied that the present control was not entirely military. He assumed that the men appointed to the proposed commission would be those who had spoken on behalf of the bill and that work would be carried on in the same manner as under the Office of Scientific Research and Development, the National Defense Research Council, and the Manhattan Project, that is, by contract with industry and universities. This he did not approve. Industries for the time being would have nothing to lose in accepting cost contracts until developments promised a profit. Meanwhile they would put their really bright young men on research of their own with a more immediate return.

It was no secret that when Szilard spoke of the OSRD, the NDRC, and the Manhattan Project he had in mind Bush, Conant, Groves, and the mechanism of the Project's Military Policy Committee through which they had controlled the atomic research laboratories. Those who followed Szilard in thus personalizing the issue were convinced that these three men, despite undoubtedly genuine assertions of wanting to be rid of their arduous responsibilities, would find that their unique experience made it a duty to serve as part-time members of the commission or, in Groves's case, as administrator. Others more ready than Szilard to admit how well these men had served their country—and even to recognize the debt they owed to Bush and Conant for making it possible, through contracts to universities, for scientists to work in congenial surroundings and in a way that maintained the dignity and integrity of their profession—yet felt strongly about the principles of civilian control and full-time responsibility.[60]

But the most disturbing feature of the bill, in Szilard's opinion, was the possible effect of the commission's virtual autonomy upon international relations. For example, the President and Congress might wish to collaborate with another government on a particular project and the administrator might issue contrary directives. Exactly this had happened during the war when the work of a mission to a Canadian project sponsored by the President had been completely sabotaged by Manhattan Project rulings that prevented scientists at the Met Lab from co-operating. Commission autonomy would also insulate it from healthy criticism, and this situation would be made worse by the stringent penalties written into the law for violation of secrecy. Those in atomic energy work would not dare to criticize the commission for fear that some past instance of picayune violation would be cited against them, and criticism from those outside the field would be considered valueless.

In sum Szilard declared himself as believing that piecemeal amendment would not satisfy the majority of scientists. He favored a continuation of the present regime while a thorough study was made. Szilard's testimony had consumed an hour and forty minutes, which the chairman seemed to think was quite enough for one witness.

The next one was Herbert Anderson (incorrectly called Harold in the printed hearings), who had written so vehemently about the May-Johnson bill from Chicago a week earlier. Presented by Szilard as a spokesman for the younger scientists, Anderson described himself as thirty-one years old and as having worked with Fermi both before and after he got his Ph.D. at Columbia in 1940; he had gone with Fermi to the Met Lab in 1942 and to Los Alamos in November, 1944. He would soon return to Chicago as a member of the new Institute for Nuclear Studies. (Twelve years later he succeeded Allison as its director.)

Anderson, considerably calmer than when he had exploded to Higinbotham a week earlier but still bumptious enough to irritate the chairman, spoke particularly about the secrecy provisions of the May-Johnson bill and their potential impact on scientific research. An astronomer needs information on atomic transformation to study the stars, Anderson pointed out; a medical researcher needs atomic

---

[60] The contribution of Bush and Conant in making war research tolerable was stressed by I. I. Rabi in the Karl T. Compton Lecture at M.I.T., March 8, 1962.

tracers. Under this law they would be able to get them only at the pleasure of the commission, and any worker who incurred its displeasure might have his tools cut off. Under cloak of secrecy, inefficiencies would be concealed. Scientists would be discouraged from entering the field. Anderson described the self-imposed secrecy on the discussion of fission that scientists had established in 1939. His own Ph.D. dissertation, the first to fall under the ban, was still under lock and key. At Los Alamos the scientists had dealt with carelessness by fining those who left classified material out of a safe or by assigning them to the evening inspection force. The rigid secrecy perpetuated by the bill would in itself, Anderson declared, be interpreted by other governments as an act of aggression. "I appeal to the Congress," he concluded, "not to place in jeopardy the civil liberties of their constituents, to beware lest in their zeal to control they stifle the very object of their control, and to leave open the road to international understanding and world peace."

Anderson read into the record a long telegram received that morning by Szilard from the Atomic Scientists of Chicago and the Association of Oak Ridge Scientists at Clinton Labs. Under eight headings it raised objections to the complete and arbitrary powers of the proposed commission, to the vagueness of the directives to use those powers wisely, to the possible employment of army and navy officers on active duty, and to the real danger of retarding research and development. All this had been said before, but this statement said it very well. It was granted that controls should be exercised by an administrative agency of the government in the interests of military security and the general welfare. "We believe, however, that the limits and objectives of these controls must be defined by the people through their elected Congress. This may be accomplished only by a law drafted after the fullest discussion, in Congress and out, of the meaning and possibilities of atomic energy and atomic bombs." The two organizations urged that the present bill be abandoned and steps taken to prepare a new one. If necessary to assure continuity, Congress might enact interim legislation empowering the present authorities to carry on for six months.[61]

Midway through the questioning of Anderson a luncheon recess was called. Most of the scientists attending the hearings spent the noon hour at what appears to have been the substitute for Compton's

---

[61] U.S. House of Representatives, Military Affairs Committee, *Atomic Energy, Hearings on H.R. 4280*, 79th Cong., 1st sess., October 18, 1945, p. 100.

Cosmos Club luncheon of Wednesday—a hastily arranged affair at
the Savarin Restaurant at the Union Station, more accessible from
Capitol Hill than the Cosmos Club. Fermi and Compton represented
the panel, and six or eight other scientists were recruited from the
morning's audience. (Those so far identified were Nickson, Borst,
Curtis, and Seitz.) The place was terribly noisy and the table a long
one, so Compton put himself at one end and Fermi at the other with
instructions to give those near him "the word." In the colloquial form
in which the episode remains in the mind of one of those present,
"the word" was that they were bad boys but would be forgiven if
their behavior improved. Fermi's heart was not in the task, and those
at his end of the table did not get the full message. The only contemporary reference to this occasion says that the panel proposed
the May-Johnson bill be amended to give more lenient security provisions, to restrict the powers of the commission, and to include a
more definite statement of the policy that should guide its actions.[62]

At two o'clock the hearings reconvened, and after the questioning
of Anderson ended, May read into the record the October 11 telegram
from Oppenheimer, Fermi, and Lawrence and Patterson's covering
letter, quoted earlier.

The next witness was A. H. Compton, the one panel member who
had not signed the telegram. It soon became clear why. For although
Compton agreed with Oppenheimer's view that control could best
be provided by some such commission as the one proposed, he had
been in close touch with the opposition and was ready to admit the
need for compromise and amendment. It was unfortunate, said
Compton, that so little was said in a positive way about the development of atomic energy. It was easier, in other words, to write in
restrictions than to write in freedom. He assumed that the drastic
penalties would never be imposed. At the same time he found it
indefensible that a commission employee should be fired and even
cut off from other employment without stated cause. The bill should
be toned down to get rid of the idea that we become strong through
secrecy rather than by building up and developing scientific work.

Representative Thomas E. Martin of Iowa concluded from the
testimony of scientists so far "that as a group you are more concerned
with seeing that you are not suppressed or retarded or discouraged
in your research and development work than anything else." Comp-

----

[62] Interview with Curtis, October 18, 1961; confirmation by Borst, February 20,
1962; AORS Daily Bulletin, October 31, 1945, AORES XX, 1.

ton agreed this was probably so and let the matter rest, but Oppenheimer reverted to this subject after he took the stand. "Scientists," he said, "are not used to being controlled; they are not used to regimentation, and there are good reasons why they should be averse to it, because it is in the nature of science that the individual is to be given a certain amount of freedom to invent, to think, and to carry on the best he knows how." As an interpreter Oppenheimer was in much better form today and Oppenheimer at his best is very good indeed. Scientists wanted assurance that scientific work would continue. He believed that the War Department would be glad to support an amendment that would give this.

Oppenheimer said he had little to add to Compton's remarks. Yet what he did say, unlike the previous day's testimony at the Kilgore hearings, was clear and unequivocal. The bill should be passed, first, because work in nuclear physics and related fields was being held up and, second, because negotiation with foreign governments to obtain international control, which all or nearly all scientists felt to be necessary, could not go forward until we had a satisfactory national administration. In framing the bill he thought that Bush and Conant (who had not made the point half as convincingly in their own testimony a week earlier) had in mind the rapidly changing picture in the atomic field and saw that a more specific bill could not be written at this time. Oppenheimer was sure that the bill was too sweeping, but he did not see how to make it less sweeping and still make it good.

Plausible as was this line of argument it did not really touch the points on which the opposition was concentrating its fire—the part-time commission, the rigid control of nuclear research, the drastic security provisions. And although, like Oppenheimer, opponents thought it vital to consider the effect of the bill on international control, they believed that its militant tone would completely vitiate the advantage he cited of having a settled domestic system from which to negotiate.

If it was not clear which side had the best of these arguments, the opposition received some aid and comfort before the afternoon was over from further revelations about the extent of the panel's acquaintance with the measure. When Compton was asked the purpose of giving so much power to the commission he hedged: "I believe—really, I am not the person to have you ask that question because I knew nothing about this bill until after it had come to your attention." In the same way Oppenheimer had been caught off guard at the Kilgore hearings. Today he repeated that he had nothing to do with drafting the bill and was not competent to judge its adequacy but he shared the confidence expressed by the chairman in the ability of the nation to produce nine intelligent, conscientious men to carry out whatever policy the country decided was right. As for the bill, he said, it

was drafted with the detailed supervision of Dr. Bush and Dr. Conant, with the knowledge and the agreement of the former Secretary of War, Mr. Stimson. I think that no one in the country carried a greater weight of responsibility for this project than Mr. Stimson. I think no men in positions of responsibility, who were scientists, took more responsibility or were more courageous or better informed in the general sense than Dr. Bush and Dr. Conant. I think if they liked the philosophy of this bill and urged this bill it is a very strong argument. I know that many scientists do not agree with me on this, but I am nevertheless convinced myself.

If other scientists had not already asked Oppenheimer and Compton some searching questions about how they happened to be supporting a bill they knew so little about, they probably did so after these hearings. A story gained currency that General Groves had given them a long oral account of the bill but had omitted those sections that left the door open to military control. Nothing that either Oppenheimer or Compton said in testimony contradicts this. As for the other two panel members, Fermi's colleagues did not expect political judgments from him and he managed to stay out of the fray; Lawrence was apparently not in Washington with the other three during this week, and according to the information given by Urey to the ASC meeting in Chicago on October 15, he had not read the bill before it was introduced. Oppenheimer and Compton, who between them were "boss" to most of the Manhattan Project scientists, bore the brunt of the explanation and criticism.

Although some rather harsh words were uttered, the younger scientists, with time and with experience of their own as administrators, have come to look back on the incident with some understanding. Compton and Oppenheimer, in the view of one, were just plain tired; they had thrown everything they had into the grueling months of planning, of decisions, of placating superiors and subordinates, and of an exhausting schedule of meetings and travel. This other unfamiliar task would have to be done by someone else. After three years of stratified organization and decisions made at the top, says another, they didn't have their feet on the ground. One might add that during the war both men had successfully subordinated divergent military and scientific viewpoints to the successful completion of the bomb and optimistically assumed the same accommodation might be carried over into peacetime. Temperamentally, Compton was well equipped for this task of conciliation; from Oppenheimer it had called forth qualities of self-discipline and leadership that astonished observers of his earlier career. They were not oblivious to the loopholes in the May-Johnson bill, but their own success in working with their military colleagues gave them a more sanguine expectation of how those gaps would be filled.

Another wartime legacy was a greater confidence in their civilian superiors, especially in Secretary Stimson whom they knew to be a sincere advocate of a radical international solution. Oppenheimer had served as consultant in the State Department in recent weeks and knew that Stimson's views were shared, if not by Secretary Byrnes, at least by influential people working under him. But he and Compton were persuaded that the already difficult path to international control would be rendered impassable if special interests and haphazard patterns of administration became entrenched while a long debate took place on domestic legislation. What these complicating factors might be was probably much more evident to Compton and Oppenheimer than to the scientists who had concentrated on technical problems.

Some among their critics perhaps reflected that delegating the exercise of judgment to those we trust, as the panel had done to Bush and Conant, is a common and necessary facet of democracy, but in the eyes of the younger men, the admission of unfamiliarity weakened the case that Oppenheimer and Compton were trying to make for the bill. It is also reported that Szilard never read it all the way through, but some of its other critics studied it with considerable care. "I had great respect for Fermi's brilliance," recalls Lyle Borst in connection with the luncheon meeting on this same Thursday, "and admired Compton very much as a person with strong ethical convictions, but I also felt that I had a mandate from two hundred or more people at Oak Ridge who were not willing to delegate their responsibilities as citizens to their former masters."[63]

By the middle of Thursday afternoon the oral testimony from scientists was complete. Representative Voorhis, not a member of

---

[63] Interview with Borst, February 20, 1962.

the Military Affairs Committee, spoke briefly on behalf of international control and submitted two statements from scientists at
unnamed laboratories.[64] Urey was in Senator Taylor's office, ready
to testify if summoned, but the chairman did not seem anxious to
call him, and his written statement was placed in the record instead.
Urey's objections to the bill, concisely and vigorously expressed, had
been largely covered by others. They centered around the broad
powers, the "almost fantastic" security provisions, and the general
approach that assumed an arms race. It was not true, said Urey, that
everyone was clamoring to work in the field, and some incentives must
be offered. The bill ought to be regarded as providing primarily for
the development of atomic power and be sponsored by the Department
of Commerce. "In view of these criticisms," he concluded, "I find it
difficult to believe that any amendments to the bill could possibly
meet my objections. The whole bill should be rewritten by other men
who have an entirely different point of view about the whole program." At the conclusion of this one day's testimony Chairman May
announced that the hearings on H.R. 4280 were again closed.

The occasion of Urey's presence in Senator Taylor's office was the
press conference suggested by Herbert Schimmel the previous evening
and called in Howard Curtis' name. Urey, Anderson, Nickson, Davies,
Curtis and about thirty reporters were there. For the scientists the
dignity of the occasion was somewhat marred by the distraction of a
pretty young press photographer crawling around the floor of the
crowded office and popping flash bulbs just as Urey got worked up to
a forensic crescendo.[65] But the more blasé reporters gave satisfactory
coverage to what the scientists had to say, especially to Urey's statement that the May-Johnson bill would create a potential dictator of
science and serve notice on the world that we were opening an arms
race. Curtis made more of this point. "The whole tone of the bill is
such," he declared, "that if I were a scientist in some other country
assuredly [I] would say to myself: 'Those fellows over in the States are
getting ready to bomb us in a big way.' Any foreign country is going
to read into it that we are an essentially aggressor nation."[66]

Urey also protested May's decision to close the hearings. No scientists intimately connected with making the bomb, said Urey flatly,

---

[64] One was "A Statement by Scientists of an Atomic Bomb Project," by the
Clinton Labs group; the source of the other, "The Control of the Atomic Bomb,"
described as "scientists of a major atomic bomb research laboratory," is not identified.
[65] Interview with Curtis, October 18, 1961.
[66] *New York Times*, October 19, 1945, p. 2.

had been consulted when the War Department bill was prepared, and many more wanted to be heard.

One of these was Lyle Borst. He had been dispatched to collect the telegrams relating to the May-Johnson bill received at the White House and had not returned when May asked if anyone else wished to testify. He obtained permission to submit a written statement for inclusion in the record.[67]

The opposition had presented a united front to congressmen and reporters, but the difference in the attitude of Los Alamos and the other sites toward the bill had not been resolved. Howard Curtis, who was going to Chicago on his way to Oak Ridge, vividly remembers his mad dash for a five o'clock train at the end of Thursday's hearings and press conference. As he tried frantically to hail a taxi, Bob Wilson pursued him from curb to curb, explaining the Los Alamos position on the relative importance of domestic and international control. Finally Curtis, on foot and suitcase in hand, ran for the Union Station with Wilson trailing behind him, breathlessly arguing his case all the way.[68]

Despite the stormy nature of the Statler Hotel conference Oppenheimer evidently saw hope of accommodation. Phoning Los Alamos on the eighteenth, he gave instructions to "tell Willy" [Higinbotham] that on the "general philosophy" of what should be done agreement was spreading and looked to have a good popular base. DuBridge and members of the panel were in complete agreement, but this did not extend to Condon and Szilard and not completely to the group from Oak Ridge. Oppenheimer was glad that ALAS had not endorsed the telegram from Clinton Labs and Chicago that had been read at the hearings. He wants you to know, the message said, that he is doing his best and that the War Department would shortly issue a statement inviting scientists to take part in discussions of the general aspects of atomic energy.[69]

Before Thursday ended straws in the wind showed a change of direction. Testifying before the Kilgore committee on the science foundation bills, General H. H. Arnold said that the first essential for preeminence in the air was scientific research. He supported the scientists in foreseeing no defense against atomic bombs; the only way would be to shoot down the carrier, and in the next war bombs would not

[67] Interview with Borst, February 20, 1962.
[68] Interview with Curtis, October 18, 1961.
[69] Notes, October 18, 1945, ALAS II, 2.

come by aircraft. Senator Scott Lucas of Illinois, usually an administration supporter but influenced perhaps by some articulate constituents in Chicago, strongly criticized the handling of atomic energy
legislation and expressed grave concern about the censorship that had
been placed on civilian scientists. He opposed the military control of
atomic energy that, all his information indicated, was being attempted.
And finally members of the House Military Affairs Committee admitted to reporters that there would be demands for many amendments to the May bill. A dispatch to the *New York Times* on Thursday evening judged the chances of passage in its present form to be
materially reduced.[70]

Friday, October 19, 1945

There was as yet no arrangement for maintaining a core of scientists in Washington, and the young men returned to their jobs in the
course of the week end. Panel members commenced a meeting with
War Department representatives to reshape the May-Johnson bill.[71]

On Friday in a memorandum to Oppenheimer Higinbotham noted
the views of the ALAS executive committee on the May-Johnson bill
for possible use in the panel–War Department talks.[72] The ALAS committee concluded that the bill should be modified but not opposed.
Their primary objections were to the commission's extremely broad
powers over even minute quantities of fissionable materials and over
scientific information and the imposition of penalties beyond those
provided in the Espionage Act. The antimonopoly section should be
strengthened. A review board of scientists to interpret the security
regulations and hear appeals might serve also as an advisory committee.

Higinbotham prophesied that the members of ALAS would confirm
these recommendations that evening, as indeed they did, but by no
means routinely, for the eight o'clock meeting lasted until nearly midnight. Great concern was expressed over maintaining the freedom of
science while the needs of national security were balanced against the
benefits to be obtained from atomic energy. The barring of military
personnel from atomic energy administration was also urged.[73]

Lyle Borst was still in Washington on Friday. Picking up threads
of the week's operations, he called on Raymond Swing. That evening

---

[70] *New York Times*, October 19, 1945, p. 2.
[71] Compton to Simpson and Henshaw, October 22, 1945, copy in AORES XVI, 6.
[72] Higinbotham to Oppenheimer, October 19, 1945, ALAS II, 2.
[73] Summary of discussion at meeting, October 19, 1945, ALAS II, 16.

Swing told his radio audience that the scientists were responsible for the reopening of the May committee hearings and presented their performance in a highly favorable light:

In the wake of the atomic bomb, which they created, now come the scientists, almost as in a procession, marching upon the stage of public affairs, and for the first time in their lives taking a lead in guiding the nation. This has been science week in Washington. It is to be hoped that the scientists, now that they have found their way to congressional committee rooms and press conferences, will continue this kind of public service. They have proved to be as impressive a group of men as ever came to modern Washington.

It somewhat astonished Washington to find that so many of these scientists—these secluded masters of intensive research—are young men in the middle thirties. Their hair is not long. Their faces are open and clear, their eyes look steadily, and as witnesses before the Senate and House Committees, and in their newspaper conferences, they were quiet, modest, lucid and impellingly convincing.[74]

Saturday, October 20, 1945

For the younger scientists the center of discussion moved to Chicago where the ASC executive committee, in almost continuous session over the week end, heard reports of the week's excitement in Washington. Nickson was back. Curtis was there on his way to Oak Ridge, and Wilson on his way to Los Alamos. John Manley and Harry Palevsky from Los Alamos also attended part of the meeting, and substitutes were found for the absent executive committee members, Szilard, Seaborg and Hill.[75]

Reports of the interviews, the luncheons, the dinners, the performance of witnesses, and currents of opinion were received with interest. But the topic that prolonged the meeting and postponed much of the prepared agenda on ASC organizational matters was the difference in point of view between Los Alamos and the other sites. Wilson reviewed the arguments for prompt passage of the May-Johnson bill that had swayed Los Alamos opinion: that international negotiation could not proceed until a domestic administration was established, and that it was better to rely upon the considered opinions of the Departments of War and State than upon the dubious prospect of educating Congress in the facts of atomic energy soon enough to get something better.

Wilson and Manley admitted the strength of Oppenheimer's in-

---

[74] Swing broadcast over ABC, October 19, 1945, text in AORES X, 5.
[75] ASC executive committee minutes, October 20 and 21, 1945, ASC VI, 12.

fluence. In the absence of official statements about international control the Los Alamos scientists, isolated as they were, had naturally relied upon one in so strategic a position to judge how it might best be achieved. This extravagant confidence obviously puzzled others at the Chicago meeting, exposed as they had been to the more iconoclastic influence of Szilard who had many warm and admiring friends but was never an object of hero worship. They lacked the direct experience of Oppenheimer's charm and magnetism or—and this was by far the most important ingredient in his hold on Los Alamos —his phenomenal capacity during discussion of subjects far from his own field to listen, to grasp, and to clarify. It seemed reasonable to suppose that he might be performing this same feat in the uncharted field of science and politics.

One important element in the Los Alamos attitude was not brought out, or noted at any rate, in this discussion. Strictly as its secrets had been guarded from outside contact, within the laboratory Oppenheimer had insisted that there be no compartmentation. Those cleared for scientific work were free to know about virtually all aspects of research and development within the scope of the work assigned to the laboratory. Both Oppenheimer and the scientists whom he had thus shielded tended to underestimate the resentment and the fear that led Clinton and Chicago to be so apprehensive about the security sections of the May-Johnson bill and about the participation of military personnel. But in the end any sense of irreconcilable difference was dispelled by Robert Wilson's good humored remark that the Los Alamos organization had not passed any resolution to believe everything that Oppenheimer told them and that it should still be possible to get together on common ground.

Further than this, discussions on Saturday and Sunday revealed some still flexible thinking about the effect of the bill on international control, the feasibility of an educational campaign, the wisdom of taking a united stand on domestic issues, and the general problem of intersite co-operation. The ground was partially cleared for the intersite meeting being planned for the following week.

In Washington on Saturday the panel and the War Department continued their conference, outlining the substance of amendments to placate critics of the May-Johnson bill. And Secretary Patterson issued the statement mentioned by Oppenheimer in his phone call to Los Alamos two days earlier—a somewhat tardy reply to the mid-

September appeals from Oak Ridge and Los Alamos to the Interim Committee:

Public discussion of great issues such as the dissemination and regulation of knowledge of atomic science is one of the basic principles on which democratic government is founded. In it all citizens have a right to participate. American scientists in particular, because of their knowledge of the technical matters involved and because of their comprehension of the full social significance of the achievement, can contribute powerfully to it. Security, of course, still requires that nothing beyond the specific subject matter contained in the Smyth Report be brought into discussion, and the use of due care that matters outside the content of this report and still under security regulations be not inadvertently encroached upon. With this sole restriction, however, which applies to all citizens, our scientists should feel that it is proper for them as citizens to join actively in public consideration for [sic] this question.[76]

It scarcely needs Oppenheimer's foreknowledge of this statement to suggest that he and A. H. Compton had some part in its timing and liberal tone. These two men believed deeply and sincerely in the right to express opinions even when, as in the days just past, such expression threatened to upset a course to which they had publicly committed themselves. As we shall see, Compton continued to explore this question of the scientist's role. Meanwhile Patterson's unequivocal statement was a meaningful conclusion to the eventful week. If it now seems an inadequate formulation of the scientist's relation to the making of national policy, that is but a measure of how times have changed.

_____

[76] As printed in the ALAS Newsletter, No. 2, October 30, 1945, FAS V, 8. *The New World*, p. 434, says that Bush had suggested such a statement several weeks earlier.

CHAPTER 4

Repercussions
October 20 to November 1

As THIS CRITICAL week of public debate drew to a close Hanson W. Baldwin, military commentator for the *New York Times*, surveyed the trend of current thinking and the prospects for atomic energy control. Into his usually chill analysis there crept something like the passion of the scientists. The eleven weeks since Hiroshima, said Baldwin,

> have been weeks in which the history of tomorrow has been shaped to the dangerous pattern of today; they have been weeks in which the world has made little progress toward either international security or international morality. They have been weeks of confusion and divided counsel, of lack of leadership, of claims and contradictions—and all the while the atomic bomb has clouded the skies of tomorrow.

Problems are being discussed in Washington piecemeal and with prejudice, continued Baldwin; misconceptions must be cleared away or our defense will be built upon quicksand. The proposed legislation must be amended to insure freedom of research and to limit the unparalleled grant of power and the whole atomic problem subjected to thorough exploration by a fact-finding commission. "There are too little imagination and breadth of vision in the halls of Congress and the streets of America, and without them the people perish."[1]

---

[1] *New York Times*, October 22, 1945, p. 4; see also October 23, p. 6, and October 25, p. 10.

1. SCIENTISTS AS CITIZENS

Whether the scientists' assault upon Washington had indeed kindled imagination and quickened statesmanlike vision it was too early to tell, but there was no doubt that it would have a powerful effect upon their own position in relation to the public life of America. When someone at the Wednesday hearings on science legislation had raised the question of educating the public, Oppenheimer remarked that the scientists were allowing themselves "to be made a circus of over this thing" because the issues involved were of enormous importance and might have to be dramatized in some odd ways. Press reactions confirmed his forebodings. *PM*, the high-minded tabloid, talked about "atom-smashing laboratory grubbers . . . rushing out of their cloistered retreats to shout a last warning to a dazed generation before it topples into the abyss." A Chicago columnist referred to "the emergence of the atomic scientists into the affairs of life, like timid butterflies crawling from their cocoons into the fierce heat of the sun."[2]

The novelty of the scientists' appearance in Washington made an impression at a number of different levels. Waldo Cohn wrote back to Clinton Labs that he wished he had made money bets on Howard Curtis' hitting the front pages of the papers. A gas station attendant and a member of the New York Philharmonic, finding he was from Oak Ridge, had asked him if he knew Dr. Curtis.[3]

Determined not to be deluded by a generally favorable reaction, the site groups resolved to make note of critical comments. The findings were slim, although there was a letter from one New York woman, slightly confused about what they were advocating, who told the Los Alamos scientists that their October 14 statement on international control was "pretty sickening." Scientists could have refused to work on the bomb, she wrote, but with wanton irresponsibility they had to experiment to see how many they could kill at once, and now during a war of nerves with Russia, they were equally irresponsible in wanting to "outlaw" the bomb.[4]

A line of criticism more likely to have an adverse effect on their campaign was the one taken by the author of the *New York Times'* "Topics of the Times," who, even before their public debut, had questioned the propriety of scientists' mixing in politics, concluding that

[2] Albert Deutsch, *PM* (New York), October 18, 1945; Willard Shelton, *Chicago Sun*, November 7, 1945.

[3] AORS Daily Bulletin, October 24, 1945, AORES XX, 1.

[4] E. Grogan to Dr. Wilson and associates, October 14, 1945, ALAS V, 8.

once the scientist emerges from his laboratory he is no more disinterested than a business man or a politician, having like them his own beliefs, aversions, his own creeds and biases. If he could keep the scientist in him from being overwhelmed by the ordinary human being, his qualifications for governing would be unanswerable.[5] The writer of "Topics" returned to the subject on October 21. Heading his column "When Scientists Speak," he declared that their statements should be placed in three categories according to whether they dealt with scientific fact, with the application of scientific fact, or with other matters. Urey's statement that the May bill would create a dictator of science should receive serious consideration; that it would serve notice on the world of an armaments race was his personal opinion and gained nothing from his status as a scientist. "When it comes to speaking of how best to make Russia behave . . . an atomic scientist carries no more authority than a non-atomic intelligent doctor or lawyer or carpenter."[6]

Objecting vigorously to the implications of this classification six young members of AORS wrote the editor of the *Times* to express their surprise that the outmoded concept of the absent-minded long-haired scientist still existed in the editorial mind of an enlightened newspaper (the last phrase occurred in their own copy but was not considered "fit to print"); they thought the persistence of this myth impeded the progress of basic science in America and wished its supporters could see what a normal daily routine they followed in Oak Ridge—"rising at 6 A.M.; a half-hour ride on a 1935 model G.I. bus; working in a room with five other scientists, two transient janitors and an occasional plumber or carpenter; queuing in a cafeteria for lunch, at the laundry, at the supermarket, at the theater, etc., ad nauseam; stoking a soft-coal furnace; changing diapers, filing income tax returns; reading good and bad newspapers and periodicals." As average citizens they had normal understanding of political and social affairs and on these matters did not intend to speak as experts. But we do have, they continued,

one distinct advantage over other citizens with respect to the present problem. We have known of atomic power and its possibilities for years. We are familiar with the potentialities of its future development for both peace and war. . . .

As to the point of leaving international affairs to the experts, we would

---

[5] *New York Times*, October 7, 1945, sec. E, p. 8.
[6] *New York Times*, October 21, 1945, sec. E, p. 8.

be very happy to do so. But first we must have an answer to the question: "Who are the experts, and where is the evidence of their handiwork?" While we recognize that the handling of problems involving human relations is infinitely more intricate than that of physical problems, we can see little evidence of the development of expert techniques in international affairs.

"Topics of the Times" opines that, while science is revolutionized every generation, the human heart is a pretty consistent performer. The persistent 20-year cycle of wars indicates that the human hearts of diplomats have been pretty consistently bad performers. Perhaps the time is ripe for some logical consistency to be injected into the art of international diplomacy.[7]

As this letter demonstrates Secretary Patterson's decree that scientists might speak as citizens was capable of more than one interpretation, and a friendly correspondence between A. H. Compton and unrelenting critics of the May-Johnson bill was attempting to define what it meant in relation to the amendments worked out in the weekend conference between the panel and the War Department. To the panel these amendments represented the limits of concern that scientists in their professional capacity might legitimately show. The dissenting scientists did not agree. Compton's close relations with the research men at Clinton and Chicago made him anxious to iron out these differences and on October 22, from the chancellor's office at Washington University, he thanked Henshaw of AORS and Simpson of the ASC for sending their joint statement on the May-Johnson bill and their objections to it. "I am glad," he said, "that your organizations were alert to these developments. Your prompt action has undoubtedly had an effect in preventing hasty action at Washington along a line, that in my opinion, would have been detrimental."

During the past three days in Washington, Compton explained, he and other panel members had recommended changes in the bill that would make it constructive rather than harmful to the development of science and industry. There still remained some fundamental points involving national and international policy which the panel, as representatives of science, did not feel they should attempt to alter. When the amended bill was reported out of committee such questions as the broad powers of the commission and its tenure could be brought into the open and further changes made if desirable. Panel members, said

---

[7] Warren R. Burgus, Raymond R. Edwards, Howard Gest, Lawrence E. Glendenin, Chas. W. Stanley, and Russell R. Williams to the Editor, *New York Times*, November 3, 1945, p. 14.

Compton, had told the War Department that they could not support
the bill in its present form or ask others to do so but that with the
proposed modifications they believed a majority of the nation's scientists would approve it. Compton considered prompt passage essential
for the continuity of research and for international agreement. And he
concluded by way of final counsel:

> I honestly believe that in its revised form, the bill is essentially good with
> regard to its effect on the strength of our national activities and that it does
> not present any policy with regard to international affairs other than that
> we intend to develop our own general strength in the field of atomic
> energy. If you and your colleagues agree with this position, might I suggest
> that with regard to the administrative and political aspects of the bill, any
> statements that you may wish to make be presented with the clear indica-
> tion that they are the expressions of the group in their capacity as citizens
> and not specifically with regard to the bearing of the bill on the growth of
> science. . . .[8]

Compton enclosed copies of the proposed changes and also of a
wire he had sent General Royall promising support for the revised
bill and summarizing the advice he was giving Henshaw and Simpson.
They promptly mimeographed this material for circulation to the site
organizations including with it an explanatory note from the War
Department to the May committee assuring its members, as Patterson
had done with the original bill, that the amended version would command the support of "the bulk of scientists in this field" and specifically of the National Academy of Sciences, the American Institute
of Physics, and the American Physical Society. This statement scientist
opponents of the bill immediately began to check.[9]

The day after Compton wrote to Henshaw and Simpson, representatives of Clinton, the Met Lab, and Los Alamos began a two-day meeting in Chicago to discuss further joint action on domestic legislation
in the course of which the letter and its enclosures must have arrived.
Three Chicago scientists had already outlined their indirect reply to
Compton in an article for *Life*, entitled "The Atomic Scientists Speak
Up." Explaining why some eight hundred scientists had abandoned
the position that the application of their work was none of their busi-

---

[8] A. H. Compton to Henshaw and Simpson, October 22, 1945, AORES III, 3; XVI, 6.
Copies went to the other panel members and to several Project laboratory directors.
[9] Compton wire to Royall, October 21, 1945; statement by War Department to May
committee to be made October 22, [1945]; and proposed amendments (copies in
Hogness' files).

ness and had pressed their views upon Congress, the authors—David Hill, Eugene Rabinowitch, and John Simpson—insisted that "scientists do not aspire to political leadership but, having helped man to make the first step into this new world, they have the responsibility of warning and advising him until he has become aware of its perils as well as its wonders." Their central theme, that old ideas about national security were no longer valid, was supported with the slogans of no secret, no monopoly, and no defense, and they called for adequate international controls.[10] Later on, when the scientists had become old hands at this sort of thing, they looked back on this *Life* article as a landmark. "A year ago a scientist who sought publicity was looked on as a hack trying to advance some personal vanity," Kay Way told a Chicago reporter. "But an article we wrote for *Life* last fall broke the ice. . . . Nothing terrible happened. Nobody's reputation was irretrievably lost."[11]

At Clinton Labs the debate with Compton was carried on more directly. He could not accept their invitation to come to Oak Ridge but wrote on November 3 to Lyle Borst a further elaboration of his thoughts. He agreed, he said, with everything in the *Life* article except the importance of prompt legislation. A more fundamental difference of opinion was whether the United States should adopt a policy of strength or weakness in atomic weapons. He thought that in calling the May bill the start of an arms race scientists were implying that we should follow a policy of atomic disarmament. This view seemed to him "fatally false and one which I must oppose with all the influence I can bring to bear." The only answer was to outlaw war itself, which could be done only by a strong world policy that had at its disposal more powerful weapons than the renegade nation could hope to acquire. Much less important to Compton were the composition and powers of the commission. He agreed that a commission appointed by the President was not democratic, but, he concluded:

As to the dangers to the democratic processes, we must rely on Congress and our representative citizens. It is indeed true that democracy can last only as long as our leading citizens are inspired by the desire to work for the benefit of the public rather than of themselves. If this spirit prevails, however broad the commission's power may be, we are in no danger. If it is absent, democracy is already gone.[12]

---

[10] Hill, Rabinowitch, and Simpson, "The Atomic Scientists Speak Up," *Life*, XIX (October 29, 1945), 45–48.

[11] *Chicago Daily News*, March 11, 1946.

[12] Compton to Borst, November 3, 1945, AORES III, 3; XVI, 6.

This letter from Compton was also mimeographed. A copy reached Austin M. Brues when he returned to Chicago after a few days' duty in Washington around November 5 and moved him to a long reply. At thirty-nine Brues was a man of assured reputation in his field; he would shortly become an authority on radiation effects in Japan and director of the division of biology and medicine at the Met Lab's successor, the Argonne National Laboratory. Still he found time to be a member and later chairman of the ASC executive committee, one of many in the local organizations who did routine tasks without fanfare but upon whose sound professional standing the movement relied for its strength and influence.

In his letter to Compton Brues first took up the question of atomic strength or weakness. He had been shocked to discover in Washington a school of thought that believed in the United Nations but wished to make it "an instrument of our national policy and maintain its headquarters and stockpile of atomic weapons in this country. . . ."

But Brues was writing chiefly to challenge Compton's views on scientists' relation to politics. He was disturbed by the consequences of repeating the cliché that when scientists spoke on public policy they should speak as citizens and not as scientists. Of course, said Brues, when he ordered a cabbage that had not been sprayed with arsenic the grocer understood that he was speaking not as a physician but as a consumer who had some special knowledge. But to reiterate the refrain appeared "to be having the effect of discrediting the witness of scientists as opposed to that, for example, of lawyers. It also puts us under suspicion as a pressure group solely interested in the comfort of scientists, which emphatically we are not. Most importantly," Brues continued,

it forgets that scientists, regardless of their great variance in political creed, have a large common denominator of social belief which, in point of fact, has been crystallized by the present crisis. . . .

This is no mystery to me. It is as clear as day that the manner of thinking and the daily work of the scientists and educators whom we have known for so long have developed in them attitudes which never had to be developed in, for example, the typical influential suburban dweller; and which, strangely enough, demand no adherence to political conservatism or radicalism in the ordinary pocketbook sense. On the individual level, these attitudes demand an enquiring analytical mind; on the national level they are biased against smugness and hypocrisy; on the world level they have brought out a striking unanimity of opinion. These men see that nationalism means war and nothing else; that wishful thinking along the old patterns can destroy us. We must not go out of our way to discredit their testimony.[13]

This correspondence did not, of course, settle anything. It did not fix the line that Compton wished to draw between those issues that scientists might legitimately try to influence at the early policy-making stage and those upon which they should express themselves only in public debate. It did not suggest how a well-known individual—like Compton himself, for instance—was to indicate that on a particular occasion his prestige did not mean a thing. Those who argued that scientists were being asked to observe a restraint not expected of other professions had a point, but they did not explain how the public was to maintain its respect for science if "scientific facts" produced quite contrary conclusions.

But these exchanges, and even more perhaps the week of October 15 in Washington, relieved anxiety about freedom of speech that had pervaded early discussions. "It has been amazing to us buried in the secret city," wrote Charles Coryell to a Los Angeles science editor on November 6,

to find out the outside world is anxious to know what we are thinking and to find that we bear for the present at least a significant weight in Washington. Our worries about being bottled up by the Army have largely disappeared for the Army is not anxious to continue its excesses of last August and early September.[14]

2. NEW RECRUITS

While this largely private colloquy was going on, a flood of pressure upon the administration and Congress was building up in the wake of Szilard's phone calls, of appeals to friends across the country from those still mysterious laboratories, and of the publicity given by a sympathetic press to the representations of earnest young scientists. There have been other causes and other occasions of public outcry against a set course. But this was a new cause, and these were novel protagonists, and in the backwash of war, to which new horrors were added with each day's news, their sincerity and their idealism made a deep impression.

The pressure came both from an expanding segment of the scientific community and increasingly from those they influenced. On Octo-

---

[13] Brues to Compton, n.d., copy in Simpson's files.
[14] Coryell to science editor, *Los Angeles Times*, November 6, 1945, AORES II, 16.

ber 23, sixty leading scientists, educators, and civic leaders wired Truman, Patterson, General Marshall, and Representative May urging withdrawal of the May-Johnson bill on the grounds that it granted unprecedented powers to an administrator responsible neither to the President nor to Congress.[15] Among the non-scientists were several with whom contact had been made earlier by travelers from Oak Ridge: Swing, Norman Cousins, Leo Cherne of Americans United, and Walter Millis of the *New York Herald Tribune* had all been interviewed by Brown, English, or Cohn in recent weeks. Following Frank Kingdon's broadcast about the Carbide Corporation's restrictive order, Cohn had a two-hour conference with him in New York, and Kingdon's October 23 commentary reported that one hundred fifty-five scientists had telegraphed Truman and members of Congress asking for further hearings.[16]

A seven-point resolution against the May-Johnson bill emerged from a second University of Chicago sponsored conference at Rye, New York, over the week end of October 27 and 28 and was forwarded to the President and other government officials. The conference of journalists, businessmen, and public figures was planned to obtain high-level support for the scientists' educational campaign, but the exigencies of the moment and the presence of Edward Levi, who had written the legal criticism for the ASC, and scientist opponents of the bill, such as Harold Urey and John Simpson, converted it into a kind of rally against the May-Johnson bill.[17]

Lines of influence and action catch the eye. Urey, for example, had been present at many of the informal talks with laymen in New York City, as reported by Waldo Cohn. He took part in a meeting of the Committee to Study the Organization of the Peace on Sunday morning, October 21. That evening as principal speaker at an American-Scandinavian Foundation dinner at the Waldorf Astoria he attacked the May-Johnson bill and called for world government. On the twenty-fourth he was in Washington for a dinner with senators, came north again for the week-end conference at Rye, and on October 30 delivered a rousing pep talk to the Association of Manhattan Project Scientists. Urey was in the process of moving to Chicago, where Patterson's statement that the National Academy of Science would support the

---

[15] *New York Times*, October 24, 1945, p. 2.
[16] Cohn, "Report on Vacation, October 13–31, 1945," AORES II, 2; text of Kingdon broadcast, AORES XIV, 2.
[17] ASC IX, 1; XXVII, 2.

amended May-Johnson bill had already been questioned. On November 3 he and five other academy members on the University of Chicago faculty (A. J. Dempster, James Franck, W. D. Harkins, R. S. Mulliken, and Sewell Wright) wrote to their three hundred fellow members asking endorsement of the Rye conference resolution. By December 1, two hundred ten had indicated their approval, and eventuallly this document, too, went to the President.[18]

On into early November academic and research centers continued to register opinions. On November 5 fifty scientists in the San Diego area signed a communication to Senator Sheridan Downey and Representative E. V. Izak of California stating their opposition to the May-Johnson bill; they appreciated the need for security, but the bill far transcended considerations of this nature and threatened "independence of American thought and aspiration."[19]

At Washington University in St. Louis a petition against the bill was circulated among the students and with several pages of signatures was given to Dean Joyce Stearns to take to Washington on November 7.[20]

Support for the bill, on the other hand, came from the Los Angeles area in an open letter, dated November 8, 1945, to the President and the Congress from nearly two hundred "private citizens" at the California Institute of Technology, Mount Wilson, the Huntington Library, and the University of California at Los Angeles. Its signers supported international control of atomic energy and believed secrecy to be ineffectual, but they declared that even if the May-Johnson bill required later modification it should be passed without delay. The signers included J. R. Oppenheimer, who had officially resumed his teaching at Cal Tech, and Robert A. Millikan, as well as some of the students who were shortly to organize the Association of Pasadena Scientists and affiliate with the FAS.[21]

For the scientists in the local associations, to whom it had seemed more important to act than to perfect the details of organization, it was a period of consolidation. The Atomic Scientists of Chicago took time to adopt a constitution while continuing to urge members to

---

[18] *Bulletin of the Atomic Scientists,* I (December 10, 1945).

[19] Copy forwarded to Lyle Borst at the Federation of Atomic Scientists office in Washington by G. P. Harnwell, director, Navy Radio and Sound Laboratory, San Diego; FAS XV, 8.

[20] Washington University petitions, FAS XI, 4.

[21] "Open Letter to the President and Congress," November 8, 1945, FAS VII, 3.

write directly to congressmen and to ask friends and relatives to do likewise.

At Clinton Labs, the Levi analysis was recommended reading, and a continuing barrage of individual protests to congressmen was encouraged.[22] Lyle Borst had returned from Washington and prepared a four-page memorandum embodying the criticisms he had been unable to present at the hearing on the eighteenth. It was unanimously approved by AORS members on the twenty-fourth and sent to the House Military Affairs Committee for incorporation in the record.[23] News of the bill was followed with interest. Milton Burton brought back a copy of the revised version early in November, which, according to the AORS Daily Bulletin on November 8, still failed to satisfy the fundamental objections to the bill.[24]

Outwardly, ALAS maintained its heterodox stand. On October 24 Higinbotham wired Urey, Condon, and Szilard at the Wardman Park that their views on the Johnson bill were not shared by the Los Alamos or M.I.T. groups. He also sent a sharp reproof to Herb Anderson, press reports of whose testimony the previous week had probably just reached the hill: "Views you express not shared by this organization. Because you appear to represent us we insist you keep quiet until you have discussed the bill with us."[25]

But almost as soon as he dispatched them Higinbotham's strictures were out of date, for developments of the past ten days had placed the bill in a different light. At a "stormy" session of the ALAS executive committee on the twenty-fifth Victor Weisskopf proposed that Oppenheimer's suggestions should be studied more critically and that future action should not be based on the assumption that the administration was "with us." A general meeting the following evening revealed some sentiment in favor of a completely new bill, but it was decided that discussion of this point should await the outcome of the intersite meeting just concluded in Chicago.[26]

In New York the Association of Manhattan Project Scientists devoted a general meeting to the May-Johnson bill, and on October 29 its executive committee held a press conference at the American In-

---

[22] AORS Daily Bulletin, October 2, 1945, AORES XX, 1.
[23] U.S. House of Representatives, Committee on Military Affairs, Atomic Energy, Hearings on H.R. 4280, 79th Cong., 1st sess., October 18, 1945, pp. 136–38.
[24] AORS Daily Bulletin, November 8, 1945, AORES XX, 1.
[25] Wires Higinbotham to Urey et al., October 24, 1945, copy in ALAS V, 4; Higinbotham to Anderson, October 24, 1945, copy in ALAS II, 18.
[26] ALAS Log, ALAS II, 2; minutes, October 26, 1945, ALAS II, 4.

stitute of Physics headquarters to announce unanimous opposition to
the bill as introduced on October 3. At a meeting the following eve-
ning, called ostensibly to discuss international control, Urey warned
AMPS members not to be fooled by amendments and described the
May-Johnson bill as the first totalitarian bill ever reported out of
Congress. The scientists, he said, were taking Washington by storm.[27]

Interest among SAM scientists, unlike that of other Manhattan
Project groups, was generated by the domestic issue. Some of them,
in fact, had at first opposed any mention of international control, but
after Urey's talk, and after Clark Eichelberger of the American Association for the United Nations had led a discussion at the October 30
meeting, they were persuaded that the two issues were closely related,
and the AMPS went on record as supporting international control and
negotiation through the United Nations.[28]

The scientists' performance in Washington had been observed
with great interest by their colleagues outside the Manhattan Project.
In the Boston area the three hundred M.I.T. and Harvard scientists
extended their organization and, after communicating their views on
domestic legislation to the War Department on October 15, prepared
for public release on October 31 a long statement on the need for
international control, for which they collected five hundred signatures. The statement did not mention the May-Johnson bill, but its
emphatic endorsement of everything else that opponents of the bill
were saying strengthened the impression that scientists were speaking
with one voice.[29]

At the University of Pennsylvania, W. E. Stephens and other
members of the Physics Department joined with a few members of
the local Association of Scientific Workers in calling a meeting of
Philadelphia-area scientists on October 22. In a statement addressed
to the President and to the military affairs committees of House and
Senate, the Philadelphia group declared its support of international
control (quoting in full the ALAS release of October 14) and its opposition to the May-Johnson bill (citing the arguments put forth by the
Association of Manhattan Project Scientists in New York). Two
thousand copies of this statement were distributed for signatures. The

---

[27] AMPS press release, October 29, 1945, FAS VI, 1; *New York Times,* October 30,
1945, p. 4; October 31, 1945, p. 6.
[28] "Federation of Scientific Organizations Proceedings" (mimeographed), November
16, 1945, pp. 29–30; AMPS Newsletter, November 2, 1945, FAS VI, 1.
[29] Camb. I; *New York Times,* October 31, 1945, p. 6.

Association of Philadelphia Scientists was formally organized on November 2, and on the eleventh it announced its adherence to the program of the atomic scientists on the basis of twelve hundred endorsements.[30]

In the New York area there were many scientists not eligible to join the Association of Manhattan Project Scientists, and when it was learned that scientists from diverse fields were organizing in Cambridge and Philadelphia, Melba Phillips and Arnold Nordsieck of the Radiation Laboratory at Columbia got Dean Pegram's permission to hold a meeting of non-SAM scientists on the evening of October 30. One hundred and fifty people turned out on twenty-four hours notice. An executive committee was elected consisting of Phillips, Nordsieck, M. Gregersen, head of the Physiology Department at the Columbia Medical School, Paul Hartman of the Bell Labs, and Hugh Wolfe, a physicist at City College on leave with NDRC.[31]

With the experience of others to guide them the Association of New York Scientists acted with speed and assurance, adopting at once the following aims:

1. Keep its members informed on legislative and other proposals affecting science and scientists, such as those now current on atomic energy;
2. Take appropriate action to influence government and the public in accordance with the sense of the meeting of October 30, *viz*:
   a) That unnecessarily restrictive measures on atomic research will be harmful to the national welfare, and
   b) That continuing monopoly of the atomic bomb and atomic energy by the United States is impossible, and attempts in this direction will be most detrimental to national security and cordial international relations;
3. Co-ordinate efforts with other groups of scientists with similar aims.

A wire was sent immediately to Representative Adolph J. Sabath, chairman of the House Rules Committee, urging a thorough discussion of the May-Johnson bill, which, even as amended, ANYS denounced as "contrary to the best traditions of this country and of science" and as potentially harmful to international and domestic welfare.[32]

By November 8 ANYS had prepared a letter to the President and

---

[30] Stephens to H. H. Goldsmith, October 23, 30, 1945; announcement of organization, November 11, 1945, FAS VII, 6.

[31] AORS Daily Bulletin, November 7, 1945, AORES XX, 1; "Federation of Scientific Organizations Proceedings" (mimeographed), November 16, 1945, pp. 69–71.

[32] As reported in AORS Daily Bulletin, November 7, 1945, AORES XX, 1.

the Congress asking a careful re-examination of proposed policies both domestic and foreign. Without presuming to suggest a detailed program the letter urged that a UN conference be called to consider control machinery and establishment of an international advisory council of scientists.[33]

This letter was circulated for signatures among potential ANYS members to reinforce similar action by over a thousand scientists in Philadelphia and six hundred in Cambridge (although the new Cambridge association was, in fact, supporting the amended May-Johnson bill). Seven hundred signatures came in within two days and, in response to a suggestion about dollar contributions, about five hundred dollars. Three hundred names were added later, two hundred of them from the SAM organization.[34]

3. WASHINGTON INTERLUDE

Not the least important result of the scientists' political debut was the forming of a joint organization with a Washington office. Following the informal meeting at Oak Ridge on September 17, the site organizations were cautiously feeling their way toward closer ties when the crisis over the May-Johnson bill precipitated them into joint action. Their political advisers in Washington recommended a united front on the domestic issue, and so, without waiting to bring together all like-minded scientists, Los Alamos, Clinton, and the Met Lab decided to mark out an area of agreement even if they could not resolve all their differences. A meeting was held in Chicago on Tuesday and Wednesday, October 23 and 24. E. G. Bohlmann came from Clinton Labs, Philip Morrison and John Manley from Los Alamos; Austin Brues; H. H. Goldsmith, and John Simpson represented the ASC, with Eugene Rabinowitch substituting for Simpson on the second day when he left for Washington. They achieved the following statement of principles:

Joint Declaration

It is our conviction that the main requirement of this legislation is that it should in no way prejudice but in every possible way assist the subsequent attempts towards international agreement on the control of atomic

---

[33] Copies of letter to the President and the Congress of the United States with space for signatures and of letter from ANYS executive committee to "Dear Fellow Scientist," November 8, 1945, FAS VI, 3.

[34] Announcement by Nordsieck, November 24, 1945, FAS VI, 3; "Federation of Scientific Organizations Proceedings" (mimeographed), November 16, 1945, p. 70.

weapons. To assure the freedom of the United States government in international negotiations, it is essential that the government retain full control
of the domestic development of atomic energy. We further believe that
the legislation on the domestic control of atomic power should stimulate
and assist the development of this new force in national and private laboratories, without infringing upon the freedom of basic research. Such
restriction will not only be contrary to the tradition of science but will
delay the development of nuclear research in this country. Advantages
which may accrue from regimenting science for military secrecy will be
more than offset in the long run by disadvantages caused by hampered
communications among scientists, difficulties of training young scientists
and general discouragement of scientific initiative.

We want to lend our collective support to the statements made earlier
by separate groups and informed individuals, that no measures of secrecy
can guarantee our exclusive possession of atomic bombs for more than a
few years and that there can be no defense which would effectively protect
our cities against an attack by atomic bombs. Even leadership in an
atomic armament race will in no way assure our safety against sudden attack by an aggressor, who might easily have enough bombs to destroy
every one of our major cities in a single day.

Therefore, we are convinced that the achievement of international controls over the military aspects of atomic power must remain the paramount
objective of our national policy. Even the best domestic legislation cannot
lessen the urgency of this task. There is no time to lose.[35]

The following day, October 25, John Simpson, Charles Coryell of
Clinton Labs, and Maria Mayer and Irving Kaplan from the Association of Manhattan Project Scientists met in Washington. Kaplan
and Mrs. Mayer endorsed the "Joint Declaration," and it was agreed
that the four organizations should form a federation, each group retaining its identity but co-operating to maintain a central office to
co-ordinate and disseminate information. Szilard and Lieutenant
Barry Commoner of the Kilgore subcommittee staff also took part in
these discussions.[36]

Simpson reported this decision by phone next day to H. H. Goldsmith in Chicago, to be relayed to Oak Ridge and Los Alamos. Each
site should have two representatives in Washington Wednesday, October 31, to organize the Federation of Atomic Scientists, one of
whom should remain at least a week to get the Washington office
started, define objectives, and plan contacts with key people. A "col-

[35] Joint Declaration," October 23–24, 1945, signed by Higinbotham for ALAS, John
Simpson for the ASC, and Paul Henshaw for AORS, ASC XIII, 11.
[36] "Coryell Odyssey, Part IV, Contacts in Washington," carbon copies in ASC IX, 8,
and AORES II, 2.

lege" for senators would meet three times a week for the next two or three months in two- or three-hour sessions "to tell the senators just what is at stake and instruct them and guide them in educating other senators." To make this project effective, said Simpson, site representatives should be mature people, with experience in teaching; they should not talk too rapidly or be too intellectual; they should remember that senators want to learn and must not be affronted. They should be capable of making independent decisions and should be so empowered.[37]

The last ten days of October were an interim period in the scientists' Washington activities in which a lot was accomplished even without centralized direction. The Wardman Park Hotel overlooking Connecticut Avenue and the Rock Creek Parkway was their only headquarters. Szilard stayed on there as a self-appointed watchdog; Condon was starting his new job as director of the Bureau of Standards further out Connecticut Avenue; and Oppenheimer was still in town advising the administration and Congress before resuming his teaching at the California Institute of Technology in Pasadena.[38]

The other scientists who had been in town for the hearings on October 17 and 18 had scattered, but one of them, at any rate, assumed continuing responsibilities. Before he returned to Oak Ridge on Saturday, October 20, Lyle Borst noted in his diary under "Things to do": select speaker for Press Club; statement for House Military Affairs Committee by Wednesday; have representative in Washington for Wednesday evening; have Curtis see Barkley (in an effort to minimize confusing crosscurrents by having the person who started a contact carry on with it); contact Voorhis; offer services to McMahon, Tobey, Kilgore, and Taylor; contact the British, M.I.T., and SAM; thank Swing; request testimony from Commoner; complete coalition between sites.

The contacts with Capitol Hill established during the preceding week were not allowed to languish, and with the aid of Herbert

---

[37] Meeting notes, n.d., and memorandum, October 26, 1945, ASC XIII, 13.

[38] "In November, 1945, I resumed my teaching at the California Institute of Technology, with an intention and hope, never realized, that this should be a full-time undertaking. The consultation about postwar matter which had already begun continued, and I was asked over and over both by the Executive and the Congress for advice on atomic energy. I had a feeling of deep responsibility, interest, and concern for many of the problems with which the development of atomic energy confronted our country" (Letter, Oppenheimer to General Nichols, in U.S. Atomic Energy Commission, *In the Matter of J. Robert Oppenheimer*, Transcript of Hearing before Personnel Security Board [Washington, D.C.: Government Printing Office, 1954], p. 15).

Schimmel of the Kilgore staff and Watson Davis of Science Service, a second dinner for scientists and senators was held on Wednesday evening, October 24. The scientists present included Simpson, Maria Mayer, Kaplan, and Coryell, who were in town for the intersite meeting next day, and Szilard, Condon, Oppenheimer, Urey, Shapley, Michelson of the Radiation Lab, and L. C. Dunn, chairman of the Zoology Department at Columbia. Nine senators were present: four Republicans; Leverett Saltonstall of Massachusetts, Tobey of New Hampshire, Forrest C. Donnell of Missouri, and Smith of New Jersey; and five Democrats; James M. Mead of New York, Abe Murdock of Utah, McMahon of Connecticut, Taylor of Idaho, and Mitchell of Washington. Senatorial secretaries and assistants were there also, among them Schimmel, Kramer, and Charles Calkins of McMahon's staff.

Coryell (who made copious notes on a whirlwind twenty-four hours in Washington) was impressed with the mellifluous flow of senatorial rhetoric, but concluded that grasp of the subject did not necessarily correspond.[39] He thought McMahon well qualified to be chairman of the special committee; Tobey seemed a great and sincere internationalist, and his warm personal interest had won the affection of all the scientists who met him.

Oppenheimer, as the chief spokesman for the scientists, did not, according to Coryell's report, directly promote their main theses; rather he talked about steps that might help to establish world confidence, such as immediately stopping the production of fissionable isotopes, a mammoth exchange program of Russian and American students on the order of five thousand on each side, and the establishment of friendly contacts with Russians at all levels of society with an emphasis upon science in general. Oppenheimer, Coryell decided, following an after-dinner discussion about the May-Johnson bill, was far ahead of the associations in his thinking. "This dinner," he concluded, "seemed to be a very effective one to strengthen contacts, to give mutual education, and build the groundwork for sound governmental and senatorial policy."

Interspersing impromptu calls with appointments, Coryell spent the following day in the Senate and House office buildings—not a unique exercise but one that only he recorded in detail. He had forty-five minutes with Representative John W. Jennings (R) of the Sec-

[39] "Coryell Odyssey," ASC IX, 8; interview with Coryell, March 17, 1959.

ond District of Tennessee (including the Knoxville area), a contact later followed up with good effect by Milton Burton. Then en route to an 11:00 A.M. meeting of site representatives Coryell made an abortive call on Representative Charles A. Halleck of Indiana, recommended by a Purdue friend as "quite liberal," and left material in the office of Representative Chet Holifield of California, receiving in exchange a Holifield speech on the nationalities of scientists working on the bomb (an interest on the part of the future chairman of the Joint Congressional Committee on Atomic Energy that was more prophetic than Coryell then realized).

Coryell returned to Capitol Hill for lunch in the House restaurant with Representative Jerry Voorhis, of California, who had already been in touch with Borst and Davies and represented, Coryell thought, the best House affiliation the atomic bomb groups had. Waiting in line Coryell met Representative J. LeRoy Johnson, also of California, whom Coryell discovered to be a member of the House Military Affairs Committee but only after he had launched an attack on the May-Johnson bill and the May committee's handling of it. Johnson told Coryell he had voted for continuance of the hearings without seeing great value in them since all scientists said the same things. (This was another contact followed up ten days later by Burton, who reported Johnson to be "one of our strong supporters.") Coryell and Voorhis shared a table with Representative Emily Taft Douglas of Illinois and an ex-officer of M 1 who had served in Yugoslavia and Istanbul. Mrs. Douglas and Voorhis agreed with Coryell that an attempt should be made to establish international control posts, but the M 1 officer cited discouraging experiences in trying to activate agreements with Russia in the field.

Coryell's next call was on the president pro tempore of the Senate, McKellar of Tennessee, predicted by Szilard "to be a hard nut to crack." Coryell had been advised to press on one point only—the chairmanship of the committee, established by the McMahon resolution, to gripe if no appointment had yet been made (which it had not) and "to bitch like hell if someone other than McMahon had been appointed." In the Senator's absence his secretary and brother, Don W. McKellar, "was very formidable," Coryell reported,

and resentful of my bothering the Senator who was not feeling well, until I spoke strongly for the Association of Oak Ridge Scientists, the Atomic Scientists of Chicago, the Association of Scientific Workers of U.C.L.A. and the Association of Cambridge Scientists. When he saw my earnestness and forcefulness, he took my arguments in a friendly fashion and promised to transmit them to Senator McKellar. We discussed atomic bomb politics briefly and I left. Within twenty-four hours McMahon was made chairman of the committee and the following Monday, Don McKellar drew my attention to that action in a letter which I subsequently answered.

It was nearly time for Coryell's plane. Senator Downey of California was out of town, but Coryell had a brief talk with his newly appointed junior colleague, William F. Knowland. Despite a delayed plane, Coryell arrived at the University of Tennessee in Knoxville in time to hear Representative Walter Judd of Minnesota speak on United States relations with Russia, China, and Japan and to talk with him afterward. Judd urged that the scientists become better acquainted with Senator Vandenberg. It had been quite a day. "End of trip," noted Coryell. "Boy was I tired!!!!!"

4. THE FATE OF THE BILL

Meanwhile what of the bill? The Senate had again placed itself *hors de combat*, first with an internal contest over the number of members on the special committee to study atomic energy, and then, after passage with Senator Vandenberg's powerful support of the resolution for an eleven member committee, with a further delay over the chairmanship. As the author of the resolution, precedent pointed to Brien McMahon of Connecticut, whose claim was strengthened because he had introduced the first atomic energy bill of the session, but McMahon was a freshman senator, and there was pressure for a chairman with more seniority. McMahon won the appointment on October 26, and with James Newman as counsel he began to prepare a period of indoctrination for his fellow committeemen. But the concern with some kind of special committee had all along served notice that the Senate was not interested in quick passage of the Johnson bill.

During the week of October 22 the House Military Affairs Committee held closed hearings, out of which optimistic reports were allowed to leak of a mutually satisfactory compromise of scientific and military views, and the bill was reported out on November 1 as H.R. 4566. The War Department amendments had modified it along the line of the criticisms offered by the Cambridge scientists. To Section 3, dealing with the general authority of the commission and the administrator, was added a more specific guarantee against unnecessary interference with scientific research that did not, however, specify the related fields to be protected (medicine, biology, and so on), as the Cambridge suggestions had done. The amended section read:

In the performance of its functions, the Commission shall adopt the policy of non-interference with the conducting and disclosure by private persons of basic research in the field of nuclear physics, or in other fields employing the results or methods of research in that field, where the release of atomic energy involved in such research, or the sources, equipment, mechanisms, or materials employed therein, are not deemed by the Commission to be of military or industrial value or to constitute a national hazard.[40]

Extensive changes were made in Sections 6, 7, and 11 dealing with licensing procedures, an area only briefly touched upon by the Cambridge scientists but one in which the original bill had been severely criticized on administrative grounds.

The security sections, which had aroused the most emotional response from scientists, were toned down. In Section 19 ("Penalties for Security Violations") the opening phrase of subsection (*a*) relating to dismissal was changed from "any violation of any regulation promulgated by the Commission . . ." to "any willful or grossly negligent violation of any security regulation promulgated by the Commission . . ." and the phrase "in connection with activities governed by this Act" inserted. The maximum fine for unintentional violation of security regulations was left at $500, but the alternative or additional penalty of thirty days in jail was dropped. For wilful violation the maximum fine was reduced from $100,000 to $10,000 and the possible term of imprisonment from ten to five years. For intentional transmission of information damaging to the interests of the United States, the maximum fine was reduced from $300,000 to $25,000 and the possible jail term from thirty years to twenty.

A dissenting report by Representatives Chet Holifield and Melvin Price, a draft of which had been prepared by Newman's assistant, Byron Miller, recommended still further amendments requiring a full-time paid commission responsible to the President, a civilian administrator, and exclusive government ownership of plutonium and other fissionable materials.[41] On November 10 further minority views were submitted by Representative Charles H. Elston on behalf of eight of his Republican colleagues, including minority whip L. C. Arends,

---

[40] From mimeographed summary entitled "Proposed War Department Amendments to the May-Johnson Bill," in Camb. I, 10, and other files.

[41] Draft in Miller's files; U.S. House of Representatives, *Reports*, Misc. V, Report No. 1186, Part I, 79th Cong., 1st sess., November 5, 1945; *New York Times*, November 6, 1945, p. 6.

opposing the May bill on the ground that the broad powers given the commission were unconstitutional.[42]

Paralleling these legislative developments were signs of second thoughts at the White House. These had commenced with the Newman-Snyder memorandum of October 15, leading to the request on the eighteenth that OWMR correlate administration views on atomic energy legislation. And presidential enthusiasm for the May-Johnson bill was further reduced by a memorandum on the twenty-second from Harold D. Smith, director of the Bureau of the Budget.

The Smith memorandum was largely the work of his assistant in charge of scientific matters, Don K. Price, a man with less science training than Newman but with an equally strong interest in the relation of science to public policy. To Smith's annoyance the War Department had not sent the May-Johnson bill to the Bureau of the Budget, but he had been informed by Price, who had seen a copy of it, that it was an extremely bad bill in that it detached a vitally important field from any political responsibility. (This was an independent judgment; at this time Price was not in touch with the scientist opposition to the bill.) The budget director had as yet no ground for submitting an opinion, but soon some of the unimportant atomic energy bills arrived in the course of routine circulation, and Smith and Price seized the opportunity to comment on the May-Johnson bill by using it as a base of comparison. Hence the memorandum of October 22. Smith and Price were not sure to what extent the President had committed himself to the bill, but they wasted no time. Within hours their comment was at the White House, and soon thereafter the Bureau of the Budget was instructed not to represent the bill as an administration measure. The Bureau, Price recalls, was invaded by more top Pentagon brass than he had ever seen, and the issue was blown wide open.

The principal issue, in the view of Smith and Price, was the same as that represented in the two chief science foundation bills currently being considered by the Kilgore committee. The Magnuson bill, which was closely related to the Bush plan, would establish a science foundation free from political interference, just as the May-Johnson bill was claimed to do for an atomic energy commission, whereas the Kilgore bill, more in line with Bureau of the Budget thinking, placed the science foundation firmly within the framework of normal government

---

[42] U.S. House of Representatives, *Reports*, Report No. 1186, Part II; *New York Times*, November 11, 1945, p. 2.

controls. In the case of either foundation or commission Smith's view was that the growing importance of scientific research and development required close integration with other activities of government. The October 22 memorandum to Truman centered, therefore, on the weakness of executive control provided in the May-Johnson bill. On October 24 Truman replied that before definite commitments were made to the bill a conference should be held between the War Department and those who had submitted criticisms.[43]

The conference was called for November 7 by OWMR as co-ordinator for the administration. Miller and Newman had begun the draft of a new bill as resolved upon after the abortive meeting between the panel and the Szilard forces, and on this draft was based an OWMR analysis of the May-Johnson bill that was circulated before the conference took place. The meeting found civilian agencies fairly well lined up against the bill, with the OWMR and the Bureau of the Budget supported by Secretary of Interior Ickes and Secretary of Commerce Wallace.[44]

Newman followed up this conference with another OWMR memorandum, which was sent to the White House in Snyder's name on November 14. Pointing out that civilian government agencies in general supported the War Mobilization Office views against the May-Johnson bill, Newman proceeded to outline and refute the War Department's arguments for retaining it. The first one—that all basic points in the OWMR analysis had been considered and rejected by the House Military Affairs Committee—was dismissed as irrelevant; the second and third points were dealt with as follows:

(2) It is urged that the Bill has had the approval of the most distinguished scientists in the country. It is further urged that the best qualified scientists have been heard at the hearings before the House Committee, and that the numerous objections made against the Bill represent a carefully organized minority opinion. The staff of the OWMR inform me that they have examined many hundreds of telegrams and letters sent to you and to me protesting passage of the May-Johnson Bill in its present form and requesting further hearings on the Bill. The staff inform me that these messages came from all over the country, from scientists and scientific groups diversified in opinion and complexion, so that it cannot be inferred reasonably that the protests are organized or centrally inspired.

---

[43] Interview with Price, June 27, 1962; Truman to H. D. Smith, October 24, 1945, copy in Miller's files; Richard G. Hewlett and Oscar E. Anderson, Jr., *The New World*, 1939–1946 (University Park: Pennsylvania State University Press, 1962), p. 438 (referred to hereinafter as *The New World*).

[44] *The New World*, pp. 443–45.

Among the known opponents of the May-Johnson Bill who were not heard by the House Military Affairs Committee are a great number of the country's distinguished scientists, including such men as Karl T. Compton, President of M.I.T.; Irving Langmuir, Research Director of General Electric; George Pegram, Dean of Graduate Faculties, Columbia University; Harlow Shapley, Director of the Harvard Observatories; Harold C. Urey, Nobel Prize Winner and Professor of Physics [sic] at the University of Chicago; and D. H. Smyth [sic], author of the Smyth Report and Professor of Physics at Princeton.

(3) It is argued, finally, that opposition to the Bill is confined to a minority of scientists who object to certain features of the Bill relating to academic freedom, and that there has been no serious opposition from any source to other important aspects of the Bill. Here again, my staff inform me that organizations and distinguished individuals in industry, business, academic life, and other professions have sent hundreds of telegrams and letters to the White House in criticism of the May-Johnson bill. (A statistical analysis of this unusually large volume of telegrams and letters, which still pour in at an unabated rate, is now being prepared and will be available to you).

The further changes suggested were essentially those proposed in the memorandum prepared on October 31 by Byron Miller for the Holifield-Price minority report.[45]

The November 7 conference, adding administration opposition to the indifference of the Senate, the bungling in the House, and the fury of the scientists, seems to have made clear to Patterson the strength of the forces arrayed against the May-Johnson bill, but a few gestures were made in its behalf. One of the bill's coauthors, William L. Marbury, defended it in a two-column letter to the *New York Times* on November 11. In regard to the security provisions that had been the chief object of the scientists' attack, Marbury admitted that much depended upon the wisdom of the commission, but he challenged his critics to find a better way of handling the problem.

Copies of Marbury's defense were distributed to the site organizations, and an answer appeared in the *Times* on November 25 from Gordon K. Lister, a patent attorney for the SAM Lab and legal adviser to the Association of Manhattan Project Scientists. Said Lister, if the Interim Committee had wanted civilian control, as Marbury contended, why did the bill not include a simple provision that the administrator and a majority of the commission be civilians? Lister found examples of this same imprecision throughout the bill; terms

---

[45] Memo from John W. Snyder to President Truman (dictated by James Newman), November 14, 1945, copy in Miller's files.

such as "military value" and "military security" were vague and subject to changing interpretation. He accused the framers of the bill
of failing to realize that substantially every nuclear disintegration involved release of atomic energy and hence of employing phraseology
that covered research on many applications of radioactive materials
remote from military ones. He foresaw endless interpretive difficulties in these and other areas.[46]

On into December the May-Johnson bill was the subject of discussion within the administration. Yet another adverse criticism
drafted by Newman was forwarded by the President to Patterson and
Secretary of the Navy Forrestal on November 30. This in turn was
analyzed by the War Department, and both were discussed at a
strategy meeting called by Patterson on December 11, together with
opinions solicited from Bush, Conant, and K. T. Compton of the now
disbanded Interim Committee, and from Oppenheimer. No public
statement of War Department intentions was issued, but the word
that reached the scientists in mid-December was that the bill had
encountered such strong opposition in Congress that it was not slated
for immediate discussion and that the House was apparently marking
time until another bill emerged from the Senate.[47]

In the coming months the May-Johnson bill remained always in
the background of the domestic legislation picture—a yardstick against
which witnesses were asked to measure their opinions on the more
popular McMahon bill, a bogey with which scientists frightened each
other whenever prospects for civilian control looked especially dark.

Comment on three points is in order; the War Department's management of the bill, the responsibility for its defeat, and the retrospective feelings of its detractors.[48]

One who is introduced to the May-Johnson bill by way of the
piecemeal information obtained at the time by the scientists who
opposed it is struck by those aspects of its management that shocked
and angered them—the secrecy about legislative plans, the ban on

---

[46] Letters from Marbury and Lister, *New York Times*, November 11, 1945, sec. E,
p. 8; November 25, 1945, sec. E, p. 8.

[47] *The New World*, pp. 452–53; editorial, *Bulletin of the Atomic Scientists*, I
(December 10, 1945).

[48] Statements in these final paragraphs are based upon discussion with numerous
scientists and in particular upon interviews with Bethe, June 24, 1959; Newman,
December 29, 1961; Borst, February 20, 1962; Bush, June 5, 1962; and Price, June
27, 1962.

open discussion, the misleading assertions of panel support, the perfunctory hearings, plus what they later learned about a seemingly offhand attitude toward the opinion of other government departments. James Newman, when asked years later if one is justifiably shocked by the way the bill was pushed through, says "at times, yes." Don Price, who shared in most respects Newman's views about the bill itself, says "in general, no"; the motives of the people involved were entirely laudable and it was all a normal part of political maneuver.

The AEC historians take a middle ground and say the bill was "badly handled," not through any fault of Patterson's, but through the cumulative effect of miscalculation. "The War Department," conclude Hewlett and Anderson,

had underestimated public interest in the measure and the sudden shift in attitude toward the military and leaders of the war effort. The same men who could command unquestioned support for a two-billion-dollar project a few months earlier were now looked upon as power-hungry connivers. The decision to hasten the bill through the military affairs committees of Congress, the clumsy impatience of Andrew May, the badgering of witnesses, the indefinite powers which the bill granted to the commission were all elements of human shortsightedness, pettiness, and folly.[49]

Patterson with his newly enlarged responsibilities at the War Department and Bush with his anxiety about orderly demobilization of secret research projects could not give undivided attention to the cosseting of a group of nervous scientists. Bush expected some reaction from the young men of the Project to the repressions of the war period, but he evidently did not think it necessary to warn Patterson that long-standing discontents might erupt to interfere with War Department plans. Perhaps Bush regarded it as futile personally to explain his views about unfettered research to the dissenters. An attempt at closer rapport might not, indeed, have affected the outcome for atomic energy; but it might have produced an earlier solution in the field of science legislation.

Although the scientists who fought the May-Johnson bill have always handsomely acknowledged the help they received from political advisers, they have happily accepted a large measure of credit for stopping it. This view was encouraged by James Newman, himself no minor claimant for prime honors in this respect, in the book about the McMahon Act that he and Byron Miller wrote in 1947. The sci-

---

[49] *The New World,* p. 435.

entists swarmed down from their ivory towers, recalled Newman and Miller,

and with energy, fervor, passionate conviction, and a somewhat unexpected talent for organization threw themselves into the battle. It may be that they were grossly naïve in politics, but there is no denying that they showed a capacity for improvisation and prompt action beyond anything the economic groups whose interests were vitally involved in the legislation were able to muster.[50]

Although with the passing of time Newman has decided that the book gave the scientists both more and less credit than they deserved in the complex battle over domestic legislation, he is still of the opinion that without their prompt agitation the May-Johnson bill would have gone through. Again Price differs, maintaining that the idea of the embattled scientists defeating the bill has been exaggerated, although as lobbies go it educated people in record time. Price believes that there was enough opposition to the bill within the administration so that the President would have vetoed it, as he later did a science foundation bill and for the same reason, that it made the federal operation of scientific research and development too independent of executive control.

As to how credit should be allotted among scientists themselves, it is generally agreed that Szilard, aided by Condon and Urey, raised the alarm and that it was the younger men at Clinton Labs and Chicago who gave it significant dimensions. The more sober criticism of the Cambridge group, though aimed at compromise rather than defeat of the bill, may actually have made more impression in certain quarters than the violent attack that struck some surprised observers as slightly hysterical.

The vehemence of scientists' opinions about the bill has been tempered by time and by the fact that in the course of compromises required for its passage the substitute measure, the McMahon Act, contained security provisions that were in some ways more stringent than those of the amended May-Johnson bill. But one scientist who had adopted this not uncommon view, having occasion to reread the original May-Johnson bill in 1962, was shocked anew by what he called the vicious and vindictive tone of its security sections.

As for the specter of military control, scientists who were then deeply

---

[50] Newman and Miller, *The Control of Atomic Energy* (New York: McGraw-Hill Book Co., 1948), p. 10. Used by permission of the publisher.

involved in protests against the bill do not admit that their fears were unfounded. Granting that the War Department and General Groves were probably sincere in wanting to turn over their responsibilities, these scientists still feel that they were right to fight against military influence even though its nominal exclusion did not, as they then hoped, either allay Russian suspicions or prevent military considerations from dominating the development of atomic energy.

The controversial administrative provisions of the bill, now as then, excite less passion than the security or military angles. Most scientists outside the administration, as their relative indifference to science legislation was to demonstrate, did not pretend to know or care much about the relation of the commission to the executive and the other points that disturbed those more familiar with administration. Their retrospective views in this area, as the value of their judgments, depend upon how close they have been to the operations of the Atomic Energy Commission. Vannevar Bush sees recent moves to replace the five-man commission by a single director as vindication of the May-Johnson bill's part-time commission and powerful administrator. From his erstwhile opponents on this point little has been heard.

But the issue relating to the May-Johnson bill that perhaps more than any other deeply disturbed the scientific community in 1945 was the secrecy of its preparation and the arbitrary manner of its promotion. To those who protested, a fight on this score seemed, and still seems, well worth making.

PART III

Launching
the Crusade

CHAPTER 5

"The Reluctant Lobby"

T HE ORGANIZATION MEETING of the Federation of Atomic Scientists was held in Washington on Wednesday and Thursday, October 31 and November 1. Two delegates were there from each of the four local associations, Paul Henshaw and S. G. English from Clinton Labs, John Simpson and Austin Brues from Chicago, Irving Kaplan and Richard Present from SAM, and Joseph Keller and William Woodward from Los Alamos. Other scientists who happened to be in Washington sat in on the discussion, from which emerged a statement for site organization approval expressing the determination to establish the Federation of Atomic Scientists to publicize the views of existing organizations about monopoly, defense, and international control and to carry out their common aims—to study the implications of the release of atomic energy, create a realization of the dangers, help establish an atmosphere of world security in which beneficial possibilities of nuclear energy could be developed, and study the relation of national legislation and international policy.

Nothing was said about officers, but it was proposed that the delegates of the four component associations who happened to be in Washington should serve as a council; a central office there would handle contacts with legislative leaders and with groups with similar aims, especially other scientists' organizations.[1]

---

[1] Statement by the Federation of Atomic Scientists, n.d., copies in ASC XIII, 11, and other files.

1. 1018 Vermont Avenue

Most of the delegates stayed on in Washington over the week end of November 3 and 4 to help launch the federation. The best that Simpson could do for office space was the loan of a small fourth-floor walk-up at 1018 Vermont Avenue, N.W.—the little used local quarters of the Independent Citizens Committee of the Arts, Sciences and Professions, obtained through Harlow Shapley, an ICC director. From there the delegates sent out the above statement and the first newsletter of typed carbons—dated November 5 and marked "confidential"—to which Brues, Simpson, English, Keller, and the new secretary, Suzanne Shuler, all contributed a few paragraphs.[2] "The office," wrote Brues, "consists of a small room which houses a desk, telephone, ancient and noisy typewriter, an inadequate number of chairs, the World Almanac, a telephone book, and $20.00 worth of newly purchased stationery supplies. There is no elevator.... We have engaged a secretary ... who so far appears to have the bear by the tail."

During the seven-week occupancy of 1018 Vermont Avenue the equipment never expanded much, and the bear's tail proved very slippery. A later visitor's inventory added a second typewriter, and bottles of aspirin and citrocarbonate in the bleak bathroom, but listed only one chair; scientists sat on the floor surrounded by copies of speeches, the *Congressional Record*, and Senate hearings.[3]

The lack of space either for workers, callers, or the rapidly mounting piles of paper was partly responsible for the indelible impression of chaos these first weeks in the Washington office left upon those who shared them. In spite of it the individuals had a pretty good idea of what they were about. Brues's report in the first newsletter turned to more general matters:

Things appear to be moving very rapidly in Washington, which is a rather wild and unpredictable environment after the mild academic atmosphere of Chicago. We have made many significant contacts and are getting a fairly clear picture of the various movements and interests which are concerned with the same aims and purposes as our organization.

The interest of many groups, particularly scientists' groups, in future control of nuclear energy and allied problems is rapidly snowballing, and various groups have approached us in the hopes that we will cooperate with

---

[2] FAtS Newsletter, November 5, 1945, FAS XV, 8.

[3] "Chain Reaction among Scientists," by Beirne Lay, Jr., manuscript, in Simpson's files.

them in different ways by endorsing their views, etc. From what we have seen here it is quite clear that within the next three days we will have to make the decision as to whether or not we are willing to support a broad, national organization to educate public opinion on problems introduced by atomic energy.

Simpson carried on Brues's story: The federation would supply speakers for a country-wide tour under the auspices of the Council on Foreign Relations; contacts had been made with the World Peace Foundation, the Foreign Policy Association, the Canadian Institute of International Affairs, and the Federal Council of Churches. The Rye conference had discussed methods of educating the public on atomic energy with substantial results. Science Service in Washington, reaching about five million readers, had asked for material and planned a special release. Contact had been established with the new scientists' group in Philadelphia.

Simpson reported briefly the dinners with senators on October 24 and 31 and added some "Notes from Capitol Hill":

Senator Morse of Oregon [Simpson's home state] was visited three times during the last ten days and expressed unusual interest in our work. He has offered to read on the floor of the Senate any memos which we feel are appropriate for such use. He strongly suggests that the Associated sites prepare brief pamphlets covering the fundamentals of atomic energy, the bomb, and the social and political implications of such weapons. A collection of these pamphlets should be given to all members of Congress since he feels that this is the only way the printed information will be used to advantage by the legislators.

Senator McMahon was visited several times in the past week and discussions were held concerning his objectives and plans for the special committee on atomic energy. . . . The Senator's secretary, Mr. Charles Calkins, is anxious to obtain background material for Senatorial speeches, both on the atomic bomb, and on peace-time applications of atomic energy.

Simpson's final items concerned a project to place copies of the Smyth report in the hands of all members of Congress with marked passages likely to further an understanding of basic implications, and the possibility of Washington delegates' obtaining an interview with Truman and Prime Minister Attlee, who was due shortly in Washington with his atomic energy adviser, Sir John Anderson.

English summarized conversations with an unnamed British scientist who had assured him "that feelings of the British scientists are essentially parallel to our own, and very strong."

Keller's section stressed the need of the federation for a permanent executive secretary, preferably a scientist who could answer technical questions, and entered a plea for the broader scientists' organization so much desired by ALAS.

While we should not fail to exploit our own positions as Atomic Scientists, there are many other scientific groups, such as the Rocket Group here in Washington, the groups in Philadelphia, Boston, and New York, who would like to affiliate with us. The Association of Los Alamos Scientists has a particular interest in such a larger group, because it is clear that be-tween the first of next year and about March 1, many of the key men at Los Alamos will have left the site to resume their peace-time work and will not be able to continue the contacts with the Los Alamos organization. We can only do one thing at a time and the establishment of the Federa-tion has been a fulltime job up til now. As soon as possible however, efforts should be made to form a federation of all interested scientists' groups of which the F.A.S. would be a unit.

Susie, the secretary, rounded off the newsletter with the offer of street maps, hotel rooms, plane and train reservations when available, and the central office "as your personal guide to a more pleasant and effective stay in Washington." (Musical chairs, perhaps, with a dose of citrocarb for the loser!) Newsletters on Mondays and Thursdays were to keep the sites well informed. This was an ironic touch, for at best the hard pressed Washington staff never managed a newsletter more often than every ten days, while with sadistic regularity those at a comfortable distance from the fray complained of not knowing what was going on.

In fact, on Monday the fifth, as this newsletter was going out, the turmoil began with the arrival of a fresh set of delegates. Lyle Borst and Dan Koshland, a young biochemist, came from Clinton Labs to take over from Henshaw and English; Brues and Simpson returned to Chicago (where Brues answered the Compton letter and Simpson presided at a series of almost daily ASC executive committee meet-ings), and their places were taken by H. H. Goldsmith and Arthur Jaffey. Kaplan and Present were down from New York for part of the week, and Robert Marshak from Los Alamos joined Woodward for a few days on his way to a meeting of the New York section of the American Physical Society, whose support he successfully enlisted for control of atomic energy through the United Nations.[4]

On Monday afternoon the delegates attended the swearing in of Condon as director of the Bureau of Standards. They talked about

---

[4] *New York Times*, November 11, 1945, p. 3.

the organization of the McMahon committee staff, to which it was hoped Condon would be made scientific adviser; they planned a Thursday meeting for congressmen in the House caucus room and a Thursday evening briefing session at the Bureau for members of the McMahon committee. These discussions carried on through Tuesday and Wednesday, and Borst's invaluable diary recalls some of the other moves in which he, at least, was involved.

On Tuesday he had a discussion with Condon, offered his services to McMahon, joined a noon conference on the international control resolution being framed for introduction in House and Senate, contacted groups to sign it, and planned a conference with non-Project scientists for November 16 and 17. In the afternoon he spoke in Condon's place to fifty people at the Washington Churchmen's Seminar (organized by John Foster Dulles) and, accompanied by Chauncey Starr of the Oak Ridge Y-12 group (the Atomic Production Scientists), talked with Representative Voorhis about the Thursday House meeting, which Voorhis was sponsoring, and about tactics on the May-Johnson bill, on which it was thought debate might start the following week.

Wednesday went much the same way. Borst studied the October congressional testimony ("understood Compton better," he noted in his diary); he discussed the removal of a world government clause from the pending international control resolution (the engineers at Y-12 wanted it in, but the other groups insisted successfully that it come out); he noted possible speakers for a National Press Club luncheon the following week (an engagement filled by Philip Morrison from Los Alamos), and made a visit to the Capitol Press Room in preparation for a press conference next day.

Each delegate was similarly engaged in exploring his own set of contacts and projects. By Thursday favorable reactions to the federation statement of November 1 had been received from the four site organizations, and the delegates held a press conference at 11:00 A.M. in the office of Senator Mitchell of Washington to announce the formation of the Federation of Atomic Scientists. Goldsmith represented the Atomic Scientists of Chicago; Kaplan, the Manhattan Project Scientists at SAM; Woodward, the Association of Los Alamos Scientists; and Borst, the Association of Oak Ridge Scientists. At the last minute the two engineers' groups of Oak Ridge, APSOR at Y-12 and AEOR at K-25, announced their adherence. The four scientists confronted some of the best of the Washington press. Borst acted as spokesman, a position he explains by saying, "Well, I had been there three days, so I knew the ropes." (Actually, Woodward and Kaplan had been there longer—since October 31—but perhaps with interruptions.) At the Capitol Press Room the previous afternoon Borst had talked with a young woman from the Hearst papers, and she was ready with a leading question: "Are you here on salary?" The negative answers clearly impressed the reporters; the further questioning was friendly, and the space they gave the new organization was entirely satisfactory.

At the press conference Michael Amrine, a young correspondent for the London *Daily Herald*, sat between two Washington veterans, Raymond Swing and Mae Craig. They shared their astonishment at this extraordinary welling up of concern and also their dismay at the scientists' rank disregard of such basic rules of the public relations game as issuing press releases single-spaced on both sides of the paper. After the conference Amrine and Richard L. Strout of the *Christian Science Monitor* talked with the scientists further, asking more questions and proffering advice. Amrine began to "run errands" and help with writing and two months later was hired as FAS publications editor.[5]

Representative Voorhis' meeting for House members took place at three o'clock Thursday afternoon. Borst recalls a crowd of five hundred people; other delegates reported that the audience included one hundred congressmen and fifty reporters. In any case the turnout showed a lively interest, and the House caucus room overflowed. Szilard spoke on international control; Urey and Joyce Stearns discussed the importance of freedom of research if scientists were to be attracted to the nuclear field, with Urey telling the congressmen that he was far less afraid of industrial monopoly of atomic power than he was of there being no research at all. Robert Marshak, a twenty-nine-year-old deputy group leader at Los Alamos, and Lyle Borst spoke on behalf of the local associations and the federation.[6]

The acoustics in the crowded room were terrible; Urey spoke fast and excitedly, and Szilard's accent seemed more obvious than usual. Borst saw that neither one was getting beyond the first row and when his turn came he spoke slowly and distinctly.

---

[5] Interview with Amrine, April 24, 1963.

[6] Borst diary and interview with him, February 20, 1962; Arthur Jaffey, "Washington Scene," November 8–17, 1945, ASC IV, 10; Marshak report to ALAS, ALAS II, 2; "late bulletin," November 8, 1945, FAS XV, 8; Goldsmith to ASC executive committee, November 13, 1945, ASC VI, 12.

"You have heard eminent scientists. You now hear a nobody," said Borst modestly. He spoke for the young men, he told the congressmen, for the anonymous 95 per cent of those who had worked on the bomb. Some of them had known nothing since leaving school but restricted wartime research, and they looked forward to being creative scientists in an atmosphere free from military control, at liberty to talk and investigate and at peace with the world and their consciences. Borst went on to tell why, as scientists, he and his colleagues objected to the May-Johnson bill; then—drawing his own line between scientist and citizen rather than Compton's—he explained that in their capacity as citizens they disliked certain features of the bill, such as the part-time independent commisson, and that also as citizens they were accepting an obligation to spread correct information. Finally, Borst announced the formation of the Federation of Atomic Scientists with a brief statement of its aims and convictions.[7]

Borst was a great success, Jaffey reported to the ASC, and saved the day. There were questions afterward, mainly about the feasibility of inspection and whether scientists had a substitute for the May-Johnson bill. Several congressmen said the meeting had changed their minds about the bill, and those already convinced on that point wanted more information about international control and inspection. Some opportunities for delegates to help with speeches for the voters back home arose from this meeting.

Congressmen were greatly impressed, Borst recalls, by the 95 per cent backing from scientists who had worked on the bomb. "As with the morning press conference," he says, "we were extremely lucky, for we were lambs in the mouths of lions." Borst came to regard this caucus room meeting as a turning point for the May-Johnson bill, as he observed that from here on its fortunes were definitely on the downgrade. (The observation was sound enough, but Borst's explanation did not take account of the previous day's White House conference at which civilian agencies had lined up against the bill.)

When the meeting ended Borst went up to Voorhis' office. Within minutes there was a phone call from a security officer: Where was Borst? What did he say? Voorhis provided the answers, then said to Borst, "We will have your speech read into the *Congressional Record*." This was subsequently done, and Borst heard no more of the incident.

This busy Thursday closed with the evening briefing for the Senate

---

[7] *Congressional Record*, 79th Cong., 1st sess., 1945, XCI, Part 13, A4914–15.

commmittee at the Bureau of Standards to which we will return later.

A well-remembered feature of this first week in the federation office was the continuing dissidence of Los Alamos expressed in a series of fractious telegrams from ALAS chairman Higinbotham. One of these protested the circulation for signatures of the Rye conference demand for a new atomic energy bill. ALAS did not support the resolution, wired Higinbotham, and wanted a new conference of all groups at some place away from interference, preferably at Los Alamos.[8] This suggestion was coolly received, and the ALAS executive committee, meeting on November 8, decided to send Higinbotham himself to Washington. No time was lost. A general meeting the following evening was informed that Higinbotham had already departed and would remain in Washington at his own expense. No one foresaw, of course, that he would stay for two years.[9]

Higinbotham flew into Washington on Saturday, November 10. The other delegates, intimidated by the ferocity of his telegrams, were delighted to find what an easygoing, friendly character he was. He spent the afternoon with Jaffey, Goldsmith, Kaplan, Borst, Szilard, and the secretary—all very sincere, he wrote next day in the first of several anguished letters scrawled by hand on trains or late at night to associates in ALAS.

Higinbotham found the office depressing and the lack of organization frightening. His first impressions continued:

The office is a dumpy suite of rooms. . . . Furniture very meager. The secretary is very good, works about 70 hours a week, is terribly overloaded. . . . So far she hasn't been paid. No one has got any money. Szillard [sic] is getting $1000 from Chicago for such expenses. No one else has tried, as far as I can see.

Politically it looks haywire, too. Szillard, Schimmel [of the Kilgore staff], etc., are the only permanent parties. Consequently any policy and action is up to them entirely. They accuse each other (when the other is not present) of trying to run things for their own ends. Everyone was very cordial to me, when I was around. . . .

The boys in Washington, under Szillard's direction are doing 2 things. (1) doing a good job from the international viewpoint. . . . Their only political advisers are the bunch Szillard has picked up. They still make many mistakes (releases, timing, etc.). They are contacting and selling a lot of people. But they could do better if there were more influential scientists here. They know that. There is no definite program, confusion reigns supreme. (2) they are trying to break the Johnson bill & get something

---

8 Wire Higinbotham to Woodward, November 2, 1945, copy in ALAS II, 18.
9 ALAS Log, ALAS II, 2; minutes, November 9, 1945, ALAS II, 2.

else. This is entirely Szillard's field and we should stay clear of it, in my mind.

Everyone is on the run every minute they can stay awake. I admire the spirit but it is a hell of a way to do things. I intend to stay out of the politicing [sic] as much as possible & try to get the big organization going. . . .

About "the big organization" Higinbotham had the impression that the others currently in Washington were lukewarm; they admit it is a good thing, he said, but sort of want to put it off. Conferences were scheduled for the next weekend, and he was trying to see that the right people got there from non-Project groups. Also, he added,

the boys are anxious for considered opinions on international control. There is no doubt that this is tough. But Congressmen and press are clamoring for dope on this. Leo [Szilard] and the boys tried to settle it over a couple of cocktails. You can't do things that way! I suggest you try to get a big group to really tear into this.[10]

2. THE INTERNATIONAL CONTROL RESOLUTION

The efforts of the Washington delegates to get the ball rolling on international control involved, as Higinbotham soon discovered, something more than cocktail conferences. For while they did not yet know quite how perfunctory Truman's Potsdam talks with Stalin had been, it was clear that no real exploration of control problems had taken place on an international level; and when it was learned that Prime Ministers Attlee and Mackenzie King, but not a Russian representative, would confer with Truman in mid-November, the scientists determined to try again. Immediately after the organization meeting on November 1 the delegates began to frame a statement, which they hoped might become the basis of a joint congressional resolution, reaffirming the principles already proclaimed by the site groups and calling for a conference with the Russians as a preliminary step toward control of atomic energy through the United Nations. They soon learned that Harlow Shapley, on behalf of the Independent Citizens Committee of the Arts, Sciences, and Professions, was soliciting signatures to a similar resolution supporting a domestic program based on full public discussion, a civilian authority, and early resumption of free research and publication in atomic physics; this statement also called for a conference with the Russians, leading toward international development "with the broadest utilization of all resources

---

[10] Higinbotham to J. Trischka, November 11, 1945, ALAS II, 18.

and the widest freedom of research and interchange of ideas," but did not include the recommendation of international control. To avoid duplication of effort, it was agreed that in further solicitations Shapley should concentrate on academic centers in the Northeast and Charles Coryell, for the federation, should make contact with those in the Midwest and West.[11]

The resolutions were sent to scientific and non-scientific organizations as well as to individuals, and many signatures had been collected by Saturday, November 10, when Attlee and King arrived in Washington. By this time, too, the scientists were assured of some congressional support. Five senators had agreed to cosponsor the resolution: Tobey, Morse, Smith, Taylor, and Kilgore; Fulbright's name was later added. In the House, where a concurrent resolution could have only one sponsor, Mrs. Helen Gahagan Douglas would introduce it, leaving time for remarks from other supporters, among whom were counted Representatives Voorhis and Holifield of California, Luce of Connecticut, and Emily Taft Douglas of Illinois.[12]

Among scientists associated with major research centers in the fall of 1945, the small minority who did not indicate positive support for international control kept very quiet—some, certainly, from an aversion to taking a public stand on non-technical questions; others from a belief that international control was unworkable (as, indeed, some who came out strongly for it also feared was the case) but that men of good will could not actively oppose it. The request for signatures to the proposed resolution exposed one center of resistance— qualified, to be sure, but from a source that could not be ignored. When Coryell learned that a group of prominent chemists and physicists at the University of California in Berkeley would not sign the federation resolution, he wired reproachfully to W. F. Giauque that only Berkeley held aloof and received a letter of amplification. Explaining that he and two others had signed the slightly less specific Shapley statement and that several more intended to do so, Giauque continued:

. . . The group here is not actually "aloof" in this matter, but we do not believe that there is any use in trying to get nations to renunciate or pro-

[11] Coryell, "To the scientists who have endorsed the formation of the Federation of Atomic Scientists," December 13, 1945, ASC X, 1.

[12] Report of Rush to AORS, November 8–19, 1945, AORES II, 2; D. E. Koshland, Jr., "Facts and Opinions from a Week in Washington," ca. November 11, 1945, AORES II, 2; FAtS Newsletter, I (November 14, 1945), FAS XV, 8.

hibit the use of instruments of war. This would seem to be particularly true of the atomic bomb, which could apparently be assembled on short notice by any unscrupulous group which acquired sufficient power to appropriate fissionable material which must be on hand in large amounts in many places if various nations are to make peacetime use of it.

We do not believe that anyone has seen any real answer to the atomic bomb problem and some of us are concerned lest too much insistence on specific non-scientific objectives by scientific groups will weaken their position in the matter. There are undoubtedly many aspects of the situation on which the scientific groups are not necessarily well, if at all, informed.[13]

Objections from within the fold had also caused "a little confusion" during the week of November 5, when Urey and a few others refused to sign the statement because it omitted any reference to the United Nations. As Koshland later explained the situation to AORS:

This had ... been purposely omitted because it was felt that the scientists should merely state the need for a conference without making any recommendations [as] to the action to be followed. It soon became evident, however, that the Senators would refuse to sign a document which did not contain a statement about the UNO. ... After extensive talks with Senators, Representatives, and members of the Government, I have the very definite conviction that one must work through the UNO. The UNO is the Senators' baby ..., any attempt to circumvent it in general falls on deaf ears in Washington. As one member of the State Department put it, the peace is fragile enough, and we should not destroy the one thing we have created. ... For these reasons it was not felt objectionable to insert the UNO into the statement.[14]

On Sunday, November 11, Truman and his guests began their discussions aboard the "Sequoia." Already on hand was a wire to the White House from the executive committee of ALAS, with the added signatures of Fermi, Bethe, Robert Wilson, Allison, and Bacher, commending Attlee's understanding of atomic energy problems as expressed in a recent speech and citing as a happy augury of fruitful

[13] Coryell to S. Shuler, November 9, 1945, AORES III, 9; Giauque to Coryell, November 10, 1945, FAS III, 1. Those associated with these reservations were W. M. Latimer, Melvin Calvin, Robert E. Connick, Joel Hildebrand, K. S. Pitzer, G. K. Rollefson, R. T. Birge, and F. A. Jenkins. Glenn T. Seaborg, recently of the Atomic Scientists of Chicago, was the only scientist from the Berkeley campus among the signers later listed in the Congressional Record (79th Cong., 1st sess., 1945, XCI, Part 8, 10942–44).

[14] Koshland, "Facts and Opinions from a Week in Washington," ca. November 11, 1945, AORES II, 2.

collaboration their own close co-operation with the British scientists assigned to Los Alamos during the war.[15]

For the federation delegates Sunday brought an opportunity for informal discussion with Washington supporters at a tea given by former Governor of Pennsylvania Gifford Pinchot and his wife. Pinchot had long been interested in public power, and he had already publicly advocated federal control of atomic energy through a fully representative commission.[16] More than once during the autumn the Pinchots opened their fifty-four-room mansion near Scott Circle to groups of scientists and congressmen and even offered the federation an office there. The young men were charmed by Mrs. Pinchot, and she in turn said she liked them because they were so delightfully inefficient. Journalists made much of the popularity of the young scientists with Washington hostesses, but delegates' memories of capitol drawing rooms do not extend beyond affairs at the Pinchots' and a few officially sponsored dinners.

Among the scientists present on this first occasion were Szilard, E. U. Condon and his wife, Borst, Rush, Koshland, Jaffey, Present, and Kaplan.[17] Senators Downey of California and McMahon of Connecticut were there, and Representatives Luce of Connecticut, and Voorhis, Franck R. Havenner, and Ellis E. Patterson, all of California. Borst and Szilard gave introductory talks; then there was discussion. The congressional guests did not need to be persuaded that some form of international control of the atom was desirable but they were persistent in their quest for specific information about inspection techniques and how violations might be punished. The need for intensive study of these questions was again brought home to the scientists as they learned of the interest on Capitol Hill in Eli Culbertson's scheme for an international army composed of national quotas and in Harold Stassen's proposal that a UN air force be armed with twenty-five United States manufactured atomic bombs. Congressmen were also talking about bacteriological warfare and concluding with the scientists that war itself, not a particular way of waging it, was the evil.

The politicians had tactical advice for the amateurs: Mrs. Luce thought the scientists ought to make a careful study of control proposals and come out strongly for one of them; Representative Patter-

---

[15] *New York Times*, November 11, 1945, p. 2.
[16] Letter to editor, *Washington Daily News*, October 9, 1945.
[17] Reports of Jaffey to the ASC, ASC IV, 10, and Koshland to AORS, AORES II, 2.

son said if they believed in world government they ought to have the guts to advocate it openly, whereas Senator McMahon advised them to pursue only achievable objectives. Governor Pinchot pointed out that the federation could get too much publicity, that it had an enviable position and should not abuse it. "As a group," Koshland reported to AORS, "we said that we wished to move very cautiously, although individuals could come out with more ambitious plans."

Scraps of political gossip were carefully noted: Mrs. Luce described how the May bill had been rushed through the House Military Affairs Committee, on which she represented the Republican minority; Senator Downey, who had attended the London conference of foreign ministers, mentioned that he had been asked by Secretary Byrnes not to discuss the atom there, thus confirming the impression obtained elsewhere by the scientists that the State Department encouraged a hush-hush policy.

Among the Pinchots' guests was Henry Field, of the Natural History Museum in Chicago, who had attended the June scientific congress in Moscow with Langmuir and Shapley. The Russians had welcomed them in a most friendly spirit, Field reported, and Kapitza had opened the congress with an eloquent plea for implementation of prewar plans for meetings and exchange of students. Field thought that Langmuir should head a delegation to Russia to try to reach an agreement on scientific matters with Russian scientists; without divulging any "secrets," the basis could be laid for later negotiation. "Every day such a conference is delayed and our present policy of secrecy continues," Field was quoted as saying, "means irreparable loss in the eyes of the Russians who are by nature extremely suspicious."

The autumn of 1945 was hardly the time to advocate openly a conference of scientists, at least for Americans who had worked on the bomb. Even the presence of James B. Conant in the delegation to the Moscow conference a month later was to make some senators very nervous. But the notion that scientists talking to scientists could clear the way for political negotiation had a wide appeal. The technique was used officially in the UN negotiations in the summer of 1946.

A lively interest in all these topics extended the Pinchots' "tea" until 9:00 P.M. Then the federation delegates adjourned to Jaffey's room at the Wardman Park to plan their next move. Earlier in the week Governor and Mrs. Pinchot had urged them to try to see the

President, but a friendly senator had told them that Truman claimed he knew the scientists' views and that as far as he was concerned they were just another pressure group. Then as they talked on Sunday evening a phone call from their new journalist friend, Michael Amrine, informed them that news coverage of the day's high-level conversations would feature Attlee's opinion that international control was impractical because it would require so many top-flight scientists. This tipped the balance in favor of the Pinchots' advice, and a telegram was sent at once by Lyle Borst on behalf of the federation asking Truman for a conference with Attlee and himself to discuss the feasibility of international control.

While delegates waited for an answer—learning only that the schedule was crowded and their request was "in channels"—they worked on a memorandum to use in the interview and talked inspection at every opportunity. They all had breakfast on Tuesday morning (November 13) with two physicists accompanying the Attlee mission, John Cockcroft, director of the newly announced atomic research center at Harwell, and Rudolph Peierls, Birmingham physicist who had recently been head of the British delegation at Los Alamos. Peierls would shortly become a leader in the British atomic scientists' movement, and there was a satisfactory meeting of minds about general aims and policies. The main topic of conversation was inspection, and despite the limited data that could be discussed in a hotel coffee shop, the federation delegates got the clear impression that the British scientists believed inspection to be technically possible.[18]

Later that day Borst and Curtis had an interview with Undersecretary of State Dean Acheson, and again the chief topic was inspection. Acheson suggested they talk to the British scientists then in Washington, and Borst and Curtis, after some rapid eyebrow signals, confessed that they had done so that morning. They also brought up the matter of a science adviser in the State Department, an idea that, like the informal international talks between scientists, would be a long time in materializing satisfactorily. Borst and Curtis regarded as more promising a continuation of the interview with Acheson's young assistant, Herbert Marks, who showed a more lively understanding of what they had to say. It is true that Marks' influence on United States international control policy was to be very great, first as a member of a State Department working committee preparing for the January United Nations General Assembly meeting and then

18 Interview with Borst, February 20, 1962; report of E. E. Minett to AEOR, ca. November 20, 1945, AORES XV, 5.

as assistant to the Lilienthal board, but if Borst and Curtis found him responsive at this mid-November meeting it was less the result of their own eloquence than of the close rapport that Oppenheimer had established with him in recent weeks as a State Department consultant.[19]

Having started at breakfast the delegates were still discussing inspection at bedtime. During the evening Curtis phoned Oak Ridge, where an AORS executive committee meeting was in progress, to sound out opinion at Clinton Labs. All members of the committee, he was told, felt that inspection was technically feasible and were ready to support a statement to that effect provided that it was carefully worded and avoided detail, a caution so generally observed by the scientists at this period as to give the probably erroneous impression that they were not thinking beyond generalities on this subject.[20]

When not discussing inspection the delegates were largely occupied with the international control resolution. Borst and his diary departed for Oak Ridge on the fourteenth, and so did Koshland, who made a full report to AORS on his week in Washington; they were replaced by E. E. Minett of the Atomic Engineers of Oak Ridge, who was also representing APSOR at the Y-12 plant, and J. H. Rush of Clinton, both of whom concentrated on resolving a series of difficulties obstructing the resolution. Some were concrete, such as Senator Tobey's departure from Washington at a critical time; others involved the delicate interplay of personalities and influence.

The quest for support for the resolution enlarged the delegates' acquaintance with congressmen and with the mores of Capitol Hill. "We had to keep in mind," noted Rush,

the necessity for maintaining something like a balance between Republican and Democratic sponsors, the factor of personal leadership attaching to some senators, the caution of Democratic senators especially as to the reaction of the Administration to the proposed resolution, the necessity for making sure the Special Committee on Atomic Energy was in no way affronted.[21]

These elementary precautions might well have been imitated by more experienced politicians, for two members of the special committee, Connally and Vandenberg, who were also chairman and ranking

---

[19] Interview with Borst, February 20, 1962; Koshland, "Facts and Opinions from a Week in Washington," ca. November 11, 1945, AORES II, 2; FAtS Newsletter I (November 14, 1945), FAS XV, 8.

[20] AORS executive committee minutes, November 13, 1945, AORES I, 6.

[21] Report of Rush to AORS, November 8–19, 1945, AORES II, 2.

minority member of the Senate Foreign Relations Committee, were extremely angry over the administration's failure to consult them prior to the Truman-Attlee-King talks.[22] Set beside the exchanges between heads of state the scientists' scurrying about congressional office corridors may seem a trivial operation, but if the record of administration-congressional relations on this matter is interpreted correctly, the scientists were doing much more than the administration to mobilize Congress in support of the general philosophy that the White House talks were promoting.

It is clear that the federation representatives were trying hard to grapple with congressional politics. Just how searching and sophisticated was their understanding of the crosscurrents within the administration that lay behind the deliberate way in which the President's endorsement of international control was being implemented, it is difficult to tell. For instance, behind the ALAS wire to Attlee and the breakfast with Cockcroft and Peierls was the assumption that exchange of atomic energy information between the wartime partners would be reappraised that week in Washington. The scientists in the federation office and certainly those who signed the ALAS wire were aware that the Quebec agreement of August, 1944, restricted exchange of information on commercial applications and fully appreciated the importance of a review of information policy to the British, for whom atomic power promised earlier benefits than for the United States. In general, federation scientists, and many others besides, approved liberal exchange with the British, both as a matter of principle and because they assumed that liberalization was a logical step toward agreement with other nations. But did they know about the wartime crises in Allied relations produced by differing views on information policy within our government? And did they understand that Bush and Conant had approved the restrictions of the Quebec agreement because they believed that a separate agreement to exchange information with Britain would prejudice the more general exchange that all scientists wanted?[23]

Federation scientists clearly knew of Secretary Byrnes' reluctance to acknowledge atomic energy as a force in international relations.

---

[22] Richard G. Hewlett and Oscar E. Anderson, Jr., *The New World*, 1939–1946 (University Park: Pennsylvania State University Press, 1962), p. 469 (referred to hereinafter as *The New World*).

[23] For discussions of negotiations on exchange of information with Britain, see Leslie R. Groves, *Now It Can Be Told* (New York: Harper & Bros., 1962), pp. 401–8; *The New World*, pp. 457–58.

But there is no evidence that they knew to what straits of unreadiness for the Truman-Attlee-King talks Byrnes' attitude had reduced the administration or how crucial a part was played by Vannevar Bush in retrieving the situation.[24]

Anxiety over the failure to prepare the United States position on international control was felt in several quarters—by Bush, by Secretary Patterson, and by members of Byrnes's own staff. Bush talked to Byrnes on Saturday, November 3 just a week before the prime ministers' arrival, and Byrnes asked Bush to incorporate his recommendations in a memorandum. On Monday, the fifth, Bush had this ready. The contents would have greatly interested the young men who were enlisting support for their resolution and who were wont to complain at this period that the administration was being advised on international matters by those who did not share their views, for in its understanding of the impact of atomic energy upon Russia's postwar attitudes it reflected the line taken by Bohr, Stimson, and the Franck Report; it anticipated the Acheson report in advocating that control be secured in carefully planned stages.

The first step would be to ask Russia to join Britain and the United States in urging the UN General Assembly to set up a special commission to supervise the dissemination of basic information in all fields of science, including a program of student exchange and laboratory visits. The United States, argued Bush, would doubtless permit publication of basic research in any case, and such an offer would provide an easy and effective test of Russia's willingness to co-operate. During the second stage of collaboration, information relating to industrial applications would be exchanged according to a previously agreed schedule and in conjunction with a UN inspection system. The final stage, which Bush warned would come only after long negotiation and trial, would see atomic weapons outlawed and atomic power devoted exclusively to commercial uses.

On Wednesday, November 7, Bush discussed the memorandum with Truman; the following day, in company with General Groves, he talked it over with Byrnes. Bush's outline was accepted as the basis for the United States' contributions to the talks that began the following Sunday as Truman and his guests sailed into Chesapeake Bay aboard the "Sequoia."

---

[24] Bush's contribution to this stage of international control planning was first made public in 1962; what follows is based upon The New World, pp. 459–69.

The Sunday papers carried long dispatches from Washington on how opinions were shaping up on control in general, on inspection, and on Russia's willingness to accept inspection.[25] No official statement on the Sunday talks was issued, but Monday morning's papers were full of reports, among them a seemingly authoritative one that Attlee had offered a plan for sharing the bomb through the agency of a strengthened United Nations, although, as Amrine had warned the delegates, he was also described as pessimistic about the success of inspection.

Secretary Byrnes and Admiral William D. Leahy had attended the Sunday meeting with Truman. Monday morning Bush was informed by Byrnes that, press reports to the contrary, there had been no Attlee offer; Byrnes and the President had submitted the Bush plan, and it had been readily accepted by the British. Now Byrnes wanted Bush to draft a communiqué. Reluctantly, since he had not been at the conference, Bush agreed. In the course of the next three days his draft was, with some difficulty, reconciled with one drawn up by the State Department's counselor, Benjamin Cohen, and, finally, on Wednesday afternoon and at an evening conference lasting until midnight, with two others prepared by the British and Canadian delegations. Working with Bush in the final stage were Attlee's atomic energy adviser, Sir John Anderson, and Canadian ambassador Lester Pearson.

If federation delegates were privy to any of these dealings, no hint of it crept into their written reports. The official communiqué of the conference was released by Truman, Attlee, and King at the White House just before noon on Thursday, November 15. Britain, Canada, and the United States declared their readiness to initiate international action to prevent the use of atomic energy for destructive purposes and to promote its use for peaceful and humanitarian ends. Basic scientific knowledge concerning the release of atomic energy would be shared freely with the United Nations; detailed information about industrial applications would be exchanged on a reciprocal basis as soon as effective enforceable safeguards against destructive use could be devised. The three leaders urged the early establishment of a UN commission to make specific proposals.[26]

---

[25] See, for example, James Reston to the *New York Times*, November 11, 1945, sec. E, p. 3.

[26] Truman's account of the conference and the text of the joint statement are in Harry S Truman, *Year of Decisions* (Garden City, N.Y.: Doubleday & Co., 1955), pp. 538–44. The AEC historians note that the final version did not depart in essentials from Bush's original proposal although "it reflected the Department of State's natural

Members of the Federation of Atomic Scientists expressed themselves as relieved by the pacific and temperate tone of the joint statement. "It leaves all of the doors wide open," Howard Curtis told a group of laymen next day. "It doesn't take us through any doorways, but the mechanics is there and the good will is there. That is essential."[27]

The delegates tried to think that their influence could be detected in the outcome of the conference. They learned with satisfaction that Senator McMahon had taken their resolution to the White House early Thursday morning and that Truman had approved it as not inconsistent with the joint declaration to be issued at noon. It was noted that certain phrases in the resolution were used in the Truman-Attlee-King statement. In the light of Bush's direct contribution all this sounds extremely ingenuous, although, as in other instances, one must not discount entirely the influence on officials of the known opinions of a large body of scientists. As for the similarity in wording, the difficulty of achieving originality in this area was brought home to scientists that very week end when the *New Yorker* published the excursions of Mr. Arbuthnot, its cliché expert, into the fertile field of the atom and the bomb. Back in New York for an AMPS executive committee lunch at the Columbia Faculty Club, Kaplan found Present convulsed over the *New Yorker,* and together they counted some sixteen phrases from their international control resolution among Mr. Arbuthnot's clichés!

The scientists and their congressional collaborators had planned to introduce their resolution in the afternoon session of this same Thursday, November 15, but the unexpectedly early release from the White House necessitated a change of tactics. It now seemed desirable to the delegates and their advisers to make the resolution a specific follow-up to the joint statement. "We all felt," explained Rush,

that this statement carried the implication of a dangerous threat to the UNO structure, in that it might lead to the development of specific proposals for international control in advance of any basis of agreement with

concern with the mechanics of translating an idea into action. . . . The revision stated effectively the plan for starting with an exchange of fundamental scientific information, but it went further than Bush had gone in emphasizing the need for controls and safeguards prior to transmitting data on practical industrial applications. In doing so, it necessarily struck a somewhat more negative note. Yet on the whole, Bush was pleased. He thought it a good statement" (*The New World,* pp. 463–64).

[27] "Federation of Scientific Organizations Proceedings" (mimeographed), November 16–17, 1945, p. 94.

Russia; we therefore felt it desirable to shape the resolution so as to emphasize the necessity for such basic agreement as the next step in negotiations.

The upshot of these consultations was that after the White House announcement on Thursday Mrs. Douglas informed the House that she was holding her resolution for further study. The scientists' resolution with its endorsements was released at a Friday afternoon press conference in Mrs. Douglas' office, with Rush and Francis Bonner of the AMPS as spokesmen.[28] The gist of the resolution, which was intended to supplement, not to criticize, the three-power statement, was

that the President of the United States immediately invite to a conference the Governments of Great Britain and the Soviet Union, in order to discuss the common danger created by atomic weapons, and to plan for the joint approach by these three nations to the other members of the United Nations Organization to the end of establishing a system of international cooperation and control of atomic energy which will prevent a competitive armaments race, safeguard world peace, and make available to all peoples the peacetime benefits of atomic energy; and

That any domestic policy instituted by the President and the Congress of the United States for the control and development of atomic energy should be in harmony with an international system of control and cooperation and that it should further provide for scientific freedom and the peacetime utilization of atomic energy in the interests of the whole people.[29]

Some fifteen representatives of the press attended the conference and gave it good coverage in next day's papers. The general reaction was that the scientists had done well to go further than the White House communiqué in proposing a definite course of action, and much was made of the many famous names among the signers. As usual it was emphasized that these represented over 90 per cent of the scientists who had worked on the bomb.

Mrs. Douglas postponed for a week the introduction of her version of the resolution in the House, and she and her staff conferred several times with Schimmel and federation delegates—Minett, Rush, and Swartz of AMPS—modifying the statement released by the scientists so as to make it suitable for congressional endorsement. Domestic

    [28] Report of Rush to AORS, November 8–19, 1945, AORES II, 2; *New York Times*, November 17, 1945, p. 4.
    [29] As printed in the *Congressional Record*, 79th Cong., 1st sess., 1945, XCI, Part 8, 10942.

aspects of the problem were subordinated to international, partly to please Los Alamos but also in the hope that it would go to the friendly Foreign Affairs Committee, which was more likely to report favorably on it than the Military Affairs Committee.[30]

The scientists also helped draft the speech with which Mrs. Douglas introduced her resolution to the House on the afternoon of Friday, November 23. Either the federation delegates had shifted their ground slightly during the preceding week or Mrs. Douglas disagreed with them on two points, for she was outspokenly critical of the Truman-Attlee-King statement, and she did not share their concern about congressional tenderness for the United Nations.

Yet her speech clearly reflected their influence. The three-power declaration, she confessed to the House, had been a disappointment. She agreed with its principles; she recognized the concern of its authors for peace and human welfare; but with the best possible interpretation, she declared,

it falls short of the necessity of this hour.... If the joint statement had been issued immediately after the two great explosions over Hiroshima and Nagasaki it would have been received as a great document. But in the months of silence that followed, voices whispering, "We have a secret. We will share nothing. It is our sacred trust. The only thing the world understands is force," have been allowed to grow until they have become dangerously loud.... We are at the crossroads. If we now even seem to rely upon force instead of friendship we will have set our feet on a dead-end street.

A UN commission, as suggested by the President and the prime ministers, was no substitute for direct consultation between the heads of state, and therefore her resolution, like that of the scientists on which it was based, called for a conference with the Soviet Union. At the suggestion of Representative Sabath of Illinois, she asked to have the scientists' resolution, as well as her own, inserted with the list of its signers into the *Record* itself (rather than into an appendix, as originally intended), and this was ordered without objection. Speeches supporting the resolution were made by Voorhis and Holifield of California and Ramey of Ohio.[31]

Mrs. Douglas' resolution went, as she hoped, to the Foreign Affairs

---

[30] Reports of Rush and Koshland to AORS, AORES II, 2; Minett to AEOR, AORES XV, 5; Los Alamos Newsletter, No. 4, November 13, 1945, and No. 7, December 4, 1945, ALAS II, 19.

[31] *Congressional Record*, 79th Cong., 1st sess., 1945, XCI, Part 8, 10940–45.

Committee. The administration had thus far given no public indication that it intended to engage in further international discussion of control prior to the first meeting of the UN General Assembly in January, but it later turned out that on November 23, the day that Mrs. Douglas spoke to the House, Secretary Byrnes cabled Moscow suggesting a pre-Assembly meeting of foreign ministers; from this followed a Russian invitation and the foreign ministers conference that convened in Moscow on December 15.[32]

Meanwhile federation delegates were not neglecting their similar undertaking in the Senate, but on the day the House resolution was presented, Trischka noted in the office journal that Senate action at the moment would embarrass the administration and the State Department. Almost daily contacts were maintained, however, by Trischka and Richard Lyon of AORS with the senators who had promised earlier in the month to sponsor a resolution—Tobey, Morse, Smith, Taylor, Downey, Fulbright, and Kilgore. In a conference with Tobey, Morse, Smith, and Taylor on Tuesday, November 27, it was agreed that before the resolution was introduced the administration should be asked to state its intentions.[33] Consequently, two days later, on Thanksgiving morning, a bipartisan delegation (Smith, Tobey, Taylor, Saltonstall, and Kilgore) went to the White House to ask what efforts, if any, had been made to include Russia in the recent conference with Britain and Canada. Introduction of the resolution would depend upon the President's answer. Again there was a close connection between display of congressional interest and State Department action. A matter of moments before the senators arrived Byrnes dispatched a tentative conference agenda by cable to Moscow. Byrnes himself, it is said, had consented to initiate the meeting in the hope of dealing with outstanding European problems, but on the agenda he proposed on November 29 atomic energy was the first item.

The President told the Senators enough about administration plans to make the Senate resolution superfluous, and before the House Foreign Affairs Committee acted on the Douglas resolution the Moscow conference was announced. The calling of this conference was only a first step on the long road to international control, but for

---

[32] For an account of the diplomacy and domestic politics relating to the Moscow conference and preparation of the United States position on control, see *The New World*, pp. 469–77.

[33] FAS History-Diary, entries for November 23, 25, 27, 1945, FAS files (Washington, D.C.).

those scientists who had long believed that no progress could be made without settling some basic points with the Russians it was a significant victory. "There is no question," reported the federation newsletter with an air of smug satisfaction, "but what the political activities of the scientific associations and the Federation have been instrumental in the atomic control question being on the agenda at this meeting."[34]

Fuller acquaintance with the background of the Russian talks does not undermine the federation's claim that the interest its members had stimulated in Congress had been an important factor in bringing them to pass. Federation scientists had little direct connection, however, with a second step urged upon Byrnes as the autumn of 1945 drew to a close—the preparation of a United States proposal for an international atomic energy authority—though they regarded it as essential and were particularly concerned with the manner of its implementation. Here the center of activity was, as it should have been, the State Department where Benjamin Cohen, coauthor of the Truman-Attlee-King communiqué, and Leo Pasvolsky, described as the chief architect of the United Nations, persuaded Byrnes to authorize the formulation of specific atomic energy proposals as part of the preparation for the January meeting of the UN General Assembly. Early in December a panel began to work on this project, in which the chief participants were Acheson's assistant, Herbert Marks, Carroll Wilson, Bush's assistant at OSRD, and Joseph R. Johnson, chief of the State Department's Division of International Security Affairs. H. D. Smyth and Oppenheimer served as consultants.[35]

A working paper was completed by this group on December 10 just before Byrnes left for Moscow. The guide lines it provided for Byrnes lent themselves to different interpretation from the procedure outlined in the three-power declaration, implying that relatively uncontroversial steps such as exchange of students and scientific personnel might be taken without waiting to resolve more difficult problems and indicating a readiness to discuss more than basic scientific information. Groves and Forrestal strongly objected to this working paper on grounds of security and mistrust of the Russians, and it also alarmed some senators to whom Byrnes showed it because,

[34] FAtS Newsletter, December 12, 1945, FAS XV, 8.
[35] *The New World*, pp. 470–77.

from the paper's flexible tone and Conant's presence in the Moscow delegation, they feared that release of technical information was contemplated.

While Byrnes was in Moscow Truman and Acheson were faced with the job of placating Connally, Vandenberg, and their associates, who were still smarting from exclusion from the Truman-Attlee-King talks, a task that became easier as the Russians consented to sponsor a UN atomic energy commission without demanding concessions in other areas. But the stormy reaction to the working paper impressed upon the President and his advisers the need to put the making of policy into the hands of a high-level, broadly representative group, and early in January Byrnes appointed a special committee under the chairmanship of Undersecretary Dean Acheson to formulate a control plan.

It would be presumptuous to suggest that men in the State Department who had helped to devise the United Nations required prodding from scientists to think about atomic energy in world terms, and in any case strong stimuli had been provided by Oppenheimer and Bush. Federation contacts with State Department planners were certainly not decisive and can scarcely have accomplished more than to underline the support that existed among scientists for a system of control based upon inspection.

CHAPTER 6

Aims and Allies

D URING THE FIRST two weeks in the Washington office the international control resolution had competed for attention with the problem of how to utilize assistance—both volunteered and solicited —from scientists outside the Project and lay organizations. To capitalize on the interest generated by the May-Johnson bill and the site statements on international control a meeting was called in Washington for Friday and Saturday, November 16 and 17, with the double purpose of organizing an enlarged scientists' federation and telling the lay groups what they could do to help.

The latter proved by far the simpler task. The public relations experts attending the second University of Chicago conference at Rye, New York, in late October had recommended that lay organizations form a national co-ordinating committee and use their existing facilities to disseminate whatever information the scientists thought the public ought to have. Michael Straight, editor of *New Republic*, undertook to initiate this step and, with the help of interested individuals in Washington, organized a meeting at the Mayflower Hotel on the afternoon of Friday, November 16, to which forty-nine organizations, with memberships totaling over ten million people, sent representatives. They came from Catholic, Jewish, and Protestant churches, from labor unions and farmers' groups, from the League of Women Voters, the National Negro Congress, the National Lawyers Guild, the General Federation of Women's Clubs (with 16,500 local groups), and the American Council of Learned Societies. It was, indeed, as Newman and Miller later observed of the scientists' following, "a large and variegated army, which it would have been difficult to unite in any other cause."[1] Some of the organizations had supported the federation's international control resolution; fifteen or so had issued their own statements about atomic energy. With the Reverend Francis W. McPeek of the Council for Social Action of the Congregational Christian Churches serving as chairman, scientists outlined what they thought needed to be done: Richard Present spoke about the magnitude of the atomic energy problem, Howard Curtis about the scientists' solution—international control—and John Simpson about the educational programs of the local associations.

An observer from the Office of Scientific Research and Development caustically summed up the reaction to the scientists' remarks as "the Atomic Bomb is just too dreadful, too awful, too-too-too— Everybody must do something about it quick. What are you doing? What am I doing? We must all get together right away and do more";[2] but the transcript seems to belie this picture of Helen Hokinson club women wagging their fancy hats in helpless dismay, giving, in fact, a contrary impression of common sense efficiency. What the OSRD visitor's comment did reflect was a feeling among government scientists that their colleagues temporarily engaged on the bomb were overly excited about atomic energy and too little concerned about long-range research problems. The AEC historians credit the federation leaders with great sagacity in isolating this naïve enthusiasm in a separate organization, but the only motivation revealed by their own records was a desire to unload a burden that they could never have carried.

Agreement on procedure was easily reached, and the National Committee on Atomic Information was promptly established. Daniel

---

[1] James R. Newman and Byron S. Miller, *The Control of Atomic Energy* (New York: McGraw-Hill Book Co., 1948), p. 11. Used by permission of the publisher. A transcript of this meeting is included in "Federation of Scientific Organizations Proceedings" (mimeographed), November 16, 1945, pp. 76–138.

[2] Report in OSRD files, as quoted in Richard G. Hewlett and Oscar E. Anderson, Jr., *The New World, 1939–1946* (University Park: Pennsylvania State University Press, 1962), pp. 447–48 (referred to hereinafter as *The New World*); the meeting took place on Friday, not Sunday, as stated in *The New World*.

Melcher, a former employee of the Treasury Department, was appointed director and with a small staff shared the new quarters to which the federation moved just before Christmas. Consultation with the committee took some of the scientists' time in the next few weeks, but they were dealing with people far more experienced than themselves in techniques of organization, and on the whole the initial phase of this collaboration went smoothly.

The scientists' own meeting of what was tentatively called the Federation of Scientific Organizations had had an opening session earlier in the day at George Washington University. The four original members of the Federation of Atomic Scientists were each represented by two or more delegates, with E. E. Minett speaking for the two engineers' associations. Seven other groups (distance from Washington and the short notice limited the number attending) sent delegates or observers.[3]

With Higinbotham as chairman the Friday morning session opened with informal remarks from John Simpson on the lessons of the past weeks in Washington. Delegates had learned to be cautious in associating with groups that might want to use the federation to further their own ends. Congressmen were favorably impressed by the scientists' apparent disinterestedness, and care must be taken in the handling of such questions as freedom of research so that congressmen would not come to regard them as just another pressure group. This was not, declared Simpson, an organization for scientists, and they should expect no benefit from wearing themselves out in Washington beyond that received by every other individual in the world. Washington and the public arbitrarily defined an atomic scientist as

---

[3] The participating groups and their representatives were the following: Association of Los Alamos Scientists (W. A. Higinbotham, J. W. Trischka); Association of Philadelphia Scientists (John Jacobs, P. H. Miller, Jr., W. E. Stephens); Science Society of Washington (M. C. Leikind, Philip N. Powers); University of Rochester Atomic Group (Robert Boche); Association of New York Scientists (P. L. Hartman); Association of New York Scientists and American Association of Scientific Workers (Melba Phillips); Atomic Scientists of Chicago (John Simpson, A. H. Jaffey); Rocket Research Group, Allegany Ballistics Laboratory (Howard Higbie, J. B. Rosser); Association of Cambridge Scientists (Arthur Roberts); Association of Manhattan District Scientists (C. D. Swartz, Francis T. Bonner); Association of Atomic Scientists, Dayton (William Argersinger); Association of Oak Ridge Scientists, Clinton Laboratories (H. J. Curtis, Russell R. Williams, Jr., M. D. Peterson, J. H. Rush); British Commonwealth Scientific Office (M. F. Day); Atomic Engineers of Oak Ridge and the Atomic Production Scientists of Oak Ridge (E. E. Minett). The Friday morning session is reported in "Federation of Scientific Organizations Proceedings" (mimeographed), November 16, 1945, pp. 3–75 g.

one who had worked on the bomb, not realizing that many Project scientists knew less atomic physics or chemistry than some outside; and although this false prestige was embarrassing, it should, perhaps, be exploited while it lasted for the honorable purposes of the federation. The release of atomic energy was not the first, nor would it be the last, major scientific event to affect society and politics, and scientists should consider the need for some farsighted group to study and publicize the broad issues that result from scientific work.

Progress reports from the four charter members of the federation (Chicago, Los Alamos, Clinton, and SAM) were supplemented by comments from Robert Boche of Rochester and William Argersinger of Dayton, representing small Manhattan Project research units with embryonic organizations that hoped to join the larger federation. At Rochester, said Boche, tight security was still in effect, and he could say only that workers there were chiefly biologists, biophysicists, and physiologists concerned with human beings rather than with material for the bomb. At the urging of Clinton Labs discussion of the amended May-Johnson bill had been attempted, but all had been too ill-informed to evaluate it properly. An organization of effective size at Rochester would have to include social and political scientists.

At Dayton the group was drawn from two small research units at Monsanto Chemicals with a technical staff of about a hundred, reported Argersinger, who then went on to tell the usual story: a few individuals, sharing private worries had found a large measure of agreement and, as their numbers increased, had sent a statement with thirty-seven signatures to members of Congress and friends urging full consideration of atomic energy problems and endorsing the international control statements of other groups. Dayton scientists wanted to emphasize long-range questions such as federal support of basic research, but Argersinger had doubts, which proved well founded, about the future of the Dayton group, for the most active members would soon return to academic jobs or were members of the Special Engineer Detachment who could not speak freely.[4]

Chief spokesman for the "non-atomic" scientists at this meeting was the chairman of the Cambridge association, Arthur Roberts, a tall, deceptively solemn figure whose fame among scientists as composer and librettist has overshadowed his contribution to the federation and perhaps even his solid achievements in physics (recordings

---

[4] Argersinger's report was made on Saturday morning (Federation of Scientific Organizations Proceedings [mimeographed], November 17, 1945, pp. 139–44).

of "The Cyclotronist's Nightmare," "How Nice To Be a Physicist," and "Take Away Your Billion Dollars" provided his colleagues with a salutary medium for laughing at themselves and their predicament in the heady days that followed Hiroshima).

It was the domestic issue, Roberts reported, that had first brought the Cambridge group together, and although it still seemed important, the international problem had top priority. Therefore, to the study and action programs outlined by other groups they had added co-operation with scientists of other countries to promote peace and understanding. Roberts was gratified by the stature of those serving with him on the executive committee, which included J. H. Van Vleck, P. W. Bridgman, and J. Curry Street of Harvard, Ivan A. Getting of M.I.T., Louis N. Ridenour of the University of Pennsylvania, and Louis A. Turner of Princeton. Other committees were functioning, and requests for speakers were coming in at the rate of three a day. The Radiation Laboratory, which had provided the core of interested people, would be virtually closed by the first of the year, but with the physics departments at Harvard and M.I.T. alone providing two hundred potential members, continuing activity seemed assured. (The Cambridge Association did, indeed, almost disappear at the end of 1945 but revived quickly as staff reorganizations took place.) Cambridge visualized a rather loose federation and until it existed had strong objections to a federation of atomic scientists speaking for all scientists. There were, he said, more nuclear scientists in the Radiation Lab than in the Manhattan Project, and even if they did not know how to make an atomic bomb, they felt competent to tell people that something ought to be done about it.

Testimony to the strong appeal of the atomic scientists' position also came from the Association of Philadelphia Scientists, whose mushroom growth had been observed with satisfaction in the federation office. However, said W. E. Stephens, despite a keen interest in international affairs and the hundreds of signatures obtained against the May-Johnson bill, there did not seem to be in Philadelphia the inclination to tackle the big job of public education proposed by the atomic scientists' groups; for the time being they would educate themselves and provide a means of expressing opinions.

Like the other non-Project groups in Cambridge and Philadelphia, the Association of New York Scientists had had its impulse in opposition to the May-Johnson bill, in connection with which its formation has already been noted. Its representative, Melba Phillips, also spoke on November 16 for the Association of Scientific Workers, a few of whose members, as in Philadelphia, had helped to organize ANYS. The AAScW, Miss Phillips reminded her listeners, was only three years old when its members began working sixty and seventy hours a week on war research, and their effort to stimulate interest in the social problems of science was only now being resumed. AAScW leaders had observed with satisfaction the spontaneous growth of the scientists' organizations and hoped that those who viewed the release of atomic energy as a special crisis would eventually take an interest in the broad social implications of science.

The Friday afternoon session also provided contact with a branch of research whose relevance to atomic weaponry was not yet fully acknowledged. Scientists working on rocket propellants at the Allegany Ballistics Laboratory at Cumberland, Maryland, hoped to contribute to a national federation, said Howard Higbie, by their relatively greater freedom to speak. Their knowledge of rockets might also be useful, for apart from the little man with the grand piano under his arm— a nice variation on the atomic bomb in the suitcase theme—rockets seemed to be the ideal method of delivery. (No one commented that before this day arrived atomic bombs would have to be much smaller and rockets far more powerful.) On the question of how scientists might be brought into the making of foreign policy, the Rocket Research Group had consulted people in Washington, including Vannevar Bush. Other rocket groups at the Bureau of Mines and at California Institute of Technology stood ready with support.[5]

M. C. Leikind spoke on behalf of thirty or forty scientists, mostly in government employ, who the previous spring had formed the Science Society of Washington to discuss problems that cut across the specialized interests of existing societies. In the beginning, said Leikind, probably none of them knew about the atomic bomb; they had been observing with interest the activities of the other groups and wished to follow plans for the national organization.

Recessing Friday afternoon for the session with the lay organizations, the scientists convened again Saturday morning at 9:30 and talked almost continuously until past ten o'clock that evening about aims, composition, nomenclature, finances, representation, and other details of organization. The sixteen people who took part were of

---

[5] A. I. Kassiakoff to H. Davies, October 19, 1945, copy in ALAS IV, 1.

comparable age and professional status, and there was no "big shot" present to push them in one direction or another as they touched on points that would be vigorously debated within their own circle in the months ahead as well as on larger questions relating to the scientists' position in public affairs.[6]

The most time-consuming task was the formulation of aims. The atomic scientist delegates flatly refused to join an organization for any purpose other than furthering world peace through international control of the atom. Others did not want to participate unless they could also champion freedom of science and promote the peaceful use of atomic energy and a national science foundation. Happily, there were two points of agreement. All those present wanted to distinguish their organization from other peace groups by emphasizing the particular contribution that scientific knowledge, freely acquired and exchanged, and scientists' experience in international co-operation could make. (Admittedly, this required delicate handling, for as Roberts pointed out, scientists themselves might think they had a particular potential for peace but to many people at the moment they appeared to have a rather marked potential for disaster.) And everyone recognized scientists' responsibility to promote the national welfare. But in the listing of aims, should national welfare precede or follow the search for a durable peace? And was it necessary to say what national welfare meant?

On the question of a concentrated or a broad program, the debate stalled for some time. Howard Curtis of AORS vigorously opposed dissipating energies on anything but international control. Twenty years hence, he said, when the main objectives were pretty well achieved, would be time enough to go off in other directions. Roberts upheld the opposite view. "If your groups want to work primarily on world peace," he said, "that is fine; . . . but if our group is particularly interested in freedom of speech and science and seeing to it that . . . [when] we get a world government . . . scientists are not all working behind locked doors, I think we ought to be permitted to work on that." What seemed to unite the two factions, observed Philip Powers of the Washington Science Society, was a realization of the need for informed opinion throughout the country; each group could determine its own emphasis. Thus reminded of their initial excuse for organizing, the delegates accepted study and dissemination of information as a basic aim.

---

[6] The Saturday sessions are reported in "Federation of Scientific Organizations Proceedings" (mimeographed), November 17, 1945, pp. 139–269.

But those who had been working in Washington had some qualifications to add. John Simpson admitted that the federation had intentionally failed to be explicit; the phrase "study and dissemination" had been adopted with an eye to the tax collector's interest in the line between educational and lobbying organizations. Studying, he explained, could mean observing individuals and working with them; and disseminating information could include giving it to congressmen in Washington. J. H. Rush, who was to become the federation's authority on tax-exempt status, added that they must not abuse their present influence by making statements without a sound factual basis. They could say that certain facts about the bomb indicated the need for control by an international agency; they could not prescribe what control mechanism the United Nations should employ. It was as well that the delegates did not try to thrash the subject through to a conclusion, for the dividing line between educational and political activities provided a thorny problem for federation leaders for months to come, and the distinction between scientific fact and political application that looked so simple in the autumn of 1945 had within a decade acquired complicated moral and political overtones.

What is remembered as the really hot issue of this week-end meeting was freedom of science. Was it possible to make clear its relevance to international understanding without appearing to be motivated by professional self-interest? Did they, in fact, all regard it as equally important? Two speakers had heard it said in recent weeks that atom bomb scientists underplayed freedom of research because they wanted to maintain their monopoly of nuclear information. This charge was, of course, indignantly denied by delegates from Project laboratories with renewed explanations of their fear that demands for relaxation of secrecy would be regarded as self-seeking and provoke further restrictions. Evidently, discussion of this issue spilled over into informal bull sessions, and a not always clear-cut division of opinion is remembered between those like Roberts (mindful of the recent declassification of Radiation Lab research), who wished to designate freedom of research as an end in itself, and the more disenchanted Project scientists, especially those from Los Alamos, who recognized that, however loud their clamor, a substantial body of information would remain classified for the foreseeable future. What could be declassified, they argued, should be held in reserve for the bargaining over international control.

Finding a formula to cover a situation about which few scientists felt entirely comfortable was a ticklish business, but by the evening session the aims had been resolved into four ways of furthering world peace and the general welfare: disseminating information, establishing free intercourse among scientists, and co-operating with scientists of other countries and with other organizations.

Regarding the composition of the new federation and the qualifications of individual members, it was readily agreed that effectiveness would rest upon members' ability to speak authoritatively as scientists and that policy should be determined only by organizations containing members of comparable scientific maturity. These limitations had to be reconciled with the need for an organization large enough to impress policy-makers and to carry on the educational campaign.

The new federation would have a council of about seventy-five representatives, based on the number of members in affiliated groups. An administrative committee elected by the council would work with the Washington office, where it was hoped that a scientist would be in charge full time.

In naming the organization the overtones of each word were considered. National was eliminated in favor of American, and council and congress in favor of federation; references to natural scientists and engineers were dropped. The name tentatively chosen was American Federation of Scientists.

Pending final acceptance of these arrangements, fund-raising would be carried on in the name of the Federation of Atomic Scientists, which was nearing the end of its $1,000 from the Atomic Scientists of Chicago and had begun looking for other benefactors. Meanwhile local associations would contribute to the central treasury on the basis of $5.00 per dues-paying member. A rough talley of the organizations represented gave a total of nearly three thousand members. This meant about $15,000 from dues but was a long way from the $64,000 that the Federation of Atomic Scientists had estimated as its annual budget.[7]

Conclusions reached in all these areas—aims, membership, structure, and finance—were circulated among interested local groups as a proposed charter. When ten associations had accepted it, the new

---

[7] The membership estimates were as follows: Los Alamos, 300; Chicago, 200; Clinton Labs, 170; Y-12 and K-25 at Oak Ridge and the gaseous diffusion unit at Columbia, 600; Cambridge, 300; ANYS, 500; Philadelphia, 500; Rochester, 75; Dayton, 100; Allegany, 80; Washington Science Society, 100—which totaled 2,925 ("Federation of Scientific Organizations Proceedings" [mimeographed], November 17, 1945, pp. 243–45).

federation would come into existence. Although only seven had done so by the time of the formal organization meeting, seventeen delegates representing twelve associations turned up at George Washington University on December 7 and 8.[8]

Acting as a constitutional committee the delegates reviewed the November 17 proposals and revisions offered by local organizations, first changing the name from American Federation of Scientists to the Federation of American Scientists, then discussing aims on the basis of a draft that Philip Morrison and Robert Bacher had prepared for ALAS. Again the chief question was whether to advocate unrestricted freedom of scientific communication. A solution was found in a phrase usually attributed to Morrison: "to safeguard the spirit of free inquiry and free interchange of information without which science cannot flourish," and next morning the aims were unanimously accepted by the delegates.

Time and referral to the local associations had not watered down the November proposals, as one might expect, but had both strengthened and extended them. Incorporated into the constitution, which included a preamble recognizing the increasingly apparent responsibility of scientists for welfare and peace and the need for them to assume a more active political role, were the aims of the federation:

1. In the particular field of atomic energy, to urge that the United States help initiate and perpetuate an effective and workable system of world control based on full cooperation among all nations.

2. In consideration of the broad responsibility of scientists today, to study the implications of any scientific developments which may involve hazards to enduring peace and the safety of mankind.

3. To counter misinformation with scientific fact and, especially, to

---

[8] Delegates to the FAS organization meeting, December 7–8, 1945: W. A. Higinbotham (chairman), Association of Los Alamos Scientists; Hugh C. Wolfe, Association of New York Scientists; Alexander Langsdorf, Jr., Atomic Scientists of Chicago; Philip N. Powers, Science Society of Washington; Melba Phillips, Association of New York Scientists; Herbert I. Fusfeld, Association of Philadelphia Scientists; Theodore Hauschka, Association of Philadelphia Scientists; Philip Morrison, Association of Los Alamos Scientists; Victor Weisskopf, Association of Cambridge Scientists; John Beek, Jr., Rocket Research Group, Allegany Ballistics Laboratory; Edwin M. Larsen, Dayton Association of Atomic Scientists; Arthur M. Squires, Atomic Engineers of Oak Ridge; David R. Goddard, Rochester Section, Federation of American Scientists; Hans A. Bethe, Association of Los Alamos Scientists; Joseph Rush, Association of Oak Ridge Scientists; André deBethune, Manhattan Project Scientists at New York; Frank R. McClure, Rocket Research Group, Allegany Ballistics Laboratory; and observers from the Canadian Association of Scientific Workers. Condensed minutes of this meeting, with copies of the Constitution, Federation of American Scientists, December 8, 1945, and by-laws, December 19, 1945, are in FAS I, 1, and other files.

disseminate those facts necessary for intelligent conclusions concerning the social implications of new knowledge in science.

4. To safeguard the spirit of free inquiry and free interchange of information without which science cannot flourish.

5. To promote those public policies which will secure the benefits of science to the general welfare.

6. To strengthen the international cooperation traditional among scientists and to extend its spirit to a wider field.

We shall endeavor to keep our members informed on legislative proposals and political developments which affect the realization of our aims, and to cooperate with other organizations in the achievement of these aims.

Other provisions of the constitution required that the aims of member associations be in accord with those of the federation, and that the local groups have at least twenty-five members, two-thirds of them with a bachelor's degree or its equivalent in the natural sciences, mathematics, or engineering, and engaged in research, development, administration, or teaching in these fields.

The constitution was completed by the middle of Saturday afternoon. The two New York associations, Los Alamos, Philadelphia, Rochester, and the Allegany rocket group were prepared to accept it at once, and since it required no minimum number of ratifications, the delegates of these six immediately became the council of the new federation. Inviting the other delegates to participate, they elected Higinbotham, Wolfe, Fusfeld, and McClure as a temporary administrative committee to circulate the constitution, bring in new groups, arrange for the next council meeting on January 5 and 6 in New York City (in connection with an American Physical Society meeting), and get the office operating with the existing Federation of Atomic Scientists' facilities but in such a way as to aid rather than interfere with its program.

An announcement of the new federation was released to the press at the conclusion of the meeting on December 8. Thereafter there existed, for a few months actively and for somewhat longer nominally, two federations, known among scientists themselves as the FAtS and the FAmS, a double identity that occasioned no small confusion outside the ranks and, as we shall see, some tension within.

CHAPTER 7

Atomic Scientists
December, 1945

THE SIX WEEKS between the first planning session for the Federation of American Scientists and the commencement of its actual
operation in early January, 1946, were by no means an idle time for
its parent organization or barren of significant developments. Late
November and December saw the emergence of new atomic energy
legislation, progress in the study of inspection by the Federation of
Atomic Scientists, and a tremendous expansion of obligations and
contacts. The original federation, having no officers or administrative
committee, continued to depend upon waves of transient labor. The
delegates who attended the November 16 and 17 meetings, still fully
articulate after two days of steady debate on principles, motivations,
and objectives, held their usual Sunday policy meeting the following
evening and turned to day-to-day tactics and deportment, renewing
their pledges to keep publicity to a minimum, to stick to the main
objectives, to keep themselves above the level of politics, and to observe the niceties of Washington etiquette. John Simpson noted these
worthy resolutions in an office journal which he began next day and
in which successive site representatives made entries more or less
regularly for the next five months.[1]

---

[1] FAS History-Diary, November 19, 1945; final entry April 10, 1946, FAS files
(Washington, D.C.).

1. EXPLORATION

But if guiding principles remained unchanged some readjustments were indicated by what the delegates learned of shifting attitudes on Capitol Hill. They observed a decreasing emphasis on the thesis that domestic legislation must precede international negotiation and a growing recognition of the need for further congressional investigation. There appeared to be no specific opposition in Washington to the federation program, but for that very reason political advisers now counseled restraint. Having done a good job in stalling the May-Johnson bill, they should now hold their fire and concentrate on the educational program. Their disclaimers to knowing all the answers had at first mystified the politicians, but it had been a mark in their favor that they were not pushing alternative legislation. In sum, the consensus was that the associations and the federation should proceed at a slower pace; they should be ready to give aid to congressmen, not try to badger them into agreement.[2]

But a resolve to remain non-political did not fix the line between supplying information and political pressure. The empirical handling of the international control resolution had highlighted this problem, and it was further explored in the policy meeting on November 18. The situation as the delegates then saw it was summed up for the Atomic Engineers of Oak Ridge by E. E. Minett:

Legally the Federation may be considered a non-lobbying, and therefore non-profit organization as long as it does not take the initiative in appearing before hearings on legislation. What is required is that we be asked to testify. The feeling was that as long as scientists had useful and reliable information to dispense ... we would be called upon to do so since the existence of the Federation is by now well known throughout Washington. ... We can consider approaching individual members of Congress or Senators without incurring disfavor. We can also make definite proposals up to the resolution stage but even here it is desirable that we sow the seed of an idea so to speak, allow the resolution to be written, and then when called upon, issue our suggestions as to possible modifications. ... Definitely, no one was in favor of the Federation or its Associations suggesting even an outline for proposed legislation, i.e., actual bills.

This renunciation was made easier no doubt by knowledge that McMahon committee counsel James Newman and Byron Miller had the draft of a new and more acceptable bill well in hand. The way

---

[2] Report of Minett to AEOR, ca. November 20, 1945, AORES XV, 5; AEOR general meeting minutes, November 20, 1945, AORES VI, 7; AORS executive committee minutes, November 26, 1945, AORES I, 6.

was now open for return to the original scheme of priorities, with international control and education at the top of the list. This meant contributing wherever possible to the exploration that the Senate special committee was about to undertake, organizing FAmS, providing guidance and material for the National Committee on Atomic Information, and extending commitments and contacts in any direction that offered an outlet for information or an inlet for funds.

The effort to cultivate useful friends, concentrated at first upon Capitol Hill, was now at the end of the autumn months branching out in many directions and bringing the federation in touch with numerous men of good will operating in and around the fringes of government. What the scientists learned from each new acquaintance bulked large in their reports.[3] Sunday lunch at the Pinchots' on November 18 for Swartz, Simpson, Trischka, and Rush developed points of common interest with several guests. Gifford Pinchot, Jr., shared their enthusiasm for bringing together scientists from many countries; a British diplomat fresh from seventeen months in Russia described the Russian people as touchy on the surface but amenable to an understandng approach; George L. Bell, director of foreign trade in the Department of Commerce, was much interested in aspects of inspection; and Mrs. Bell, with whom this lunch provided one of the first contacts, would later become a staunch ally of the scientists in their fight for civilian control.

Delegates dropped in at the weekly teas at the Office of Scientific Research and Development, and Higinbotham in particular began developing some useful perspectives on the federation's position. People in industry, he learned, felt their contributions to the bomb were receiving too little attention; and chemists thought physicists took too much the center of the stage.

Taking the pragmatic approach to public relations, the delegates spoke to any group of Washingtonians that would listen. Their November circuit included invalid soldiers at Fort Belvoir, the Methodist Ministers Association, the Federation of Government Workers (AF of L), the Women's League for Peace and Freedom, and over ward loudspeakers, patients at Bethesda Naval Hospital. Watson Davis of Science Service offered its outlet to five million readers and as a starter interviewed three delegates on CBS. Nor did the scientists

---

[3] Unless otherwise indicated material in this section is drawn from entries in the FAS History-Diary or from the FAtS newsletters for November and December, 1945, in FAS XV, 8.

do all the talking themselves. "In the late evening hours in our hotel rooms," John Simpson wrote later, "we could many times be found writing speeches for prominent citizens and officials in Washington, who were anxious to present an intelligent discussion of atomic energy."[4]

Although travelers returning from Europe reported greater concern with food and fuel for the coming winter than with the atomic bomb, which was considered an American sensation, the renewal of foreign contacts was felt to be vitally important and was discussed whenever opportunity offered. Dr. Alexander King of the British Scientific Office reported progress in his correspondence with societies and individuals about a world scientific congress and a world-wide charter of principles, and federation encouragement was given to Harlow Shapley in negotiating for such a congress at the forthcoming UNESCO meeting to which he was the United States delegate.

Determination not to offer specific plans for international control did not preclude co-operative study of the subject, and on November 26 several delegates joined Urey and Szilard in a conference in Washington with James T. Shotwell, professor of political science at Columbia, and Clark Eichelberger, associated with Shotwell on the Carnegie Endowment's Committee to Study the Organization of the Peace, and were invited to help plan a Carnegie sponsored conference on control measures in New York at the time of the January FAmS council meeting. These conversations were continued next day with officials at the State Department. The federation was also represented at a large New York dinner of the newly amalgamated Americans United for World Organization on November 28.

Opportunities for the pooling of skills and experience with social scientists were followed up. The Society for the Psychological Study of Social Issues offered to help with writing and research; the Rockefeller Foundation's Social Science Research Council proposed consultations; and the Department of Agriculture asked the federation to co-operate in its program to educate farmers in science and international relations.

Many of the new contacts were well-known commentators and journalists like Edgar Ansell Mowrer and Frieda Kirchway. Joseph Alsop met Urey and the younger scientists at a reception that followed a United Nations forum and took them all home for an impromptu

---

[4] Simpson, "Scientists in Washington," *University of Chicago Magazine*, XXXIX (November, 1946), 5.

discussion afterward. ("Interesting and apparently influential," noted one of the young men.) And there were the staff writers sent by the big magazines and networks to get a story. Frances Henderson of *Time*, Beirne Lay of *Life*, Sam Shaffer of *Newsweek*, and Tris Coffin of CBS took a keen interest in the federation, became friendly with the less temporary delegates, and though their findings were not always used immediately, had a good deal to do with the federation's generally satisfactory press in the months to come.

The delegates saw a lot of Shaffer and his photographer during the week of November 19, and on December 3 *Newsweek* devoted a section under "National Affairs" to what it christened "The Reluctant Lobby," with subtitles, "Babes with an Atom" and "In the Washington Woods." There were pictures of the current crop of delegates, looking, said *Newsweek*, more like college sophomores than the popular conception of men of science. "Some sport crew haircuts, tab collars, and bow ties. They know as much about politics as congressmen know about nuclear physics. Controlling no blocs of voters, they compel attention because they are the men who attached a detonating device to the basic power of the universe and stopped a war dead in its tracks."[5]

The self-effacing delegates, who had needed five hours' persuasion to pose, were Trischka and Higinbotham from Los Alamos, C. D. Swartz and Edward Adler from New York, and Russell Williams and Merlin D. Peterson of Clinton; their ages ranged from Peterson's thirty-six to Williams' twenty-five. John Simpson from Chicago managed to avoid the photographer. A list of Ph.D. theses and articles with incomprehensible titles helped to build up a picture of men highly qualified for some job other than the one at hand. "Their lack of political know-how," *Newsweek* reported,

complicates their task. Pleased whenever a legislator listens sympathetically, they fail to consider whether he controls any vote besides his own. Often, the congressmen who have been won over are approached the next week by new delegates who do not know their predecessors have been over the same ground. . . . When asked whether they have been "to the Hill," they think the questioner is referring to the laboratory at Los Alamos. . . .

These political gaucheries, probably contributed by the delegates themselves, merely lent interest to an otherwise favorable picture of young men driven by a strong sense of moral responsibility and de-

---

[5] The Reluctant Lobby," *Newsweek*, XXVI (December 3, 1945), 42.

termined to reject the "you-help-me, I'll-help-you" kind of deal customary in Washington.

The wholehearted absorption in an unfamiliar task made some observers downright sentimental. "Those who visited the Federation's original headquarters on Vermont Avenue," wrote one visitor, ". . . were confronted with a test-tube of unadulterated democracy. The organization had no president or chairman, because nobody wanted to be czar. The members came to Washington, not to get something, but to give something—to give the most precious commodity in existence: knowledge." Without salary, without a publicity director, without political know-how, without staff or office equipment, without Pullman reservations, and without arrogance, they had come, bringing knowledge, sincerity, patience, humility, and a desire to perform a public service.[6]

Not all these euphoric reactions got into print, but still the delegates who had figured in the *Newsweek* article felt uncomfortable about the effect of their notoriety on the boys back home, and the "Newsletter" tried to set things right:

Such publicity as the *Newsweek* article is painful to us but it is necessary. In the first place, we have sufficient news value that we will be written up anyway so we should cooperate and try to get the best possible treatment. We know that the factual information which we distribute is true and that the conclusions we urge are based on sound judgment. We have to compete with fakes, misinformation and poor logic. To give authority to our expressions we must invite favorable publicity.

2. WAYS AND MEANS

But "unadulterated democracy," so moving to a casual visitor, was a trying atmosphere in which to work. "My strongest impression after a week in Washington," Rush told the AORS executive committee when he got back to Oak Ridge about November 20, "is of the urgent need for one competent man to head our office there and for delegates to stay longer than one week whenever possible. No one has been in position to oversee the activities there and to develop the 'feel' for the whole situation that is so important for continuity of effort."[7]

An attempt was made at the November 18 meeting to rectify the situation by dividing responsibility between John Simpson and Willy

---

[6] "Chain Reaction among Scientists," by Beirne Lay, Jr., manuscript in Simpson's files.

[7] Report of Rush to AORS, November 8–19, 1945, AORES II, 2.

Higinbotham, both of whom had arranged several weeks leave of absence. Simpson was to reorganize the office and establish more consistent practices in making contacts and meeting the press; Higinbotham would concentrate on setting up the expanded federation. But this division of duties was no sooner made than Simpson found his time fully taken up with testimony and reports for the McMahon committee, and Higinbotham took over the management of the office, about which he again unburdened himself to friends back at Los Alamos. It was hard to describe the troubles, he said; everybody was trying to do ten times as much as he could, and all of it seemed essential, with every day a constant stream of reports, interviews with influential people, requests for information; the secretary could scarcely keep up with the phone. Last week there had been eight delegates, now six, tomorrow five.[8]

Two days later Higinbotham wrote more cheerfully. They were looking for new office space and for more secretarial help. The search for funds, which he himself had carried to New York, promised results. Once the international control resolution was introduced into Congress they would not offer to help on such matters until they had more manpower; visits to congressmen and influential people would be continued but not emphasized. Obtaining and distributing information from the sites would be put on a more businesslike basis.

Then just as order seemed in sight the secretary's departure caused a relapse, and for several days papers went unfiled, letters unanswered, and communication with the sites broke down. A raw set of delegates had recurrently to be shown the ropes. According to Daniel Lang, a newly arrived scientist would climb the several flights of stairs, look around in bewilderment while he caught his breath, and gasp, "I'm Dr. So-and-So from Columbia. What do I do?" A stenographer would call, "Fellow here from New York. Got anything for him to do?" And Higinbotham would shout back, "Tell him to go over to the Unitarian Church tonight. They want a speech."[9]

F. C. Armistead of K-25 at Oak Ridge, viewing the chaos with an engineer's eye, drew up a chart of man-days spent by delegates during his tour of duty from December 10 to 15—the only extant record during the entire autumn of who was there at a given time—and concluded that the trouble was not lack of ability but shortage of

---

[8] Higinbotham to Lennie [Jossem], November 21, 1945, ALAS II, 18.
[9] Daniel Lang, "A Reporter at Large," *New Yorker*, XXII (November 16, 1946), 76–87.

people and lack of a plan of operation. The job required, he thought, not one full-time scientist but four, one as administrative head and front man, the other three as executive, editorial, and legislative assistants.[10]

No one paused for breath long enough to use Armistead's efficiency survey, but new office space at least provided more elbow room. This had been the object of considerable search. The Vermont Avenue quarters were crowded, and rooming with the Independent Citizens Committee did not square with the determination to avoid close entanglements with other organizations. Independence likewise prompted refusal of one of the Pinchots' fifty-four rooms and of space in a diocesan building offered by another friend, the Right Reverend Angus Dun, Episcopal bishop of Washington, although Kaplan, who spent a lot of time on the office hunt, recalls that fear that noisy arguments late into the night might seem lacking in dignity to the Pinchots' friends and the Bishop's staff was also a consideration.[11]

A new office was finally found at 1621 K Street—a good location but a mediocre building—and a six-month lease obtained at $100 a month. Alex Langsdorf from Chicago supervised the purchase of furniture from government surplus and the application of paint in time for moving day on December 22. The federation had two offices and a conference room in front and the NCAI a large office in the rear. Again more businesslike operations were confidently predicted.[12]

The confusion that stemmed from shifting personnel and reluctance to establish a line of command was compounded by inability to hire enough help. The federation was indeed operating on a shoestring in these early weeks. Member associations, although paying no direct levy, contributed substantially by paying the expenses and making up the salaries of their representatives out of local dues and contribu-

---

[10] Report of Armistead to AEOR, ca. December 15, 1945, AORES II, 2. Armistead's chart of delegates present during the week of December 10 was as follows:

Delegates	Monday	Tuesday	Wednesday	Thursday	Friday	Saturday
Simpson (ASC)	x	x	x	x		
Higinbotham (ALAS)	x	x				
Trischka (ALAS)	x	x	x	x		
Jaffey (ASC)	x	x	x	x		
Ferminhac (AORS)	x	x				
Williams (AMPS)	x	x	x			
Weinberg (AORS)	x	x	x			
Armistead (AEOR)	x	x	x	x	x	x
Rush (AORS)				x	x	x
Swartz (AMPS)				x	x	

[11] Interview with Kaplan, April 3, 1962.
[12] Report of Ralph Ferminhac to AORS, ca. December 11, 1945, AORES V, 2; FAS Newsletter, January 3, 1946, FAS XV, 8.

tions. The on-leave-without-pay status of the delegates that had so impressed reporters on November 8 had been worked out with each laboratory director. Monsanto, for example, allowed Clinton Labs scientists to count trips to Washington as laboratory business, and AORS accepted the time off but not with salary. However, it was not considered out of line for individuals going east from Oak Ridge, Chicago, or Los Alamos on professional business to fit in speaking engagements, interviews with congressmen, and bull sessions on federation policy. Los Alamos had the most expensive travel problem, which Higinbotham, who was a bachelor with inexpensive tastes like folksinging and square dancing, solved for ALAS by staying in Washington for many months without salary. Those with family responsibilities often had to ask their executive committees for travel advances and overdue salary replacements.[13]

The federation was able to function during November only by virtue of the $1,000 passed along by the Atomic Scientists of Chicago out of their $10,000 grant from Chancellor Hutchins. This paid four weeks' salary for the secretary and a phone bill of $700. The Allegany rocket group sent $50 to help defray expenses of the November 16 organization meeting. The only other November income, and the federation's first unsolicited gift, was five dollars from a young social scientist in Berkeley who wished to show his satisfaction at the scientists' organizing for political and social action. His name was Richard L. Meier, and two years later he succeeded Higinbotham as executive secretary of the FAS.[14]

Things looked a bit brighter in December. The William Volker Charities Fund in Kansas City contributed $5,000; a *Collier's* article, written by Amrine and signed by Urey, brought in $1,500, and other contributions totaled $150. A second $5,000 came from the Carnegie Endowment for International Peace. About $700 went into rent, repairs, and office equipment, $400 for office salaries, and just over $1,000 for expenses and salaries of scientific personnel, it having been decided midway through the month that the federation could now pay travel expenses, hotel bills, part of salary replacements, and a $2.50 daily allowance for cabs and the like. The back phone bill was paid, and $374 spent in recording the meetings on November 16 and 17. This left a balance of $3,925.48 to start the new year, a nest egg

---

[13] Henshaw to Whitaker, November 9, 1945, AORES II, 2.
[14] Meier to FAtS, November 14, 1945, and Simpson to Meier, November 23, 1945, FAS XIX, 2.

that complicated the absorption of the FAtS into the larger federation.[15]

3. LEADERSHIP

Fortunately, the Federation of Atomic Scientists had some positive assets to balance financial and other handicaps. Chief among these, John Simpson thought, was that they were of one mind about the ultimate objective, with no personal axes to grind. And scarcely less important was the quality of support and counsel they attracted in official and unofficial Washington, in press and radio, and in other academic disciplines.[16] But if the youth and earnestness and even the anonymity of those who ran the federation had a certain value in outside contacts, the absence of a recognizable hierarchy required some internal adjustments. The delegates of one site organization were often unknown to the others until they met in Washington. Clinton Labs and Chicago felt that Higinbotham was pushing the FAmS too vigorously, while the ALAS leaders perhaps took his confidences about confusion too literally and underestimated what he and his associates were accomplishing. Concluding that the atmosphere of the Washington office was not conducive to farsighted planning, two members of ALAS proposed that one or more eminent scientists serve full time in Washington to think about atomic energy problems. All political activity to date, they said, has consisted in giving science education to congressmen who are sympathetic or neutral; it has involved no political thinking. We need, they argued, a more aggressive lobbying group to press our views upon government officials, especially upon the President who seems to be subject to pressure from those who do not share our views. One of the federation planners should be Oppenheimer because his strong convictions on important subjects agree with ours; we respect his judgment; he is qualified to analyze political as well as scientific problems; he is a logical and convincing arguer, better acquainted than most scientists with the ways of Washington.[17]

Thoughts on how to improve or save the FAS were to be a dime

---

[15] FAtS financial statement, December 1945, in Rush's files; wire Simpson to Brues, December 6, 1945, ASC XXV, 4. The December financial statement does not mention this Carnegie grant, but a summary of December 17, 1945, in FAS XVII, gives a total income of $12,655, "mostly from foundations."

[16] Simpson, "Scientists in Washington," *University of Chicago Magazine*, XXXIX (November 1946), 3–8.

[17] Proposal from H. Polevsky and I. Block, November 28, 1945, ALAS III, 2.

a dozen in the next few years. This one received no more than passing notice, but the imbalance on the side of youth that inspired it was the subject of a good deal of comment and even misrepresentation. The early site organizations, J. H. Rush observed, were not really the juvenile uprisings they were represented to be; young men predominated because they predominated in the Manhattan Project. Actually, during the war it had been the senior men who took the lead in developing and expressing ideas on implications and use of the bomb. On continued military control it was Allison who spoke out, and Urey, Condon, and Szilard who went to Washington—all then in their forties and early fifties. But when it came to organizing for continuing action, it was the young men who moved decisively. They organized the local associations and they ran the Washington office, where during November there were twenty-three delegates at one time or another, ranging in age from twenty-three to forty-three; only six were thirty-five or older, and most were between twenty-nine and thirty-two.

This does not include Urey who was always helpful but did not spend much time in the office or take a systematic part in planning for the federation. It does not include Condon, who was a Project consultant but not attached to a laboratory where a site organization developed. Nor does it include Szilard, who, though on the ASC executive committee, was not an official delegate. In any case Szilard was the antithesis of the organization man, even of an organization so loosely conceived as the Federation of Atomic Scientists, and it was characteristic of him that having provided a spark he was now off on new tangents, making fresh contacts in New York and Washington. Some of them proved useful to the federation, but he was not in the usual sense its leader or even at times an entirely co-operative member, and the younger men, much as they valued his help, learned to accustom themselves to not knowing how he was presenting their case or when he was taking off after some quarry of his own. "He was a great objector to other people's statements," says one of his admirers, "but he seldom consulted us about his own." It became a byword around the office that to reduce the Russians to helpless confusion it would only be necessary to parachute Szilard into Moscow.[18]

In all the site organizations the senior men served as elder states-

---

[18] Interview with Higinbotham, October 18, 1961; Rush to the author, March, 1964.

men: on advisory committees, in fund-raising, and in speaking. Eugene Wigner often went from Princeton to New York for meetings of the Association of Manhattan Project Scientists and, making no particular fuss about his participation, gave the young men a feeling of strong support. Urey was for some months the movement's most effective publicist. In large numbers the elder scientists went on record as opposed to the May-Johnson bill or in favor of the goals of the federation, as on the impressive roster of names appended to the international control resolution.[19]

It is true that two distinguished physicists, Enrico Fermi and Ernest Lawrence, were part of that 5 to 10 per cent of Manhattan Project scientists whose support the federation did not claim. Although always ready to put their knowledge at the service of the government, these two men held aloof from, or in the case of Lawrence even discouraged, participation in an organization of scientists for non-scientific ends. In Fermi's case the aloofness pertained only to his personal conduct, for wherever he was, conversation about the role of science and policies on which it had a bearing was likely to flourish and to be brought into perspective by his realistic and not illiberal approach.[20]

In his story of the Manhattan Project General Groves makes some provocative comments on the character of the scientists' movement:

... There had been, and continued to be, widespread public discussion about how the U.S. should conduct its atomic affairs. Much of the written material and the most vocal of the various protagonists took what would be called the liberal position. In general, they wished the United States to proceed with full confidence in the Russians and with good will toward all mankind. They also claimed, most erroneously, that the success of our project had been due entirely to international science, and implied that the United States had no particular rights in the matter.

---

[19] Interview with Kaplan, April 3, 1962. To one query about the attitude of older, well-known scientists, ALAS replied by citing the support of George Kistiakowsky (the eldest and not quite forty-five!), Hans Bethe, Robert Bacher, Kenneth Bainbridge, Donald Kerst, Cyril Smith, and Robert Oppenheimer himself (E. L. Jossem to G. Cowan, November 1, 1945, ALAS IV, 5).

[20] Mrs. Fermi, in a private communication to the author, explains that her husband did not join the movement because his experience under dictatorship had convinced him that international control, desirable as it was, was a hopeless cause so long as Russia remained a closed country. Of those who did campaign for international control, a number had also experienced dictatorship; others, both in the federation and outside—Bush, Conant, Oppenheimer—were scarcely more optimistic than Fermi about agreement, working for it only because the alternative seemed so grim. They differed from him only in recognizing a very remote chance that Russia might regard control as sufficiently desirable to open the door a little way. It seems to me that willingness to take part in the movement was a matter of temperament. Fermi's friends and admirers understood and respected his independence in this matter.

Unfortunately, the scientific leaders of the project who normally would have been the spokesmen for their colleagues were preoccupied then with getting back to their peacetime occupations at their own universities and I have always felt that they simply did not realize what was developing. The result was that a new and vociferous group of spokesmen arose from among the younger scientific people, few of whom had had any experience outside the academic world, and who even there had served in only very subordinate capacities. There were a few others, of course, some of whom sought personal prestige and some of whom wished to forward extreme social points of view. The propaganda emanating from these sources was eagerly seized upon by various ambitious political figures, and by a few people in the State Department who seemed to me more concerned about the momentary good will of other nations than about the welfare of the United States.[21]

There is nothing in this estimate of which one cannot say, "Well, of course that is the way it looked to Groves." But it is not true that the older men did not know what was going on. As we have seen, A. H. Compton and Oppenheimer were in almost daily touch with what was being said and done at Chicago, Oak Ridge, and Los Alamos in the early autumn. They did indeed counsel restraint and on some points differed openly with their younger colleagues, but in their hearts they understood and sympathized. As for what might be called the next lower echelon of senior scientists, one can think offhand of numerous instances of co-operation that went far beyond general expression of support: Warren Johnson's taking the Clinton Labs protest to the Interim Committee to Chicago for signatures; the help given by Bethe, J. R. Zacharias, Allison, and Teller in the drafting of the first Los Alamos "document"; many letters in the files— personal explanations directed to a particular group or individual—on the need for international control and the federation stand. These things indicated not only an awareness of what was going on but an involvement in it, too.

Grove's charge of seeking personal prestige is an easy one to make in any context and an almost impossible one to refute. Although he mentions no names, it is no secret that the three older men who had, so to speak, led the march on Washington were not favorites with

[21] Leslie R. Groves, *Now It Can Be Told* (New York: Harper & Bros., 1962), p. 410. In view of the animosity displayed toward him by some federation scientists in the months after the war, Groves's restraint is remarkable; he is doubtless aware that his forthright defense of Oppenheimer in 1954 divested him of his villain's robes and produced such a wave of admiring gratitude among his erstwhile foes that probably no one of them has uttered unqualified criticism of him since.

Project administrators. Condon's rebellion against security in refusing to remain with the Los Alamos project in its early stages had not been forgotten. Szilard's attitude on security and other procedures had made his superiors constantly uneasy or annoyed; and Urey's impulsive outspokenness had kept him out of the inner councils of the Project, where many of his colleagues thought he ought to be.

And "extreme social points of view" is a meaningless concept unless one defines the center line. If there were people in the Project site organizations whose views seemed extreme to Groves, it would only be because he had approved their clearance and had supposedly been satisfied that youthful left-wing connections had been firmly severed. One of the few individuals in this category has since remarked that they, by virtue of their earlier experience, were the conservatives in the federation. So great, in fact, was the determination of the leaders of the organization to avoid being tarred with a radical brush that they risked internal charges of injustice and intolerance by dismissing questionably connected employees and by spurning affiliation with groups that might have been helpful to their program. A very large proportion of the "new and vociferous spokesmen" are now solidly entrenched in the most respectable academic and industrial establishments, hold responsible posts in the AEC administration, or direct research at the national laboratories at Oak Ridge, Los Alamos, Argonne, or Brookhaven and without any appreciable re-orientation of social philosophy.

If the older men were for the most part in agreement with the goals of the federation, why then did they not become its leaders? I. I. Rabi is quick and firm in his answer. "They didn't need us," he says. "They were doing just fine, and we older men would have spoiled the show. I was all for them," he added, "and I wish the young scientists would go to Washington and do it again."[22] The older scientists usually gave the quite legitimate excuse of pressing responsibilities either for winding up a wartime project or, as Groves suggested, for organizing some new peacetime job. But one must suppose also a certain psychological hurdle. It was harder for those over forty to change their ways; they were willing to abandon the traditional (if often in history, inoperative) detachment of their profession and speak to a particular issue, but to form an aggressive pressure group, as the younger men were prepared to do, meant too radical a departure from an established

[22] Interview with Rabi, March 4, 1962.

pattern of behavior. Despite the hard work in conditions of rather marked discomfort, the Washington enterprise had about it something of an adventurous, if very high-minded, lark, and this held considerably less appeal for their elders, who had had enough professional makeshift and adventure during the war to last them for quite some time.

And finally, though the demand for leadership was to be a recurrent one—and though the failure of the scientists' movement to accomplish more dramatic results is now attributed by some people to the lack of it—one cannot but speculate as to what would have happened had one of those "eminent scientists" stepped into the federation office, however tactfully, to mastermind activities there. The suspicion displayed toward the army and the scientific "brass" at Chicago and Oak Ridge and the devoted but wary attitude at Los Alamos toward Oppenheimer's influence make the answer fairly obvious. It would have been vigorously resented, and the point is not without significance for those both within the profession and outside who periodically regret that scientists do not always present a united front. It is easy to make a good working team of people whose work depends as much upon collaboration as does scientific research; it is not easy to make docile followers out of those whose professional success depends upon independent evaluation of evidence.

The scientists' movement was predominantly masculine for the same reason that it was predominantly youthful, because men far outnumbered women on the scientific staff of the Manhattan Project and the other wartime laboratories. They joined the local associations in proportion to their numbers, and several of them were extremely active: Maria Mayer with the SAM group in New York, then with the Atomic Scientists of Chicago; Hoylande Young and Katharine Way in Chicago and Miss Way later at Oak Ridge; Joan Hinton, who came from ALAS to the ASC; and Jane Hall, who was a member in Chicago before going to Los Alamos, where she served on the executive committee of ALAS. The only woman who played a prominent part in the national organization was Melba Phillips, one of the organizers of the Association of New York Scientists, who worked in the Washington office two or three days each week for the first six months of 1946.

CHAPTER 8

Toward Control

THE CENTRAL THEME of the scientists with whom this study is concerned was that the old concepts of defense, either by destroying the attacker or by monopolizing superior weapons, were no longer valid and that the only way to prevent a nuclear arms race was to establish a world-wide atomic authority. That they sometimes talked as if technical data supported both halves of this proposition exposed them to the charge of claiming more for scientific knowledge than it could legitimately bear. If their rhetoric was sometimes faulty, their procedures were sound; and having given wide currency to the idea of international control through manifestoes and resolutions, they turned to technical studies of how control might be carried out in the hope that feasibility would provide a persuasive argument for it.

1. THE FEASIBILITY OF INSPECTION STUDY

Those who made preliminary contacts with international planners brought back to their site organizations requests for more specific information. So did the delegates who talked with congressmen about the international control resolution in early November. What evidence did they have, congressmen kept wanting to know, that control was feasible? At what points between mine and bomb or power plant could inspection take place? Wariness in offering advice to politicians began to break down, and it was with a certain relief that scientists turned from offering vague generalities to the American public to a

253

task more suited to their training and talents, a study of feasibility of inspection and control.

By way of preparation those in Washington urged the local associations to consider the general question and to solicit opinions from senior men, among whom Fermi and Oppenheimer had already expressed themselves as believing that control merited the most serious consideration.[1] From the federation office they pursued their own investigation as opportunity offered. In addition to their conference on November 13 with Cockcroft and Peierls from Britain, the delegates made contact with those to whom they guardedly referred as some people with experience in detecting scientific installations in Europe before and after the end of hostilities, meaning members of the Alsos mission then being disbanded in Washington. They were, of course, fascinated by this first authoritative glimpse of the extent of German atomic progress, fear of which had provided a major argument for their own work on the bomb. They were also interested to learn that ordinary spies had proved ineffectual for ferreting out technical developments and that the most useful information about what the Germans were doing had been turned up by engineers who knew what to look for. The delegates concluded that specially briefed college graduates in chemistry, physics, and engineering could adequately man an international inspection system and that it would not require a large corps of top-level scientists.[2]

These consultations furnished substance for the memorandum that the delegates prepared during the week of November 12 in the hope of a White House interview, and although it never served its original purpose, it proved a useful base for their own further thinking about inspection. It listed possible inspection points: control at the mines of uranium ore and beryllium, and checks on critical materials (such as graphite, heavy water, and even stainless steel and nickel), large construction jobs, production plants, and scientific and technical personnel. It suggested that some legal means be found to encourage technical people to report violations in their own country. It recognized that the success of any proposals for control depended upon political arrangements for free access and co-operation.[3]

---

[1] FAtS Newsletter, I (November 14, 1945), FAS XV, 8.
[2] Report of Jaffey to the ASC, November 8–17, 1945, ASC IV, 10. On the Alsos mission, see Samuel A. Goudsmit, *Alsos* (London: Sigma Books Ltd., 1947), and Leslie R. Groves, *Now It Can Be Told* (New York: Harper & Bros., 1962).
[3] Report of Jaffey to the ASC, November 8–17, 1945, ASC IV, 10.

This was about as far as a general statement could go, and at their policy meeting on November 18 the delegates decided to inaugurate detailed studies of the feasibility of inspection at successive stages of the several processes, hitherto employed or envisioned, in the production of atomic weapons. This could only be done by those with access to classified material, and some way would have to be found to make the studies useful to policy-makers, but altogether it was a project that fitted admirably within the declared purpose of the federation, to study and inform.

John Simpson, who with Arthur Jaffey had conceived the idea, was put in charge of its execution as part of his assignment as the federation's liaison man with the Senate special committee that was preparing to open hearings on November 27. The proposal was promptly converted into a formal request from Chairman McMahon for classified reports on inspection and for an unclassified summary of their contents.[4]

There is not good documentation in the scientists' own files for what some now consider to have been their most constructive contribution to international control, for Simpson made initial arrangements by phone or personal contact and with a few exceptions the reports themselves are still classified. Simpson originally planned three types: (1) classified reports on various phases of international inspection; (2) unclassified reports based on them that would be discussed at all the sites and integrated into a single report by a federation committee, with added studies of mining, personnel, and other topics on which Project scientists were not qualified; (3) an integrated classified report by a specially cleared committee of scientists, engineers, and administrators.[5] This integrated classified report was in the end taken over by a special War Department committee in accordance with a recommendation made by the federation.

Simpson left the assignment of topics to the local associations. He asked for first drafts by December 11, with classified material going to him at the Met Lab since there were no facilities for keeping it in the federation office. He worked out the program in collaboration with E. U. Condon, scientific adviser to the McMahon committee, and

---

[4] FAS History-Diary, November 29, 1945; FAS files (Washington, D.C.); FAtS Newsletter, I (December 1, 1945), FAS XV, 8; *Bulletin of the Atomic Scientists*, I (February 1, 1946), [8].

[5] Simpson to all FAtS executive committees, January 11, 1946, in *Bulletin of the Atomic Scientists* files.

again consultations were direct and unrecorded. The one exception is an undated memorandum, distributed to member associations about December 10, entitled "Proposal for Submitting Information to the McMahon Committee concerning the Feasibility of International Inspection of the Utilization of Atomic Energy,"[6] which described the two weeks of hearings held thus far as seeking answers to two general questions: (1) Is it technically feasible to set up a system of international inspection and control to prevent the manufacture of atomic bombs? (2) If control is feasible, how soon must such a system of inspection and control be put into effect? The memorandum emphasized that because of compartmentation of knowledge on the Project no one man, except General Groves, had access to all information needed for an informed answer to these questions, and warned that

a variety of unreliable answers will be the principal result of asking these general questions of witnesses who have not had detailed knowledge of all the pertinent facts. The questions must be answered individually for each project and for each phase of the individual projects: research, engineering development and design, and operation.

(This was tactfully presented as prediction, but it was already a matter of observation that the first series of hearings was producing very little in the way of illuminating information or insights for the guidance of the Senate committee.)

After outlining his scheme of reports Simpson suggested expert study of the possibility of detecting illegal operations in seven types of plants: isotope separation by gaseous diffusion, thermal diffusion, electromagnetic process, and centrifugal separation; production of plutonium; manufacture of bombs; and production of power from which diversion of fissionable materials for bombs might be taking place. The classified reports should be detailed, and all members of a writing team should have access to all material. Much of this work could be done by the six affiliates of the Federation of Atomic Scientists working independently; the one on the prevention of illegal diversion of materials would need the assistance of Los Alamos scientists familiar with the amount and purity of materials necessary for bombs, but collaboration between them and other groups was not permitted under existing army regulations. If a co-ordinating committee for the integrated classified report was appointed promptly, it could simplify

---

[6] ASC X, 7, and other files.

its own task by advising those who were working on the detailed studies.

Here by implication the problem of compartmentation was extended from the field of research, where scientists had already pointed out its stultifying effects, to that of policy-making. At a fairly early stage in the evolution of a control plan, it was necessary to restrict what might have been a useful exchange of ideas and delegate this collective thinking to a committee. Unhappily, time has only magnified the problem, and on many crucial matters, opinion that might contribute to solutions is disqualified through limited access to information.

Simpson invited the non-Project groups about to affiliate with the Federation of American Scientists to write reports on such topics as rockets, radar jamming, and checks on personnel.[7] It is not clear whether there was any response to this and the classified reports remained essentially a FAtS project.

While waiting for the special studies to be completed, individuals and groups were encouraged to formulate general statements on the feasibility of control. At Clinton Labs a paper entitled "Universal Atomic Energy Control Program" reached only an experimental draft.[8] In Chicago Rabinowitch framed a general statement on technical feasibility, which appeared as an editorial in the second issue of the *Bulletin of the Atomic Scientists of Chicago* on December 24.[9]

Discussion of the general problem continued also in the Washington office, and a three-page statement on "Feasibility of International Inspection of Atomic Energy (Technical Aspects)"—the lineal descendant of the memorandum prepared for Truman—was distributed to the local associations on December 10 with the instructions for preparing the special reports.[10] This concise summary drew on many kinds of Project experience to suggest surveys needed and materials, processes, equipment, and laboratories to be inspected. The idea of "an international laboratory staffed with top-flight men working on the problem of atomic energy, to try to insure that no single nation could get ahead in developing new methods which may make inspection procedures obsolete," made its appearance. The human compo-

---

[7] FAtS memorandum, December 17, 1945, FAS II, 9.

[8] "Universal Atomic Energy Control Program," by R. R. Edwards and J. R. Raper, copy in *Bulletin of the Atomic Scientists* files; ASC executive committee minutes, November 13, 1945, ASC VI, 12.

[9] *Bulletin of the Atomic Scientists*, I (December 24, 1945), [1].

[10] FAtS memorandum, December 10, 1945, in *Bulletin of the Atomic Scientists* and other files; printed with minor changes in the *Bulletin*, January 10, 1946, and identified as the Federation of Atomic Scientists' preliminary attack on the control problem.

nent was considered from three angles: checks on training and employment, the use of personnel to report violations, and the liberal exchange of scientists and information as a preventive measure against clandestine activity. The familiar points were stressed, that the problem of inspection and control was primarily political and that under current limitations an integrated study of feasibility was impossible. The longer the delay in setting up a control system, the harder it would be to make it effective since technical processes tend to become more efficient and plants smaller; hence violations would be easier to hide.

With this summary of informed opinion as a guide, work went forward on the classified and unclassified reports on special topics, though less rapidly than Simpson hoped. Few papers had come in by his original deadline of December 20, and for the next month urgent reminders and promises were exchanged with his local deputies. The date for final drafts was put off until January 18, with the expectation that unclassified versions would be available at all sites for discussion a few days later.[11]

One of the first to be completed was an unclassified seventeen-page statement dated December 5 on the "Feasibility of Inspection of the World for Plants for Concentrating Uranium 235 by Gaseous Diffusion," by Manson Benedict of the Atomic Engineers of Oak Ridge at K-25.[12] With two young colleagues, Cuthbert Daniel and Arthur Squires, Benedict had recently become interested in applying statistical methods to the problem of accounting for materials and to the determination of how many samples of uranium and U-235 would be needed to indicate to inspectors what was going on.[13] Not all their findings could be included in the unclassified FAtS report, but Benedict offered the conclusion that diversion of U-235 could be prevented only by careful inspection of the plant and by continuous accounting of the U-235 in the material received for treatment. If a sufficiently elaborate system of overlapping inspection was instituted,

---

[11] A meeting of site representatives to work on the composite unclassified report was proposed for January 26–28, but I have found no record of it (Simpson to all FAtS executive committees, January 11, 1946, in *Bulletin of the Atomic Scientists* files). The information about the reports that follows is culled from minutes and memorandums and is not necessarily complete; nor do references to work in progress always indicate whether a given report was to be secret or unclassified.

[12] Copy in AORES XIX, 1.

[13] Interview with Benedict, September 13, 1962.

it should be possible to detect the construction of a gaseous diffusion plant, but one built before controls began could be made very difficult to detect. With encouragement from an international organization, said Benedict, scientists and engineers could be useful in suggesting the existence of unauthorized operations. "If international control of atomic energy becomes the expressed policy of all the major nations, these men will be among the first to realize that they can serve the whole world as well as their own nation by the widespread exchange of technical workers and ideas."

From K-25 also came a report by F. C. Armistead on the centrifuge process. At Y-12 Chauncey Starr of APSOR wrote one on electromagnetic separation. Lyle Borst and Jack Kyger were working at Clinton Labs on reports on the plutonium process and metal refining. At the SAM Lab Clarke Williams, Elliott Montroll, and I. Kershenbaum were in charge of studies of gaseous diffusion, thermal diffusion, and heavy water plants.

At the Met Lab Glenn Seaborg, Arthur Jaffey, L. I. Katzin, J. R. Gilbreath, and H. H. Hyman worked on a chemicals separation report, with Seaborg undertaking to draw the various parts of it together. By January 16 a non-classified version of this report was ready: "Feasibility of International Inspection of Chemical Processing Plants Associated with Piles Using or Manufacturing Fissionable Materials.[14] A physics report was assigned to a committee, with A. Wattenberg and A. S. Cahn doing the actual writing.[15]

At Los Alamos by the end of November Leonard Schiff and Jerome Wiesner had completed an unclassified report on "Countermeasures and Defenses," and David Hawkins and Vernon Cannon, one on the mechanism of control, probably also unclassified, as both were available in the ALAS office.[16] These would seem to belong in the category of general statements requested by Simpson for use by scientists testifying before the McMahon committee and may also have been used by those who drafted the general analysis of December 10.

Los Alamos was also responsible for more comprehensive and probably classified studies of inspection. In response to an urgent wire from Higinbotham, E. L. Jossem replied on December 4 that one of these was still "cooking" with Eldred Nelson, Cannon, and the "big shots"

[14] Copy in ASC IX, 1.
[15] ASC executive committee minutes, January 5, 1946, ASC VI, 12; Jaffey to Simpson, January 16, 1946, ASC IX, 1.
[16] Los Alamos Newsletter, No. 6, November 27, 1945, ALAS II, 19.

and would include discussion of checks on personnel, mines, factories, and finished materials. It was tough to get people not to quibble, said Jossem, but he hoped the report would be ready by the week end. At the end of December Philip Morrison, Hawkins, and Nelson were working on a report on the detection of atomic bomb laboratories, testing sites, and assembly plants, and Jossem was responsible for one on the preparation of metals.[17]

Anxious as he was to get the studies finished Simpson cautioned that thoroughness was more important than haste. Those prepared at the Met Lab, Jaffey reported in mid-January, had of necessity been somewhat off-the-cuff; though useful in their present form, another month of full-time work would be needed to do a really good job. The Chicago group, said Jaffey, urged that a highly qualified man from each site be assigned to devote full time to the inspection problem for the next few months.[18]

Quite likely Simpson had suggested that the ASC give an extra push to his earlier proposal for an official integrating committee. At the time Jaffey wrote, appointments to a War Department committee were being made by General Groves at the request of Senator Mc-Mahon. With Manson Benedict of K-25 as chairman, its members were Lyman A. Bliss of Union Carbide, like Benedict a specialist in the gaseous diffusion process; Chauncey Starr of the electromagnetic plant at Y-12; Spofford G. English, Clinton Labs chemist; L. W. Alvarez, R. F. Bacher, and Philip Morrison; Los Alamos physicists; Frank H. Spedding, director of the plutonium research unit at Ames; and A. B. Kinzel, a metallurgical consultant from Union Carbide. Colonel Walter J. Williams, associated with the construction at K-25, and later Colonel J. R. Ruhoff of Groves's staff, represented the army. To the federation scientists these appointments brought assurance that their inspection study would be brought to a fair and competent conclusion. Groves later told the McMahon committee that although he himself knew of no way to inspect an atomic bomb internationally he had been careful to see that proponents of international control were represented on this committee and he thought three—perhaps as many as five—members were in favor of it.[19]

[17] Wire Jossem to Higinbotham, December 4, 1945; copy in ALAS II, 18; ALAS Log, December 29, 1945, ALAS II, 2.

[18] Jaffey to Simpson, January 16, 1946, ASC IX, 1.

[19] Simpson, "Scientists in Washington," *University of Chicago Magazine*, XXXIX (November, 1946), 6; *Bulletin of the Atomic Scientists*, I (February 1, 1946), [8]; Morrison to ALAS executive committee, January 21, 1946, ALAS II, 2; U.S. Senate,

Sixteen years later neither Benedict nor Bacher remembered that the Federation had originally launched this project although they agreed that the War Department committee was given some earlier explorations of various topics to start with. Beginning in late January they spent two months preparing a report. Also hard at work was the Lilienthal board of consultants to the State Department committee charged with evolving a United States proposal for international control. The use that was made of the feasibility of inspection study by the Lilienthal board and later by the UNAEC will be discussed in a later chapter.

2. THE FEDERATION AND THE McMAHON COMMITTEE

Parallel with the technical studies, there was going on that supposedly intensive investigation of political implications by the Senate Special Committee on Atomic Energy that scientists had demanded and to which it was originally intended that their inspection reports should contribute. McMahon's appointment as chairman was very much to their liking. His committee had a strong conservative cast. For the Democrats, there were Edwin C. Johnson (Colorado), who had introduced the War Department bill, Richard B. Russell (Georgia), Tom Connally (Texas), Harry F. Byrd (Virginia), and Millard E. Tydings (Maryland); and for the Republicans, Arthur H. Vandenberg (Michigan), Warren R. Austin (Vermont), Eugene D. Millikin (Colorado), Bourke B. Hickenlooper (Iowa), and Thomas C. Hart (Connecticut).[20]

On October 28, two days after McMahon was named chairman, he summoned James Newman from the atomic energy conference at Rye and asked him to be the committee's counsel; he appointed a young lawyer, Christopher T. Boland, as executive officer. Scientists were asked to make recommendations for technical adviser, and the choice fell on E. U. Condon, who was high on all their lists. His appointment was announced with that of Newman and Boland on November 5. Lyle Borst, freshly arrived from Oak Ridge, noted in his

---

Special Committee on Atomic Energy, *Atomic Energy Act of 1946, Hearings on S. 1717*, 79th Cong., 2d sess., January 22–April 4, 1946, p. 482; interviews with Benedict, September 13, 1962, and Bacher, September 14, 1962. For corrected list of Benedict committee membership, see *Bulletin of the Atomic Scientists*, III (January, 1947), 32.

[20] U.S. Senate, Special Committee on Atomic Energy, *Hearings on Senate Resolution 179*, 79th Cong., 1st sess., November 27, 1945–February 15, 1946. *The New World, 1939–1946* (University Park: Pennsylvania State University Press, 1962), by Richard G. Hewlett and Oscar E. Anderson, Jr., makes use of Senate committee files (pp. 435 ff.; referred to hereinafter as *The New World*).

diary that evening that "the internal structure of the committee goes our way."[21]

The choice of Condon was a natural one for Newman to make in view of their contacts over the May-Johnson bill and Condon's position as director of the Bureau of Standards. If the atomic scientists, just settling their new federation in its first Washington office, had anything to do with these appointments, it happened through the satisfactory relationship developing between McMahon and John Simpson. The two men had first met at the dinner for senators and scientists on October 24. Perhaps they talked about McMahon's original atomic energy bill, which had startled the scientists with its loosely conceived generalities about national benefit and the exclusion of private interests. At any rate McMahon asked Simpson to come to the Senate cloakroom next day, where, in addition to seeing McMahon again, he talked at length to the Senator's ghost writer, feeding him information relevant to the domestic issue for a speech that McMahon was to give over NBC. A few days later Simpson had dinner with McMahon and his wife. By that time the Senator had seen the *Life* article in which Simpson, Rabinowitch, and Hill had stated their basic convictions about the bomb and was impressed with their presentation of the case.[22]

The junior senator from Connecticut became something of a hero to scientists and other supporters of civilian control, but those closest to the scene of action—though they liked him and were thankful for his stubborn advocacy—realized he was no knight in shining armor. Taking their cue, perhaps, from more experienced observers, they describe him as "one of the sharpest, smoothest apples" then on Capitol Hill and a good man not to have against you. But Newman has pointed out that although in the later stages of the campaign for the bill that bore his name McMahon's contribution was somewhat obscured by that of others, notably Senator Vandenberg, he at first "stood alone and fought alone for those essential features of the legislation that were finally upheld."[23]

With less dramatic flair and easy fluency than some of the leading

[21] Suggestions for scientific adviser from AORS and from Director Doan of Clinton Labs are in AORES III, 3, and IV, 1. *New York Times*, November 6, 1945, p. 6; interview with Borst, February 20, 1962.

[22] Interviews with Higinbotham, October 18, 1961; and Simpson, July 9, 1962.

[23] James R. Newman and Byron S. Miller, *The Control of Atomic Energy* (New York: McGraw-Hill Book Co., 1948), p. x. Used by permission of the publisher.

atomic scientists, Simpson was not, perhaps, the obvious choice to impress a smooth-talking politician. But his affability, quiet competence, and drive have proved highly effective over the years in promoting whatever cause has currently absorbed him—civilian control of atomic energy, cosmic ray research, or the International Geophysical Year—and with McMahon in November, 1945, he developed a working friendship through which he exerted considerable influence on what McMahon said in public.

Implicit in the demands for more careful consideration of atomic energy legislation had been the idea of providing congressmen with some elementary technical information. Newman outlined a program of education for the McMahon committee before it began to consider specific bills,[24] and Simpson communicated his ideas about a "college for congressmen" to the site organizations. An enthusiastic beginning was made on this adult education project on the evening of Thursday, November 8, when the federation delegates capped a busy day that had included the House caucus meeting and the press interview by attending a physics class for senators at the Bureau of Standards. Harold Urey lectured on fission; L. F. Curtiss of the Bureau staff and Lyle Borst did experiments. But the senators had also had a busy day, and even the popping flash bulbs of photographers recording the novel occasion did not keep them awake. Said Senator Connally to Condon, who was playing host, "Well, Doctor, I don't think you can expect to make scientists out of senators." "Well, Senator," replied Condon, "I wasn't counting on hiring you for the Bureau of Standards."[25]

This seems to have been the one and only formal tutorial session in which federation scientists took part although the "education" of senators quickly became a part of the legend of their accomplishments. There was plenty of conversation at the Pinchots' and on other social occasions, says Condon, and a great deal of running around buttonholing congressmen, but even his own expounding of the Smyth report during the next two weeks of closed meetings did little, he thinks, to improve the committee's grasp of the fundamentals of nuclear science. By that time some on-the-spot demonstrations seemed in order, and a trip to Oak Ridge was arranged for November 20 and 21. When word reached Oak Ridge of the senators' impending visit, rivalry developed between the scientists and the army as to which

---

[24] *The New World*, p. 440.
[25] Borst diary; interviews with Borst, February 20, 1962; and Condon, July 29, 1962.

was to get the committee's good ear. AEOR members at K-25 planned a dinner for the senators and invited representatives from Clinton and Y-12, about twenty-five scientists in all. This conflicted with army plans, but when Chairman McMahon arrived on the twentieth and was presented with the two propositions, he hastily weighed, as one account put it, a general and two colonels against a couple hundred scientists and accepted the AEOR invitation. This meant last-minute improvising of facilities and program. Charles Coryell of Clinton Labs served as master of ceremonies and, anxious that the senators receive an unforgettable impression of the bomb's destructiveness, he asked Colonel Shields Warren to talk about Hiroshima, but General Groves refused permission, saying this was on the schedule for next day. Coryell thought he had Alvin Weinberg primed to do the job, but Weinberg chose the constructive approach and spoke instead about peacetime applications. So in the end Coryell ad-libbed a description of what an atomic bomb could do to such cities as Chicago and St. Louis and warned the senators that this would be its chief use. The AORS "Daily Bulletin" reported that Coryell, with some help from others, had "badgered and drubbed the Army . . . but always on a friendly basis."

There were opportunities at dinner and again during the "official walk-around" next day for individual contacts, which were followed up with personal letters to committee members expressing satisfaction at the pleasant exchange of views and reminding the senators that the scientists with whom they talked at Oak Ridge felt that the future of civilization depended upon firm control of the military aspects of atomic energy at both the domestic and the international levels. The Oak Ridge scientists and engineers were pretty well satisfied that the right impression had been made upon the committee. They had noted with interest the presence of David Lilienthal among the official visitors, and a week later Borst, Curtis, and Davies from Clinton Labs called on him at TVA headquarters to discover what light the TVA experience might shed on mechanisms for controlling atomic energy.

The Oak Ridge dinner demonstrated, however, the dangers of indulging publicly in the kind of speculation to which scientists were accustomed among themselves. When Hans Bethe stated at a committee hearing two weeks later that a nuclear explosion would not blow up the world, he was asked how this squared with a remark the senators had heard at Oak Ridge. The Washington office immediately dispatched a memorandum to all associations urging that hereafter speakers stick strictly to facts on which they themselves were authorities or consult colleagues before speaking.[26]

Open hearings before the Senate committee began on November 27, and McMahon announced that no legislation would be considered until all the facts were known. He had good reason to prolong the study period, for at the moment the two possibilities were the May-Johnson bill, still held in committee, and the not very serious contender S.1557, which Senator Joseph Ball of Minnesota had introduced on November 5. The drafting of the Newman-Miller bill was now nearing completion, and McMahon intended that this should be the main object of committee consideration, as indeed it became after he introduced it in the Senate as S.1717 on December 20.

The first witnesses were Alexander Sachs, who had taken the Einstein letter to Roosevelt six years before, and General Groves. "The hearings in the Senate Office Building," reported Anthony Leviero to the *New York Times,*

are attracting a crowd of fascinated citizens. Kleig and flashlights flare for the camera man. The sessions are marked by touches of humor, with Senators and the public joining in the laughter, although the most calamitous past events and the terrors of the imagined future are discussed. The easy atmosphere, however, belies the serious intent of the Senate's select committee....[27]

The hearings, which were to go on intermittently for the next four months, did not always maintain this level of interest. In fact, Simpson soon became concerned about the limited news coverage they were getting outside Washington, or as he put it, "the Senators were worried" because the information they were receiving in testimony was not being adequately relayed to the public. It was important not to reflect on the committee, he wired the site organizations, as it was doing an excellent job, but all means of access to local news media should be exploited. Chicago and Oak Ridge responded promptly. The ASC got in touch with the editors of all Chicago papers, and

---

[26] Interviews with Coryell, March 17, 1959; Borst, February 20, 1962; and Condon, July 29, 1962; AORS executive committee notes, November 19, 20, 27, 1945, AORES I, 6, and II, 5; AORS Daily Bulletin, November 20, 23, 1945, AORES XX, 1; FAS History-Diary, November 21, 1945; FAtS Newsletter, November 24, 1945, FAS XV, 8; Borst to Senator Hickenlooper, November 26, 1945, AORES V, 10; FAtS memorandum to all associations, December 5, 1945, AORES XIX, 1. See also *The New World*, p. 449.

[27] *New York Times*, November 29, 1945, p. 4.

Clinton Labs sent out a hundred and fifty letters asking individuals and groups to "support" the McMahon hearings and talked personally with commentators, including Swing, Kingdon, Mowrer, and Shirer. The editorial committees of AEOR and APSOR jointly prepared articles for Nashville and Knoxville papers summarizing the testimony.[28]

Although the federation scientists must by this time have given up any thought of systematic instruction, they still had great hopes of the hearings as a platform and kept a close watch upon the pre-Christmas series. Transcripts of all testimony were supposed to be sent regularly from McMahon's office to the site organizations, where statements were to be checked and points noted for inclusion in later federation testimony that Simpson, with the help of other delegates, was preparing. He was also consulting with scientists who were testifying independently. Condon remembers very little contact between the committee staff and the young men in the federation office at this period; John Simpson says there was a great deal but all of it personal and direct. Perhaps there was no need of much, for with Condon and Newman responsible for calling witnesses it was certain that views that the federation considered sound would have a fair hearing.[29]

During this first series of hearings scientists were the principal witnesses, providing eight days of open testimony. They were Urey, Langmuir, Bush, Oppenheimer, Bethe, Morrison, Goudsmit, Szilard, and —representing the Federation of Atomic Scientists and the younger men in it—John Simpson, Clarke Williams, and Alvin Weinberg; and finally two navy scientists, Ross Gunn of the Naval Research Laboratory and Commodore W. S. Parsons, wartime head of the ordnance division at Los Alamos. The December hearings closed with three days of testimony from high-ranking naval officers and spokesmen for industrial concerns associated with the Manhattan Project.

The scientists' reticence on matters relating to domestic legislation kept the discussion where both they and the senators obviously wanted it—on general questions of the impact of atomic weapons and research policy. By the time the federation representatives appeared,

---

[28] Wires Simpson to all sites, December 5, 1945, ASC XIV, 4, and FAS XI, 7; ASC correspondence with Chicago editors, December 10, 1945, ASC XIX, 10; Bohlmann to Urey, December 11, 1945, AORES VI, 2; report of AEOR and APSOR editorial committees, December 20, 1945, AORES VI, 9.

[29] Notes on Henshaw phone call to Cohn, November 29, 1945, AORES I, 6; FAtS Newsletter, December 1, 1945, FAS XV, 8; memorandum of Ferminhac to all sites, December 4, 1945, AORES VI, 1.

those senators who took an active interest in the proceedings were clearly impressed by the gravity of the situation. They had heard much about the present and potential destructiveness of atomic weapons, the need to consider radically new solutions, and the bearing of unfettered research upon national welfare. Two topics dominated the discussion when Weinberg, Simpson, and Williams testified on December 12: What was the relation between peaceful and military applications of atomic energy, and how could one be had without the other? And what concrete steps toward international control did the organized scientists recommend?

Weinberg's prepared testimony described, as had his brief talk at the Oak Ridge dinner, the possible applications to agriculture, industry, and medicine. But, he told the senators, although his list was already long because the field was so vast, this was nothing to what it could be if scientists ceased to be preoccupied with military applications and were freed from the compartmentation that denied to nuclear engineers such pertinent facts as knowledge of the availability of uranium supplies. And exclusion of non-Project scientists from access to information, said Weinberg, had made the really original ideas that come from new blood remarkably scarce. We stood at the threshold of a new era, and yet our ideas for using the new source of power were generally much less revolutionary than the initial application of it to the bomb.

Scientists were making a great deal at this period of the bright future for peaceful applications, but this was one of the rare occasions when they said anything specific. And Weinberg, employing a simple economy of expression, turned his procession of possibilities into an argument for international control and the freedom of science. The international aspects with which previous testimony had been chiefly concerned would determine, he said, our domestic developments, for only with satisfactory controls would the United States feel free to develop peaceful uses. Weinberg did not agree with those who wanted to halt work on atomic power in order to lessen the risk of military use. "We cannot, and we must not," he told the committee, "keep atomic power in a Pandora's box—afraid to open it because we fear what might happen if it is misused. Rather we must develop atomic power, and we must develop the power to control it."[30]

Clarke Williams gave the senators a clear statement of some of

[30] *Hearings on Senate Resolution 179*, p. 339. The possibilities Weinberg had in mind had been discussed in Section V of the Jeffries Report, November 18, 1944; see Appendix A.

the problems involved in inspection, showing that if scientists were preparing to advocate it as an instrument of control it was not because success seemed easy or assured.

John Simpson's testimony related to the federation—its wartime background, the spontaneous development of the site groups, and the astonishing unanimity of their recommendations. Although it was now clear that the federation's inspection studies were not going to be suitable reading for the Senate committee, Simpson described the project that had been undertaken, he concluded deferentially, in the recognition that "the most probable solution of the overall problem rests in the hands of our statesmen."[31]

Simpson's prepared testimony, it should be noted, related not to how senators should solve the problem of control but how they could get the information necessary for decisions. His statement, like the federation's report project, lay well within a conservative interpretation of its assumed obligation "to study and inform," but the questions directed at Simpson, especially by Senator Tydings, indicated that something more was expected and exposed the dilemma that scientists would face as their contacts with politicians increased. Tydings wanted the federation to think collectively about the actual steps to be taken with reference to prohibition of atomic developments, to treaties, and to inspection. Inspection should be weighed in the context of an armaments race, on the one hand, and a partial agreement covering the licensing of peacetime applications, on the other. Senator Millikin asked in addition for a specific statement as to the point at which the United States should destroy its bombs and level its bomb-making plants. Chairman McMahon endorsed this proposal, adding that the scientists had been restrained by modesty from moving further than the inspection reports they had undertaken at his request.

Armistead sent back to the Atomic Engineers of Oak Ridge a rather gloomy report of the federation's day in court. Few senators were present, and the discussion had not been highly instructive because the senators frequently got the scientists off on irrelevant points and outtalked them. Armistead thought certain topics should not have been discussed: destruction of bombs and facilities, the arming of a United Nations air force with atomic bombs, or steps to international control.[32]

---

[31] *Hearings on Senate Resolution 179*, p. 306.

[32] Notes on a phone call from Armistead, December 12, 1945, AORES VI, 7; report of Armistead on Washington, December 10–15, 1945, AORES II, 2.

Compared with later hearings, the atmosphere in which the young scientists were questioned was friendly, even encouraging. Senator Tydings called Simpson's statement outstanding among many fine ones the committee had heard. But no one could have missed the note of warning in Senator Millikin's remarks. The scientist, he said, was in a true and not disparaging sense an internationalist because he was accustomed to meeting people from all over the world, but with his intensive specialization, he underweighted human nature and the causes of war. The committee was trying to fit together a jigsaw puzzle; both scientists and the military presented them with pieces that were too big and had to be cut down to size. He was delighted to hear what Simpson had to say, but he would have to discount it somewhat.

"The mental struggle that goes on as the committee and witnesses cope with so unusual a thesis [as the brotherhood of man] often gets excruciating for the onlooker and must be painful occasionally for the participants," observed *Times* reporter Leviero as the hearings progressed.[33] Happily, there were lighter moments, chiefly preserved in the recollections of E. U. Condon, whose ear for the ridiculous delights his admirers as much as it has annoyed his critics. "Who was that guy Lizard you had in here yesterday?" Vandenberg inquired after Szilard had testified. A cloak-and-dagger mentality sometimes asserted itself with security officers making a meticulous search of chair seats and chandeliers in the ordinary hearing room but raising no objections when a session was suddenly moved to larger quarters.

Condon recalls one harrowing afternoon when Oppenheimer, Groves, and Patterson were to testify in executive session. Trying a little compartmentation of his own, McMahon decided that Groves and Patterson should not hear what Oppenheimer had to say. "Put 'em somewhere," he said to Condon, who, using the only available space, shut them in a small document storage room with a high window and two stools. Oppenheimer, as Condon puts it, proceeded to hold the committee spellbound with his fancy triple subjunctives, and when four o'clock arrived McMahon dismissed the committee, picked up his papers, and prepared to leave. "Brien," said Condon in horror, "Patterson and Groves are still in that closet." "Tell 'em to come back tomorrow," snapped McMahon. "No," said Condon firmly, "you do it."[34]

---

[33] *New York Times*, December 16, 1945, sec. E, p. 6.
[34] Interview with Condon, July 29, 1962.

Simpson, influenced by his pleasant relations with McMahon, thinks that these early hearings accomplished something of lasting value in establishing a degree of mutual respect and understanding between scientists and politicians. It is true that scientists spoke deferentially of legislative skills and that senatorial doubts about the ability of intellectuals to grapple with a nasty world were expressed with courteous restraint. But most observers experienced a certain disenchantment about the curiosity and diligence of committee members. A "thorough study" did not mean to politicians quite what it meant to scientists and lawyers, and it was remarked that only Senator Johnson of Colorado, who once brought to Condon his own conjectured design of an atomic bomb sketched with child's crayons, had so much as a popular science view of technical matters. After the first few sessions, three, four, and five of the eleven members were regularly absent. The most diligent, Vandenberg and McMahon, were regarded as a political careerists.

For anyone who had noted what scientists had told other congressional committees, the December hearings brought out little that was new. Questions sometimes drew from witnesses a few more figures or more detailed speculation; they showed the scientists what points in their thinking seemed most vulnerable to the politicians—hints, which they did not always care to understand, of trouble spots in less happy days to come. Condon calls the hearings just a shambles as far as producing systematic information was concerned, and Newman and Miller found that "an analysis of the testimony offered reveals little more about the nature of impending changes than the conviction that they will come and that they will be important." In the somewhat more objective view of the AEC historians they were "a dismal fizzle."[35]

The judgment of Condon and Newman was influenced by a bitter wrangle in which they and the Senate committee engaged in late November with Secretary Patterson and General Groves in an attempt to obtain access for the committee to classified information— one skirmish in the battle that was still going on behind the scenes between supporters of the May-Johnson-bill approach to domestic control and the McMahon-Newman forces. It has been suggested that Groves was worried not so much about what the committee might learn as that classified information would reach Condon and perhaps

---

[35] Newman and Miller, *The Control of Atomic Energy*, pp. 5–6 (used by permission of McGraw-Hill Book Co.); *The New World*, p. 454.

his allies Urey and Szilard, with all of whom Groves had differed sharply during the war over information policies and whose discretion he frankly did not trust. With Patterson's support Groves won the contest.[36]

The federation scientists were not drawn into this struggle, but knowledge of it quite likely prompted the strong statements they made about adequate information for policy-makers in connection with their program of reports on inspection. And the contest certainly influenced the disposition of the reports. When he testified on December 12 Simpson suggested three alternative ways of using them: the Manhattan Project could appoint a committee to receive and digest all material; the Senate committee could hear individual experts and attempt on their own to integrate what they learned; or it could arrange for the appointment of a panel of experts to do it for them. The success of Groves and Patterson in persuading the President that the Senate committee ought not to have unlimited access to information eliminated all but the first of Simpson's alternatives, and recognition of the senators' limited inclination for serious study easily reconciled the federation scientists to turning over their reports to the Benedict committee, which Groves appointed.

3. A NEW BILL

A third focus of federation interest in the closing months of 1945 was the new atomic energy bill that was being drafted by Newman's assistant, Byron Miller. Newman's various memoranda on the May-Johnson bill, the Levi and Bureau of the Budget analyses, and the scientists' comments together provided the basis for a new approach to domestic control and the bill of which Miller completed the first draft on November 5. He had been in touch with Condon and Szilard, and early in November he took his draft to Chicago to discuss it with his friend Levi at the Law School and with a group of ASC members who were taking a particular interest in legislation. Working always closely with Newman, Miller made several revisions before the final version was ready for McMahon to introduce on December 20.

The site representatives in the Washington office, fully occupied with the growing pains of their two federations, with the inspection reports and Senate committee hearings, made no attempt to take

---

[36] *The New World*, pp. 449–52; interview with Condon, July 29, 1962.

part in this highly technical process. Insofar as scientists made a direct contribution to the McMahon bill, the channels for it were Szilard and the ASC. Among those in the Chicago organization who made a special study of domestic legislation were Francis Friedman, chairman of the ASC legislative committee, Thorfin Hogness, and Arthur Jaffey. Harold Urey was often involved in discussions. The contact with Edward Levi at the Law School had been closely maintained, and Levi, too, was drafting a bill, not without knowledge of the Newman-Miller draft, but with the object of putting in orderly form the conclusions reached in frequent discussions with the scientists. His draft was examined at an ASC executive committee meeting on December 1 and again at a general meeting on the twelfth. Interest naturally centered on those areas where the May-Johnson bill had seemed defective: the make-up of the commission; assignment of responsibility for distribution of materials, production plants, and military applications; dissemination of information; and the character and control of nuclear research. The scientists did not inquire deeply into the complexities of patents, contracts, and licences, about which they admittedly knew very little.[37]

Meanwhile Miller made other trips to Chicago and acknowledges the scientists' help in clarifying technical points. It shows up the shortcomings of documentation, on the one hand, that the only draft to which the ASC records refer is Levi's and of remembered history on the other, that one much involved scientist later stated without hesitation that the McMahon bill was written across the campus in the Law School after President Truman sent Miller to request that Chicago write a new bill.

Szilard's influence, not necessarily at variance with that of more group-minded ASC members, but brought to bear independently, is, as always, hard to pinpoint. Going back and forth between Washington and Chicago, he conferred frequently with Levi, Friedman, Hogness, and others, drawing them into luncheon conferences at the Quadrangle Club or long evening sessions at Levi's house, supplemented, if Szilard was running true to form, by phone calls in the dead of night to elaborate or try out some new idea. What all this adds up to is hard to say for Szilard's influence never lent itself to quantitative analysis, and he usually considered his job complete when others began to think and formulate. Miller did not accept Szilard's ideas

---

[37] ASC executive committee minutes, December 1, 1945, ASC VI, 12; ASC general meeting notes, December 12, 1945, ASC XXVI, Vol. IV.

uncritically—for instance, his notion of a nuclear research division with an independent budget—but he dates his great admiration of Szilard as a gadfly and a mental stimulant to this period when he was drafting the bill.[38]

Whatever the proper assignment of credit may be (and let it be clear that here, as at other points where we shall discuss it, this is a historian's concern, not the participants'), Simpson summed up a widely held impression in federation circles when he said that the Chicago scientists had made substantial contributions to the formulation of the new bill. But it must be remembered that a common viewpoint had drawn Newman and the scientists together in the first place. They found him fully sensitive to the challenge of the new age, sharing with them the belief that in a peaceful world science could provide great benefits for mankind and needing no instruction about the factors conducive to flourishing research, such as the unpredictable cross-fertilization of ideas and direct personal communication. Miller proved equally understanding. Therefore, one cannot say that contact during the period when the bill was being drafted proves influence. One can only show that the contact existed.

On December 27 and 28, a week after McMahon introduced the bill, representatives of four atomic scientists' associations met in Chicago to discuss it—Harrison Davies from Clinton, Irving Kaplan and G. Lister from SAM, Bernard Feld and Aaron Novick from Los Alamos, and Francis Friedman and Thorfin Hogness of the ASC. The loyalty of ALAS to the May-Johnson bill, which had once threatened the unity of the cause, had quietly subsided, and the delegates had no difficulty in agreeing that S.1717 offered reasonable prospects for the satisfactory handling of atomic energy. For the benefit of federation members and to provide a basis for eventual endorsement, they analyzed those provisions of the bill that they considered important or on which scientists' opinions might carry weight. Their primary satisfaction derived from the conclusion that the McMahon bill would permit, and even encourage, a solution to the international problem by recognizing the possibility of international control and placing the bomb in proper perspective in relation to the whole field, as they believed the May-Johnson bill failed to do. They also applauded the provision that future international agreements should supersede pro-

---

[38] Interviews with Hogness, January 18, 1960; and Miller, January 20, 1960.

visions of the present act, although the conference recommended an even more explicit statement to this effect.

The bill promised a balance between basic and applied research and impartial support of government and independent laboratories in the assignment of funds and research materials. Although the commission would control the release of basic scientific data in the nuclear field, it would also be responsible for its effective dissemination. The security sections, which in the May-Johnson bill had evoked such an emotional response by turning the pursuit of scientific knowledge into a hazardous undertaking, were found to be a vast improvement in that the penalties did not go beyond those in the Espionage Act and the commission was not granted extraordinary powers to issue new regulations. Quarterly reports of past activities and future plans seemed to assure adequate public review and appraisal. Studies of social, economic, and political implications (which the Senate committee later deleted) would serve as a basis for additional legislation and would keep the public informed about trends and prospects. As during the framing process, the details of patents and licensing were left to the experts, but the analysts at the Chicago meeting displayed a strong general anxiety that private industry should not acquire, either by grant or by default, rights that would inhibit research or withhold research equipment. They were glad, therefore, to see the commission made the sole producer and distributor of fissionable materials, as a guarantee against private monopolies, and to have the use of devices or processes controlled by commission licensing.

Finally, a full-time salaried commission, appointed by the President and responsible to him, would provide "a responsible and efficient administrative organization" and fill the specifications of the experienced government administrators who had criticized the May-Johnson bill in regard to the commission's responsibility to President and Congress. A clear distinction was made between the policy-making function of the commission and the administrative duties of the division heads, which, among other advantages, would enable the commission to serve as a relatively impartial board of review and appeal from administrative decisions.

On the whole the McMahon bill conformed admirably to what the scientists had been saying was desirable in domestic legislation. As a matter of tactics it was recommended that the security provisions should be given explicit support, not submerged in blanket approval. A few minor revisions and clarifications were suggested. Others were discussed but inconclusively. One of these was whether the bill ought to be specific about distribution of isotopes to other countries, an area where the Chicago conferees were correct in sensing trouble, for some years later a shipment to Norway, which most scientists regarded as falling well within the legal limits of research and clinical use, was challenged by AEC commissioner Lewis Strauss and members of the Joint Congressional Committee on Atomic Energy, providing an early instance of friction between Strauss and Oppenheimer, who was then chairman of the AEC's General Advisory Committee.[39]

The Chicago analysis was mimeographed for distribution with the injunction that its contents and the McMahon bill itself be studied and discussed preparatory to the federation's taking a public stand soon after Congress convened in January.

In the light of later developments it is interesting to note the absence in the analysis of explicit reference to civilian or military control of policy. Support of the civilian principle was clearly implied in the satisfaction with the makeup of the Commission and its position relative to the division heads, and it is virtually certain that the failure clearly to define the issue stemmed not from failure to recognize its importance but from a wish to keep the negative element of the now dormant feud with the army out of the legislative contest.

---

[39] Report of conference on domestic legislation, December 27–28, 1945, ASC X, 7; FAtS memorandum, n.d., FAS X, 5; report in *Bulletin of the Atomic Scientists*, I (January 10, 1946), [6].

CHAPTER 9

FAtS and FAmS

W<small>HILE THE</small> atomic scientists were keeping a watchful eye on the McMahon committee hearings and promoting the inspection studies, preparation was also made in the Washington office for the first council of the Federation of American Scientists, which was held in New York on January 5 and 6, 1946, overlapping a meeting of the American Physical Society. Nine local associations sent delegates: Rochester, Chicago, Los Alamos, the two New York associations, Clinton Labs, Pasadena, Philadelphia, and the Allegany Rocket Research Group. Cambridge, Dayton, and the newly formed Oak Ridge Engineers and Scientists had not yet voted to affiliate but sent observers.

The two most important topics did not at the moment require debate: policy on domestic legislation had been settled at the conference in Chicago the previous week, and the framework for international negotiation was being set up at the UN General Assembly meeting in London. So the council dealt chiefly with the tiresome but necessary details of organization. An administrative committee of seven was elected: W. A. Higinbotham, John A. Simpson, J. H. Rush, Philip Morrison, Louis Ridenour, Melba Phillips, and Leonard Schiff, of whom the first four came from Federation of Atomic Scientists groups. Higinbotham was elected chairman, Phillips, secretary, and Rush, treasurer; these three were to staff the Washington office,

Higinbotham and Rush full time, and Miss Phillips three days a week.[1]

In a lengthy discussion of the relationship of the new federation to its parent organization, it was agreed that the FAmS should be strengthened as rapidly as possible, but no date was set for the dissolution of the FAtS, whose members wanted to complete their two major jobs—the reports on feasibility of inspection and the program of dinners for senators.

Relationship of the new federation to the American Association of Scientific Workers was also considered. Suggestions for exchange of material and joint sponsorship of an atomic energy program at the March meeting of the American Association for the Advancement of Science were favorably received and later carried out, but a proposal for closer affiliation was firmly turned down. In the future there were to be occasional complaints about duplication of effort, especially in Cambridge, where before the war there had been an active AAScW group, but on the FAS side amalgamation was never seriously considered.

The Federation of American Scientists immediately began to expand. Before the second council meeting in March the Oak Ridge Engineers and Scientists, Dayton, Cambridge, and the Northern California Association of Scientists, centered in Berkeley with nearly two hundred and fifty members in the bay area, had been admitted; Pittsburgh and Ann Arbor, with a hundred members each, were voted in at the March council. Eastern Iowa, Wisconsin, and Cornell joined in April; and a Washington, D.C., association in June. Except for the disbanding of the Allegany Rocket Research Group, some of whose members became active elsewhere, there were no further changes in member organizations in 1946. Groups in the Schenectady area and at Fort Monmouth did not become formally affiliated until the following year. In other places, although the enthusiasm of a few people had produced embryonic organizations, they did not survive long enough to join the federation.

With officers and the prospect of income from dues and contributions to pay a more adequate staff, Higinbotham, Rush, and Phillips began to pursue the always elusive goal of an orderly office routine and regular communication with the site organizations. By the end of January Michael Amrine had joined the staff as publications editor. If

---

[1] FAS council minutes, January 5–6, 1946, ASC XIV, 2.

conditions never quite reverted to the chaos of the autumn, neither did they achieve monotonous stability. "For the past month," wrote Rush to Waldo Cohn at the end of March, "this office has resembled an animated model of the Kinetic Theory." The greatest financial stringency seemed to coincide with crises necessitating a staggering amount of paper work, but fortunately, the cause and its adherents attracted volunteers, at one time an ex-girl friend of Higinbotham's, at another a secretary at the British Embassy who devoted evenings to typing, addressing, and mailing. Delegates were no longer a regular part of the office scene although they sometimes came to do a specific job in connection with legislation or international control.[2]

The pious hope of the first FAmS council that amalgamation with the FAtS would be quick and painless proved overly sanguine, and instead there followed several months of sometimes acrimonious debate, which in retrospect seems slightly ridiculous and to have absorbed time and energy out of all proportion to its long-range significance. The controversy had been gathering momentum ever since the November planning session for FAmS, and the considerations raised at that time had by January taken shape as arguments for one side or the other. The protagonists of FAmS pointed out that its larger membership would be a more effective political and educational force, provide more recruits for the Washington office, and by adding to the range of specialties, enable the organization to speak with greater authority. Scientists leaving the Manhattan Project could still take part in local associations or as members-at-large. It would be a step toward a world federation; and it would remove the misleading distinction between atomic and non-atomic scientists.

Although not disputing any of these points, the more intransigeant supporters of the FAtS resisted absorption with the argument that only a small compact organization could act with the unanimity responsible for their successful stand against the May-Johnson bill. The word "atomic" had proved an "open sesame," the force of which they could not afford to ignore; and the atomic scientists' groups had taken on obligations to supporters and contributors that could not be delegated. "We at Chicago," explained Eugene Rabinowitch, one of the FAtS less choleric champions, to Louis Turner at the Radiation Lab,

2 FAS Newsletter, No. 1, January 27, 1946; Rush to Cohn, March 29, 1946, FAS VII, 1; interview with Amrine, April 24, 1963.

are all in favor of the new Council but want to avoid its dissipating its energies in fields not related to new weapons; it should not acquire partisan color or become an organization to defend professional interests of scientists. For this reason we want to keep its direction in the hands of "genuine" scientists' organizations with active members and prevent its being swamped by any "paper" organizations run by a small partisan group. . . . I hope your views coincide with ours.[3]

Much of the argument now seems petty and ephemeral, and any larger relevance it had lay in the uncertainty it revealed as to the purpose of a scientists' organization for nonprofessional ends. Scientists are accustomed to a frank and unceremonious appraisal of each other's ideas and projects, and for all its asperity, the FAtS-FAmS dispute left no real scars. Some of the parties to it had the grace to note the irony of bickering over how to promote world peace, and the altercation was largely kept private. A history of the movement, however, can hardly ignore anything that left so voluminous a residue in the files although only those with a reminiscent interest may care to read even the severely compressed account that follows.

Clinton Labs and Chicago, with some support from the engineers at K-25 and Y-12, vehemently upheld the FAtS; while Los Alamos and the SAM scientists (their numbers rapidly dwindling at the end of 1945) and the non-Project groups in Cambridge, New York, and Philadelphia supported the FAmS. This large but on the whole less-dedicated group was willing to tolerate the existence of the FAtS so long as it could exert a special influence whereas the atomic scientists were sensitive to any step taken by the Washington office that seemed likely to hasten their dissolution. Memorandums and minutes show how strongly some felt; and a common recollection of the period is the incessant and ubiquitous argument heatedly pursued by Hy Goldsmith of the ASC on behalf of the small, compact association.[4]

ALAS tried to moderate the stand of Chicago and Oak Ridge with conferences and correspondence. The FAtS, argued ALAS, would

---

[3] Rabinowitch to Turner, December 3, 1945, Camb. II.

[4] Wire Cohn, Stangby, and English to Simpson and Weinberg in Washington, with copies to all groups, December 11, 1945, FAS I, 2; AORS executive committee minutes, December 18, 1945, AORES VI, 4; FAtS memorandum, December 17, 1945, FAS XVII, 1; report of Armistead to AEOR, ca. December 15, 1945, AORES II, 2; AMPS Newsletter, December 13, 1945, FAS VI, 1; wires Rush to Higinbotham, December 28, 31, 1945, FAS I, 2; J. J. Nickson to Simpson, November 26, 1945, in Nickson's files; ASC executive committee minutes for December, ASC VI, 12; ASC general meeting notes, ASC XXVI, Vol. IV.

soon represent a small fraction of the erstwhile "atomic" scientists. By the end of January, 1946, half the ALAS members, many of the best known among them, would have left Los Alamos, and the epithet "small-fry scientists," with which someone had tagged the FAtS, would be even more appropriate. Two organizations with identical aims were a waste of manpower and would divide the scientists' movement because others could not understand the reluctance of FAtS to co-operate. A full account of the FAtS-FAmS debate was included in the Los Alamos Newsletter that was due to appear on January 1, but someone prudently recognized that outside readers might magnify this lapse in unanimity, and the whole issue was withdrawn.[5]

The dissident groups did in the end join the FAmS—Clinton Labs on January 4 in time to send a delegate to the New York meeting, and the Oak Ridge engineers and scientists (ORES) on January 24 when the merger of APSOR and AEOR was completed. Chicago debated affiliation of several weeks, finally deciding upon it on February 9.[6]

But to join the FAmS was not to acquiesce in the extinction of the FAtS. In the ASC *Bulletin* of February 1 Rabinowitch emphasized the tactical value of the prestige attaching, even if undeservedly, to those who had worked on the bomb and the indelible stamp this experience had left upon them, making them willing to subordinate all other tasks to the fight for international control. It remained to be seen, he said whether a similar unity and uniqueness of purpose could be developed in a nation-wide organization, and for this reason the Atomic Scientists of Chicago preferred that the FAtS remain a separate entity working in close and friendly co-operation with the newer group.[7]

In private FAtS enthusiasts did not always speak so temperately, and the partisanship of a hard core became stronger as they recognized their tactical error in allowing so keen a supporter of FAmS as Willy Higinbotham to take charge of the Washington office. Having been sent by ALAS for the express purpose of promoting the broader fed-

---

[5] Olum and Weisskopf to Cohn, December 20, 1945, AORES III, 8; ALAS Log, December 21, 1945, ALAS II, 2.

[6] The ASC was erroneously listed as an affiliate at the January council meeting. AORS general meeting notes, January 4, 1946, AORES IV, 3; Minett to Higinbotham, January 24, 1946, FAS XXI, 2; ASC executive committee minutes, February 9, 1946, ASC VI, 12.

[7] "The Atomic Scientists and the Federation of American Scientists," *Bulletin of the Atomic Scientists*, I (February 1, 1946), [4–5].

eration, Higinbotham had done so quite openly in the weeks before Christmas in the belief that the upsurge of interest from scientists outside the Project should not go unacknowledged while the in-group haggled over details. He was chosen to head the office by the FAmS council on January 6, not by virtue of any marked political sense (although this he did turn out to possess), but because he was available. Of the other members of the Washington staff, Rush, who had been charged by Clinton Labs to see that the FAtS did not disappear while no one was looking, had never personally sympathized with the FAtS extremists, and Melba Phillips had always been a FAmS supporter. Simpson, who favored a gradual turnover of FAtS responsibilities, was in Washington only intermittently after Christmas. Outside commitments, Simpson believes, can be combined with science only by rigorously cutting them off at the point of maximum return, and as 1946 opened he foresaw that contacts on Capitol Hill would yield diminishing results and that international control would be a long time coming.

So Higinbotham, Rush, and Phillips conducted the affairs of both federations from the office at 1621 K Street, not always, it is true, making clear which one they represented. The FAtS still had no officers, and its members, although complaining about the way things were handled, showed decreasing inclination to spend time in Washington. Critics might have been mollified by full reports and explanations, but the office staff was busy attending McMahon committee sessions, reporting testimony, hunting for money, cultivating new contacts, planning movies, radio programs, and articles, and helping the National Committee on Atomic Information gets its educational campaign started. Higinbotham made frequent reports to the new FAmS administrative committee and memorandums on particular points went to local associations, but five weeks elapsed between the first and second numbers of the FAmS newsletter. Rush, meanwhile, had to put up with some fairly pointed remarks from his friends in AORS, which sometimes took account of the faulty organizational structure that forced the Washington staff to make policy decisions but were on occasion uncomfortably personal, directed at Higinbotham for highhandedly promoting the interests of FAmS and at Rush himself for not resisting.[8]

Patiently Rush replied to these strictures with careful explanations

---

[8] Henshaw to Rush, February 2, 1946, AORES VI, 1.

of problems and policy. Although never one of the publicly acclaimed "atomic scientists," he became a key figure in the development of their organization. A thirty-four-year-old Texan with a shy and diffident manner that seemed to belie his origin, Rush thought clearly, wrote well, and had an equable disposition and a willingness to let other people do the talking, which had some merit in the highly articulate circles in which he moved. With only a master's degree in physics, Rush held a job where he was not indispensable, and having proved his ability as a formulator of statements in the early days of AORS, he had been sent as its delegate to the autumn organization meetings of FAmS and to the January council. Rush went to the council determined to demand a strict accounting of FAtS funds and with a feeling that its interests would best be served if someone other than Higinbotham became chairman of FAmS, but the elections put them in the saddle together and they were soon working harmoniously, with Rush a good foil for Higinbotham, who was quick and perky and never at a loss for a word. A month later Rush resigned from Clinton Labs and moved with his wife and two sons to Washington.

"It is impossible to imagine the FAS in those early days without Joe Rush," says Higinbotham. "He never said much in meetings so that people sometimes forgot he had been there, but he could make sense afterward of what they said and when he talked with people alone he was a very effective interpreter of the FAS." Rush refused to capitalize on his position. "Most of us who worked on the atomic project," he told a boy scout who wanted his signature for the troop collection of autographs of great leaders, "are not great men and women; we just happened to be working on a great job, and I don't think we should like to have our names listed as 'great scientists'. . . ."[9]

As treasurer of FAmS Rush also had charge of the FAtS account and did all kinds of tedious financial jobs, investigating the involved subject of tax exemption for the Federation and its affiliated groups and then explaining over and over in letters and memoranda what this meant in terms of permissable political and educational activity. Rush was in a crucial position in the FAtS-FAmS debate because one argument for the continuing existence of the FAtS was its superior appeal to contributors. It was as "atomic scientists" that the ASC had received the $10,000 from Chancellor Hutchins of the

---

[9] Rush to Ben Kohn, November 27, 1945, copy in Rush's files.

University of Chicago, and from Oak Ridge Borst wired Simpson in alarm that the $5,000 Volker Fund contribution for education and its continuing support assumed the existence of the Federation of Atomic Scientists. Four months after solicitation of funds for FAmS began, the FAtS was still receiving more money from more sources, and the FAtS protagonists argued that the overlapping campaigns confused and discouraged donors.[10]

Even the joint income did not cover mounting obligations. The site organizations, Chicago in particular, had advanced money to FAtS during the previous autumn for delegates' expenses, and the FAtS treasury in turn supplied the salaries for FAmS in the early part of 1946. So FAmS owed FAtS, and FAtS owed the sites, and this train of financial obligation, as in any family relationship, complicated independence. At intervals lump sums were transferred from FAtS to FAmS until the account was closed in September, 1946.

As February and March of 1946 came round, the partisans of FAtS fed their continued disaffection with the observation that the new federation was having no such dramatic impact on Washington as their improvised attack on the May-Johnson bill the previous October. Having demanded a thorough study of all aspects of atomic energy, they now became impatient at the deliberateness of the Senate committee's review, complaining that the non-Project associations were not joining vigorously enough in bringing pressure upon Congress. As the first flush of enthusiasm waned and scientists again became absorbed in research or teaching, the FAtS leaders turned to reorganization as a means of instilling new life into the cause, concluding that the FAtS position might be stronger if it had officers and the normal mechanism of organization. On the insistence of Clinton Labs a FAtS conference was held in Chicago on February 21 and 22, at which James Stangby and Merlin Peterson for AORS, Bernard Feld for ALAS, and Arthur Jaffey and Francis Friedman for the ASC (with Leo Szilard and Aaron Novick also taking part), in a kind of deathbed marriage, formally organized the Federation of Atomic Scientists, electing John Simpson as chairman, Harrison Brown as vice-chairman, and Rush as secretary-treasurer. They proposed that FAmS should be composed of regional and professional councils, with FAtS as the atomic council, an arrangement that would make

---

[10] Wire Borst to Simpson, December 15, 1945, FAS VII, 1. In March, 1946, FAtS received $1,745 from fifteen donors, and FAmS $1,235 from twelve (financial statements, FAS IV, 4).

possible authoritative statements by specialists in atomic energy, rockets, radar, missiles, and so on. This plan was circulated—somewhat arbitrarily, since ORES had already recommended that FAtS be dissolved, Los Alamos had opposed most of the motions on the ground that formalizing FAtS would only accentuate the controversy, and Irvin Kaplan, on behalf of the AMPS at Columbia (then debating a merger with the non-Project ANYS), expressed the opinion that unless FAtS wished to become merely an exclusive alumni club it should be dissolved by July 1 at the latest.[11]

A change in structure, the Chicago memorandum admitted, was no substitute for adequate internal communication or for good men with mature judgment willing to spend time in Washington. Szilard, in fact, began agitating to put Harrison Brown, who would shortly move from Clinton Labs to the University of Chicago, in charge of the Washington office, a suggestion vigorously vetoed by Higinbotham and Rush. They readily acknowledged their need for help and leadership and welcomed Brown's assistance, but as officers of FAmS they could hardly accept the vice-chairman of FAtS in a supervisory capacity. The matter was quickly and amicably settled in a conference in Washington on March 9 between Higinbotham, Rush, Brown, Simpson, and Henshaw. Brown concluded that his presence in the office could cause nothing but confusion, that the strengthening of FAtS should be abandoned and the structure of the FAmS changed so as to bring out new leadership; he suggested to the others that a panel of atomic scientists within the federation might be responsible for atomic energy problems.[12]

This was the last serious effort to reinvigorate the FAtS, though its fate was discussed throughout the spring concurrently with proposals for the improvement of FAmS. The June council meeting of what will now be called the FAS gratefully accepted from FAtS the $5,000 Volker Foundation contribution for state conferences, and the next council in September recognized the absorption of the FAtS and accepted its obligations and its assets.

[11] Minutes of FAtS meeting, February 21–22, 1946, proposal for reorganization, and related material, ASC XIII, 15.

[12] Phone call from Henshaw to AORS executive committee, March 10, 1946, AORES IV, 4; Brown to Henshaw and Simpson, March 19, 1946, and Henshaw to Higinbotham, March 20, 1946, FAS I, 1.

PART IV

To Study
and Inform

CHAPTER 10

Education

To a large extent the central federation owed its influence, as well as its troubles, to the strength of its constituent parts, which had quickly adopted all the paraphernalia of organization lacking in the Federation of Atomic Scientists. Back of the belligerence of the older site groups was a legitimate sense of accomplishment in having promptly provided information and identified issues.

1. CHICAGO

The determination to inform and educate was nowhere stronger than in Chicago, where, rooted in the wartime formulation of ideas, it received added impetus from fear that Midwest isolationism might revive to block international control. While meticulously shaping their first public statements and haggling over tactics on the May-Johnson bill, the Atomic Scientists of Chicago set up a complex committee structure designed to harness enthusiasm and distribute the load, all properly sanctified by a constitution—circulated, revised, and adopted—under which a new executive committee took office on November 7. Simpson, the new chairman, Rabinowitch, Brues, and Nickson carried over from the temporary executive committee, and Arthur Jaffey, Robert Moon, and Francis Friedman replaced Szilard, Seaborg, and Hill; H. H. Goldsmith became secretary and L. C. Furney treasurer. To make sure that the prestige of the enterprise was clear to those familiar with professional standing, an advisory committee was appointed, consisting of Thorfin Hogness as chairman, Kenneth C. Cole, Farrington Daniels, James Franck, Robert S. Mulliken, Glenn T. Seaborg, H. C. Urey, and Walter Zinn. Daniels, as director of the Met Lab, continued to play a sympathetic, if sometimes cautionary, role; Hogness and Urey gave far more than nominal backing in advice, speechmaking, and fund-raising.

Alternates, subcommittee members, and guests shared policy discussions at the two weekly executive committee meetings, which the novelty of subject matter and techniques prolonged interminably. Even after office help was hired and the first rush subsided, the time contributed each month was estimated at thirty man-days on conferences, twenty on speeches, twelve on movies and visual aids, and eight on radio broadcasts, a total, not counting the *Bulletin of the Atomic Scientists,* of some seventy days with a cash value of $5,000 in salaries.[1]

A copious legacy of minutes, outlines, and correspondence, dull and repetitious though they sometimes are, convey the concern and excitement with which the ASC program was launched. Evenings and weekends, once spent in the laboratory, were now devoted to meetings and speech-writing. Yet it is not so much the changed pattern of time that is vividly remembered as the upheaval in accustomed attitudes and the mounting sense of urgency.

Much informal canvassing of interest, from the Independent Voters of Illinois to *Esquire,* had preceded the inception of the publicity and contacts committee in early October under Katharine Way's chairmanship. Subcommittees were made responsible for contacts with newspapers, radio, and organizations (subdivided into world government, religious, women's, and scientific) and for letter-writing, editing, collection of materials, promotion of magazine articles, and a speakers' bureau. A sample letter to a hometown newspaper explained that the writer wanted his former neighbors to know about the bomb's implications and offered a series of articles.[2]

---

[1] Simpson to M. E. Leeds, April 29, 1946, in Simpson's files; ASC statement for Emergency Committee of Atomic Scientists, November, 1946, ASC XXII, 12. Unless otherwise indicated this section is based on the ASC executive committee minutes for 1945–46 in ASC VI, 12 and 13.

[2] Chairmen of the subcommittees established in October, 1945, were Richard Adams, Melvin Freedman, Leonard Katzin, W. Rubinson, L. C. Furney, R. Platzman, Jane Hall, Katharine Way, and Alex Langsdorf.

This was no paper organization, unless one counts the volume left behind. Leonard Katzin's editorial group started at once on a primer of basic technical facts about atomic energy directed primarily at members of Congress. The first twenty-five hundred copies of this pamphlet, *The Atomic Bomb*, ready in mid-February, were soon exhausted, and another ten thousand were ordered with further printings dropped only when curtailment of National Committee on Atomic Information funds cut off the principal outlet. Much ASC effort also went into a booklet by the semanticist S. I. Hayakawa entitled "One Minute War," but by the summer of 1946 when it was finally ready, so alarmist an approach seemed unwise.

Thick correspondence files testify to the industry of the committee charged with magazine contacts. The ASC's debut in the periodical field, the *Life* article of October 29, had altered somewhat the scientists' own feeling that addressing a mass audience was a kind of indecent public exposure and raised great hopes for this medium, but editors were really interested only in big names, and Kay Way, peddling projected articles in New York, had frustrating interviews with editorial assistants who persisted in treating her as a struggling young author and kindly recommended obscure little journals. Katzin's "The Industrial Uses of Atomic Energy," in the February, 1946, *Scientific American*, was cited as a model for semipopular technical articles, but few scientists had developed the knack for this sort of thing, and fewer still would take the time. ASC authors were more frequently represented by brief comments on international control or secrecy in slightly highbrow journals—*Nation, Christian Century,* or *New Republic*.

For all this systematic canvassing of the publishing field, the most successful venture had a fortuitous beginning in notes for a symposium on atomic energy jotted on an envelope one January evening as Kay Way and physicist Gale Young rode home on the bus from the Met Lab's offshoot in suburban Argonne. When Miss Way talked to an old friend, Dexter Masters of McGraw-Hill in New York, he suggested that he and Miss Way become joint editors of the proposed collection of articles. Other scientists were hastily assembled, and Miss Way is not sure whether they were more impressed by the opulence of lunch in the McGraw-Hill executive suite or by the dispatch with which their suggestions were implemented. Reached by phone in Princeton, Einstein, as a prospective author, commented gloomily that "sometimes these great men are so hard to get together with," but his fears proved excessive, and the book, entitled *One*

World or None was in print on March 18, 1946, with articles by General H. H. Arnold, Walter Lippmann, and Bohr, Urey, Einstein, Condon, Langmuir, Morrison, Ridenour, Seitz, Wigner, Young, Szilard, A. H. Compton, Oppenheimer, Bethe, and Shapley. An FAS statement was included.[3] At a dollar a copy for the paper edition, sales at home and abroad had netted over $7,000 by the end of June, plus some $2,500 from reprint and translation rights. In the end nearly one hundred thousand copies were sold. Miss Way and Gale Young gave their royalties, over $600 for the first three months, to the Atomic Scientists of Chicago for publicity, and those from several other contributors went to the FAS or one of its affiliates.

A measure of success attended the scientists' efforts to establish rapport with Chicago newsmen. Once a scientist became known to reporters his phone was likely to ring early and late with requests for technical background or off-the-cuff comment on atomic politics. Impersonal pronouncements from the ASC office lacked the appeal of an irate or witty explosion from Allison, Szilard, Urey, or Teller. Reporters often listened sympathetically to sober explanations of implications, but editors were more interested in blasts at army censorship. "My story on the atomic scientists, which I worked on quite hard, and considered of some significance, wound up inside," complained a friendly *Daily News* reporter to Kay Way, "while a sensational piece on roadhouses which I unearthed with considerable ease was slopped all over page one."[4]

In radio, too, Chicago scientists had the advantage of proximity to a responsive urban community and frequent opportunity for talks and interviews. With political and social scientists they discussed international and domestic control, security, and freedom of research on the University of Chicago Round Table programs, then attracting a national audience. But what counted more in the long run than direct discussion of issues was the slant regularly given to atomic energy news by professional commentators and columnists. Among the radio men in close touch with the ASC was Clifton Utley, a former political science instructor at the university who not only gave publicity to the scientists' views but was generous with advice on politics and public relations. And there were others in press and

---

[3] Dexter Masters and Katharine Way (eds.), *One World or None* (New York: McGraw-Hill Book Co., Inc., 1946); interview with Way, April 20, 1959.
[4] Jack Mabley to Way, ca. March, 1946, ASC XXIII, 17.

radio whom the scientists in Chicago and elsewhere called on whenever they felt an issue was not being adequately or fairly presented.

But the area of public relations into which Chicago scientists poured most time and effort was in speaking directly to Midwest audiences. If platform manner sometimes lacked polish this merely confirmed the picture of men of science wrenched from their blackboards by the exigencies of the moment and did the cause no harm, although, in fact, some of these men, already known as inspiring classroom performers, turned out to possess an equal appeal for laymen, and enthusiastic letters poured in from churches, technical societies, high schools, and clubs. "Dr. Teller did a magnificent job," wrote the pastor of Plymouth Church in Shaker Heights, Ohio, where a two day conference had brought together a thousand people.

With superb skill he put us through a course in nuclear physics and then with a force of conviction that is rare indeed, he persuaded his audiences of what needs to be done about it. I don't know which won people more, the greatness of his intellect or the greatness of his character and personality, but certainly few men have come to Cleveland and made so profound an impression as did Dr. Teller. He is a rare soul, indeed, ... and countless numbers of people have spoken, telephoned, and written ... in appreciation of him and his effort here.[5]

Alex Langsdorf, in charge of speaking assignments, filled an average of one request a day during the winter of 1945–46 from a list of some forty ASC members. Audiences ranged from twenty to five hundred; fees usually ran around $25 to $50, occasionally as high as $250, and were generally, perhaps always, turned over to the ASC, which up to November, 1946, received $1,155 from this source.[6] From the varied audiences available, the pick in size and potential influence were assigned, of course, to the better-known scientists, with the younger men being given a choice of suburban Lions or Kiwanis Club luncheons, local synagogue groups, pastors' institutes, teachers' conferences, and science clubs from Cleveland to Fond du Lac. At first they explained the elementary facts of atomic energy and its revolutionary implications. While the McMahon bill was in committee and before the Congress, they stressed civilian control and the excesses of military secrecy; with publication of the Acheson-Lilienthal Report

---

[5] M. H. Krumbine to Adult Education Council, May, 1946, ASC XX, 6.

[6] Simpson to Emergency Committee of Atomic Scientists, November 16, 1946, in Rush's files. Material relating to speaking engagements is scattered through ASC files; see especially boxes IX, XX, XXVI, and XXVII.

in the spring of 1946 and subsequent opening of United Nations negotiations, they tried to stimulate informed discussion and support for the United States control proposal. With the day-to-day picture sometimes changing rapidly, it was hard for these part-time publicists to keep abreast of all developments, especially when on tour with a schedule of three or four speeches a day on different topics. The ASC legislative committee stood ready with copies of bills and summaries, and the testimony, articles, and clippings gathered by the materials committee were arranged as a reference library in the Physics Building by H. W. Ibser, who also prepared bibliographies and lists of materials available for public distribution.[7]

At first there was novel satisfaction in the warm response of fascinated listeners, but often the audiences were small and unsophisticated. Szilard maintained that the whole educational program was not worth a few well-chosen contacts in Washington. Rabinowitch, on the other hand, argued that only the long slow process of education could bring about the new climate of opinion necessary for the acceptance of international control. The seven months' campaign for the McMahon bill was to demonstrate the usefulness of both approaches and also of a middle course that the ASC adopted early in 1946, that is, conferences of leaders in fields where the mechanism for disseminating ideas already existed. Sponsored jointly by the ASC and the University of Chicago, the first one brought some forty Midwest religious leaders—pastors, educators, and editors—to the campus on February 5, 6, and 7 to be briefed on the elementary physics, chemistry, biology, and politics of the bomb by ASC scientists, including Allison, Urey, and Warren Johnson, and other eminent faculty members. Queries about technical points, tactics, and economics reflected a lively interest but were also a reminder that six months after Hiroshima information about atomic energy, even among the relatively well informed, was at a pretty rudimentary level. Nor does it seem that the guests were eager to discuss the particular challenge of the new weapon to their own profession. When a scientist raised the moral issue, the clergymen replied that for centuries the Church had been wrestling with man's propensity to employ force and that as professional teachers of morals they had long faced the dilemma now confronting the scientists of how to alert people to danger without scaring them to the point of cynicism.[8]

---

[7] ASC I, 5; X, 10.
[8] Transcript of the Conference of Religious Leaders and related material in ASC II, 6; III, 15, 16; IV, 8.

Although the written record thus leaves some doubt that beyond a recognition of common responsibility any real meeting of minds occurred, at the time the conference was regarded as a great success, in part because it passed and dispatched to President Truman and Senator McMahon a strong resolution in support of civilian control. A continuing committee of twelve, with six scientists and six Protestant, Catholic, and Jewish clergymen joined the National Committee on Atomic Information and sponsored other conferences in Grand Rapids, Flint, and Toledo.[9] An April 1 conference for fifty labor leaders (representing four million workers) heard, according to an awed participant, "one of the most terrifying stories ever told to a labor group." It too set up a continuing committee, and labor gave valuable support to NCAI and the campaign for civilian control.[10] Business executives were brought together in the same way in April, though with less apparent impact. In June the ASC initiated a June conference for radio executives in New York City and helped organize other conferences on domestic or international control in Midwest communities, for which they provided scientist speakers, including Joseph and Maria Mayer, Herbert Anderson, and Harrison Brown.

To manage these conferences the ASC executive committee had hired a former Met Lab secretary, Beth Olds, who soon added the job of executive secretary of the ASC and, in the summer of 1946, executive secretary of the fund-raising Emergency Committee of Atomic Scientists, as well as playing girl Friday to Szilard's successive schemes for resolving the atomic crisis. With Beth's warm welcome for visitors, her intelligent comments, and her hand on the long distance phone, the crowded basement room in the university's Social Science Building that housed the ASC and the *Bulletin* became a secondary nerve center of the scientists' movement, sometimes better informed than the FAS office in Washington.

Some observers were much impressed by this transformation of masters of equation and test tube into political mentors; others found the phenomenon a little frightening, not always realizing the scientists' own misgivings or how conscientiously all the site organizations

---

[9] Kenneth Cole, Warren Johnson, David Hill, Thorfin Hogness, Robert Moon, and historian Louis Gottschalk went to Grand Rapids on March 19; Francis Friedman and Herbert Anderson to Flint on March 21; Cole, Brues, Hill, and Donald Hughes to Toledo on May 20 (ASC II, 14, 15; VII, 9).

[10] Speakers were R. G. Gustavson, Alvin Weinberg, and H. C. Urey (*Bulletin of the Atomic Scientists*, I [April 1, 1946], 18).

adopted programs of self-education and tried to exchange information with specialists in other fields. This was fairly easy at the University of Chicago where Chancellor Hutchins and members of the law and political and social science faculties had been so immediately co-operative and where the Office of Enquiry into the Social Consequences of Atomic Energy encouraged collaboration. To provide a background for their own technical studies of inspection and to help evaluate the various control schemes in preparation, all the local associations in the winter of 1945–46 tried to learn about past and present attempts at international co-operation by listening both to historical treatments of the subject and to advocates of particular proposals for world government. In Chicago some important converts were made to world federalism—Harold Urey, Harrison Brown, and Edward Teller; but officially the ASC remained loyal to the concept of international control under the United Nations and urged scientists to concentrate on technical aspects of the control problem.

These exchanges, which were part of a nation-wide attempt by intellectuals to pool their skills in the cause of peace, bore some fruit in international planning and domestic legislation. But to the extent that the object was mutual education, one senses disappointment with the result. To physical scientists, the specialists' expertise in some of the areas they explored seemed little more than formulated common sense, whereas to social scientists, the laboratory method of choosing a problem and isolating it seemed a highly unrealistic approach to human difficulties. Behind the scientists' humble readiness to learn one detects a slightly arrogant belief that what social and political scientists had to teach could be grasped in a few easy lessons, though they were, perhaps, equally oversanguine about the brief courses they frequently offered in nuclear physics.

The most concrete manifestation of the Chicago scientists' desire to educate themselves and others—indeed the most enduring symbol of the whole movement—was the *Bulletin of the Atomic Scientists*, conceived in the somewhat unlikely setting of the local Stineway Drug Store where Hy Goldsmith and Eugene Rabinowitch, drinking coffee with their sociologist friend Ed Shils, held long passionate discussions in the early autumn of 1945 on how the adjustments to the atomic age might be adequately weighed and recorded. The project authorized by the ASC executive committee on November 24 promised weekly committee reports, items from other site newsletters, and "good" statements about atomic energy as well as "terrible stuff" from the public press. Goldsmith was instructed to proceed with a biweekly publication and was soon ready to order a thousand copies of the first number for the sum of $35.40.

AORS at Clinton Labs already had its daily duplicated newsletter and Los Alamos its one-page printed weekly when Volume I, Number 1, of the *Bulletin of the Atomic Scientists of Chicago* appeared on December 10, 1945. This first six-page issue, now something of a collector's item, featured a press release of December 7 by Harold Urey and the ASC executive committee entitled "Pearl Harbor Anniversary and the Moscow Conference" and a brief statement about the ASC; it reported formation of the Federation of Atomic Scientists, plans for the larger federation, and news of other site groups. Two pages of congressional news included the status of the May-Johnson bill and testimony before the Senate Special Committee on Atomic Energy, which had opened two weeks before. The attempt to provide comprehensive coverage was quickly abandoned. Subsequent issues displayed the less parochial spirit of the Stineway discussions, with activities of local associations yielding space to aspects of the control problem, documentation of United Nations Atomic Energy Commission negotiations, the effect of the bomb on defense, secrecy and research, and in time, almost any issue relating to science and government.

Always soundly professional in spirit, the *Bulletin*, like the movement of which it was a part, had an incurably amateur quality. Crises in the legislative campaign or major statements on international control repeatedly upset deadlines, and early issues were the fruit of midnight vigils, with Goldsmith at times dictating directly to the typesetter. After he moved to New York in the spring of 1946 and Rabinowitch to Urbana, their periodic visits to Chicago were the occasion of interminable and often heated arguments, not about their fundamental view of the *Bulletin* as a vehicle for authoritative exploration of issues, but about the immediate means to this end. Although critical and contentious, Goldsmith had warm friends and wide contacts outside science that helped at once to set the *Bulletin* apart from other site newsletters, but because of his deep aversion to writing, it preserves no direct evidence of his great contribution. Rabinowitch, on the other hand, had a natural facility in writing, which had already been enlisted by his friend Franck and the ASC. His July memorandum to the Met Lab Committee on Panel Discussions had discussed the dire need of atomic education, including education for scientists themselves, and it was to this dual task of enlightenment that he dedicated himself with a selfless perseverance that has survived all the disappointments of the postwar years and the loss of his chief collaborator when Goldsmith died in a swimming accident in 1949. The *Bulletin* was the creation of these two men, though Friedman, Jaffey, and Simpson, of the first editorial board, and Shils, Teller, and Langsdorf gave their time generously to *Bulletin* problems, as did later recruits from Oak Ridge, Harrison Brown, Harrison Davies, and Clyde Hutchison.

The need of a source of information and a forum for discussion had been correctly judged. One battered copy of *Bulletin* Number 6, wrote an ASC visitor to State College, Pennsylvania, was the prize possession of a local minister and was eagerly passed around. By April, 1946, ten thouand copies were being printed, and the site organizations adjusted dues to include the *Bulletin*. Clinton Labs suggested a change of name to "Bulletin of the Federation of Atomic Scientists," with each site contributing articles and sharing costs. The ASC executive committee preferred the *Bulletin of the Atomic Scientists*, and "of Chicago" disappeared from the title with the issue of March 15. But this was as far as the editors were willing to go, and the *Bulletin* never became the official organ of the FAS. Their independence was resented in some quarters, and the FAS administrative committee, disturbed because Rabinowitch's editorials were sometimes accepted as organization policy, finally persuaded him to initial them. University of Chicago sponsorship, a tempting solution to financial stringency, was also refused.

Success seemed to justify some long-range planning. Certain editorial refinements, lacking in the first hastily assembled issues, were introduced, such as numbered pages, authors' names, and in due course, the dignity of a cover. In June, 1946, the *Bulletin* became a monthly, eventually settling on ten issues a year. The circulation figures, up to sixteen thousand at the end of the first year, were highly satisfactory, but there was a large free list, mainly of foreign scientists and libraries, and sales brought in only $1,500 per month. Costs rose with expanded format, and although the editors received no salary and the university no rent, the financial situation was always parlous. In order to claim tax exemption *Bulletin* accounts were separated in May, 1946, from those of the ASC (although it, too, was eventually granted tax exempt status), and the following autumn the *Bulletin* received help from the Emergency Committee of Atomic Scientists, which later recognized the periodical's unique contribution by making it the beneficiary of remaining funds.

From the scientists who formed the core of *Bulletin* readers, a mixed reaction was inevitable. Some called for greater variety, others for a continuing pattern and more self-criticism; still others denounced the *Bulletin's* persistently middle-of-the-road editorial position or found the authoritative articles on which Rabinowitch insisted unnecessarily academic and dull. Yet, on the whole, scientists have been proud of the *Bulletin*, recognizing that it has introduced and kept alive many an important issue and that it uniquely expresses the crisis of conscience that science experienced in the wake of Hiroshima. Early issues were the only source of certain materials for newsmen and popular writers and are now indispensable for students of the changing relationship of scientists to public affairs.

The Chicago scientists' job of public relations was for a brief period successful beyond any reasonable expectations, but it had been terribly time-consuming, and in the spring of 1946 the ASC executive committee hired a professional, John H. Skinner, Jr., for a six-month trial period. Skinner seems to have done a workmanlike job, taking over many tasks from hard-pressed members, exploring new film and radio projects, studying income, expenditures, and contributed time, and planning future expansion. The mimeographed material became more abundant than at any time since the early formulation of principles. But Skinner's outline of proposed educational activities for the winter of 1946–47 is a kind of milestone in the scientists' crusade, for its twenty pages contain no touch of the evangelical fire that had lit the most prosaic of the early memoranda; it referred to kits and visual aids, promotional publicity, and estimated coverage with but the merest hint that it was selling the salvation of civilization, not socks or lawn mowers.

Skinner never completed his program. The executive committee was preoccupied with United Nations negotiations, the organization of the domestic Atomic Energy Commission, and FAS policy and, ignoring the law of diminishing returns, decided that the educational campaign was falling short of expectations. His contract was terminated at the end of six months.

It was not a shortage of funds that curtailed Skinner's program. Despite the growing competition of other interests the Atomic Scientists of Chicago was still a vigorous organization in the autumn of 1946. Always the rich relation among the scientists' groups, the ASC was the only one at this time not heavily handicapped by lack of money. The $10,000 from Chancellor Hutchins' special funds had enabled it to advance expenses for federation delegates, to start the *Bulletin,* and to subsidize the booklet *The Atomic Bomb.* The university had also helped pay for conferences and provided useful, if not luxurious, office space. Up to March, 1947, ASC scientists themselves had raised over $12,000 in contributions; lecture fees had brought in over $2,400, dues $1,550, and articles $1,372. Receipts for the eighteen-month period totaled $28,617.64.

Although there is no intention of following the financial affairs of all associations, it is instructive to see how one of them spent its money. As of March, 1947, $5,000 had gone into travel expenses, $13,000 for salaries and office maintenance, and $400 for FAS dues. *The Atomic Bomb* had cost some $1,100 over and above sales; $1,600 had been spent on distribution of other materials, nearly $200 on the reference library, and another $200 on the religious leaders' conference. Nevertheless, the ASC treasury had a net surplus of $5,300.90, and the next six months showed a continuing increase of both income and expenditure, though a gift of $2,500 to the *Bulletin* slightly reduced the surplus.[11]

2. ASSOCIATION OF LOS ALAMOS SCIENTISTS

With almost identical aims and techniques each association developed a special character, the product less of the brooding presence of the ancient foothills of the Smokies or the snow-capped Sangre de Cristos than of the availability of a local audience, exposure to certain human stimuli, and the immediate future of the particular laboratory.

Scientists at Los Alamos had to choose between complete capitulation to the desire for peacetime ways by leaving for familiar campus or tempting industrial job, or continuing under the fairly rigorous regime that still pertained on the mesa. The forty-eight-hour week remained in force; censorship of personal mail continued until early December, 1945; and the gates were firmly guarded, although visitors' passes were easier to obtain. The future of the laboratory depended upon decisions of national policy, both domestic and foreign, and there was much speculation about its possible dissolution either by

---

[11] Financial statements with ASC executive committee minutes, in ASC VI, 13.

official decree or by loss of key men. Its survival owed a great deal to the steady hand of the new director, Norris Bradbury, who accepted the difficult task of stepping into Oppenheimer's shoes and quietly provided a meaningful objective in a thoroughly unsettled situation. Their job, Bradbury told his associates, was to set up as nearly as possible an ideal project to study the use of atomic energy on an operating basis and be ready to turn it over to the agency established by Congress. Weapons research would have to continue, however strong the wish that they should never be used, but he hoped the laboratory might also explore peacetime applications. No pressure would be applied to keep people at Los Alamos, but from those who stayed he expected work consistent with a creative holding operation.[12]

This did not allow much relaxation of effort, and though several group leaders found time to serve on the first ALAS executive committee, the main work of the organization was done by the younger men. The first Los Alamos Newsletter on October 25 outlined the duties of a dozen committees,[13] and file drawers in scattered offices soon overflowed with their memoranda. Higinbotham's complaint to Bradbury that ALAS business—of vital concern, he said, to five hundred people—was interfering with work in electronics produced a windowless storeroom in the Tech Area T Building for an ALAS office. One volunteer typist soon proliferated into a women's auxiliary, headed by Mrs. John Manley, with its own committees for typing, writing, fact-finding, radio auditing, organization listing, and local publicity. Mrs. Robert Brode's clipping committee reported on nation-wide reactions to the May-Johnson bill and international control.[14]

A unique facet of ALAS public relations was a brief blossoming of friendship with residents of Santa Fe with whom a guarded conversation on folk art or local history in library or museum had

[12] Notes on a talk at co-ordinating council, October 1, 1945, in *Project Y: The Los Alamos Project*, by Edith C. Truslow and Ralph Carlisle Smith, Vol. II of *Manhattan District History* (Washington, D.C.: Office of Technical Services, U.S. Department of Commerce, 1961), pp. 115–25.

[13] A. Fact-finding Committee—R. Marshak, chairman; B. Membership—M. Deutsch, chairman; C. Publicity Committee—J. Trischka, chairman (releases, P. Olum; writing, F. Reines; correspondence, L. Jossem; speeches, H. Richards; clippings, L. Helmholz; Hill publicity, A. Grubman; Newsletter, W. Sherrer); D. Legislative Committee—M. Perlman and R. Williams, chairmen; E. Publications Committee—C. Critchfield, chairman.

[14] Higinbotham to Bradbury, October 22, 1945, copy in ALAS I, 11; Los Alamos Newsletter, No. 1, October 25, 1945, ALAS II, 19.

stretched the limits of permissible contact. But in the early autumn of 1945 a link between mesa and valley was provided by Dorothy McKibben, a widow in her mid-forties who ran the Santa Fe office of the Manhattan Project in the vine-covered adobe patio at 109 East Palace Avenue. Mrs. McKibben's charm and discretion had made her the confidante of Los Alamos leaders and the comforter at one time or another of most of its residents. Impressed by the reaction of her "hill" friends to the use of the bomb, she wanted the citizens of Santa Fe, puzzled and resentful at the invasion of their beloved mountains by the populous secret project, to understand and support the efforts of ALAS.

The first encounter took place at the Laboratory of Anthropology on the outskirts of Santa Fe on the evening of November 26, when some fifty people from Los Alamos were invited to meet a picked group of the artists, writers, wealthy New England spinsters, and gentlemen ranchers who live in Santa Fe and the neighboring valley. Mutual curiosity had produced a cordial atmosphere by the time the formal program began. Enrico Fermi demonstrated apparatus for detecting and counting neutrons; Philip Morrison showed pictures of Hiroshima and Nagasaki and talked with great effect of what he had seen in Japan. And with loving nostalgia Victor Weisskopf described the development of nuclear physics, dwelling upon the prewar years when scientists from his native Vienna, from Hungary, England, Germany, and America had worked together with Fermi in Rome, or Bohr in Copenhagen, and then how many of them had gathered at Los Alamos reluctantly to make a nuclear weapon. The audience was deeply stirred. Science, like art, wrote one of the painters next day, has no national boundaries and must be so kept.[15]

A Santa Fe Citizens Committee on Atomic Information was quickly formed and sponsored a public meeting on December 8 with Bernard Feld and John Manley of ALAS and John van Neumann, Princeton mathematician and Project consultant, as speakers. At another atomic age rally in Taos, sixty miles to the north, Edward Teller and Cyril Smith wondered what the blanket-clad Indians from the Pueblo, sitting stolidly among the local artists and townspeople, made of their message about the emergent politics of the atomic bomb. Also in the audience was Peggy Pond Church, whose father had founded the Los Alamos Ranch School and whose husband

---

[15] *Los Alamos Newsletter*, No. 7, December 4, 1945, ALAS II, 19; Will Shuster to ALAS, November 27, 1945, ALAS V, 4.

was its acting headmaster when it was dispossessed by the Project. Offering to ALAS the profits of her next book of poems, *Ultimatum for Man*, she explained: "I had many many happy years at Los Alamos and can hardly bear the thought that the name is beginning to symbolize only destruction in so many people's minds."[16]

Cocktail and dinner parties followed these first contacts, and for a few weeks Los Alamos social life, active enough after its fashion but somewhat standardized in mirror-image apartments, took on new dimensions. Within the blank adobe walls of Santa Fe were now revealed secluded gardens, handsome carved portailles, and sun-shielded rooms filled with Spanish colonial treasures or choice hoards of pre-tourist Pueblo craftsmanship. Los Alamos tried to reciprocate one December evening, but the party coincided with the worst water shortage the mesa had experienced; ingenious domestic makeshifts seemed suddenly crude when seen through the eyes of these exemplars of casually gracious living; nor did it help that the guests arrived in a mild state of shock from their first sight of the once silent, pinon-covered mesa scarred by fences, barracklike buildings, trailers and macadam. Nascent friendships that survived this affair were soon interrupted by departures from Los Alamos, but happily, some who stayed on shared the artistic and archeological interests of their valley neighbors and re-established the connection on a less frenetic basis.

As in Chicago, it was a rare audience that was counted in hundreds, and most ALAS speechmaking was to bankers, church groups, and service clubs, with the Rio Grande Knife and Fork Club providing a local accent. But the reaction of the scattered audiences was gratifying. "I do not know when we have had anyone in this community that stirred up a like amount of interest," wrote a school superintendent after Theodore Jorgenson had made eight speeches on a three-day tour of Colorado high schools and urged his adult listeners to write their Congressmen in support of civilian control.[17]

The thousands of non-technical workers at Los Alamos were not forgotten either, and at a November meeting Robert Williams explained the elementary facts of the phenomenon they had helped to produce, and Philip Morrison again described the destruction in

---

[16] Mrs. Church to ALAS, May 30, 1946, ALAS IV, 5. A later book by Mrs. Church, *The House at Otowi Bridge: The Story of Edith Warner and Los Alamos* (Albuquerque: University of New Mexico Press, 1959), preserves the spell of the Pajarito Plateau and the memory of an important figure in the life of wartime Los Alamos.

[17] Los Alamos Newsletter, No. 28, May 16, 1946, ALAS II, 19; James H. Wilson to ALAS, February 13, 1946, ALAS files.

Japan. The mesa radio station broadcast news of ALAS and its aims, and for a wider audience a series of ten evening broadcasts over KOB-Albuquerque began on April 2, 1946, with ALAS members describing Alamogordo, Hiroshima, and the Bikini tests and discussing the Acheson-Lilienthal Report and peacetime applications. West Coast stations repeated the series.[18]

ALAS, too, looked hopefully to the magazines, but articles in the *American Teacher* and the *Saturday Review of Literature* are about all that can be traced to a copious correspondence with editors. An ALAS atomic primer, *Our Atomic World*, by Robert Marshak, Eldred Nelson, and Leonard Schiff, with a foreword by Enrico Fermi, was promptly accepted by the University of New Mexico Press, but a fuss over color illustrations held it up until June, 1946, and within two months its distribution, like that of the similar Chicago booklet, was curtailed with the cut in NCAI funds.

From Washington Higinbotham forwarded suggestions for supplementing ALAS' limited educational opportunities—a fact sheet for science teachers and authoritative treatment of certain topics. For instance, he said, irresponsible discussion of the danger of igniting or poisoning the atmosphere was not doing the "cause" any good, a point shortly underlined by *Time* magazine, which referred to scientists' itchy fingers and reported a bet offered by Fermi at Alamogordo on whether the test would work—a callous acceptance, said *Time*, of the possibility of blowing up the world. A joint reply from the ALAS executive committee and Fermi deplored *Time's* portrayal of scientists as madmen, explained that explosion of the atmosphere had been established as impossible, and denied that Fermi had made a bet at Alamogordo but drew from *Time* only the concession, "O.K. not really mad, just very very inquisitive."[19]

On the whole the scientists' efforts to attract attention were dignified and decorous, but ALAS provided a notable exception when, despite mutterings about "cheap publicity" from two dissenting executive committee members, samples of earth from the Alamogordo bomb crater, christened "Trinitite" after the code name of the test, were sent to the mayors of forty-two cities with the request that they

---

[18] Complete scripts are in FAS XXII, 2 and 6, and all except Nos. 9 and 10 in ALAS V, 10. Speakers were Frederick Reines, Harold Agnew, Philip Morrison, Maurice Shapiro, Willard Stout, Jane Hall, Raemer Schreiber, John Manley, Dale Corson, and Joseph Keller (Los Alamos Newsletter, No. 28, May 16, 1946, ALAS II, 19).

[19] Higinbotham to Jossem, November 23, 1945, ALAS II, 18; *Time*, XLVI (December 3, 1945), 50; and XLVI (December 24, 1945), 8; correspondence in ALAS V, 5.

be prominently displayed as a reminder that the city would probably be destroyed in the first hours of a conflict. "We hope that you, Mr. Mayor, charged with the passive defense of your city in time of war, will testify at the very important hearings of the McMahon Committee. . . . We believe, with most other experts in this field, that only international control of these weapons can prevent the utter destruction of urban civilization within our lifetime." The fused sand offer made the front page of the *New York Times*, and requests poured in. Belatedly granting that they had started not an upsurge of public awareness but a collector's boom, the committee drew up a form letter regretting that no more requests could be filled.[20]

Amidst these experiments in education and publicity, particular issues were studied and debated—the May-Johnson bill, the merits of the national scientists' organization, the feasibility of inspection. ALAS' public statements and its internal dialogue continued to focus on international control, and there was less interest in more comprehensive panaceas than in Chicago or Oak Ridge. As long as they stayed at Los Alamos prominent members of ALAS gave the organization effective backing: Bacher, Bethe, Morrison, Weisskopf and Teller. The predicted post-Christmas exodus was reflected in the new executive committee, on which only Manley and Keller carried over, and a general contraction of compass was evident as 1946 opened.[21]

But seeds had been planted. Wherever ALAS people went—to Cambridge, Chicago, Ithaca, Washington—they strengthened forces already demonstrating that scientists were determined to be responsible members of the body politic. They left with a sense of obligation and opportunity all the more compelling because of a speech that Robert Oppenheimer made to five hundred ALAS members and wives on the evening of November 2, shortly after his resignation as director. Ask any Los Alamite what he remembers about this period, and though he may have forgotten everything else about ALAS, he will begin, "Well, I remember Oppie's speech." What Oppenheimer said about why scientists had worked on the bomb, why they were defending freedom of research, and what the special conditions

---

[20] Los Alamos Newsletter, No. 14, January 22, 1946; material in ALAS II, 2, 4, and III, 14; New York Times, January 19, 1946, p. 1.

[21] The new members were Philip Morrison, David Hawkins, Jerome Wiesner, Maurice Shapiro, G. F. Friedlander, and Willard Stout, who also left before his term as chairman was up (ALAS meeting notes, December 28, 1945, ALAS II, 4).

were that made the times at once so full of peril and so full of hope have been quoted at earlier points in this narrative. The advent of atomic weapons was important, said Oppenheimer, not so much because they provided a new argument against war—there had always been good arguments—nor even because of the unknown but sure industrial and scientific benefits of atomic energy, but because in this new field there existed the possibility of realizing those changes in relations between nations that were needed if there was to be peace. In this change, said Oppenheimer, it was hardly thinkable that the international traditions of science, the fraternity of scientists, should not play a constructive part. "It is a new field," he went on,

in which just the novelty and the special characteristics of the technical operations should enable one to establish a community of interest which might almost be regarded as a pilot plant for a new type of international collaboration. I speak of it as a pilot plant because it is quite clear that the control of atomic weapons cannot be in itself the unique end of such operation. The only unique end can be a world that is united, and a world in which war will not occur. But those things don't happen overnight, and in this field it would seem that one could get started . . . without meeting those insuperable obstacles which history has so often placed in the way of any effort of cooperation.[22]

This was Bohr speaking, as well as Oppenheimer, and the substance of this passage has inspired much continuing effort.

3. CLINTON LABS

Although the future of all parts of the huge atomic energy development was unclear in the autumn of 1945, there was less uncertainty at Oak Ridge than at Los Alamos, where all effort had been directed toward achieving a bomb. Scientists at Clinton Labs, the largest research project at Oak Ridge, had worked on earlier stages of the fission process, which were applicable however atomic energy was used. Nor did scientists there feel quite the direct revulsion over the bombing of Japan that clinched many a decision to sever connections with Los Alamos. Of the one hundred ninety members of the Association of Oak Ridge Scientists in October, 1945, only twelve had left by the middle of January. In June there were still one hundred thirty-nine members plus fifty-four alumni.[23]

---

[22] The speech was printed and distributed at Los Alamos (copy in author's files).

[23] To help dispel the confusion of similar names and initials in the Oak Ridge organizations, the reader is reminded that the Association of Oak Ridge Scientists (AORS)

As we have seen, the Clinton Labs scientists reacted sharply to political issues, and their location off the main line of travel did not prevent their full participation in the May-Johnson bill fight or in the affairs of the two federations. Scores of carefully composed letters went to editors, congressmen, hometown newspapers, and friends describing the Oak Ridge experience, outlining the conclusions about the need for control to which it had led, and asking for action and support. Often one individual, exploiting his migratory status, wrote to senators and representatives in his home state, his adopted state of Tennessee, and the one where he intended to settle. The immediate impact of this activity was so great that the SAM group at Columbia wanted to know how AORS accomplished so much. The secret, Waldo Cohn replied, lay in striking out in all directions but controlling all strikes. Clearly, people didn't know the ABC's of the atomic project—how the sites were related, what kind of research went on, how other countries could build their atomic industries, or even what scientific research meant—hence anywhere one turned it was possible to enlighten someone.[24]

Daniel Lang's giggling physicist, unaware of the purpose of his work, was not in evidence when Louis Falstein, reporting for the *New Republic*, visited Clinton Labs in early November, where he was greeted by a large sign outside the Laboratory: "Dawn of Peace. Let's Make it Forever." Attending an AORS executive committee meeting, at which everyone present was under thirty. Falstein was impressed by the maturity of the group. "There is an urgency about them now," he wrote, "and deep concern in their faces. They've fashioned a terrible weapon and consider themselves the Responsibles." Though the scientists were dubbed "longhairs" by the east Tennessee workers, Falstein's wanderings in the residential area turned up a normal lot of young people. One was training his dog Pluto (short, of course, for plutonium) to roll over when asked if he would rather work for duPont or be a dead dog. Another was reading the comics, which he liked very much, he told Falstein, but

---

was at Clinton Labs; the Atomic Production Scientists of Oak Ridge (APSOR) was at the electromagnetic separation plant, Y-12; and the Atomic Engineers of Oak Ridge (AEOR) was at the gaseous diffusion separation plant, K-25. In December, 1945, APSOR and AEOR combined to form the Oak Ridge Engineers and Scientists (ORES); in June, 1946, ORES and AORS merged to form the Association of Oak Ridge Engineers and Scientists (AORES).

[24] AORS Daily Bulletin, November 5, 1945, AORES XX, 1.

at the moment Orphan Annie's politics (stressing the "secret" of the bomb) made him mad.[25]

If the public relations work of AORS is not presented in detail, it is in kindness to the reader and not for lack of material, for its editorial, information, records, and legislative committees and speakers' bureau were as active and left nearly as voluminous a record as those in Chicago. A book by Harrison Brown of AORS, *Must Destruction Be Our Destiny?* published by Simon and Schuster in February, 1946, was an effective and widely read statement of the implications of atomic weapons, and the author's royalties swelled the AORS' treasury. Oak Ridge speakers took the whole South as their responsibility and the demand from Nashville, Houston, Tulsa, Louisville, Birmingham, and smaller communities in Kentucky, Tennessee, and the Carolinas, if not exactly overwhelming, still kept them busy. AORS sent specially briefed speakers to fifteen religious conferences in the summer of 1946.[26]

The Oak Ridge scientists made perhaps their greatest contribution to public discussion through the medium of state conferences on atomic energy, a movement started when Lyle Borst, attending the University of Denver's Rocky Mountain Conference on Atomic Energy in December, 1945, so impressed the head of the Volker Fund of Kansas City that $5,000 was given to the Federation of Atomic Scientists and $500 to AORS to subsidize a speaking tour of Kansas. This took place in the first ten days of April, 1946, with Borst, Paul Henshaw, and Harrison Brown of Clinton Labs, J. J. Nickson and David Hill of Chicago, Theodore Jorgenson of Los Alamos, and Dean Joyce Stearns of Washington University, St. Louis, going along for all or part of the tour. Accompanied by social and political scientists from the University of Kansas, they moved from town to town on a tight schedule, with each man speaking several times a day, concentrating on the nature of the atom and its military significance in the morning and discussing social and political implications in the afternoon. There were talks also on the economics of atomic power and the recently published Acheson-Lilienthal Report on international control. Nickson was gratified that there appeared

---

[25] Falstein, "The Men Who Made the A-Bomb," *New Republic*, CXIII (November 26, 1945), 707–9. Orphan Annie's creator was also reproved from Los Alamos; see R. W. Williams to Harold Gray, November 10, 1945, ALAS IV, 10.

[26] Material relating to speaking engagements is in AORES IV, 4, 6, and XX, 1; and in FAS VII, 1.

to be no evidence of isolationist sentiment and that audiences seemed disposed to consider these novel questions on their merits. Action was encouraged. At Wichita three resolutions expressed support of the Acheson proposal and recommended a community committee on atomic energy and study of the social and political implications of atomic energy in the secondray schools.[27]

After the final merger of the Oak Ridge scientists' groups, the state conference program was carried on by a mass education committee, led first by Borst, then by K. Z. Morgan. Again supported by the Volker Fund, the new series began in Tennessee in August, 1946, with the University of Tennessee issuing three to eight hundred invitations in each of eight cities, and five of its faculty members assisting a half-dozen AORES speakers. The same pattern was followed in North Carolina in November (here a Virginia Quaker paid the speakers' expenses), and money was available for fifteen more, of which only five actually took place—Virginia in February, 1947, Florida in April (plenty of speakers volunteered for the Florida conference, commented the chairman), Georgia in May, Louisiana in June, and Alabama in October. No one could be found for a swing through Texas; still the area covered was substantial, and letters of appreciation showed that some impression had been made, although the local "councils on the atomic crisis," which it was hoped the conferences would inaugurate, were formed in only a few places.

The Oak Ridge community itself, where shortly before the war ended population had reached a peak of seventy-five thousand and employment in its plants and laboratories eighty-two thousand, offered considerable scope for atomic education. Teachers, the Women's Club, and a Forum Council for discussion of current issues that AORS helped to organize provided responsive audiences. With the advice of AORS scientists, Philip E. Kennedy, a high-school English teacher, set up a Youth Council on the Atomic Crisis, whose sponsors hoped that it might be the nucleus of a national youth movement. "An Open Letter to Modern Youth," in the Christmas, 1945, number of the school paper *Oak Leaf* showed what fervor the atomic scientists were capable of generating in their disciples.

We, the students of the high school at Oak Ridge, believe that our Christmas service to the world should be to tell it what we think about

---

[27] *Bulletin of the Atomic Scientists*, I (May 1, 1946), 14; correspondence in AORES V, 8, and ASC XX, 6; Nickson's report in ASC XXV, 5.

the atomic bomb. . . . To stop a war and save the lives of millions, our fathers and our brothers made this bomb. It served its purpose well. . . . We have listened to those of them who are our scientists. . . . We do not want to die a needless death. As you do, we want to live. Long years hence, we want to share our children's Christmases. . . . We wish that you could know Oak Ridge, know what is is to grow up almost in the shadows of these massive factories which can bring glory to the world or utter desolation. You would listen then when our scientists speak. . . .

Expressing alarm at the lack of attention paid to the testimony being presented to the Senate Special Committee on Atomic Energy, the letter concluded with an exhortation to the youth of America to help people see the handwriting on the wall and insist that atomic energy be used henceforth for peaceful, constructive purposes.[28]

It is easy now to be disturbed by the tense emotionalism running through the eight paragraphs of this letter, but it was quoted with approval on radio and in other school papers, and the reporters, including one from *Time*, that it brought to Oak Ridge were impressed with the sensible and mature way in which discussion of atomic energy was developed, especially in Kennedy's English classes. A special February issue of the school paper continued to pick up the scientists' current emphases, this time reproving Major de Seversky for playing down the destructiveness of the atomic bomb, and struck such a high moral note with a series of student opinions on how to prevent the use of the bomb that even a mild skeptic is relieved to come upon a column of particularly noxious teen-age jokes and a Student Council request for more "refined" conduct in the cafeteria.

AORS remained a lively activist organization through the nine months of its independent existence. Internal communication was at first covered by a daily news bulletin, which after the first hectic three months became a weekly one. A single issue of "The Soapbox," which had promised a continuous bull session on policy, was succeeded by an equally short-lived scheme of laboratory wards with representatives responsible for taking opinion polls and listening to gripes. A tendency to collective introspection became even more marked at Oak Ridge in late 1946 and 1947 as the whole scientists' movement adjusted to the postponement of success, and the periodic policy polls, as stipulated in the AORES constitution, provoked Fred-

---

[28] Reprinted in a special atomic energy issue of the *Oak Leaf*, III (February 19, 1946), 4, copy in ASC XV, 18.

erick Seitz to remark that when such an organization revealed truth it should be by more than majority vote.[29]

4. ENGINEERS AT OAK RIDGE

When the Clinton Labs scientists organized in September, 1945, there was talk of asking engineers at K-25 and Y-12 to join them, but the consensus of opinion was against it. At first no one knew how the army would regard communication between the plants and laboratories, but even after Secretary Patterson's assurance that discussion of political implications was in order, the men at Clinton Labs held off. They intended to be an action group, and the unanimity needed to get things done would be difficult with a larger membership not in daily contact; they were more confident of being able to work with the academic scientists at Chicago or Los Alamos, among whom they had friends, than with the engineers a few miles away whom they did not know. For their part the engineers at Y-12 and K-25 thought Clinton Labs unduly sensitive about army control, which they accepted as an interim necessity, and did not wish to campaign for its removal.

As explained in an earlier chapter, the Atomic Production Scientists of Oak Ridge at Y-12 developed when a dozen people interested in world government were encouraged by scientists at Clinton Labs to set up a formal organization at the end of October. Within four weeks, APSOR acquired one hundred twenty-five members, who were polled on their attitude to the May-Johnson bill, science legislation, and civilian versus military control. An editorial committee dispatched letters to a hundred college presidents on the military control issue, prepared material for congressional witnesses, and encouraged letters to congressmen. The world government study was revived by the four charter members and remained a primary interest of APSOR.[30]

The Atomic Engineers of Oak Ridge at the Carbide and Carbon Chemicals Company K-25 plant seems to have sprung up entirely under the influence of Clinton Labs and the impact of May-Johnson bill hearings the week of October 15. A statement of intent was cir-

---

[29] "The Soapbox," ed. R. P. Lyon and P. C. Tompkins, November 19, 1945, AORES XX, 1; AORS education committee memorandum, January 18, 1946, AORES IV, 4; Seitz quoted in AORES Newsletter, January 2, 1947, AORES XX, 4.

[30] APSOR material, including newsletters, is in the AORES files; see especially AORES VI, 10, 11; XX, 1.

culated and an executive committee elected. On November 2, when AEOR was formally organized, ninety-three people joined. A month later there was a paid membership of two hundred forty-eight, but in the interval 30 per cent of those originally enrolled had dropped out because the membership fee of $1.00 a month seemed excessive.[31]

AEOR members also commenced an active correspondence with editors, radio commentators, and public officials. They commended Dorothy Thompson, Drew Pearson, and Thomas L. Stokes for views expressed in their columns. Candidates for president of the American Chemical Society were asked to go on record in support of the views of the atomic scientists' associations. In December the combined editorial committees of AEOR and APSOR wrote articles for Tennessee newspapers summarizing testimony before the McMahon committee.[32]

The first enlistment of members at Y-12 and K-25 went fairly well. But later developments justified the fears of Clinton Labs about unanimity. One reluctant recruit, identified only as "an applied scientist," was scathing in his comment:

They then started trying to form an association and they sent around the circular for the fellows to sign up.... They tried everything to get me to sign but I wouldn't do it. "D" who was a big shot in the outfit wouldn't even speak to me.... Finally it got so bad that somebody was talking to me about five or six times a day and I signed the damn thing so I could get some work done. "A" shook my hand and I never before realized how important my signature was.... The trouble is that "A," "B," "C," and "D" [all pure scientists] and others are putting the pressure on and all of the other dumb oafs, such as myself are falling in line. I still don't know what they're talking about.... I think the main thing they want to do is to get all information released on the bomb.[33]

The conclusion that while this was an extreme case of resistance it was not an isolated one is supported by membership figures, for neither of the engineers' groups reached anything like the potential numbers hopefully cited—eighteen hundred for AEOR and five hundred

[31] AEOR executive committee members were: J. A. Armitage, F. C. Armistead, W. C. Beard, Jr., H. A. Nowak, C. B. Slade, A. M. Squires, and T. Williamson; AORS Daily Bulletin, October 24, 31, 1945, AORES XX, 1; AEOR committee reports, and other material, in AORES VI, 7.

[32] Correspondence in AORES III, 8; VI, 9; XVI, 2.

[33] Quoted by Margaret Smith Stahl, "Splits and Schisms, Nuclear and Social" (Ph.D. dissertation, University of Wisconsin, 1946), p. 259.

for APSOR. In March, 1946, the two groups together had four hundred fifty members.

They did include, however, two dozen or so deeply committed individuals. AEOR and APSOR quickly announced adherence to the Federation of Atomic Scientists when it was formed in early November and immediately sent E. E. Minett as their joint delegate to the new Washington office. Before he went Minett discussed with his fellow engineers whether, and in what ways, they differed from research scientists in their fundamental approach to atomic energy. Should atomic engineering research continue under private corporations as during the war, and to what extent should these projects be controlled and assisted by government? How would engineers fit into an international control scheme? What precautions should the profession take to see that a few unscrupulous members, perhaps employed by a company under contract to a foreign government, did not misuse their technical knowledge to the disadvantage of the United States? What positive engineering program could be recommended to further world peace by raising living standards in other countries?[34] The answers unfortunately are missing, but it is significant that the questions were raised. Minett reported that his associates in Washington, Szilard excepted, felt that engineers could broaden the base of the federation in a useful way, and AEOR sent H. A. Nowak, "a real engineer" rather than a Ph.D., as Minett's successor. As had Minett, Nowak also represented APSOR, which had raised enough money to send three delegates but was less successful in finding candidates, and he was followed in turn by other AEOR members, A. M. Squires and F. C. Armistead.[35]

In December, 1945, a painless amalgamation of the two engineers' groups took place, and on January 8 the first meeting of the Oak Ridge Engineers and Scientists, known as ORES, took steps to join the new Federation of American Scientists rather than the Atomic Scientists, to which APSOR and AEOR had belonged.[36] The ORES bi-weekly newsletter, "The Atomic Engineer and Scientist"—eight

[34] Minett memorandum, November 9, 1945, AORES VI, 8.

[35] AEOR executive committee minutes, November 16, 1945, AORES VI, 7; November and December entries in FAS History-Diary, in FAS files (Washington, D.C.).

[36] The ORES officers were Lyle Brewer, chairman; W. C. Beard, Jr., vice-chairman; H. A. Nowak, executive secretary; and J. A. Armitage, treasurer; assisted by a planning committee consisting of D. A. McRae (chairman), W. G. Stone, J. L. Waters, F. C. Armistead, and Cuthbert Daniel ("Atomic Engineer and Scientist," February 2, 1946, in AORES files).

mimeographed pages with a mushroom cloud on the front—provided excellent summaries of atomic energy news and reading lists but made no attempt at the extensive documentation or the exploratory articles of the Chicago *Bulletin,* with which its sponsors at one time spoke hopefully of amalgamation. In mid-March of 1946, when civilian control was much in the news and relevant material was perhaps given more than a passing glance, ORES was sending copies to 531 members of Congress, 800 editors and publicists, 150 college presidents, and 350 organizations and friends. A log book commenced by ORES continued as the official record of the fully merged Oak Ridge associations until October, 1948, when the final entry tersely noted the closing of the office.

Meanwhile ORES joined in the critical appraisal of atomic energy bills that was proceeding in the early weeks of 1946 and turned out statements and telegrams at critical points in the McMahon bill campaign. But on the whole, members of ORES were less exercized about the domestic issue than the other groups originally forming the Federation of Atomic Scientists. Passionate involvement on the part of ORES members was reserved more often than not for international matters; the practical engineers specialized in study committees on UNESCO, international control, and world government, whereas the research men went in for political action.

The ORES world government committee eventually absorbed the one on international control and helped organize world government groups among both women and teachers at Oak Ridge. In the early summer of 1946, the Youth Council on the Atomic Crisis helped ORES conduct a world government poll in which 70 per cent of those questioned, described as twelve hundred representative Oak Ridge residents, expressed the opinion that the United States government should work for world government immediately, and 53 per cent thought world government could prevent war. From ORES circles also came a "Credo of an Atomic Engineer," elaborating the theme that only by establishment of world justice and order can war be abolished. Efforts to get the "Credo" published through the FAS were unsuccessful; the scientists' movement was not adverse to slogans, but it drew the line at creeds.[37]

---

[37] Henshaw to Swing, December 21, 1945, and Swing to Henshaw, December 24, 1945, AORES V, 9; Higinbotham to Stout, January 25, 1945, in FAS chronological files (Washington, D.C.); memorandum from ORES members to L. Brewer, March 21, 1946, AORES VII, 1; report on ORES poll, Balderston to Q. Wright, July 15, 1946,

Although Clinton Labs had decided not to take part in the December AEOR-APSOR merger, the winter saw collaboration on legislation, speaking, and writing, and in March AORS and ORES began to share an office in the Roane-Anderson Building in the Town Site area. The response to a proposed women's auxiliary of AORS and ORES wives was disappointing, but a few women, led by Mrs. Paul Tompkins, loyally typed, filed, and answered the phone.

Toward the end of April, 1946, amalgamation was again suggested, this time by AORS members, among whom the growing manpower shortage seems to have induced a change of heart. After a trial period of joint meetings a constitution was drawn up for the Association of Oak Ridge Engineers and Scientists, known as AORES, and on July 10 E. E. Minett, originally of AEOR, became chairman of a twelve-man executive committee, six from AORS and six from ORES.[38] The merger was taking place just as the McMahon bill began its stormy journey through House committees and floor debate, a period made especially critical for Oak Ridge scientists, as we shall later see, by a visit in early June from the chairman and counsel of the House Un-American Activities Committee and subsequent charges in the House of subversion at Oak Ridge. It was a good time to be united.

5. HOLLYWOOD, PRESS, AND PUBLIC

This singling out of the older associations for biographical treatment may seem unjust to some who worked hard in other places, but it is a fact that the impetus and the pattern for the educational campaign were provided by Chicago, Oak Ridge, and Los Alamos, and as records of the other associations are meager by comparison so were their activities.

Later it was a different story. After early 1947 the FAS would have made a poor showing without Northern California and the Committee for Foreign Correspondence, Cornell and its study of clearance procedures, Mohawk Valley's technical aid to foreign

---

AORES IX, 3; copies of the "Credo" and correspondence in FAS XXI, 2 and XXIII, 1. Chairman John Balderston frankly admitted that the world government committee shouted loudest and wrote most in the hope of getting the Oak Ridge scientists committed to it; in this it never succeeded, although in early 1948, the committee, independently of AORES, established an Oak Ridge chapter of United World Federalists.

[38] From ORES: W. A. Arnold, Walter C. Beard, Cuthbert Daniel, E. E. Minett, H. Pearlman, J. D. Trimmer; from AORS: Lyle Borst, Waldo Cohn, Paul Henshaw, K. Z. Morgan, James Stangby, Paul Tompkins (AORES executive committee minutes, July 10, 1946, AORES VIII, 1).

scientists, Rochester with its foreign student program, or the Washington, D.C., group to staff the office and carry on special studies. By 1951 when Oak Ridge and Los Alamos were virtually dormant, New York scientists were still providing motive power for a local committee on atomic information. And now years later it is not from Chicago that protests are heard about overreliance on fallout shelters or the oversaturation of the arms program—although some who made such commotion in 1945 are still there—but from Cambridge.

When the expanded federation began to function in January, 1946, it did not take over local educational projects but tried rather to provide a clearing house and fill in gaps. This tactic resulted on occasion in too many fingers in the public relations pie, a tendency highlighted by one of the more tumultuous chapters in Federation affairs—its participation in the major film about atomic energy, M-G-M's *The Beginning or the End.*

Films and movies had early occurred to the site groups as a promising medium for keeping alive the impact of Hiroshima, but the M-G-M connection had a fortuitous start at Oak Ridge in a congratulatory letter received by Edward Tompkins of Clinton Labs from a one-time high-school science student, M-G-M actress Donna Reed. Acknowledging her note, Tompkins facetiously expressed surprise that Hollywood did not have a movie about the Project ready for release. He promptly received a call from Miss Reed, introducing her husband Tony Owens, a Hollywood agent who thought the film a great idea and wanted to come to Oak Ridge to discuss it.

Tompkins, of course, consulted the AORS executive committee, which began a cautious appraisal: they must see what other sites were doing; they must inform General Groves; any picture they sponsored must be first class. More phone calls disclosed that L. B. Mayer of M-G-M was enthusiastic and that United Artists was also interested. Clinton Labs men themselves began sketching out sequences; one manuscript in their files depicts the nuclear holocaust and the subsequent reversion of civilization to 100,000 B.C. with a positive flair for the banal.[39]

Tony Owens, accompanied by producer Sam Marx, arrived in Oak Ridge on November 5. They spent two hours with the AORS executive committee, seemed to grasp at once what the scientists wanted

---

[39] E. Tompkins to Donna Owens, October 26, 1945, AORES V, 3; the same folder also contains notes of phone calls, executive committee minutes, scripts, and later correspondence on which the following account is based.

to say, and taking Tompkins and Stangby along as consultants, set off for Washington to get General Grove's approval. The negotiations with Groves went smoothly (though the AORS newsletter could not resist the crack that he wanted a shot of the scientists sitting on his knee). Not so the dealings with the new Federation of Atomic Scientists, which had just set up shop in its borrowed quarters on Vermont Avenue. The confusion in the dingy attic office made a most unhappy impression on the gentlemen from Hollywood. Delegates, improvising in all directions, rushed in and out; the phone rang constantly, and the succession of young men who joined the discussion seemed pathologically suspicious of Hollywood. Muttering that they couldn't work with such an outfit, Marx and Owens took their leave, and only Tompkins' skilful blandishments got them to a breakfast conference next morning. Even there the scientists' sense of crisis produced phone calls and abrupt departures; the tenuous contact was only just kept alive, though with no clear understanding of what the federation would approve.[40]

Marx, however, advised Tompkins that given official approval M-G-M would move ahead on the largest possible scale; he asked Tompkins to act as technical adviser, and an M-G-M contribution to the federation was mentioned. Seeking official blessings at the highest level, Marx and Owens obtained an appointment with President Truman, to whom they outlined their plans. The President's answer was, "Make your film, gentlemen, and tell the world that this is either the beginning or the end." "Mr. President," replied Marx, "you have just chosen the title of our film."[41]

As the original sponsoring organization, AORS also made Tompkins its representative, and in mid-January he began a stay of ten uneasy weeks in Hollywood. The story prepared by Robert Consodine was highly satisfactory, but the subsequent manipulations of scriptwriter, producer, and art director played such havoc with the authenticity of certain scenes involving scientists that Tompkins found the later stages of his assignment a harrowing experience. Typical incidents were the transformation of the starkly simple setting of the first chain reaction into a chrome plated nightmare with colored lights and ringing bells and the dictum of the producer that it was

---

[40] AORS Daily Bulletin, November 12, 14, 1945, AORES XX, 1; Borst diary for November 7, 8, 1945; interview with Borst, February 20, 1962.

[41] As reconstructed by Edward R. Tompkins in a letter to the author, September 25, 1964. I rely at several points upon Dr. Tompkins' helpful elaboration of the documents.

not important how a scientist would talk but how the public thought he would talk.

At the same time Project scientists wanted the movie to be worthy of its subject, and everybody put in a word. Oak Ridge urged a strong push for world government. The Columbia group forwarded suggestions from anthropologists Margaret Mead and Gregory Bateson. Chicago was touchy, as indeed was Clinton Labs, about the *quid pro quo* involved in accepting an M-G-M "contribution," and a check for $5,000 was passed around like a hot potato. M-G-M wanted the FAtS seal of approval and its help in obtaining permission for impersonation from individuals, for which their check was apparently considered payment, but the FAtS leaders (it still had no officers) protested that they could not accept payment for specific services though they expected to give a generous endorsement if the movie was good. Gratuitous and sometimes querulous advice of this sort, conveyed in phone calls to Tompkins, was recorded, it later turned out, for the benefit of M-G-M executives and confirmed the unfavorable impression that producer Sam Marx had earlier formed in Washington. Thanking Norman Cousins for "setting us fairly right with the more important scientists in the Project," Marx expressed admiration for Szilard and Urey, whose outlook was vast and their understanding great; but, he continued, he was concerned about the younger and less important scientists whose critical attitude he attributed to "their youth, inexperience, and, regrettably enough, smaller minds." They seemed to dislike the idea of putting any entertainment in the film, and Marx wondered if it was worthwhile trying to educate them.[42]

Marx's examples of docility were not well chosen, and Tompkins, reporting that Marx had threatened to fire him and get Szilard out to Hollywood, commented that then Marx would really know what trouble was! Indeed, it was not long before word circulated that both Szilard and Urey had told Marx that the script was "lousy." Szilard, it seems, not only insisted on the inclusion of a certain scene about himself but wrote it as well!

In a belated effort to improve relations with M-G-M, J. J. Nickson of the ASC was made head of a FAtS committee to supervise films. FAtS representatives meeting in Chicago and motivated by idealism, legal advice, and word that Szilard and Einstein would allow them-

---

[42] Marx to Cousins, January 10, 1946, in Simpson's files.

selves to be impersonated only if the federation received a sum approaching $100,000, decided to return the $5,000 check to M-G-M. But while they were stalling over it, M-G-M had obtained some permissions, and Nickson could do little more than record individual decisions, some of which changed as different versions of the script were read. A few scientists, notably Niels Bohr and Lise Meitner, never granted permission, and those who did, to Marx's distress, would accept no money in return.[43]

But having returned the check the federation had little excuse for interfering. Tompkins was needed at Oak Ridge, and so, declaring that his own ignorance of movie-making was balanced by Marx's ignorance of how to handle scientists, he surrendered the job of technical adviser to General Groves's nominee, physicist H. T. Wenzel, formerly technical information officer at Oak Ridge.

The ill-starred liaison closed on a happier note in the late spring of 1946 when David Hawkins went to Hollywood at Oppenheimer's request and with Marx's consent to keep an eye on portrayal of character and technical details. A thirty-three-year-old philosopher from Berkeley, in charge of technical personnel at Los Alamos and very knowledgeable about science, Hawkins' versatility acquired still another dimension during the month that he and his wife occupied M-G-M's Beverly Hills guesthouse, but his preconceptions about Hollywood remained pretty much intact as he observed the delivery of slot machines for a director's party and noted the haphazard arrangements for sound and light to accompany the world's first nuclear explosion. But he liked Sam Marx, contending bravely on the one hand with straight-laced scientists and with the M-G-M executive officer on the other. When Hawkins arrived Marx was trying to tie in the prologue—an idea bought on speculation and fitting well, M-G-M thought, the cosmic character of the atomic bomb. The contents of a time capsule, buried in the California Redwoods and containing a copy of the Bible and the script of *The Beginning or the End*, was being explained by the hero of the movie to an audience yet unborn. His quaint language, he told them, was English; his jacket was woven from the coat of a sheep; his necktie was made of silk. The identity of the hero, however, was yet to be decided.

---

[43] Marx found it ironic that the army men all accepted payment for granting permission to be impersonated and then never gave any trouble. Marx to L. Robertson, December 10, 1962 (letter shown to the author by Mrs. Robertson); and correspondence in Nickson's files.

Marx maintained he was J. Robert Oppenheimer; the executive officer claimed he was General Groves. Marx won his point, Hawkins recalls, on the specious grounds that the General could not wear a necktie.

Marx did not always win his arguments, nor did Hawkins. Filming done before he arrived could not be changed. He substituted a few Los Alamos stories for some execrable jokes but was never able to persuade M-G-M technicians that the sound of the bomb should come after the light or convince the executive officer that a superb speech of Oppenheimer's would be a more forceful commentary on Roosevelt's death than a stock crowd scene. We cannot, was the dictum, be partisan![44]

A wholly favorable verdict on the finished product from the critical scientific audience was too much to hope for. Harrison Brown, one of those young men Marx found so difficult, deplored the film's poor character portrayal and modification of history to suit the plot. Whereas the first chain reaction at Stagg Field had taken place in abnormal stillness, M-G-M sound effects were like the walls of Jericho. More serious was the false impression that Hiroshima had been showered with leaflets warning of an atomic attack. It was true, said Brown, that Americans would get some picture of nuclear bombing, but he thought the film's optimistic implications that things would work out should have been tied to what individuals could do about it.[45]

After the Washington preview Higinbotham remembers only a feeling of relief that the film was so dull, but at a similar event in Chicago roars of laughter greeted Fermi's thick fruit vender's accent, and Oppenheimer's mannerisms seemed hilariously funny. But when the lights went on the faces of M-G-M representatives bore a look of puzzled disappointment.

Much of the film-making projected in the first flush of enthusiasm for atomic education never came to fruition. Bradford Shank, a young employee in Los Alamos procurement who aspired to be a Hollywood agent, commenced negotiations with the Disney Studios, the Society of Independent Motion Picture Producers, and the Academy of Motion Picture Arts and Sciences about an industry-wide film. M-G-M's early start checked that scheme, but ALAS and then the FAS partly subsidized Shank for several months in order to have someone in Hollywood promoting their viewpoint and keep-

---

[44] Interview with Hawkins, April 5, 1963.

[45] Harrison Brown, "The Beginning or the End: A Review," *Bulletin of the Atomic Scientists*, III (March, 1947), 99.

ing a weather eye on developments. Paramount began an ambitious documentary but eventually sold its rights to M-G-M; Presentation Associates planned and dropped a film on the peaceful uses of atomic energy. The *Encyclopaedia Britannica* completed a film for high-school students on atomic physics but abandoned one on social implications. Although federation scientists had not directly inspired all these efforts, they were drawn into much consultation and correspondence. It was the more modest projects that succeeded. The Philadelphia association sponsored a one-reel animated film strip, *One World or None*, released in the autumn of 1946 by Film Publishers for the National Committee on Atomic Information, and collaborated on a cartoon strip, *How To Live with the Atom*. Chicago scientists gave technical advice on Society of Visual Education films, one called *The Atomic Bomb* and others on medical and industrial applications. Scientists' enthusiasm about a "March of Time" film, *Atomic Power*, released in August, 1946, showed that it was not impossible to please them. But when it came to dramatizing atomic energy, it was hard to devise anything to compete with the bomb itself, and the mainstay of the film repertory were the items distributed by Los Alamos and used by scientists all over the country to point up their message—the slides of the test shot at Alamogordo and the films of Hiroshima and Nagasaki.[46]

Such educational projects as the Washington office initiated followed the pattern of speaking, writing, and invoking the help of influential people already begun by the site organizations. When no great clamor greeted offerings from local editorial chairmen, it was supposed that co-ordination of effort would produce better results, and in January, 1946, the FAS hired Michael Amrine, the young journalist who had been so helpful in the autumn, to keep track of press coverage and to edit and place articles. Amrine and Higin-botham hit it off at once. They both got a slow start in the mornings but usually worked until midnight, and even their Saturday night beer parties, shared by visiting scientists and office volunteers, were devoted to singing parodies about what Amrine calls their obsession. In many ways he identified himself with the scientists' cause, but he despaired at times at their purist attitude on movie and radio contracts, at the erratic leadership provided by some of the older men,

---

[46] Material on various film projects is in AORES and ASC executive committee minutes, AORES IV, 4, and ASC VI, 12, 13; see also AORS I, 6; II, 10; V, 3; XVI, 7, 9; Armistead report, ca. December 15, 1945, AORES XIV, 1; FAS I, 8; and XVI, 1.

and at what he (more than some other lay associates) considers their incurably apolitical outlook. When one of the frequent office bull sessions had descended to the level of suggesting that the world ought to be governed by scientists, Amrine banged his fist on the table and shouted, "I'd rather be bombed!"

Keeping an eye on atomic energy news was a big job in these days, and on the whole the federation was alert to what was going on and enjoyed a remarkably good press. At FAS instigation the de Seversky article, "Atomic Bomb Hysteria," in the February, 1946, *Reader's Digest* was answered in the same magazine by Robert Littell's "What the Bomb Would Do to Us"; and on numerous other occasions Amrine or Rush wrote to correct published statements.

Amrine also worked hard at the job of getting and placing articles. Before joining the FAS staff he had written a vivid discourse on the dangers of atomic warfare, which, with Harold Urey's signature and the title "I'm a Frightened Man," appeared in the January 5, 1946, issue of *Collier's*. He later interviewed Einstein for the *New York Times Magazine* and edited pieces by Higinbotham for leading newspapers and the Labor Press Association. A luridly illustrated *Look* article of March 5, "Your Last Chance," reflected the scientists' worst forebodings, but in the autumn Amrine helped arrange a more sober *Look* symposium, whose contributors included Oppenheimer, Higinbotham, Henshaw, and Hawkins.

But most of Amrine's overtures to magazine editors met the same fate as those of local committees. The long atomic energy section of the *Readers' Guide* for 1945–46 includes a substantial number of scientist authors but mostly in journals whose readers may have been strong on influence but were small in number. Amrine tried to jog FAS writers onto more popular tacks with a stream of memoranda suggesting Alamogordo anniversary articles and, for Los Alamos scientists, article titles such as "I'm Still Making Bombs" or "Why the Bomb Is No Secret." Next he tried a list of slightly more specialized topics: atomic power as a practical reality, radioactivity, dispersal of cities, Russian progress in nuclear physics, caves as shelters. But the impulse to write was now expending itself, where possible, in scientific papers or in the semitechnical pages of the *Bulletin of the Atomic Scientists*, which demanded no radical adjustments in literary style.[47]

Daniel Lang's first *New Yorker* descriptions of life and work at

---

[47] Material in FAS II, 7; V, 3; 4; VI, 2; XIX, 1.

Oak Ridge and Los Alamos were done without direct contact with the atomic scientists, but the Washington staff was often in touch with him while he was doing the later articles on Morrison's impressions of Japan, on the Y-12 plant at Oak Ridge, on the work of the Lilienthal panel, and finally, on the FAS (November 16, 1946), a generally sympathetic story featuring Higinbotham, entitled "That's Four Times 10^{-4} Ergs, Old Man."

Radio, by virtue of its ephemeral character, was better able to use amateur talent than the other media and more disposed to tackle a subject still unclear in its outlines and meaning. Urey, Franck, Bethe, and Oppenheimer gave intermission talks on the CBS Sunday afternoon broadcasts of the New York Philharmonic, Higinbotham arranged for speakers or filled in himself on numerous programs in Washington, and every local association sponsored and took part in a radio series of some sort.

Higinbotham carried on contacts made by site organizations in New York and Washington and tried, often against heavy odds, to co-ordinate what other people were doing. In the spring and summer of 1946 he dealt at length with a proposition from Tony Owens that the FAS sign a seven-year contract and give exclusive support to a radio series starring Orson Welles. Undeterred by M-G-M's experience, Owens was prepared to state that "all the minds connected with atomic science have joined forces to make 'The Atom Story' the one significant, official radio series." This kind of talk sent a collective shudder through local executive committees, and thinking wistfully of what $1,000 a week would do for their empty treasury, FAS leaders turned down Owens' contract.[48]

The Chicago-sponsored conference for executives of major networks was held in New York on June 5, at a time of particular concern about how the United Nations Atomic Energy Commission discussions opening the next week and the forthcoming Bikini tests would be reported to the public, but Urey and the other speakers seemed to talk over the heads of their audience, and contact with radio magnates was less rewarding than with friendly broadcasters like Swing and Utley.[49]

---

[48] Higinbotham diary, entries for May and June, 1946; correspondence and contracts in FAS XXII, 2, 4; ASC executive committee minutes, May through August, 1946, ASC VI, 13.

[49] Professor Fred Eastman of the Chicago Theological Seminary, whose field was religious education, acted as agent for the ASC in planning the radio conference; see ASC executive committee minutes, April 9, 1946, and later meetings, ASC VI, 12, 13, and other material in ASC III, 12, and FAS XXII, 1.

At the same time a more satisfactory way of using radio was opening up through the Advertising Council, a New York organization formed to promote worthy causes through contributions of time, space, and services. Since March negotiations had been going on between the FAS, the NCAI, and the Council about adoption of international control as one of these causes, a step urgently supported by Oppenheimer, who felt that popular understanding might be crucial to acceptance of the recently completed Acheson-Lilienthal plan. In early June, the Council gave the project its stamp of highest priority. With G. Edward Pendray as co-ordinator, Young and Rubicam as the volunteer agency, and the FAS as official adviser, a fact sheet was distributed to major networks with short plugs to be inserted between programs. A series of printed advertisements began in the fall. Higinbotham watched developments carefully, checking the implications of copywriters' statements with the latest pooling of opinion by FAS scientists and those attached to the United States delegation to the UNAEC. He was enthusiastic about the Council's contribution, and indeed the number of listener impressions registered between July, 1946, and February, 1947, estimated at 658,295,000, could not fail to excite amateur publicists accustomed to reaching audiences of fifty to a hundred at a time.[50]

An inevitable result of courting public attention was a vast quantity of mail—requests for technical information, inquiries about the federation, sincere offers of help, some exceedingly welcome, others no less heartening for not being highly literate or precisely to the point. Letters often mentioned the articles in *Collier's*, *Life*, or *Look*, and the *New Yorker* article of November, 1946, brought what Higinbotham called a touching response, including a check for $50 from a Socony Vacuum employee in Egypt in place of Christmas presents for himself and his wife. "Sister and I are glad the scientists of America are organizing," wrote a retired costume designer who wanted to promote a fund drive in her New Jersey suburb, and an unemployed member of the International Ladies Garment Workers enclosed a dollar and a list of possible contributors.[51]

Some correspondence found its way into "crackpot" files in Wash-

---

[50] J. J. Nickson to Theodore Repplier, Executive Director, War Advertising Council, February 14, 1946, in FAS chronological files (Washington, D.C.); report of Hagemann to the ASC, ca. March 2, 1946, ASC files; Higinbotham to A. Wilson, September 26, 1946, FAS IV, 5; Higinbotham to Emergency Committee of Atomic Scientists, January 17, 1947, FAS XV, 4; annual report of the Advertising Council, March 1, 1947, FAS IV, 5.

[51] Correspondence in FAS III, 4, 7; XVIII, 1.

ington and the sites, although the nature of the subject and the situation in which the contrivers of the bomb had placed themselves made the line an awkward one to draw, for some of the discoveries and devices offered were not a whit less improbable than the atomic bomb, nor were the panaceas more revolutionary than the Lilienthal panel's proposal for international control. An engineer wanted the opinion of the site groups on his estimate of the number of seconds required to lower the Empire State Building into the ground; another presented his theory of the origin of energy in the motions of the Unseen Fluid Ether. A laboratory director was warned that the beam of light recently observed was not, as he might think, the aurora borealis but a focusing of ultramicrowaves originating in Omsk or Tomsk, of which he was the target. The world's scientists should unite for a standard fair wage scale, wrote another. Or all medicines were poison, so what did the FAS mean by claiming that atomic medicine had already saved thousands of lives (a question raised also by several FAS members, following an optimistic but imprecise release on the subject)? Much unsolicited literature accompanied these comments: poems privately printed, a pamphlet entitled "The Inventor's Magna Charta," a manuscript on the classless America. Even the most muddled discourse often made a telling point. The old world of Christianity was gone, lameted one woman as she closed a rambling account of her troubles and fears for her son. "What are you great scientists going to do, live in the old world and a new world and believe in both?" What, indeed!

6. The Emergency Committee and the NCAI

The principal agent of the federation in educating the American public was the National Committee on Atomic Information, which the Federation of Atomic Scientists had helped to organize in November, 1945. Using the communication facilities of existing organizations did in some cases—church groups, labor unions, and the League of Women Voters—multiply many times and with a minimum of expense the initial impulse; others were less suited to this purpose and their affiliation was largely nominal.[52]

After the first meeting with the scientists on November 16, the NCAI quickly completed its own organization with Ralph McDonald,

---

[52] NCAI files are deposited in the Library of Congress, but duplicate material is scattered throughout the files of the FAS and the local associations, see especially FAS XIX; XXIV, 1; and ASC III, 6; XIV, 5 XVII, 13, 14; XVIII, 1, 2, 3; XXVII, Vol. IX.

chief of the Division of Higher Education of the National Education Association, as chairman, Mrs. Helen Dwight Reid of the American Association of University Women as vice-chairman, Mrs. Joy Falk of the United Council of Church Women as secretary, and Father E. A. Conway, S.J., of the Catholic Association for International Peace as treasurer. They, with representatives of eleven other organizations, formed the executive committee that enlisted the support of distinguished lay sponsors and a panel of eminent scientists. John Simpson represented the federation on the NCAI executive committee, and he was succeeded in turn by Higinbotham and David Hawkins.

The director, Daniel Melcher, credited with an outstanding job at the Treasury Department in promoting the sale of war bonds in schools, shared the FAS office at 1721 K Street, and by June, when the two organizations moved to larger quarters at 1749 L, the NCAI staff was dealing with many of the miscellaneous contacts that had so overwhelmed the scientists. Early in March it began to distribute a fortnightly bulletin, *Atomic Information*, designed to provide the ten million members of its affiliates with bibliographies, discussion guides, lists of articles, and brief popular articles, interspersed, sometimes with more liberality than discrimination, with quotations about the significance of atomic energy. Its pages were brightened with the work of Herblock and other cartoonists who shared the scientists' views of the military or political figures who seemed to stand in the way of civilian or international control. If the ten thousand copies being printed in early April were read and used as directed the impression made should not have been negligible, nor was it, to judge by the burden carried up the seventy-seven steps by the postman and one day's catalogue of orders for literature, offers of help, movie and newspaper contacts, and the like. The backbone of the NCAI program was the distribution of atomic energy literature, which included the Acheson-Lilienthal Report on International Control, study kits and discussion outlines, a cartoon film strip, the *Bulletin of the Atomic Scientists*, reprints of articles, plays, and NCAI publications. By June, 1946, thirty thousand copies had been sold of a six-page NCAI pamphlet, "Education for Survival," telling what organizations and individuals could do.[53]

A mid-June summary indicates some success in the fanning out of effort. The Young People's Division of the Congregational Church

---

[53] Melcher to Simpson, April 29, 1946, FAS XI, 8.

was re-enacting hearings of the Senate Special Committee on Atomic Energy at a summer conference of three hundred delegates from every state in the union. Americans United for World Organization was keeping a team of speakers on atomic energy in the field all summer. The National Council of Jewish Women had sent to all its sections an official call for action and with it analyses of the McMahon bill and the Acheson-Lilienthal Report. The American Association of University Women had chosen atomic information as the topic for its annual dinner, and the League of Women Voters had made civilian and international control the first item on its two-year agenda. Boston's Joint Council on International Organization, made up of thirty-nine organizations, had sponsored a rally on "Atomic Energy in War and Peace," with members of the M.I.T. faculty presenting Louis Ridenour's dramatization of accidental nuclear war, "Pilot Lights of the Apocalypse."[54]

With the public reacting strongly on the civilian control issue in the spring of 1946, Melcher saw no limit to what he might accomplish, given money and staff. A New York fund-raiser, Harold L. Oram, thought that $20,000 a month could be raised for atomic education, and early in May arrangements were concluded between him and the NCAI for a major drive. Oram advised seeking high-level sponsorship, and he and Melcher went to Princeton to see Einstein, a member of the NCAI scientific panel. What happened next is not entirely clear. Perhaps Oram and Einstein together proposed an "emergency committee," though one observer suspects that the vagueness of the original proposals left Einstein somewhat out on a limb, from which Szilard, Urey, and others united to rescue him. Perhaps they merely wished to extend the benefits of the campaign to the FAS and others concerned with atomic education. In any case in June—over the protests of Higinbotham and Rush at creation of still another entity in the field—they organized the Emergency Committee of Atomic Scientists, with Einstein as chairman, to back the drive. Its relations with the FAS and other parts of the scientists' movement will be discussed later. In the early summer of 1946 the prestige of the Emergency Committee, as it was usually called, greatly aided Oram's efforts, and the first appeal brought in nearly $100,000.

Some of this was in hand by the time Melcher submitted his financial report for the six months ending June 30, 1946, and ac-

---

[54] *Atomic Information*, I (June 17, 1946), 2.

counted for the fact that expenditures of over $28,000 were more than balanced by an income of $67,200, of which nearly $64,000 was in contributions. (Sales of literature had brought in $3,383.85.) This happy condition encouraged Melcher to propose that three field workers, an editorial assistant, and a radio contact man be added to the staff when the NCAI executive committee met on July 7.[55]

Melcher himself was not invited to this meeting, and the reason soon became evident. For some time, it turned out, the executive committee had been uneasy on a number of points: Melcher's failure to consult them about hiring staff, mounting evidence that he was antagonizing important sources of outside support, and an increasing display of animosity toward the scientists with whom he had been hired to work, especially toward Higinbotham. All this was brought to a head by a letter from FAS representative John Simpson, also unable to be present on July 7. Reflecting particularly the sentiments of the strongly interested Chicago group, Simpson complained that NCAI policy had lagged behind that of the scientists and that *Atomic Information* sometimes misrepresented their views. Avoiding personalities, he pointed out that lack of a strong NCAI policy group had forced the director to assume this function but that, with the likelihood of ample funds, it was more than ever essential that a complete overhaul of policy be made by the NCAI executive committee, the FAS leaders, and the new Emergency Committee. Simpson's reference to this tripartite control laid bare one of the roots of the trouble. It was not the first time, nor would it be the last, that too many cooks were in evidence in the scientists' affairs, and Melcher's tendency to create tension, of which his employers complained, was probably due in part to desperation at having too many bosses and to their interference with his fund-raising plans for the NCAI. Whatever the cause, his relations in all three directions seemed to have deteriorated beyond repair. The executive committee held several more meetings *in camera*, trying to resolve the administrative problem without jeopardizing the extended program that now seemed possible. Melcher refused to consider working under a new director, and his connection with the NCAI was terminated at the end of July.[56]

---

[55] NCAI financial statement and outline of program, FAS XIX, 3.

[56] Copy of NCAI policy committee minutes, July 27, 1946, with relevant correspondence, FAS XIX, 3.

The attention given to this personnel problem is justified only because of its repercussions and the dilemma it pointed up. Everyone agreed that in some directions Melcher had done a good job. Understandably he felt ill-used and could not accept as adequate the explanation of personal incompatibility that NCAI Chairman McDonald, citing a good deal of supporting evidence, maintained was the only reason for dismissal. Knowing that another reason had been mentioned in the executive committee, Melcher claimed that he was the victim of politics, and indeed, there was present just enough political apprehension about the NCAI staff to make the situation awkward.

As mentioned earlier, from the time they first organized a handful of FAS scientists had been extremely nervous about association with any group whose composition they could not vouch for. In particular great care had to be exercised in what the scientists said about sharing atomic information lest they inadvertently follow the Communist party line. An editorial in *Atomic Information*, defending British physicist Alan Nunn May, had caused considerable alarm, as had some statements in the secrecy and science issue. All NCAI material was supposed to be submitted to the FAS staff for approval, but whether by design, inadvertence, or because of strained relations, this had not always been done. Amrine, whose job it was as FAS publications editor to view critically anything said in the scientists' name (and who was himself sometimes criticized for acting without consultation), felt strongly that something was wrong. On the basis of information he provided, one NCAI board member raised the question—at which Simpson's reference to misrepresentation had hinted —of extreme left-wing bias of NCAI material, but Chairman McDonald firmly maintained, as did Higinbotham in his replies to protests from FAS members who heard the rumor of "politics," that Melcher's personal difficulties had been the reason for his dismissal and that no others had been seriously considered.

Whatever his shortcomings in other directions, Melcher's relations with his own staff were good, and all but one of its fourteen members resigned in protest. Melcher's story reached a good many people in the next few weeks. No public statement was made by FAS or NCAI; the only published reference to the incident was a long, and in some ways misleading, article by Nat Finney in the Minneapolis *Tribune* on how the scientists' federation had cleared itself of Communist infiltration and had caught onto attempts by party liners to slant

NCAI publications. No one admitted having leaked the information to Finney, who said he had got all he needed from Attorney-General Clark's office and Representative Mundt. He had usually done a better job than this in interpreting the scientists' position, and it looked as if he had been briefed by some one taking a more extreme view of the danger than most FAS scientists.

Trying not to let this unhappy episode interfere with its work, the NCAI executive committee placed the office temporarily in charge of its vice-chairman, Mrs. Reid, and recruited new staff. E. A. Casgrain, formerly chief of group liaison for UNRRA, was put in charge of relations with member organizations and Livingston Hartley, a writer on foreign affairs, was made publications editor, with the understanding that when the proposed overhaul of policy took place a director would be put over them. At a point that in retrospect appears to be the beginning of contraction of the scientists' movement, NCAI leaders were thinking in large terms—correlating the distribution of *Atomic Information* and the *Bulletin of the Atomic Scientists* so that all important groups in the country were covered, running an international information center in the United States to work with similar agencies abroad, and establishing regional offices of NCAI. The new director should be a man of prestige—Chester Bowles and Donald Nelson were suggested—who could co-operate with State Department, foreign embassies, and scientists at home and abroad in developing an international education program.[57]

Two things were taken for granted: one was the success of the fund-raising by the Emergency Committee, which promised its first $200,000 to the NCAI; the other was close collaboration between NCAI, FAS, and the influential scientists on the Emergency Committee. Neither of these conditions was fulfilled, and like the other operations-bootstrap undertaken by the scientists in the coming months, NCAI accomplishments fell short of stated hopes. Fluctuating income made long-range planning impossible, and for the remaining year and a half of its existence, no radical change took place in the NCAI program. *Atomic Information* became a monthly publication with less editorial comment, fewer quotes out of context, and a decided lowering of evangelical tone. The list of available study kits and reprints of pamphlets, articles, and official reports doubled. NCAI put out some publications of its own, such as Living-

---

[57] Simpson to NCAI executive committee, September, 1946, ASC XIII, 16.

ston Hartley's analysis of the Baruch proposals, and inspired others, among them an excellent pamphlet in the Foreign Policy Association's Headline Series, *Atomic Challenge*, by Higinbotham and Ernest K. Lindley of *Newsweek*. A twelve-panel atomic energy exhibit, developed for the NCAI by the Enoch Pratt Library in Baltimore, was routed across the country. In collaboration with other local groups, NCAI set up a District of Columbia Council on Atomic Information. Institutes for organization leaders were held in the spring of 1947 in Philadelphia, Cleveland, and Los Angeles. George Glasheen, formerly of the Retraining and Reemployment Administration, became NCAI director in May, 1947.[58]

Comparing the opportunity and the need for atomic education with the visible results, scientists tended to be negative in their evaluation of what their own and other groups accomplished, but they admitted that NCAI put literature about the implications of atomic energy into the hands of millions of Americans and made it possible for the FAS to rally support for the McMahon bill, the Acheson-Lilienthal Report, and confirmation of the first Atomic Energy Commission. All we had to do, Higinbotham later remarked, was to pick up the phone, call the Washington representatives of NCAI organizations, and say, "This is your problem." Without NCAI contacts, Higinbotham thought that the McMahon bill would not have passed or the AEC been confirmed.[59]

Amrine and, he claims, a few others thought of the NCAI as an instrument of long-term collaboration between the press and science (which he regarded as a fifth estate) to guide adjustments to the new era. But the NCAI's scientist sponsors—even the few, like Rabinowitch, who fully appreciated what a long, slow, repetitive process atomic education was bound to be—seem to have thought of it, as they thought of their other ventures in public relations, as an emergency measure to mold official policy and public opinion in such a way that a nuclear arms race would not get started. The alliance represented by the NCAI amply demonstrated its value on the domestic control issue, but a quick resolution of the problem of inter-

[58] Higinbotham to FAS administrative committee, November 21, 1946, FAS I, 8; Rush to FAS administrative committee, December 15, 1946, in Rush's files; NCAI Order Sheet, July 25, 1947, FAS II, 7; *Atomic Information*, II (May 20, 1947), 10; Casgrain, "Case History," August 1, 1946, FAS XIX, 5.

[59] Higinbotham to Emergency Committee of Atomic Scientists, May 15, 1947, FAS XV, 5; Higinbotham memorandum on tax exemption, December 29, 1947, AORES XVII, 10.

national control by means of education now appears to have been a hopeless objective. Fifteen years would pass before those of the scientists' observations that had real validity would permeate even semipopular thinking, and then, as they had indeed predicted, it was the bomb and its more terrifying successors that proved to be the great educator.

CHAPTER 11

International Relations
in Science

As this account has frequently had occasion to emphasize, scientists feel great pride in the internationalism of their profession. In the mid-twentieth century this concept enabled native-born Americans to share a rich heritage to which their own country had contributed but meagerly. To Europeans, transplanted by the upheavals of the thirties, it was a homeland of the mind.

1. The Committee for Foreign Correspondence

But above all, in the early days of peace, the restoration of the bonds between scientists seemed to offer a means of healing some of the wounds of war and became a primary aim of FAS policy. Scientists in Washington exploited every opportunity for discussion with European colleagues as the autumn of 1945 brought some slight renewal of travel and contacts, but the first concrete step was taken in the Cambridge Association in December when Amasa Bishop, a physicist at the Radiation Lab, and other young scientists set up a Committee for Foreign Correspondence with the central purpose of explaining their ideas about international control and enlisting the help of scientists abroad.[1] When Bishop moved to the University of California in March, 1946, he took the heardquarters of the com-

---

[1] P. Axel to ASC, December 18, 1945, ASC XVI, 2.

mittee with him to Berkeley, where interest in it contributed to the rapid growth of the Northern California Association of Scientists. By vote of the March council the Committee for Foreign Correspondence became an official FAS activity, but its management remained in Bishop's dedicated hands.

Members of scientific societies in the United States were asked to report names of foreign scientists, how well they knew them, whether they would be willing to write personal letters, and how freely the recipient might be able to answer. The committee soon had over a thousand names. Those in Britain and Canada were excluded from the program because contact was being satisfactorily re-established, but to each of the others the American scientist who knew him best was asked to write a personal note. The committee then forwarded a package of reading matter, accompanied by a form letter asking for reactions to American atomic energy policy, what steps scientists in the recipient's country were taking to promote international control, what could be done to hasten exchange of fellowships and basic scientific information, and finally, what could be done to prevent war. This letter was translated into French and Russian and carefully checked, Bishop reported, for clarity, interpretation, and warmth. As of August, 1946, when the packages began going out systematically, they contained copies of the *Bulletin of the Atomic Scientists*, NCAI's *Atomic Information*, a brochure about the FAS, the Acheson committee's report on international control, *One World or None*, and Urey's "I'm a Frightened Man." As supplies ran out, other items were added, such as John Hersey's *New Yorker* article on Hiroshima.[2]

To avoid misinterpretation of this communications project a release about the committee was made on June 17, 1946, from the FAS office with simultaneous announcements in Berkeley, Chicago, and Cambridge. Reaction in eastern papers was favorable, but Bishop was unhappy about the Berkeley press conference for which he had corralled eleven important scientists. Only three newsmen turned up; nothing appeared in the press for a week, and then the *San Francisco Chronicle* ran a short article headed "Scientists To Give Away

---

[2] Copy of the questionnaire and explanatory material distributed by the Committee for Foreign Correspondence ca. February 12, 1946, in FAS XIII, 8. See also Los Alamos Newsletter, No. 19, February 27, 1946, ALAS II, 19; Bishop to Higinbotham, May 19, 1946, and July 14, 1946, FAS XIII, 6; report of Committee for Foreign Correspondence, September 18, 1946, ASC XIII, 18; Committee for Foreign Correspondence minutes, February 25, 1947, FAS XIII, 7.

Atom Secrets."[3] In Washington Higinbotham was chiefly concerned about the House Un-American Activities Committee; but since its more excitable members preferred vague charges of espionage at Oak Ridge (with which they shortly confused the House debate on the McMahon bill) to an attack on a committee blessed by Einstein, Oppenheimer, Arthur and Karl Compton, and DuBridge, no trouble developed. The State Department requested a hundred reading packets for United States Information libraries and made it possible for visitors to Japan, Germany, and Russia to take this material with them before direct mail service was available.

Returned travelers soon reported a warm reception, including that from three U.S.S.R. scientists, to the personal letters and reading matter. Written replies were more guarded, but by early 1947 it was clear from a thick file of more than formal thanks that something had been done to relieve a dire shortage of information and to create sympathetic understanding, if not behind the Iron Curtain, at least among former colleagues in Germany and Japan. The committee, the FAS, and the *Bulletin* were deluged with requests for journals and inquiries from students.[4]

Saturday volunteers wrapped the packages, but hard cash was needed for postage and reprints. When the first large consignment was ready Bishop asked the FAS for $700, but Rush, who had become something of an expert in robbing Peter to pay Paul, could only suggest that when the Northern California Association paid its dues they could be credited against the committee's back expenses. To avoid holding up the program Bishop dug into his own pocket and advanced over $1,000 the first year. By October, 1946, four hundred packages had been sent; a hundred and fifty waited postage, another hundred had been committed, and ten requests came in each day. Bishop filled orders from odds and ends and, with an occasional hundred dollars from the California association, kept the work going until a two-thousand-dollar grant came from the Emergency Committee in January, 1947. To be eligible for these tax free funds the Committee for Foreign Correspondence was transferred from the politically active FAS to the new Association of Scientists for Atomic Education.

---

[3] FAS press release, June 17, 1946, FAS XIII, 8; Bishop to Higinbotham, June 24, 1946, FAS XIII, 6.

[4] For Bishop's correspondence with Higinbotham and Rush, 1946–47, and other Committee for Foreign Correspondence material, see ASC XV, 1; FAS VII, 5, and XIII, 6, 7.

As scientists watched the developing stalemate in the United Nations in the winter of 1946–47 and wearied of making the same speeches to small audiences, many thought the committee their most worthwhile activity. But Szilard, who had earlier disparaged the domestic educational campaign, was now advocating that scientists concentrate on state conferences. Top scientists abroad were now sufficiently informed, he said, and there was no point in spending money to educate the European public, much of which had no vote.

This typically Szilardian *volte-face*, though it may have influenced the Emergency Committee's final assignment of funds, did not discourage Bishop and his committee from planning an expanded program. To the thirteen hundred fifty names on their mailing list they added three hundred Russian scientists during the summer of 1947. The one reply from Russia expressed full support for the Gromyko plan, but the committee thought this less remarkable than that any at all was received. By early 1948, material had been sent to three thousand scientists, two hundred seventy-five libraries and scientific organizations, and one hundred fifty foreign newspapers. Scientists in sixty-five countries had answered. Plans to publish these replies and to establish a technical information service were doomed by failure of the Emergency Committee's 1948 fund drive. Gradually the Committee for Foreign Correspondence ceased operation.[5]

2. INTERNATIONAL ORGANIZATIONS

Handicapped as were many FAS members by explicit knowledge of how to make an atomic bomb, the program of foreign correspondence was an ingenious way of making their influence felt abroad. The delicacy of its position in relation to secrecy, plus determination not to become entangled in extraneous causes, kept the FAS apart from the main stream of international organization, but this independence did not go unchallenged.

Three principal media for scientific co-operation existed or developed in the first year after the war. The oldest was the International Council of Scientific Unions, founded as the International Research Council in 1919, and reorganized as the ICSU in 1931, which was composed of academies and scientific societies; its United States affiliates were the National Academy of Science and the Na-

---

[5] Association of Scientists for Atomic Education directors' minutes May 17, 1947, September 13–14, 1947, in Rush's files; "Committee for Foreign Correspondence: History and Accomplishments," *ca.* March 15, 1948, AORES XVIII, 9.

tional Research Council. In 1946, its committee on science and social relations published a survey of the views of scientific bodies on problems arising from research, and its member unions (of mathematics, physics, and other fields) gradually resumed their international congresses—the only ones for some years attended by Russians.

The United Nations Educational, Scientific and Cultural Organization (with which the ICSU later became affiliated) took shape after a preliminary conference in London in November, 1945. Its constitution required ratification by twenty countries, and the endorsement of American scientific organizations was considered important in obtaining congressional approval. The FAS as usual was cautious about spreading out in too many directions, and when the June, 1946, council finally passed a resolution supporting UNESCO, it spurned the broad statements about an instrument of world peace and a world congress of scientists offered by the internationally minded engineers at Oak Ridge and tied support of UNESCO to the FAS stand on control of information by civilians, which in its domestic aspect was then in jeopardy in the House Military Affairs Committee debating the McMahon bill:

> The Federation of American Scientists is concerned about the present status of the liaison between scientists in the United States and those in other countries. The only existing official channel for such liaison is, by default of civilian agencies, through U.S. armed forces sponsorship. Profitable international cooperation in science can be more effectively achieved by U.S. participation in UNESCO, by passage of a National Science Foundation Act, by increased appropriations for scientific liaison to the Division of Cultural Relations of the State Department.[6]

A third major organization emerging in 1946 was the World Federation of Scientific Workers, of which the most potent forerunner was the British Association of Scientific Workers, founded in the 1920's by people of liberal and left-wing views who were concerned with the applications of research and the professional status of scientific and technical workers. In the following decade a vigorous counterattack on the stultifying effects of planned research was mounted by the Society for Freedom in Science, but at the end of the war the British AScW, with Professor P. M. S. Blackett of Manchester as presi-

[6] Bart J. Bok to Higinbotham, January 21, 1946, FAS XXIV, 4; FAS council minutes, March 23–24, 1946, ASC XIV, 2; FAS memorandum on UNESCO, May 16, 1946, in *Bulletin of the Atomic Scientists* files; ORES memo on UNESCO, May 23, 1946, and Higinbotham to Minett, June 10, 1946, FAS XXIV, 7; FAS UNESCO resolution, in *Bulletin of the Atomic Scientists*, II (July 1, 1946), 23.

dent, still had sixteen thousand members, including many prominent scientists; similar organizations had been founded in South Africa, Australia, Canada, France, and the United States.

It was the British Association of Scientific Workers that picked up the idea of a world congress, so much discussed in the autumn of 1945 as a means of renewing contacts, and called a conference on "Science and the Welfare of Mankind" for February 15 to 17, 1946, in London. John Simpson represented the Carnegie Foundation for International Peace, which paid his expenses, and the FAS. As a moving spirit in the ASC and FAtS, a member of the FAS administrative committee, and a representative of the FAS on NCAI, Simpson was well qualified to explain what American scientists were doing. He had missed the older physicists' customary term of foreign study, and now at twenty-nine this was his first trip abroad. He brought back a conscientious report of the conference (and of two weeks' further discussions in France and England) on the needs of scientists in Holland, Belgium, Czechoslovakia, Poland, and the other half-dozen countries represented (Russia was not among them), the usefulness of nuclear power to Britain, the hope of obtaining United States isotopes for research, concern about how German science would be reconstituted, and the anxiety about United States isolationism in scientific information. He reported the desperate need of technical journals and equipment in the liberated countries and the hopes being placed in UNESCO. One needs to recall the barriers that war had raised to appreciate how much Simpson's report provided in the way of news and confirmation.[7]

Much of this was reflected in future FAS "foreign policy." Of immediate interest was the formation of a committee on atomic energy by the British Association of Scientific Workers, composed of eighteen scientists prominently associated with nuclear research, both members and non-members of the AScW. Simpson attended a meeting of this committee, talking about the FAS program and arranging for exchange of materials. He noted an inclination on the part of some members to become independent of the AScW, and this separation took place on March 8, when, with the committee and a group

---

[7] Simpson's report was distributed to all associations; for a summary, see J. A. Simpson, Jr., "A Scientist's Visit to England and France," *Bulletin of the Atomic Scientists,* I (April 1, 1946), 16–17. Simpson and Holbrooke MacNeille, London representative of the United States Navy's Bureau of Research, were the only United States scientists present.

at Oxford as a nucleus, the British Atomic Scientists Association was formed. Its members published a newsletter, talked on the B.B.C., made a critical study of the British atomic energy bill (a less controversial measure than the McMahon bill), and dispatched a memorandum on international control to the UNAEC.[8]

A closer link with government planning made it at once more difficult for British scientists to speak publicly and at the same time made them better able than those in the United States to influence official policy; for this reason and perhaps also because of a less immediate sense of responsibility for the bomb, they did not attempt such an extensive program of public education as did scientists in the United States.

The idea of an international organization to promote the peaceful uses of atomic energy bloomed briefly in the latter months of 1946. The British Atomic Scientists Association took advantage of an international physics conference in Cambridge in July to hold a three-day discussion of atomic energy problems in Oxford. With the press excluded, what was described as a large and representative gathering pooled information about domestic control plans and debated atomic power, anticipating frequent and fruitful exchanges on these topics. As a matter of fact nine years would elapse before scientists again found themselves discussing these questions with relative freedom at the Geneva Conference on Peaceful Uses of Atomic Energy in 1955. For all the optimistic talk, the Oxford conferees were prepared to agree only upon a skeleton arrangement to facilitate exchange of accurate information (with Professor Pryce of the Clarendon Laboratory, Oxford, as temporary secretary) and upon the desirability of an international information office, probably in New York City under FAS auspices. This proposal later reached the stage of a tentative $25,000 annual budget but foundered with other new educational projects of 1947 for lack of funds.[9]

Close liaison between the British and American groups was maintained, but nothing more was heard of the international atomic sci-

[8] Officers and council of the British Atomic Scientists Association: president, N. F. Mott; vice-presidents, R. E. Peierls and M. H. L. Pryce; general secretary, P. B. Moon; council members: W. J. Arrol, P. M. S. Blackett, E. H. S. Burhop, N. Kurti, W. G. Marley, H. S. W. Massey, N. F. Mott, M. L. E. Oliphant, R. E. Peierls, T. G. Pickavance, J. Rotblat, and H. W. B. Skinner.

[9] Henry A. Boorse, "Two International Scientific Meetings in England," *Bulletin of the Atomic Scientists*, II (September 1, 1946), 5–7; FAS council minutes, September 22–23, 1946, and March 15–16, 1947, ASC XIV, 2; ASAE proposal, April 18, 1947, FAS XVII, 4.

entists' organization. Effective collaboration, especially for United States scientists, had to wait upon the clarification of national policy. This was true even of peacetime applications, but here a major inhibiting factor was that scientists, for all their optimistic general talk, were as yet thoroughly unsure of the extent and timing of these applications.

An additional reason why atomic scientists' groups did not push formal organization was that from a third conference held in England in July, 1946—of existing national scientific workers groups—there grew the more broadly based World Federation of Scientific Workers that linked itself with UNESCO and quickly acquired members and influence in Europe and later in Asia. For the most part its aims were in close harmony with those of the FAS—utilization of science for peace, and exchange of scientific personnel and basic research information. But they also included that concern with the status of scientific workers that the site organizations, and later the FAS, had firmly abjured, as well as a vaguely phrased commitment "to encourage scientific workers to take a more active part in public affairs, and to make them more conscious of and more responsive to, the progressive forces within society." Plans included the relief of food shortages and the recovery of science in war devastated countries, improvement in science teaching, and consideration of a code of rights and duties for scientists, all of which found much sympathy in FAS circles but could not have been adopted without dissipating its resources.

This problem of aims would doubtless have been solved had it not been for communist influence in the new organization. It was recognized that the older groups of the Association of Scientific Workers were made up predominantly of middle-of-the-road liberals, but it was not clear what might happen to the new ones or to the world federation under the leadership of two eminent scientists who were also avowed Marxists, F. Joliot of France, the president, and J. D. Bernal of England, a vice-president. However strongly American scientists might feel about freedom of political opinion, they had to admit that their influence as supporters of international control would be greatly reduced if they joined a communist-led international body.

When the question of affiliation came before the FAS council in September, 1946, a negative decision was reached on the grounds that activity of the trade union type was excluded by the aims of the

FAS and that under existing conditions in Europe the WFScW was likely to be dominated by those with extreme political opinions. Later councils, fortified by the argument that the FAS could barely support its own limited program, maintained this position but not without incurring criticism abroad or creating a lingering uneasiness at home at this failure to implement the internatonal spirit of science. This did not prevent exchange of material or having FAS observers present at WFScW meetings.

3. German Scientists in America

Another kind of challenge to the internationalism of science arose as news of friends and colleagues in Germany disclosed instances of heroic resistance to Nazi pressure as well as cases of ambivalent behavior and collaboration. For refugee scientists of the thirties, this was a painful subject fraught with memories of their own balancing of principles, professional interest, and family safety. Few cared to make public judgments about this complicated aspect of scientific responsibility, though it was much discussed privately among scientists in 1945 and 1946.[10]

The question arose, however, whether the FAS should take a position on the bringing of German scientists to the United States to work on military research projects. Although the press had reported in November, 1945, what was intended to be the secret arrival in New York of a first contingent of eighty-eight, no one seemed to have given it much thought when Victor Weisskopf brought up the matter at the January FAS council meeing. The question was called to the attention of the site groups, but they had their hands full with domestic legislation and education programs; and even official disclosure by Secretary of War Patterson on February 14 that some hundred and thirty German scientists were temporarily in this country reconstructing V-1 and V-2 rockets did not create a stir. No names were mentioned; the work was in fields unfamiliar to most members of the federation, and the isolation of the visitors was complete, at least as far as scientists likely to raise questions were concerned. No

---

[10] The seriousness with which the Germans had pushed the uranium project was later discussed in Samuel A. Goudsmit's *Alsos* (London: Sigma Books, Ltd., 1947), in which he reported his expedition into Germany in the spring of 1945 as head of a United States scientific team, and in exchanges between Goudsmit and the German physicist Werner Heisenberg in the periodicals *Nature* and *Bulletin of the Atomic Scientists*. It was more widely publicized in Robert Jungk's *Brighter than a Thousand Suns* (London: Victor Gollanz, Ltd., 1958).

one felt disposed to challenge the temporary employment, even of possible Nazi sympathizers, in this useful piece of technological detection.[11]

War Department announcements in September, 1946, and again in December, put a rather different complexion on the matter, for they suggested that a more extensive use of German scientists and technicians was contemplated and that, on completing their military work, they might be given jobs in industry and at universities and perhaps eventually citizenship. The FAS council in February, 1947, took a decidedly adverse view of this preferential treatment of those who had, however reluctantly, worked along with the Nazi regime —at the same time that the victims of that regime were often refused asylum—and it authorized an open letter to President Truman expressing deep concern over the implications of this War Department program. "Certainly not wishing to jeopardize the legitimate needs of national defense, and not advocating a policy of hatred and vengeance toward our former enemies," the letter went on,

we nevertheless believe that, during this critical postwar period of national and international adjustment, importation of scientists is not in keeping with the best objectives of American domestic and foreign policy. . . . We, therefore, respectfully urge that the use of Nazi scientists by the armed forces be held to an absolute minimum, that none of them be granted citizenship, that none of them be given employment in industrial or academic installations, and that all of them be sent back to Germany as soon as possible.[12]

Higinbotham sent the FAS letter to the White House, but before making it public he took the precaution of confirming the War Department statements and finding out where the State Department stood on the question of citizenship. He was assured by Secretary Acheson that it was State Department policy not to bring in anyone of known Nazi sympathies and that the German scientists could become citizens only by leaving the United States and coming in on the unfilled German quota.[13] Higinbotham's caution in releasing

---

[11] *New York Times*, November 17, 1945, pp. 1, 6; and February 15, 1946, p. 6; FAS council minutes, January 5–6, 1946, ASC XIV, 2.

[12] FAS council minutes, February 1–2, 1947, p. 6, and Appendix 3, AORES XVII, 1. For comments on employment of German scientists (Goudsmit presenting both sides, Hans Bethe and H. S. Sack protesting), see *Bulletin of the Atomic Scientists*, III (February, 1947), 64–65.

[13] Higinbotham to Acheson, February 14, 1947, and other government officials, and Acheson's reply, March 13, 1947, FAS XVI, 7.

the letter won him a reproof at the March council meeting, at which critics discounted Acheson's assurance by pointing out that experienced university teachers, if they had a promise of two years' employment in the United States, did not need to come in under the quota. It was also reported that the staff of one university had been requested, and had refused to appoint a German military scientist.

But the complexity of the situation was becoming evident. Chicago opposed any action on the German scientist issue; others said the complaints were too generalized and that accurate case histories were needed. It was agreed that relevant information should be sent to the Washington Association of Scientists which would compile a report. Release of the letter to the President the following week brought out more violent disagreement within the FAS; the letter, it was said, revived wartime hatred and suggested fear of competition. Exploration also revealed a marked lack of agreement on what if anything the FAS should say. Pressure had been relieved by publication of the letter, and by the time the next council met, the issue, as far as the FAS was concerned, had collapsed like a balloon.[14]

---

[14] FAS council minutes, March 15–16, 1947, pp. 3–4; and May 4, 1947, p. 4, AORES XVII, 1, 2; FAS press release, March 22, 1947, AORES XVIII, 4; Higinbotham to FAS administrative committee, April 1, 1947, FAS I, 8.

CHAPTER 12

Secrecy
and the Army

WHILE THE atomic scientists and their new associates in the FAS carried on their efforts to prepare friends at home and abroad for eventual decisions on international control, the immediate focus of much activity in the first seven months of 1946 was the campaign to get the McMahon bill through Congress. Speeches, articles, conferences—all the techniques and channels established to publicize the international issue—were now employed to advertise the domestic one as well. The scientists justified this marked diversion from their prime objective on the grounds that the McMahon bill, by providing for civilian control of atomic energy, would facilitate international agreement, just as the May-Johnson bill, with its loophole for military influence and its emphasis upon secrecy, would have hindered it. The representatives of the Federation of Atomic Scientists, analyzing the McMahon bill in Chicago on December 27 and 28, had made much of this point.

1. SECRECY AND FREEDOM

Early in January two members of the McMahon committee staff, Condon and the staff director Christopher Boland, spent two days in Chicago talking with Urey, Szilard, Jaffey, Friedman and other

ASC members, bringing back what were described as valuable suggestions. The outcry promoted by the scientists against the May-
Johnson bill had demonstrated the importance of having their
support, and this may have been as strong a reason for consulting
them at this stage as their technical knowledge.[1]

The promoters of the McMahon bill were also taking care to obtain
a unified administration position, for Newman and Miller were not
going to repeat the tactical errors made by May-Johnson bill sponsors,
one of which, it is reported, was to have a copy presented to a cabinet
member by a uniformed officer with the demand that he read and
return it at once. The concurrence of the Bureau of the Budget,
whose objections to the May-Johnson bill had influenced Truman's
withdrawal of support, was especially important. On January 2 Don K.
Price, on behalf of the Bureau, submitted to Newman a generally
favorable reaction to the McMahon bill, though Price objected to
its provisions for special boards to control fissionable materials, patents, information, and security dismissals and recommended the addition of a general manager. These and other modifications were
accepted by Newman and Miller and later by the Senate committee.[2]

Sketching in the background for the second series of Senate committee hearings, which began on January 22, the authors of *The
New World*, the official AEC history, ascribe a growing public concern about military influence to the manipulations of James Newman
and his associates on the committee staff. Two dinners to rally
support for the McMahon bill had been held on November 29 and
December 18. On the second occasion leading Washington columnists heard McMahon, Newman, and Condon talk about the bill
and the issues. A direct result, seemingly, was a series of articles
by Marquis Childs in the *Washington Post*, commencing January 4,
which reviewed the controversy over the May-Johnson bill, the suspicion of its opponents that it was intended to keep Groves in power,
the scientists' dislike of Groves, and the fight between the General
and the Senate committee over access to information. Other journalists picked up the theme. Charles Calkins of McMahon's staff
told the Senator that the issue of civilian versus military control

---

[1] Los Alamos Newsletter, No. 12, January 8, 1946 ALAS II, 19; correspondence in
ALAS IV, 12,

[2] Richard G. Hewlett and Oscar E. Anderson, Jr., *The New World, 1939–1946*
(University Park: Pennsylvania State University Press, 1962), pp. 482–84 (referred to
hereinafter as *The New World*).

might be worth pushing to the point of an attack on the army's conduct of the Manhattan Project if, as now seemed possible, the Mc-
Mahon bill stalled in committee.[3]

There is no evidence that any of the federation leaders knew of
Calkins' suggestion or that they were privy to concrete plans, if such
existed in the minds of Senate committee staff, for sharpening the
civilian control issue in the period just after Christmas. Nevertheless
they contributed to the building up of this issue in two ways—by
discussion of secrecy and research and, contrary to earlier resolves,
by allowing their specific complaints against the army and General
Groves to reach the public ear.

From the beginning, as their memorandums and meeting notes
show, they had seen the wide implications of the fight they were
engaged in but had good reasons for not broadening the base of the
argument themselves. Although firmly believing that what was important to science was also important for more basic values—respect
for truth, individual freedom, human dignity, co-operation—they
thought that freedom of science, not human rights in general or the
safeguarding of them through democratic processes, was the particular freedom they were best qualified to explain and defend. But the
question of what they should say publicly, even about the limited
issue of secrecy and military influence, had been a touchy one. The
progress of science had suddenly become of the utmost importance
to the nation. On the conditions most conducive to its continued
flourishing, they could speak with authority; but how could they
present the issue so as to avoid the imputation of special pleading
and of concern—to use Rabinowitch's phrase—for their "traditional,
free, and secluded way of life"? And how could they argue that
military control of science endangered human welfare without seem-
ing merely to be slapping back at the army for the disagreeable
experience of wartime security?

That scientists did not agree among themselves on the answers had
been evident at the November organization meeting of the larger
federation when Manhattan Project scientists replied to the charge
that they were not interested in the freedom of science by explaining
that they were only trying to soft-pedal their disagreement with the
army. And it was partly because of this de-emphasis that the most

---

[3] *The New World*, pp. 485–88; the Calkins memorandum in the files of the Senate
Special Committee on Atomic Energy was written between January 14 and 22, 1946.

effective blast against secrecy came not from Manhattan Project ranks but from Louis N. Ridenour, a nuclear physicist at the M.I.T. Radiation Lab, where relations with the military in the application of radar had been highly satisfactory. In the November, 1945, issue of *Fortune* Ridenour argued that keeping a secret that did not exist could only be harmful to the United States. He therefore urged removal of all security barriers to the publication of basic scientific information in nuclear physics (as distinct from bomb technology) and careful examination of the various aspects of atomic bomb technology (as distinct from basic nuclear physics) to determine whether continuation of the present policy of concealment was wise.[4]

There were two approaches to security, said Ridenour, one by concealment, the other by achievement. The military had long been accustomed to thinking in terms of operational information, which by its very nature is compact, universally understandable (on both these counts easy to steal), arbitrarily chosen, subject to change, and essentially perishable; concealment was reasonably easy to maintain. By contrast the scientific information on which new weapons are based is diffuse (a report of five to ten million words was being prepared on the work behind radar); it is meaningful only to scientists, who, being naturally straightforward fellows, do not make good spies (the exceptions that were to prove the rule being then unknown to Ridenour). Scientific information is not arbitrary, and unlike operational data, it cannot be changed to fit the need. And finally, scientific information, if correct, is eternal, and if we try to conceal the workings of nature from our enemies, "we are committed to ending the free international scientific publication that has been the chief glory and support of our present age of science." Since what we have to fear from an enemy, Ridenour continued, is not science but its applications, we must seek security through achievement, not by concealment. From his extensive knowledge of the wartime use of radar, he cited instances when concealment had lost more than it gained. "In effect," he concluded,

the problem of policing or of organizing the world, if it is raised at all by the development of the atomic bomb, must be actively and not passively solved ... within the next two or three years. Any security by concealment that the U.S. attempts meanwhile can gain us little time at best,

---

[4] Ridenour, "Military Security and the Atomic Bomb," *Fortune*, XXXII (November, 1945), 170 ff.

can create unjustified illusions of national safety, and will damage our prospects for scientific progress.

Ridenour's statement was enthusiastically cited by his fellow scientists in the FAS, and reprints were widely distributed. Since it avoided philosophical or sentimental clichés about freedom and human welfare, it seemed the kind of argument that might impress those responsible for national defense, as in some cases it undoubtedly did. But in general the scientists' attempts to be realistic and confine themselves to an area of *expertise* backfired. Even the generally sympathetic authors of the McMahon bill felt that the scientists' interest was a narrow one and that they were concerned primarily "with the effects of a military regime on the progress of science and the life of scientists rather than with the broader political issue of the appropriate functions of the military departments in a democratic state."⁵ Here again was the familiar trap: if scientists spoke about administration and government they were speaking out of their field; if they discussed freedom only as it related to science they were being parochial.

The tactical consideration of making their opposition to military control appear as disinterested as they sincerely believed it to be had also led Project scientists to play down their feud with the army. At the same time, anxiety about War Department intentions in certain areas—the suppression of free speech and the railroading of legislation—abated somewhat after Patterson's assurance in late October that they were free to speak and organize and while the May-Johnson bill was allowed to remain in committee. Then, too, a few people paused to reflect that, after all, civilian scientists had applied the principle of compartmentation to nuclear research before the army took over and that in wartime the administration of atomic development was a legitimate War Department function. It was also sobering to hear that both at the Radiation Lab and in the execution of the Alsos mission liaison with the military had been relatively smooth. From the end of October until mid-February, when federation scientists suspected Groves's influence behind the Senate committee's interest in introducing stronger military liaison provisions into the McMahon bill, their own files give the impression that their quarrel

---

⁵ James R. Newman and Byron S. Miller, *The Control of Atomic Energy* (New York: McGraw-Hill Book Co., Inc., 1948), p. 13. Used by permission of the publisher.

with the army and even with the General himself was to some extent in abeyance.

Yet behind the scenes the contribution of this feud to the argument over legislation in the form of antimilitary and anti-Groves anecdotes was not inconsiderable. If the scientists did not often tell these stories publicly, their journalist friends had no such compunctions. Links between the two groups are not hard to trace. Marquis Childs, who wrote the January *Washington Post* articles, had been an early contact of the Allegany Rocket group; Samuel Shaffer of *Newsweek* had been in close touch with federation delegates when he did the "Reluctant Lobby" article; Frances Henderson of *Time*, Al Friendly of the *Washington Post*, Stewart Alsop, and other journalists sometimes joined the office staff for dinner or a beer.

On the evening of January 27, a few days after the McMahon committee hearings reopened, the scientists found themselves with a particularly receptive audience when Edward Levi of the University of Chicago Law School, in Washington to help with the atomic scientists' testimony before the committee next day, arranged a gathering at the Arlington home of a friend in the Antitrust Division. Davies of Clinton, who was to testify, Kaplan of SAM, George Sacher of Chicago, and Roy Thompson and Bernard Feld of Los Alamos were there, as was Urey, who led an informal discussion on the implications of the bomb. A scattering of their friends in the government were also present—Thurman Arnold, Representative Jerry Voorhis, and Calkins and Boland of the McMahon committee—and at least seven representatives of radio and the press, including the *New York Times, Christian Science Monitor, Time,* and Scripps-Howard papers. A State Department representative was noticeably silent, and one reporter advocated arming to the teeth as the only protection against the Reds, but otherwise everyone was extremely friendly, and the scientists yielded to the temptation to recount amusing or ironic incidents resulting from the unnatural association of scientific and military minds. As one of them noted in the office journal, "His nibs took quite a beating."[6]

The stories told on this and other occasions were usually designed to underline the stupidity of compartmentation or of having military men administer research. One incident cited to expose "the cellular system of research" had occurred in 1940 before the army took over:

---

[6] FAS History-Diary, January 27, 1946, FAS files (Washington, D.C.).

Szilard had calculated the amount of U-235 needed to explode a bomb but thought the figure exceeded the amount that could be separated by known methods, while Urey, unknown to Szilard, had developed an improved method of chemical separation but did not know how much U-235 was required for a bomb. Only when British findings on critical size, obtained under less rigid secrecy rules (and from work done, it is said, because Britain did not know how else safely to employ her refugee scientists), were communicated to the Americans did Szilard and Urey usefully pool their information. Later under the army, Urey, the discoverer of heavy water, was not permitted to talk to the duPont men charged with manufacturing it. Compartmentation of knowledge, the scientists told their journalist friends, could be dangerous as well as stupid. According to the army, Oak Ridge scientists had no need to know what quantities of fissionable materials could be brought together without exploding, but at Los Alamos, where they knew a lot about critical size, one of the scientists (reportedly Teller) guessed there must be some explosive material accumulating at Oak Ridge and began to worry about how they were storing it. Finally, someone was dispatched to find out and by giving the Oak Ridge scientists forbidden information averted a catastrophe.

The scientists also liked to recall trivial instances of army bungling, such as Fermi's finding in his mail box the censor's instruction sheet for checking his letters. But some of the anecdotes had an unpleasantly personal tone, designed to show that General Groves—or any military man without advanced scientific training—was not qualified to control the exchange of scientific information. Attending a technical meeting at the Met Lab, Groves, it was recalled, had expressed official approval of mathematical formulas on the blackboard that turned out to be jottings left from a freshman physics class. Another Chicago story quoted Groves's definition of basic knowledge as something either generally known or easily found out (upon which *New York Times* science reporter Waldemar Kaempffert commented that this would rule out Newton's law of gravitation, Einstein's theory of relativity, the discovery of X-rays, and much of atomic physics including the fission of uranium by neutron bombardment).[7]

---

[7] "General Groves on the Future of the Atomic Bomb Projects," *Bulletin of the Atomic Scientists*, I (December 24, 1945), [2]; "Secrecy Hampers Atomic Research," *New York Times*, February 3, 1946, sec. E, p. 9. The most comprehensive collection of such stories appeared in a series of eight articles by Alfred Friendly in the *Washington*

One revives these stories with a certain sense of injustice to the General, whose 1962 reminiscences, although not entirely uncritical of scientists, avoid personal recrimination against those individuals who had seemed to him most obstructive. "We were not," says Groves, "engaged in a popularity contest, but in an extremely serious undertaking." "The scientists and I have one thing in common," he was reported to have said at an early conference on the M-G-M movie; "they want me out of this job and I want out."[8]

Some scientists now declare that they always liked and respected Groves personally even though they disagreed with his policies and that they deplored the tendency to make him the scapegoat for what they disliked in traditional military attitudes and methods. Even at the time the impersonal view was the one publicly adopted. "The scientists' revulsion at military repression of research information," wrote Aaron Novick in the New Republic, "is not a matter of personal differences with the Army and Navy. It is a conflict between types of work which by their nature cannot dwell in the same house." It was not the need for secrecy during the war that scientists were challenging, said Novick, but its excessive applications, continuation of which in the future would be intolerable.[9] Nevertheless, the stories were part and parcel of the scientists' discontent with military supervision and an easy way of illustrating and justifying their more general complaints.

A less well-known aspect of the scientist-army feud was the overtures that Groves made to both Clinton and Met Lab scientists in the late autumn of 1945. At Oak Ridge during the week of December 3, flanked by two members of his Washington staff, General T. F. Farrell and Major W. A. Consodine, and by the commanding officer at Oak Ridge, Colonel Kenneth D. Nichols, Groves had a conference with members of AORS—Henshaw, Cohn, Nordheim, Coryell, Edward Tompkins, English, and Weinberg—but they respected his wish that the discussion be kept confidential.[10] In Chicago Groves talked first with Met Lab director Farrington Daniels, who in turn advised

Post beginning on March 20, 1946, in time to support the fight against the military liaison amendment with the argument that scientists would not continue to work under the government if control of information policy was not relaxed. Alfred Friendly, "Civilian vs. Military Control of Atomic Age," Washington Post, March 20–27, 1946.

   [8] Leslie R. Groves, Now It Can Be Told (New York: Harper & Bros., 1962), p. 46; AORS Daily Bulletin, November 14, 1945, AORES XX, 1.

   [9] Aaron Novick, "A Plea for Atomic Freedom," New Republic, CXIV (March 25, 1946), 399–400.

   [10] AORS executive committee minutes, November 19, 1945, AORES I, 6.

the ASC executive committee on November 21 that a tapering off of
Washington activities might be wise. Groves himself talked to a
meeting of Met Lab scientists on December 18, and although the
atmosphere remained superficially friendly, the incompatibilities were
clearly visible. This occasion was fully reported in the ASC *Bulletin*.[11]

Groves spoke first of the difficulties caused by "unnecessary delay
in legislation," and his expectation that something very like the
May-Johnson bill would come out of the Senate committee, which
was finding the subject too complex for detailed planning. If he had
written the May-Johnson bill, said Groves, he would have incorporated some of the suggestions made later by the scientists. Groves
assured his audience about the continuity of the Los Alamos, Clinton,
and Chicago laboratories, as well as the work at some universities
and colleges. He spoke of the declassification study being made by a
high-level Project committee and the prospect of a prompt decision
to release information in certain wide fields of basic research. He
asked their forbearance during this indeterminate transition period
when inexperienced military personnel was taking over.[12]

In keeping with Groves's wish to bury the hatchet and with the
scientists' determination to keep it out of sight, the *Bulletin of the
Atomic Scientists* reported all this in an even tone, but from the
questions it was obvious that anxiety still lingered as to whether the
army was going to follow what scientists considered a reasonable
policy in release of basic information. James Franck, as their principal
spokesman, suggested that "the delineation between secret and non-
secret information should be left to scientists working directly in the
field and not to the Army or its top scientific advisors." He was supported by Arthur Dempster, who cited the self-imposed restrictions
of 1940. But Groves commented that then only a few people knew
the facts and there was no outside interest. Franck pressed further
questions about compartmentation and the problems it raised for
those trying to negotiate international control or inform legislators,
but Groves, who years later declared that "compartmentalization of
knowledge, to me, was the very heart of security,"[13] answered that

[11] ASC executive committee minutes, November 21, 1945, ASC VI, 12; "General
Groves on the Future of the Atomic Bomb Projects," *Bulletin of the Atomic Scientists*, I (December 24, 1945), [2].

[12] These difficulties are described in chapter xxviii of Groves's *Now It Can Be Told*.

[13] Groves, *Now It Can Be Told*, p. 140.

Project directors had instructions to give each person all the information he needed for his work and none that he did not need, and that it was sufficient if witnesses at congressional hearings spoke as experts in their own fields, thus demonstrating once again that he and the scientists simply did not understand each other when they talked about the wellsprings of creative research. It was at this meeting that Groves provided the definition of basic knowledge mentioned earlier.

If Groves did not always search for phrases that would sooth and mollify, he had taken, or would take in the next few months, several steps calculated to still some of the critics, although it is safe to say that none was made contrary to the counsel of his inner circle of scientific advisers in Washington. The declassification committee to which Groves referred at the Met Lab meeting, consisting of Richard C. Tolman, chairman, Arthur H. Compton, Ernest O. Lawrence, Harold C. Urey, J. Robert Oppenheimer, Robert F. Bacher, and Frank H. Spedding, inspired a confidence that their report of February 4, 1946, justified. Expressing the belief that release of information would in the long run enhance national welfare and even security, it dealt with three broad categories of material: (1) non-secret, (2) secret but probably suitable for declassification, and (3) material of a military nature that must remain secret. Specific topics were recommended for declassification.[14]

On the basis of the committee's report a system of declassification by document, rather than by field, began to operate in April, 1946. A declassification manual was issued on May 1 (giving the routing for each of the required six copies). The Manhattan Project declassification authorities proudly noted that at the June Physical

[14] Report quoted in *Bulletin of the Atomic Scientists*, I (February 15, 1946), p. 11; Tolman's release reported in *New York Times*, February 5, 1946, p. 9. Testifying at the Oppenheimer hearings in 1954, Groves expressed satisfaction with the results of the first committee report although he thought later declassification had gone too far. The criterion in that first declassification study, he explained, "was established by a committee of eminent scientists, but like all committees, it was under pretty rigid control by me, because I had the chairman, Dr. Tolman, who was in complete sympathy with me as far as I know, I had the secretary, who was an officer and a distinguished chemist handling that end—and they were told in advance what should be the criterion and they got the board to agree to that criterion. Nothing was recommended for declassification where it was felt that would be of any assistance to the Russians in developing the bomb" (U.S. Atomic Energy Commission, *In the Matter of J. Robert Oppenheimer*, Transcript of Hearing before Personnel Security Board [Washington, D.C.: Government Printing Office, 1954], pp. 175–76). Scientists would once have been outraged by this statement, but at the time Groves made it he was stoutly defending Oppenheimer, and his former antagonists were in a forgiving mood.

Society meeting forty-six of a hundred and one papers were available by virtue of the new system and that other declassified material made possible a two and one-half day symposium on fluorine and fluoro-carbon chemistry at the American Chemical Society meeting in Sep-tember. During its first year the declassification office released twelve hundred papers.[15] Those who did not have to process the hundreds of papers and check details were less impressed with the progress.

The appointment by Groves in January, 1946, of the Benedict committee to co-ordinate inspection reports also somewhat mollified his critics. And in the early spring he established the Advisory Com-mittee on Research and Development, to lay the ground work for the system of national laboratories that later developed under the AEC and for its sponsorship of research in university and private labora-tories, instances of farsighted planning for which scientists occa-sionally remember to give Groves credit.[16]

2. THE JAPANESE CYCLOTRONS

But these conciliatory moves were long-range affairs. In January and February, 1946, when scientists were concerned about secrecy in re-lation to the McMahon bill, they were at best in the promissory stage. Gradual declassification of basic information, however wel-come, would not help the Senate committee to decide about legisla-tion or enable other countries to evaluate proposals for control. At the very time that Groves was arranging his autumn peace conferences at Oak Ridge and Chicago, he was underlining the gulf that existed between his views and the scientists' by stating to the Senate com-mittee his strong objections to international inspection and control.

And beginning in late November such marked disagreement on two matters of policy developed between federation scientists (in-deed, virtually the whole scientific community) and the military that it obscured and negated the conciliatory long-range moves that Groves was making. One was the destruction of Japanese cyclotrons; the other was preparations for atomic bomb tests in the Pacific.

News of the destruction of the five Japanese cyclotrons broke after Groves had arranged for the Oak Ridge and Chicago conferences but before they were held. Most scientists probably heard it, directly

---

[15] Lieutenant Colonel W. S. Hutchinson, "The Manhattan Project Declassification Program," *Bulletin of the Atomic Scientists*, II (November 1, 1946), 14–15.
[16] This advisory committee consisted of Robert F. Bacher, Arthur H. Compton, Warren K. Lewis, John R. Ruhoff, Charles A. Thomas, Richard C. Tolman, and John A. Wheeler; it first met March 8, 1946 (*The New World*, p. 633).

or indirectly, through a dispatch from Lindsay Parrott in the *New York Times* of November 24. Date-lined Tokyo on the twenty-third, the article was based on an announcement from Allied Headquarters that two machines at Osaka University, one at Kyoto University, and two in Professor Yoshio Nishina's laboratory in Tokyo had been destroyed in line with War Department policy of eliminating Japanese war potential. One of those in Tokyo was a 220-ton machine, virtually a twin of Lawrence's Berkeley cyclotron and purchased in the United States about 1938. "Today," reported Parrott, "under orders to destroy them, engineers and ordnance men from Lieut. Gen. Robert L. Eichelberger's Eighth Army here and General Walter Kreuger's Sixth Army in Southern Japan, moved into the plants armed with welding torches, explosives and other equipment and began to take the machines apart. Parts of them will be loaded on barges, taken out to sea and sunk."

The machines, none of which were in working order when the Allies found them, had been under guard, but the Japanese apparently knew nothing of the intended destruction until troops arrived with cutting torches and demolition charges. The officer in command claimed, according to Parrott, that the cyclotrons were capable of extracting U-235, but this had been denied by Professor Seishi Kikuchi of Osaka, who was quoted as saying that intensive work on the mass separation of unstable elements had been considered by the Japanese up to 1941, when it was dropped because other nations were far ahead and Japan had no substantial deposits of uranium. The electromagnets had been saved, perhaps to be used in China or elsewhere in the Far East.[17]

Some poignant and ironic details of the seizure were later added by Professor Nishina. On October 15 he had filed a request with the Supreme Commander of the Allied Powers for permission to operate the two machines in his laboratory for research in biology, medicine, chemistry, and metallurgy. This was first granted, then later restricted to biology and medicine. He and his associates were preparing for experiments when the orders for immediate destruction arrived. At SCAP headquarters, where Nishina and a representative of the Central Liaison Office went to seek an explanation for the sudden shift in policy, they were told that of course American scientists had been consulted, particularly K. T. Compton, who had recently been in Japan as head of the Scientific Intelligence Survey. They later found

---

[17] *New York Times*, November 24, 1945, pp. 3, 18.

that this was untrue and that Compton and other members of the survey had, in fact, recommended that permission to operate the cyclotrons be granted.[18]

Even without these later details the matter-of-fact phrases of the *Times* report conjured up a sufficiently horrifying picture of hatchet men at large in laboratories, and the reaction from American scientists was immediate. Beginning next day with Clinton Labs, as usual quick to take alarm and quick to act, the site organizations issued angry press releases and telegrams of sharp reproof to the President, Secretary Byrnes, and Secretary Patterson. Calling the destruction "wanton and stupid," AORS likened it to the sacking of the Louvain library—a crime against humanity. "Men who cannot distinguish between the usefulness of the research machine and the military importance of a 16-inch gun," its release said, "have no place in positions of authority." (We were proud of our righteous blast, recalls Joe Rush, until Karl Compton returned from Japan a few days later; his statement made ours look pallid!) The ALAS release also referred to the burning of books and concluded: "It is the declared policy of the United States to help the Japanese whom we liberated from their militaristic leaders to attain a normal democratic society. The wrecking of scientific instruments will be a permanent detriment to the forces working toward this end." In a letter to Secretary Patterson, Chairman Ridenour of the Cambridge Association wished to know whether the cyclotrons had been destroyed in conformity with established army or War Department doctrine or whether it was the irresponsible act of subordinates misinterpreting a generally worded directive. If the first explanation was correct, the Cambridge Association took strong issue with the principle; if the second, they demanded that those responsible be disciplined. The destruction of the cyclotrons, said Ridenour,

implies that it is our intention to deny the Japanese—so far as this is in our power—knowledge of the way in which the Universe is made and works. The consequences of this doctrine are far-reaching and extremely frightening; it implies, in effect, that the War Department opposes the advancement of basic science. We cannot bring ourselves seriously to believe that this is, in fact, the official doctrine....[19]

---

[18] Yoshio Nishina, "A Japanese Scientist Describes the Destruction of His Cyclotrons," *Bulletin of the Atomic Scientists*, III (June, 1947), 145, 167.

[19] AORS press release, November 25, 1945, AORES II, 7; *New York Times*, November 26, 1945, p. 2; AEOR report of wires sent in AEOR Newsletter, No. 1, Novem-

Reports that General Groves had ordered the cyclotrons destroyed were not denied, and the protest that AORS had wired President Truman on the twenty-fifth was answered by Secretary Patterson on the twenty-ninth with the formula that the step had been taken in compliance with the War Department policy of preventing military research. AORS then wired Patterson asking what his own attitude in the matter was. Ten days later Patterson replied with what was to remain the official explanation, namely, that General Douglas MacArthur had received a radio message in Patterson's name that Patterson had not seen; the advice of scientists should have been sought, and he regretted the hasty action of his department.[20]

General Groves has recently explained that the destruction of the cyclotrons, which he calls stupid but not wanton, followed a directive from his office. On October 30 a Joint Chiefs of Staff cable to Pacific commanders had ordered seizure of atomic research equipment and research workers. (Groves does not mention Nishina's request of October 15 to use the cyclotrons for research or the authorization he was given.) Groves intended that the cyclotrons should be "secured," not destroyed, but did not make his wishes entirely clear to a new subordinate, insufficiently briefed in his customary procedures, and a message sent from his office on November 7, in Patterson's name, ordered the destruction after all available technical and experimental data had been obtained. On November 24 the Joint Chiefs of Staff was informed by General MacArthur that destruction had begun that day. Nine people in authority, including Groves, were sent copies of this cable; in each case a subordinate initialed and filed it, despite "the detailed instructions that existed in every headquarters to prevent just such an occurrence." The destruction should have stopped at this point, says Groves, but not until the news broke in the newspapers, which he places on November 30, did it "come to the attention of persons at the policy-making level."[21]

The reader of Groves's book cannot but be moved by his willingness to reconstruct the event and accept responsibility. However, the *New York Times* reported the destruction of the cyclotrons *not*

---

ber 27, 1945, FAS XXI, 3; ALAS press release in Los Alamos Newsletter, No. 7, December 4, 1945 ALAS II, 19; Association of Cambridge Scientists press release, December 1, 1945, Camb. I, 2; Rush to the author, February 28, 1964.

[20] AORS wire to Truman, November 25, 1945; reply from Patterson, November 29, 1945; AORS to Patterson, December 5, 1945; and Patterson to AORS, December 15, 1945 in AORES V, 11.

[21] Groves, *Now It Can Be Told*, pp. 367–72.

on November 30 but on November 24, the day of MacArthur's cable. It is strange indeed that no one "at the policy-making level" read as far as page three of the *New York Times* or learned of the angry protests with which scientists bombarded the White House and the War and State departments (also reported in the *Times*). Action on the twenty-fourth would have saved something. Groves's explanation, even if Patterson had allowed him to make it at the time, would scarcely have mitigated the scientists' wrath. Indeed, they would have said, this is exactly how we expect such matters to be handled by a military hierarchy and provides the best possible illustration of why science should not remain under military control; for in their view the most elementary understanding of the limited capabilities of the Japanese cyclotrons would have prevented the needless setback to basic research and peaceful applications.

For some time scientists in the United States worried about how they might make amends. Higinbotham explored the question the following spring in response to a request from the Pasadena group and reported that most FAS members would give priority to the repair of Allied laboratories. When Higinbotham was chairman of the FAS in 1951, he sought the reaction of the State Department to a campaign to raise money to replace the cyclotrons but was told that replacement, even by private funds, might be interpreted by the American public and in Asia, too, as giving aid to the Japanese in a strategic field. State Department opinion favored the more cautious approach—a stepped-up educational program, especially in basic research, a possibility that the FAS might consider in reaching a decision on whether to raise money for cyclotrons.[22]

3. THE BIKINI TESTS

Another issue on which a large number of scientists disagreed with official policy and on which their disagreement fed their continuing reluctance to see military control of the atomic energy program perpetuated was the testing of atomic bombs on ships, first mentioned publicly as a possibility at the end of October, 1945.[23] The immediate reaction of delegates in the new Federation of Atomic Scientists office was that such a demonstration might provide a

---

[22] Higinbotham to R. Noyes, March 6, 1946, FAS VII; FAS correspondence on Japanese research in 1947, and G. Arneson to Higinbotham, September 19, 1951, FAS XVII, 4.

[23] Arthur Krock's column, *New York Times*, October 24, 1945, p. 4.

useful lesson for legislators in the power of atomic weapons, but the FAS attitude had changed by January when the navy announced plans to drop an atomic bomb among ships in the Marshall Islands' Bikini atoll about May 1, followed by a surface test early in July and an underwater explosion at some later time. The scientists were especially disturbed by a request from the House Naval Affairs Committee on January 30 that any results prejudicial to the United States should be kept secret, and Chairman Higinbotham, interviewed the same day, said he did not see much point in the tests because damage to a large fleet spread out across the lagoon was not likely to be impressive.[24]

This opinion was elaborated in an editorial in the *Bulletin of the Atomic Scientists* of February 15: The early date of the first test gave little time for the development of the necessary test instruments. No provisions were indicated for studying the effects of the bomb's radiation on ships' crews. From the point of view of mechanical damage to the ships, the overhead blast might reveal nothing that could not be estimated in advance from measurements already made. Furthermore, ground areas that had been affected in Japan were roughly four miles in diameter, whereas ships in a lagoon measuring twelve miles by twenty-seven would be farther apart than that; and since naval vessels were mechanically stronger than buildings, the amount of destruction would be misleading. The effects to be expected from underwater blasts were less clear, and no conclusions should be drawn until that test had been held. International repercussions should be carefully weighed, for if foreign observers were excluded, the tests could only be viewed by the rest of the world as secret maneuvers in atomic warfare.[25]

Reactions from other local associations also centered on the danger that test results would encourage the public to underestimate the bomb. Pasadena stressed the incompatibility of the tests with the expressed intention of the United States government to discourage military use of atomic energy.[26] The FAS council meeting on March 23 and 24, although principally concerned with the Vandenberg

[24] Report of Minett to AEOR, ca. November 20, 1945, AORES XV, 5; *New York Times*, January 31, 1946, p. 8.
[25] *Bulletin of the Atomic Scientists*, I (February 15, 1946), 1, 12.
[26] Atomic Engineer and Scientist (newsletter of ORES), February 2, March 16, 1946, AORES XX, 3; FAS Newsletter, March 1, 1946, AORES XXI, 5; Pasadena Association Newsletter, No. 6, March 26, 1946, FAS VII, 4.

amendment for a military liaison committee, gave opportunity to develop a unified policy and to discuss the postponement of the first test until July, as announced the previous day. The results of this discussion, sorted out by a subcommittee and released to the press, summarized what was henceforth the FAS position—and that of many non-federation scientists as well—in regard to the tests:

The President's announcement of postponement of the atomic bomb tests at Bikini Atoll we believe will contribute to a more favorable atmosphere for the meeting of the Security Council and the projected meeting of the UNO Atomic Energy Commission. We feel it would have been unfortunate at this time to focus the attention of the world so dramatically on our military preparations.

The Navy tests will have a purely military value. Scientists recognize that such bombings will not add anything to fundamental scientific knowledge—they are not significant from the standpoint of development of atomic energy for peaceful purposes.

Scientists believe that in the atomic age no amount of military preparation can give us real security. If there is another war with atomic weapons we and all the world will suffer irreparable losses no matter who may be the "victor." We must put all our best thought on organizing the world for peace.

To this end, we urge full support of the United States program for international controls over atomic armaments, and for the UNO program of collective security as opposed to primary reliance on armed might.

The great experiment to which this nation and its leaders should devote their greatest attention and energy is under way in the United Nations Organization. There we are making the fateful test of whether nations can work out their problems without resort to war.

We do not need further bombing tests to tell us that if this larger trial of world order fails the great UNO experiment will end in the most destructive explosions our earth has ever seen.[27]

The council statement omitted certain points as being more suitably handled by others, and some of these provided the basis of an attack on the tests a few days later when Senator Scott Lucas of Illinois, a friend of the Chicago scientists, and Senator James W. Huffman of Ohio called for their cancellation. The senators, too, deplored the timing of a martial gesture, but they also objected to the enormous expenditure of ships and manpower. However, both on the Senate floor and by the Joint Chiefs of Staff speaking through the President, the tests were defended as promising to pro-

---

[27] FAS council minutes, March 23–24, 1946, ASC XIV, 2; press release in Los Alamos Newsletter, No. 24, April 10, 1946, ALAS II, 19.

vide much needed information to designers of ships, aircraft, and military ground equipment as well as to strategists, tacticians, and medical officers.[28] But these arguments did not carry great weight with scientists and were challenged by some responsible ones outside the federation orbit. President Compton of M.I.T. suggested that a test over land on a mock city specially constructed with every kind of structural material might be more to the point.[29] And Lee A. Du-Bridge, wartime head of the Radiation Lab and newly appointed president of California Institute of Technology launched a strongly worded attack—"What about the Bikini Tests?"—in the May 15 *Bulletin of the Atomic Scientists,* based upon the doubtful military and scientific value of the experiments, their cost, and their international implications.

No doubt, said DuBridge, hundreds of secret reports would be written on the variation with distance from the impact point of damage to masts, gun turrets, radar, rabbits, and field kitchens, but volumes of empirical data would still leave unanswered "the basic strategic question of whether navies or armies are obsolete and how future warfare might be conducted." The scientific results—in the unlikely event of their publication—would not make a ripple on the surface of basic nuclear science, and the hundred million dollars might be better spent on controlled laboratory tests or in education toward preventing another war. Nor should the possibilities be ignored that the whims of meteorology might dump radioactive debris on a ship full of observers or an unsuspecting populace hundreds of miles away, or that some malfunction in the bomb might put many men in danger. Although leaving the specialists to judge the effect of the tests on international relations, DuBridge was certain it was not in the direction of improvement and that at this critical hour they were, at the least, in poor taste.[30]

It was a great asset of the FAS at this period that on every important issue there were a few senior men not identified with the federation who spoke out in corroboration of its stand—Dempster on compartmentation and K. T. Compton and DuBridge on the tests—providing by this independent testimony more effective assistance

---

[28] *Congressional Record,* 79th Cong., 2d sess., 1946, XCII, Part 3, 2790–95, 3548–50.

[29] *Bulletin of the Atomic Scientists,* I (April 15, 1946), 18.

[30] DuBridge, "What about the Bikini Tests?" *Bulletin of the Atomic Scientists,* I (May 15, 1946), 7, 16.

than had they been listed as nominal supporters. There were, of course, scientists who supported the tests either because they thoroughly believed in them or because it was part of the job they had undertaken, and they were numerous enough to provide the necessary civilian personnel. At the same time, as with its other activities, no group of scientists actively tried to counter the federation's position, as it continued throughout the spring to emphasize that the tests were being held for military, not scientific, reasons. The March council had asked the Los Alamos association to make a further study of the technical features of the tests, and a summary by Frederick Reines of the ALAS findings, supplemented by comments from Hans Bethe and Louis Ridenour, was released by the FAS on May 26 to controvert statements in the Senate and elsewhere that the tests would furnish scientific information.[31]

Meanwhile scientists attempted to insure some non-military assessment of results and Senator McMahon successfully urged the President to appoint a civilian evaluation commission that would report to him independently of the Joint Chiefs of Staff's Evaluation Board. The membership of both boards was announced at the end of March, with E. U. Condon's name being added to the civilian commission just before the tests took place.

Condon, who has extracted what humor he could from a series of unhappy brushes with the arbiters of security and clearance, draws from his fund of what he calls "silly stories" an ironic incident connected with his appointment. For the June meeting of the American Physical Society in Chicago a trip was arranged to the Argonne Laboratory outside the city—the new site of Met Lab operations and opened for the first time to visitors. While Condon waited in the bus a young man put his head in the door and called out unceremoniously, "Is Dr. Condon here? You don't have clearance for this trip." The other passengers were highly amused for Condon was then president of the Physical Society and no public insinuations about his loyalty had been made. But seeing no point in argument he went back to the Quadrangle Club, and as he whiled away the afternoon reading magazines a call came from the White House asking him to serve on the President's Civilian Evaluation Commission.

---

[31] Reines' report in Los Alamos Newsletter, No. 29, June 1, 1946; ALAS II, 19; FAS press release, and other material, May 26, 1946, FAS XVII, 1.

Those who attended the July tests on behalf of the President were Senators C. A. Hatch and Leverett Saltonstall, Representatives W. C. Andrews and Chet Holifield, Bradley Dewey, president of the American Chemical Society, W. S. Newell, president of the Bath Iron Works Corporation, Fred Searls, Jr., of the State Department, K. T. Compton, president of M.I.T., and E. U. Condon, director of the Bureau of Standards.[32]

---

[32] W. A. Shurcliff, *Bombs at Bikini* (New York: Wm. H. Wise & Co., 1947), p. 183; see page 182 for membership of the JCS Evaluation Board. Dewey and Compton were members of both groups.

PART V

Domestic Legislation and International Control

CHAPTER 13

The McMahon Act

THE SCIENTISTS' concern with all the ramifications of secrecy and with military policies affecting research and international agreement formed a backdrop for their participation in legislative developments during the first seven months of 1946. In brief these developments were as follows: Beginning on January 22 the McMahon bill was considered by the Senate Special Committee on Atomic Energy in open and closed hearings. On April 19 it was reported with amendments to the Senate, which passed it on June 1. The House then tried further emasculation through amendments both in committee and on the House floor, but after conferences with the Senate both houses passed the bill in a form not very different from the Senate version of June 1. President Truman signed the bill on August 1, 1946.

The readjustments of postwar politics and the novelty of the subject made this progress not uneventful even for experienced politicians. To the scientists the crises were unfamiliar and ominous. In every stage the federation, especially the atomic scientists, took an active interest. In some stages they played a conspicuous and probably a decisive part, although their share of the credit was not always quite what they thought it to be at the time; nor is it possible even now to assign it with accuracy, so complex had the political picture become by the time the bill was passed. Again, the full story based upon generally inaccessible official documents can be found in *The*

New World. The present account concentrates on the scientists' attitudes and activities.

1. THE McMAHON BILL

To make their support of the McMahon bill effective required that the scientists look both to Congress and to the public, and in neither direction did they act alone. In mobilizing public support they had crucial assistance from citizens' committees, and in their relations with Congress they had leadership and guidance from the staff of the McMahon committee in deciding when to fight, when to compromise, and when a massive expression of public opinion was in order. As they were accustomed to do among themselves, the scientists freely challenged advice; on occasion they acted without it; but on the whole the collaboration was a smooth and successful one.

Hints in office memorandums that after the Christmas recess Newman was advising the scientists to curtail their direct contacts with Congress are confirmed by the course of events. The grandiose schemes for educating senators were quietly allowed to lapse. When the studies of inspection and control were diverted from the Senate committee to the War Department's co-ordinating committee, nothing took their place. There was recurrent talk of dinners for scientists and congressmen like those that had successfully opened up communication in the autumn, but Higinbotham reported on January 16 that for the present McMahon committee contacts considered them politically unwise. Small affairs with senators and scientists dining "dutch" at the Cosmos Club would be better. This idea was in turn abandoned when hostesses were found for small dinners, but Szilard was soon complaining that these "lacked seriousness."[1]

Those who staffed the Washington office quickly grasped the complexities of the political picture and realized how many interests and pressures—some of their own making—had appeared on the scene since the atomic scientists had rushed impulsively to Washington three months before. The two full-time staff members, Willy Higinbotham and Joe Rush, developed considerable aptitude for distinguishing between what they wanted and what they could get but were caught between the advice of the professionals and the

---

[1] Higinbotham to Phillips, January 16, 1946, and Higinbotham to FAS administrative committee, January 31, 1946, FAS I, 8; Jaffey to ASC executive committee, February 16, 1946, and Nickson and Higinbotham reporting to ASC executive committee, February 19, 23, 1946, ASC VI, 12.

reluctance of their colleagues outside Washington to recognize that badgering congressmen while the special committee was at work might do more harm than good. Scientists were encouraged, however, to continue their interest in the legislation itself, partly for support, partly for advice, and partly to make them better propagandists. The newly formed Oak Ridge Engineers and Scientists began their own evaluation of the bill during the Christmas holidays, collecting opinions also from non-members at K-25 and Y-12, and forwarded suggestions to the McMahon committee through Chauncey Starr. McMahon asked all the local associations for similar contributions,[2] and during January they discussed the bill in committees and at general meetings, aided by charts prepared in the Washington office that compared the various measures thus far introduced. Although freewheeling in Washington was discouraged, those at a safe distance were reminded, as they would be many times in the ensuing months, of the importance of individual letters and telegrams to Senate committee members and other congressmen, and many of these went out from Oak Ridge, Chicago, and elsewhere expressing and soliciting opinions about the McMahon bill.

With the advice of Newman and Condon it was decided that a representative of the Federation of Atomic Scientists, capitalizing on the special experience of its members, should communicate its endorsement of the bill to the Senate committee on January 28. Francis Friedman, chairman of the legislative committee of the Atomic Scientists of Chicago, was charged with preparing the testimony, using as a starting point the analysis provided by the FAtS Chicago conference of December 28 and modifying it in the light of suggestions from all the FAmS groups. Assisting Friedman, but working in the Washington office, was Bernard Feld (on his way from Los Alamos to M.I.T., where Friedman would shortly join him). There was nothing very glamorous now about a delegate's life in Washington, reported Feld to friends in Los Alamos; it was mostly routine—answering letters from well-wishers, grinding the mimeograph machine, talking to other scientists and newsmen. Still it was part of a scientist's liberal education.[3]

While Feld worked on testimony, Roy Thompson, also of Los

[2] Atomic Engineer and Scientist (newsletter), January 6, 1946, AORES XX, 3; McMahon to Novick of ALAS, January 16, 1946, ALAS IV, 12.

[3] Feld to "Lennie," January 10, 1946, ALAS IV, 9; Feld to H. Linschitz, January 16, 1946, FAS chronological files (Washington, D.C.).

Alamos, was serving for a few weeks as liaison between the office and the committee staff. The outlook for increased publicity on committee hearings was not very bright, he wrote Friedman the day after they opened; the federation had been told that the most helpful thing it could do was to prepare a two- or three-page digest of each day's testimony and the FAS reaction to it. Thompson forwarded the first of such reports to Senate committee members two days later, but it is not clear how long they were kept up or whether they merged into the scheme of digests that the FAS inaugurated for its own members. During the three weeks or so of open hearings, complete transcripts of committee testimony were sent on alternate days to the Atomic Scientists of Chicago and to the SAM groups at Columbia, whose members promptly made digests for distribution to other associations.[4]

By January 28, when FAtS testimony was presented, the second series of hearings had been going on for several days. Budget director Harold D. Smith and Secretary of the Interior Ickes had both testified in favor of the McMahon bill, and support from academic circles had been presented in a University of Chicago Round Table discussion between Chancellor Robert M. Hutchins and three distinguished colleagues in sociology, science, and law, Robert Redfield, R. G. Gustavson, and Edward Levi. But the testimony that had made most impression on the committee—particularly on Byrd, Hickenlooper, Johnson, and Millikin—was Secretary of the Navy Forrestal's criticism of the bill on the grounds of inadequate liaison between the commission and the military. This issue was very much in the minds of the seven members—a large attendance for this second series—who heard the representative of the Federation of Atomic Scientists testify on January 28.[5]

The FAtS witness was Harrison Davies, a thirty-four-year-old biochemist who had been at Clinton Labs since 1943, a choice that reflected some lessons of recent months. "Aren't there any scientists with good American names?" one senator is reported to have asked. Added to Davies' satisfactory name was his impeccably Anglo-Saxon appearance and the fact that without being too suavely articulate to overawe or annoy the senators he was a very able fellow. S. 1717, declared Davies, had "the strong support not only of more than

[4] Thompson to McMahon committee members, January 25, 1946, FAS XI, 7; FAS Newsletter, No. 1, January 25, 1946, FAS X, 5.

[5] U.S. Senate, Special Committee on Atomic Energy, *Atomic Energy: Hearings on S. Res. 179*, 79th Cong., 1st sess., November 27, 1945–February 15, 1946.

fifteen hundred Manhattan Project scientists and engineers, but of thousands of other scientists." The collective testimony he offered showed that the month of discussion since the Chicago conference had produced no change of viewpoint; suggested alterations in the bill were so minor, said Davies, that they were being held for later referral to the committee lest they detract from the wholehearted support the federation wished to give it. The only substantial addition to the Chicago analysis was undoubtedly made after Forrestal's testimony five days earlier:

We wish to go on record most strongly as favoring complete exclusion of the military from any policymaking function on the commission. By this we do not mean to exclude efficient liaison between the commission and the armed forces. Provisions making this liaison mandatory as suggested by Secretary Forrestal would not be opposed by the Atomic Scientists. However, it is in the best tradition of American government that policy be made by civilians. A subject fraught with such tremendous significance to our foreign policy as the development of atomic energy in this country must certainly be freed from every vestige of military control.[6]

Davies' manner is hardly one to invite acerbity. Yet the senators' questions were less deferential and more calculated to put him on the spot than those directed at John Simpson six weeks earlier. In the interval the senators had been made wary not only by Forrestal's testimony but by publicity given to scientists' complaints about Groves and army security policy and by the news from the London UN Assembly meeting, where two committee members with the United States delegation, Senators Vandenberg and Connally, had expressed grave concern lest commitments to discuss international control involve too many revelations. In Vandenberg's absence, Senator Hart immediately challenged what he interpreted as federation support of military exclusion, employing the common argument that atomic energy would be under civilian supervision because the President and Congress control the military. Davies' counterquestion— "but is that control directly exercized?"—reflected the fears of the civilian control camp of a stereotyped formula that only seemed to subordinate military influence. Davies did a good job at elaborating the federation's views on military versus civilian control, a considerable service in view of the prominence this issue was shortly to assume. He was on less happy ground when lured by the senators' questions into quasi-political judgments on the effect of the bomb on interna-

---

[6] *Hearings on S. Res. 179*, pp. 135–59; *New York Times*, January 29, 1946, p. 4; *Bulletin of the Atomic Scientists*, I (February 1, 1946), pp. 1, 4–5.

tional relations and, as commonly happened, he was in turn sharply criticized for overstepping his competence by the very people who asked him the questions.

On January 31 the Senate special committee heard testimony from Secretary of Commerce Henry A. Wallace, the McMahon bill forces' closest ally in the cabinet. After emphasizing the bill's importance for international agreement and discussing some points relating to his own department, Wallace lined up all the arguments in its favor, including a strong statement about civilian control.

That afternoon President Truman was asked about Wallace's testimony at a press conference. He replied with a seemingly off-the-cuff endorsement of the principle of civilian control. The following day, using a draft provided by James Newman, the President wrote to Chairman McMahon making more explicit his support of a civilian commission, government ownership of fissionable materials, a licensing system for atomic energy devices, freedom of scientific research, and arrangements that would facilitate international agreement. "To your committee, pioneers in legislation of vast promise for our people and all people," the President's letter read, "there beckons a place of honor in history."[7]

The President's letter received first-page coverage in newspapers over the week end, and on Monday the FAS office wired all the associations urging congratulatory telegrams to Truman and a barrage of communications to McMahon's office; lay groups and public figures should also be requested to write or wire. This was followed up with an FAS press release expressing complete agreement with the principles cited in the President's letter to McMahon, principles that deserved the support of all enlightened citizens; if civilian control were not established soon atomic science in America would suffer grievous interruption, an argument, it will be noted, that had not carried much weight with these same scientists when offered four months earlier by supporters of the May-Johnson bill.[8]

---

[7] Truman to McMahon, February 1, 1946, copy in FAS XI, 7. Hewlett and Anderson suggest that Newman and Condon were responsible for the contents of Wallace's testimony and for the President's endorsement (Richard G. Hewlett and Oscar E. Anderson, Jr., *The New World, 1939–1946* [University Park: Pennsylvania State University Press, 1962], pp. 489–91 [referred to hereinafter as *The New World*]).

[8] Phillips to all associations, February 4, 1946, FAS, XI, 4 (the folder contains letters conveying federation approval of favorable testimony to Ickes, Wallace, *et al.*); FAS press release, February 5, 1946, FAS XVII, 1.

Throughout the three weeks of open hearings the federation continued to have observers present and to circulate daily digests, of which further condensations appeared in the Chicago *Bulletin*. One of the purposes of this vigil was to counter statements that seemed unsound. When George E. Folk, for the National Association of Manufacturers, called for minimum government controls and talked about "harmless" fissionable materials, the FAS issued a special release to say that harmless fissionable material did not exist and that if Folk's advice was followed any crackpot or subversive could make bombs. Knowing that Major de Seversky's testimony would try to minimize atomic bomb damage, the federation had Philip Morrison, whose description of Hiroshima and Nagasaki had so impressed the committee before Christmas, on hand to answer him. But de Seversky's two-hour testimony came in the morning, and the reporters did not return after lunch to hear Morrison's rebuttal—the kind of ineptness in public relations, Higinbotham told fellow scientists, that they must learn to avoid.[9]

On the whole there was little occasion for corrective statements, for witnesses from industry generally backed the bill or criticized it in areas where the scientists claimed no competence. Testimony from individual scientists, not speaking for the federation, was also favorable, although detailed recommendations varied. Like some of his more conservative colleagues, Harlow Shapley advocated a single administrator with full-time divisional directors and an unpaid advisory board; I. I. Rabi spoke for a completely civilian commission with adequate military liaison. Others testified not so much about the bill as about the principles behind it, Louis Ridenour repeating the practical arguments against strict secrecy in his *Fortune* article, and John von Neumann eloquently explaining the importance of freedom of research and his belief that the war had delayed rather than accelerated the development of nuclear physics, in which he foresaw great advances in the next five years.

Throughout these open hearings, Secretary Forrestal's had been the only major dissenting voice. Secretary of War Patterson had been abroad, and his testimony on February 14 was awaited with interest by those who had differed strongly with him over the May-Johnson bill. Their supposition that Patterson had not changed his

[9] FAS press release, February 8, 1946, FAS XVII, 1; Higinbotham to ASC executive committee, February 23, 1946, ASC VI, 12.

views turned out to be correct, though the story behind his testimony cannot have been widely known at the time. Three days earlier a careful War Department analysis of the McMahon bill had been sent to the White House and then to the Bureau of the Budget to be reviewed for consistency with administration policy, a test it failed to meet because Patterson's recommendations for putting military officers in staff positions was inconsistent with the President's recent endorsement of civilian control.[10] The evening before he testified Patterson conferred with the President on how this split in administration opinion should be handled, and although Truman did not insist on unqualified support, Patterson next day endorsed the principle of civilian control, approved a full-time three-man commission, and advocated free publication of basic scientific information, with civilians, not the military, drawing the line between basic science and military applications. But in his response to questions, Patterson's lack of enthusiasm for the McMahon bill became apparent; he recommended that the armed forces should have custody of atomic bombs; they should be allowed to conduct research in military applications of atomic energy; and they should be consulted about security regulations, which should not rest solely on provisions of the Espionage Act. All these points were to be of particular concern to the federation scientists in the coming months.[11]

If the Senate committee staff was not particularly eager to have the scientists' help in dealing with Congress, it was delighted to have their assistance in arousing public interest. The FAS prepared a petition to the Congress of the United States with arguments for the McMahon bill distilled for quick and easy comprehension and phrased to attract the widest possible support. The principles fundamental to a satisfactory domestic policy on atomic energy were declared to be full control of developments by the federal government and the exercize of control through a civilian agency fully responsible to the President and Congress; science must not be hamstrung "by shortsighted and unrealistic policy based on the belief that military security can be achieved by imposition of secrecy in scientific research. . . .

---

[10] See *The New World*, pp. 499–500. Budget Director Harold Smith sent the War Department analysis to the Office of War Mobilization and Reconversion, where James Newman, along with his job as McMahon committee counsel, was still the Director's right-hand man. "Whatever Smith's intentions," comment the authors of *The New World*, "his action was tantamount to killing the War Department report."

[11] *New York Times*, February 15, 1946, p. 3; *Hearings on S. Res. 179*, pp. 389–409.

National legislation must not obstruct but smooth the path for the future creation of international control." The control and development of atomic energy must not become a partisan issue. About February 5 these petitions went to some forty research centers, to organizations, and to individuals, accompanied in some cases by a sample letter to "Dear Friend" that could be used for solicitation of more signatures. The receipt of four thousand names at the end of a ten-day period was considered very satisfactory.[12]

The help given by local associations at this juncture was somewhat uneven, for ALAS, Cambridge, and SAM were handicapped by loss of members and the new groups getting under way in February seemed to draw their strength from interest in international rather than domestic problems. Members of the Atomic Scientists of Chicago, however (since if they moved at all, it was mostly from the Met Lab to the University of Chicago), maintained their intense interest in domestic legislation and responded to the appeal of February 5 with a prompt assignment of duties relating to the McMahon bill—promotion of letters and telegrams, preparation of a resolution on the bill, and contacts with radio commentators and newsmen and with universities, scientific organizations, and other sites. By chance the conference for midwest religious leaders opened on the campus the very day the call for help came from Washington, and after the not signally successful effort to exchange scientific fact for spiritual insight, the affair turned into a rally for the McMahon bill. The forty-odd clergymen not only wired the President and Senator McMahon their support of civilian control but went home prepared to spread the word in their communities. Two Michigan meetings organized by the continuing committee of the conference had, as we shall see, a significant influence on the military liaison issue.[13]

2. THE CANADIAN SPY SCARE

Supporters of civilian control hoped that the President's endorsement and Patterson's nominal backing would check the interest of the Senate committee in strengthening military liaison. But on Saturday, February 16, two days after Patterson testified, these hopes were

---

[12] Petition and related material in FAS XI, 1, 2; FAS Newsletter, I (March 1, 1946), AORES XXI, 5; report of Hagemann to ASC executive committee, February 19–March 2, 1946, in ASC files.

[13] ASC executive committee minutes, February 5, 1946, ASC VI, 12; proceedings, correspondence, etc., of conference of religious leaders in ASC II, 6; III, 15, 16; IV, 8.

dashed by news from Canada that arrests had followed the defection of a Russian cypher clerk with documents taken from the Soviet embassy vault. A week earlier a new version of the May-Johnson bill had been introduced in the Senate as S. 1824, and the scientists and their allies now faced the probability that the Canadian affair, as yet unknown in its extent or United States implications, would be used either to push this bill through or drastically to amend the McMahon bill. The effect of the spy case on both legislators and scientists was heightened by the fragmentary release of information, liberally interlarded with rumor and speculation. Headlines referred to "atom" spies even when the articles denied that atomic energy was involved, and along with official statements that no United States scientists were implicated, rumors spread of more extensive espionage in this country. And alarm was caused on both sides of the border by Canadian special orders in council under which suspects were arrested, by suspension of habeas corpus, and by denial of legal counsel.

Trying to disentangle truth from rumor, FAS leaders prudently withheld comment, but discussions of the affair were fraught with real anxiety. In Chicago an ASC executive committee meeting on February 19 heard a report from Washington that some kind of military board was inevitable and began to think in terms of a compromise formula limiting its control to the bomb itself. James Franck, a man not subject to hysterical reactions, was quoted as saying that all scientists were being called spies and that Secretary Patterson should be asked to clarify the situation. ASC leaders regarded the spy scare as a smoke screen to force passage of the May-Johnson bill, and a phone call by Szilard to Byron Miller during the meeting revealed the same suspicion among McMahon bill supporters in Washington. Miller's advice was to stress this point rather than make a direct attack on the May-Johnson bill, and to this end the executive committee made immediate contact with columnists and commentators— including Raymond Swing, Walter Lippman, Elmer Davis, Clifton Utley, Walter Winchell, Drew Pearson, and Dorothy Thompson— climaxed a few days later with a conference for Chicago radio commentators at which Szilard and some younger ASC members explained their views on the relation of the spy scare to domestic legislation.

A renewed push was given to circulation of McMahon bill petitions by the ASC, and a postcard campaign was directed at the Senate committee. Efforts to organize an FAS affiliate of non-Project scientists and engineers in the Chicago area were intensified. Two hundred and fifty students at Armour Research Foundation were implored to write letters in support of the bill, and Harold Urey helped organize a group of doctors. Urey was also assigned the task of converting Colonel Robert R. McCormick of the *Chicago Tribune* to the cause of civilian control, but he failed to turn in a progress report. A visit from FAS chairman Higinbotham on February 23 found these efforts in full swing; he brought little encouragement from Washington— only the bad news that the tide of mail supporting the McMahon bill had dropped to a trickle after the spy case broke.[14]

There were disturbing minor repercussions. Swing's broadcast on the twenty-second revealed that a visa had been denied to Niels Bohr. And one that seemed very ominous was an army statement— attributed, of course, to General Groves—that from disclosures in Senate committee hearings and loose talk among irresponsible scientists more information about the atomic bomb had leaked out in the last four weeks than in the entire course of the war. This roused particular anger at Clinton Labs. One of the pre-Christmas witnesses, Alvin Weinberg, wired Urey, Simpson, Teller, and Szilard, urging that scientists who had appeared before the committee sign a statement that their testimony had not jeopardized security and had been essential to its deliberations.[15] There is no record of such a joint statement, but Weinberg's colleagues in AORS shared his indignation. In addition to a vigorous campaign by the political action committee to get members and friends to write and wire the President and Senate committee members, AORS released a statement that said in part:

> The Army ... would like to keep atomic energy exclusively as a military weapon, thus insuring that it would never be used for the good of mankind. It would like to continue to manufacture more and more atomic bombs, thus plunging the world into an atomic armaments race, leading inevitably to atomic war, against the express wishes of the people, the President, the Secretary of State, and the United Nations Organization.[16]

On February 21 and 22, while this angry reaction was in full tide, the representatives of AORS, ALAS, and the ASC met in Chicago

---

[14] ASC executive committee minutes, February 19–26, 1946, ASC VI, 12.
[15] Weinberg to Urey et al., February 19, 1946, ASC XXV, 8.
[16] Quoted by Raymond Lawrence, *Oakland Tribune*, March 4, 1946, p. 20; AORS memorandum, n.d., AORES IV, 7; AORS Newsletter, February 27, 1946, AORES XX, 1.

for that belated election of FAtS officers already described and to propose a major reorganization of the FAmS, actions that were not unrelated to the gloomy outlook for civilian control. Said the resulting memorandum with more pith than elegance:

The present political crisis has found us with our Washington political pants down. There has been insufficient building of political fences by continued contact with members of Congress and the Administration. At times, politically unwise press releases have been made. A good deal of this is due to the relative inexperience of our representatives in Washington. Much could be done, however, if greater use were made of a number of politically-wise men in Washington—men who have already shown strong sympathy for our program.

Liaison of the Washington office with member groups has been very poor. Except for occasional phone calls and telegrams, the local organizations have received little immediate information from Washington. Policy has effectively been determined by the few people in Washington, rather than by the FAmS Council, which has not met since the beginning of January. There has been little attempt to gather information and opinions from the local organizations before action has been taken in Washington. Communication has been largely an after-the-fact business, via a delayed news letter.[17]

It is not clear whether Higinbotham, who was in Chicago next day, was on hand on the twenty-second to defend the Washington staff and the less aggressive policy toward Congress recommended by its political advisers; but he did try to improve communications, and within a few days a report on the legislative situation went from the FAS office to all member associations: the response to the McMahon bill petition had been good—an informal count at this point showed four to five thousand signatures—but still more wires and resolutions to congressmen from scientists and laymen were needed. The committee might conclude its hearings by March 11 (an estimate that was off by just a month), and speed was essential.[18]

For the press an FAS release on February 27 was directed not to the particular episode of the spy case but to the general subject of secrecy. Secrets were leaking, it pointed out, wherever the nature of the universe was being studied. The momentary advantage of the

---

[17] "Proposal for Reorganization of the Federation of American Scientists," ca. March 13, 1946, ASC XIII, 15. The Philadelphia association also complained that lack of communication was leading to doubts about the usefulness of the federation (Fusfeld to Higinbotham, February 26, 1946, FAS VII, 5).

[18] FAS memorandum to all associations, February 26, 1946, FAS XI, 4; Phillips to Newman, February 27, 1946, FAS XI, 1.

United States was its two-billion-dollar investment in plants. Scientists did not want to give away military secrets, but the American public could not judge the next war without knowing about radiation damage at Hiroshima and about bacteriological warfare. The top military men had not told the American people the real story of science in war because they themselves had not been authorized to develop a new security policy geared to the atomic age. The past week of spy hysteria, concluded the release, was an example of what was to come.[19]

The day this FAS release was issued there occurred a second event that stirred the McMahon bill camp to even further heights of alarm and activity. On February 27 the Senate committee reopened its public hearings to listen to the views of General Groves on military liaison. Speaking for himself, not the War Department, Groves recommended a nine-man commission of whom perhaps four should be military men and from which nuclear physicists, or heads of institutions having large nuclear physics laboratories, should be excluded as not being disinterested. If any bill is adopted, said Groves, "which does not include men with military background on the Commission, the Commission should be required by law to submit to the Joint Chiefs of Staff all matters of policy prior to adoption and before publication." This seemed to describe exactly the control of policy that scientists were trying to prevent and overshadowed the General's blander comments to the effect that after the past five months he would be most reluctant to accept the post of administrator and that the bill should look to the future and not indicate that we thought of atomic energy only in terms of a weapon.[20] With nerves already on edge after ten days of scare headlines on the Canadian spy case, the FAS this time did not allow a cooling off period. It issued a statement next day drawing attention, somewhat unjustly, to the militaristic character of Groves's testimony.

The discovery of atomic energy, developed by civilians for peaceful uses, under a system of world order and law, offers greater hope for plenty than any single thing since man discovered use for fire.... Today, however, the men who think of atomic energy mainly as a super-weapon to kill millions

---

[19] FAS press release, February 27, 1946, FAS XVII, 1.
[20] U.S. Senate, Special Committee on Atomic Energy, *Atomic Energy Act of 1946: Hearings on S. 1717*, 79th Cong., 2d sess., January 22–April 4, 1946, pp. 467 ff.; *New York Times*, February 28, 1946, p. 12.

where once bombs killed thousands ... are urging mankind to keep playing with the toys of war until the flaming end.[21]

As far as the scientists were concerned it was now almost impossible for Groves to say the right thing. Outside the hearings he suggested salary increases for scientists for the purpose—or at least so he was quoted—of saving the country. Higinbotham wired all sites for reactions. Jaffey reported by phone from Chicago that he and his colleagues thought economic security was definitely not a reason people were leaving the Project, though polls should be taken to find out. ALAS chairman Maurice Shapiro wired on March 1: "If General actually said 'to save country,' we say raising scientists' salaries is pleasant but irrelevant.... Best hope of saving country from sudden devastation is world collaboration for control of atomic energy. National atomic armament is a false basis for national security." And Waldo Cohn informed a Senate committee member that AORS considered Groves ill qualified to pass on scientific secrets, commenting that the General had not led the Project but had commanded and domineered it.[22]

The Association of Oak Ridge Scientists went ahead with the plans already outlined. Duplicated material under date of March 1 included a two-page statement on atomic energy legislation, a memorandum to "Members and Friends of AORS" quoting the February 26 call to action from Washington, and a model letter to "Dear Friend," ending in each case with a list of Senate committee members and an exhortation to write or wire. The model letter contained a typical example of propaganda and prophesy:

Whether the bill the [Senate] committee sends to the Senate has the progressive features of the present McMahon bill or the restrictive ones of the ill-famed May-Johnson bill depends upon what the committee hears from the public.

It is not too much to say that the future course of the world may depend on the action taken in Washington on this subject within the coming days and weeks. If atomic energy is left in the hands of the military we may expect the continuation of the present situation, in which the War Department stockpiles atomic bombs while the State Department and U.N.O. delegates make vain gestures towards the international control of atomic energy. We have, as a result of the War Department's action, initiated an

---

[21] FAS press release, February 28, 1946, FAS XVII, 1.

[22] Higinbotham wire to Jaffey and memorandum of phone call, February 28, 1946, ASC XXV, 8; Shapiro wire to Higinbotham, March 1, 1946, FAS V, 8; Cohn to Senator Johnson of Colorado, March 1, 1946, AORES V, 10.

atomic armament race, vitiated the efforts of the UNO and our own State Department, demoralized the Projects and forced the better scientists out of them; we have crippled our own atomic energy research and spurred the rest of the world into mistrust and fear of us.

AORS also distributed a March 3 column by the *New York Herald Tribune's* military columnist, Major George Fielding Eliot, supporting civilian control and chiding General Groves for lack of confidence in the American people. (They did not apparently feel an equal interest in a *New York Times* article of the same date by Arthur Krock expressing some sympathy for the General's side of the argument.) And finally yet another AORS statement, dated March 4, described the critical situation of the McMahon bill and again urged communications to Senate committee members, because "we technical workers" feel that we cannot stem this tide alone.[23]

Reflecting an equally strong reaction in Chicago to Groves's testimony, a *Bulletin* editorial of March 1 called his recommendations a program to drive away the best scientists in the country and continued:

To the military mind, one scientist may be as good as another; if one leaves he can be replaced by another one. This is the spirit in which Hitler let the best German scientists leave the country. . . . This is the spirit which dryed [sic] out military research in this country between the two World Wars.

. . . Will the Congress, in despair over the momentary—and perhaps passing—international troubles, enact legislation which will create, in the tissue of our public life, a malignant tumor of irresponsible military rule; which will stifle science in the name of a futile "security," create a "Maginot line" of a stock of atomic bombs, and start the whole world on the road to disaster?[24]

On a practical level the ASC determined to see that it was effectively represented in the Washington office. Since Christmas there had been difficulty in finding people to go, but toward the end of February Albert Cahn spent a short time there, and when he indicated his willingness to return for an indefinite period, the executive committee agreed to underwrite his salary.[25] Cahn soon became the scientists' chief link with the Senate committee staff and with supporting citizens groups. His connection with Kansas City political figures, it will be remembered, had given Szilard an entree to the White House in the

---

[23] The five AORS releases are in FAS VII, 2.
[24] *Bulletin of the Atomic Scientists*, I (March 1, 1946), 12.
[25] ASC executive committee minutes, March 6, 1946, ASC VI, 12.

spring of 1945. Acquaintance with Senator McMahon through his wife's family in Connecticut now gave Cahn another useful contact.

The sending of Cahn reflected the critical attitude that the old-guard atomic scientists continued to maintain toward the larger federation. The implication—somewhat lacking in political realism—was that more energetic action in the Washington office would have prevented the Senate committee from developing doubts about the McMahon bill in its original form. As for the local associations, Clinton Labs and Chicago complained that although other groups produced letters, telegrams, and signatures for the McMahon bill petition they did not send volunteers to Washington or originate aggressive action.

There was, indeed, some justice in this observation, but as individuals adjusted to new jobs and new associates, several of the "non-atomic" groups became effective in their own way. At this time, in fact, a vigorous new FAS affiliate was developing in Berkeley. Toward the end of January the Washington office had learned that a dozen people there were interested but hesitant about organizing because of Lawrence's known opposition to political activity, but these fears were soon overcome, and early in February the Northern California Association of Scientists was formed. The nucleus was a group of young men interested in the Committee for Foreign Correspondence and in a social science project concerned with atomic energy; but the NCAS owed to the military control issue the fact that in the first five weeks it acquired three hundred members, with an additional one hundred and fifty applications on hand. It organized a meeting in San Francisco on March 1 at which the University of California's distinguished chemist Joel Hildebrand talked about the challenge of atomic energy to an overflow audience of two thousand. The McMahon bill petition was circulated at the meeting, and by March 12 the NCAS sent in fourteen hundred signatures. Enthusiastic progress reports went almost daily to the Washington office.[26]

Although some scientists felt that not enough was being done, a quite contrary reaction was expressed by a few outside observers. The *New York Times* "Topics" editor, who had questioned scientists' qualifications for politics after the May-Johnson bill debate, now raised the issue again and denounced the AORS' February 27 blast at the

---

[26] FAS History-Diary, January 22, 1946, in FAS files (Washington, D.C.); reports from Leo Brewer to Higinbotham, February and March, 1946, FAS XX, 4.

army as an example of angry, passionate partisanship. Rebuked for this remark by an unidentified woman scientist at M.I.T., the "Topics" editor returned to the subject the following Sunday. He did not want scientists to go back to their ivory towers; he only wanted them to make clear when they spoke as scientists and when as citizens and—since opinions among scientists clearly differed—not to be so violent.[27]

A West Coast columnist took up the theme. Messianic motivation was understandable, wrote Raymond Lawrence in the *Oakland Tribune*, but the army had already lost its fight for military control and the public didn't need educating. Citing the AORS statement of February 27 and the San Francisco McMahon bill rally, which he had attended, Lawrence continued:

In this process of educating the public and defeating the Army, many of these scientists have become tub thumpers whose intemperate vituperation and intense passion might arouse the envy of Gerald K. Smith. The popular notion that the scientific temperament is restrained, judicious, quiet and soundly balanced is belied by some of the recent antics....

The language of the learned journals has turned acrid and acidulous, but we do not believe sarcasm and vituperation, regardless of the deficiencies of the military education, will accomplish the purpose....

...These scientists could be better guides in atomic thinking and policy, and would elicit more support, if they returned to their own method and spirit....

To a remonstrance from the Northern California Association Lawrence replied in a second column with some sensible remarks about conflicting views on research and security without retracting his statements on intemperate propaganda.[28]

For the most part what the scientists read in the papers was from more sympathetic pens. By a kind of autocatalytic process news of current developments was fed back to them, at least in the papers they most respected like the *New York Times* and the *Washington Post*, by newsmen whose views on atomic energy they themselves had helped to form. But in reacting strongly on the military liaison issue, the local associations were responding not only to published news but also to private reports from Washington. The spy scare had completely changed the picture, wrote Higinbotham to a friend at

---

[27] *New York Times*, February 24, 1946, sec. E, p. 8; March 3, 1946, sec. E, p. 8.
[28] Lawrence, *Oakland Tribune*, March 4, 1946, p. 20, and March 8, 1946, p. 32; M. Kasha to Lawrence, March 5, 1946, FAS XX, 4.

Los Alamos. The committee got scared and called on Groves and perhaps they would now report his bill to the Congress. Higinbotham was not sure what to do next, but the FAS staff was getting all the advice possible. "In any event," he said, "an all-out attack on the General is in order since he has spoken as an individual and contrary to the President's position."[29]

Returning to Chicago about March 2 French Hagemann told the executive committee that the picture looked very black. General Groves's testimony had found a majority of the committee with him, and references had been made in committee circles to "crackpot long haired scientists." Newman and Condon, bearing the still incomplete McMahon bill petition with some five thousand signatures, had seen the President and urged that he speak again in favor of civilian control but with inconclusive results.[30]

From the FAS office the first formal newsletter in six weeks assessed the damage suffered in the fortnight since the Canadian spy story broke: there was now grave danger that something like the May-Johnson bill would be reported out by the Senate committee; as propaganda against genuine civilian control the spy hysteria could not have been better timed if it had been planned that way. But there were indications that committee members were still influenced by letters and telegrams, and support given the FAS McMahon bill petition had been excellent. Science legislation, hitherto regarded by federation scientists as a distraction from their main business, was now, in Senator Kilgore's compromise version, recommended to members for study, with the admonition that the issue of administering science for peace or war might be the same for both pieces of legislation. A supplementary memorandum from Higinbotham referred to last-ditch efforts by the office staff to save the McMahon bill, adding anti-climactically but not irrelevantly, "At this inopportune moment we are broke."[31]

One of these last-ditch efforts is documented by correspondence between Melba Phillips and certain leading scientists. Although an impressive number of prominent ones had testified in favor of the

[29] Higinbotham to M. Shapiro, March 1, 1946, FAS files (Washington, D.C.).

[30] Report of Hagemann to ASC executive committee, February 19–March 2, 1946, in ASC files.

[31] FAS Newsletter, I (March 1, 1946), AORES XXI, 5; Higinbotham memorandum to all sites, March 1, 1946, Camb. II. The FAS attitude toward science legislation is discussed in a later chapter.

McMahon bill or publicly supported it and the petitions were bringing in signatures from many more, a perhaps decisive blow would be struck in its favor if those who had previously backed the May-Johnson bill could be shown to have changed their minds. The FAS leaders decided to try. On February 27 letters to Conant, Bush, Lawrence, Oppenheimer, Fermi, and A. H. Compton pointed out that the cause of civilian control would be greatly strengthened if they would join in supporting the principles set forth in the petition for the McMahon bill.[32]

Answers were requested by telegram; some may have been phoned. The only ones in the files are from Bush and Fermi—both prompt, careful, and negative. Fermi could not support the bill because he disagreed with it on ten counts, which he elaborated in an attached memorandum; these included, he noted with characteristic fairness, only points of disagreement, not those of which he approved.

In the first place the McMahon bill tended to discourage industrial developments, especially atomic power.

> While I realize that atomic industry on a large scale may make the problem of international control of the production of weapons more laborious I think that the passage of such legislation would be a deterrent to the progress in the field, since many people will be unwilling to work for an objective which at present is forbidden on the chance that it may be permitted in the future. I also believe that in the present international situation it is in the best interest of the Nation to further and not to discourage large scale development in the atomic field. I also doubt the soundness of the argument that showing no intention to expand rapidly this field will improve the chances of international agreement. I am rather inclined to believe that the main incentive for some foreign powers to accept an agreement may be the conviction that they should be left behind in the industrial development if one were to come to an armament race.

Fermi questioned the operation of installations by the commission instead of by contractors as this would involve huge administrative machinery and the handicap of low government salaries. The bill's statement of policy, Fermi noted, omitted any reference to atomic energy as contributing to national safety. More precise definition was needed of "fissionable materials" and of what constituted irrelevant amounts. Fermi's last two points related to civilian control: the army should be given authority over research and development of military applications and should have custody of atomic weapons.

---

[32] Phillips to Conant et al., February 27, 1946, FAS XXVI, 1.

He agreed that weapons production should be possible only under specific authority from the President, but the requirements of quarterly renewal of this authority would prevent long-term commitments and hamper production.[33]

The reply from Bush came a few days later in a friendly letter to Higinbotham. He had given much thought to domestic policy and approved the May-Johnson bill, especially as amended in late October (H.R. 4566). "I am fully aware, however," said Bush, "that many of the most competent scientists who worked on the atomic fission project favor a different type of organization . . . and I have kept an open mind on the subject so that I may fully understand their viewpoint." He had studied S. 1717 and concluded that it had serious deficiencies that should be remedied before the Senate committee reported it, and he enclosed a copy of a seven-page letter he had sent to Chairman McMahon on January 22 discussing these matters in detail. Bush's first two points dealt with the conduct of research by government agencies as opposed to the private and university sponsorship that he strongly favored. There was also a lengthy discussion upholding a part-time commission, a point on which Bush when interviewed in 1962 expressed as strong an opinion as he did in 1946. He also gave McMahon his views on licensing, patents, and other points.

Blanket endorsement of the McMahon bill, Bush told Higinbotham, was a very serious responsibility that should not be undertaken without the considered conclusion that in all respects it answered the problem. This conclusion he had not reached and he hoped the bill would be amended. In any case Bush thought it improper for him as a government official to join in a group petition of private citizens to Congress. At the same time, he concluded, "I want to urge you and the other members of your Federation and its member associations to continue to take an active part in these legislative matters that so vitally affect us as scientists and citizens."[34]

Bush's testimony before the McMahon committee had preceded the introduction of the McMahon bill, but if his views as expressed in the confidential letter to McMahon caused no surprise in the FAS office neither did they convince. One reader, quite likely Higin-

---

[33] Fermi to Phillips, March 1, 1946, and "Comments on the McMahon bill on atomic energy," FAS XXVI, 1.

[34] Bush to Higinbotham, March 4, 1946, and enclosure, Bush to McMahon, January 22, 1946, in FAS XII, 7.

botham himself, made some marginal comments. By the section opposing government control of research, he wrote, "Nuts, we have Los Alamos and Clinton." On control of research, he noted "argue," but on licenses "no argue."

Local associations also tried to get endorsement from important individuals. Again it was a refusal that got into the record when Lee A. DuBridge, who had led an attack on the original May-Johnson bill but supported its amended form, told Robert Mulliken of the ASC advisory committee that he thought a full-time commission was preposterous, though he would withdraw his objection if anyone could name for him five highly intelligent men who would accept the jobs at $15,000 a year.[35]

Arthur Krock, in a long *New York Times* article about the attacks being made on General Groves and his information policy, also showed an interest in the opinions of "leading scientists"—Bush, Conant, A. H. Compton, Oppenheimer, Lawrence, Urey, and Szilard —only the last two, Krock said, disagreed with Groves on any major point. Urey, he added, had advised against expansion of an Oak Ridge plant for extracting U-235 on the grounds that it could make no important contribution before the war was over, and he could be wrong again.[36]

Krock's "leading scientists" were those whose names had been most often in the papers, and the category was thus weighted on the side of official status in the Manhattan Project. One might add that none of those he mentioned as agreeing with Groves, whatever their current views, was now taking public part in the debate on domestic legislation. Bush was busy demobilizing the numerous OSRD research projects; Conant was back at Harvard; Oppenheimer was immersed in the State Department study of international control; and Compton was concentrating on his new duties as chancellor of Washington University, though he did take public issue on March 6 with the demand of the World Council of Churches that the manufacture of atomic bombs be stopped by pointing out to its president, Bishop G. Bromley Oxnam, that war itself needed to be outlawed but that we could not at present abandon bombs.[37] The efforts of the FAS to draw these men back into the fray were notably unsuccessful.

---

[35] DuBridge to Mulliken, March 4, 1946, ASC VIII, 7.
[36] *New York Times*, March 3, 1946, sec. E, p. 3.
[37] *New York Times*, March 7, 1946, p. 10.

As for those who disagreed with Groves, Szilard, who since the 1930's when he had tried to interest Chaim Weizmann in a foundation to control the atom, had never ceased to think of its relation to war and peace, was for the present out of the Washington picture (or was, at any rate, eluding the firm rein of Newman) and was exploring the—for him—new field of biology at the University of Chicago. Szilard's thoughts, as usual, had jumped ahead of events and were now directed toward facilitating international agreement by some kind of direct communication with Russian scientists, a dream that was not fulfilled until the Pugwash Conferences began ten years later. Urey, however, was in the thick of things, and this fact inspired a suggestion from Oak Ridge on how to counter Groves's February 27 testimony. The Senate committee will listen to Groves because he is one and we are many, wrote Waldo Cohn to Rush in the Washington office; we should choose one leader—Urey—and let him battle Groves where, as, and if, he chooses. "This is no time for palavering on organizational activities," Cohn concluded; "the battle of the bill is on, and no holds are barred."[38] Urey would never officially have entered the lists against Groves, but in his impetuous, sputtering way he was continuing to speak out and did so, in fact, on the day that Cohn wrote from Oak Ridge, telling reporters in an interview at the New York office of Americans United for World Organization that if the people of the United States were awake they would realize that they too had a quarrel with the Manhattan District, as indeed the whole world had.[39]

General Groves, whose public utterances had so often made the scientists angry, did not counterattack, but through Oppenheimer he conveyed to Higinbotham the hope that in the future he and the federation might confer upon issues as they arose. Higinbotham's note to the General acknowledging these overtures was polite but chilly and said little more than that he was sorry they did not agree.[40]

Closely related to its bearing upon the fate of the McMahon bill was another angle to the Canadian spy case that caused much private concern to the FAS leadership, namely, its effect upon the standing of scientists in relation to security. The problem of keeping the

[38] Cohn to Rush, March 2, 1946, FAS VII, 1.

[39] As reported in the *New York Times*, March 3, 1946, p. 12; with Urey were Bernard Feld of Cambridge, Aaron Novick of Chicago, Irving Kaplan and Clarke Williams of the SAM Lab, and Lyle Borst of Clinton.

[40] Higinbotham to Groves, March 14, 1946, FAS chronological files (Washington, D.C.).

organization free from taint of fellow-traveling had worried some people a great deal, especially those on the Manhattan Project who fully realized how easily their campaign for international control could founder, despite the blessing of conservative statesmen, if they became associated with individuals or groups whose motives for negotiating with Russia could be impugned. This consideration accounted in part for the insistence on an organization of limited scope and specific objectives. Their problem was not an internal one, for the Project's G-2 and other security agencies had done the purging of awkward associates at an earlier stage, but situations developed that required poise and sometimes toughness, and the burden fell on the Washington staff, who, unable to discuss the problems frankly, got caught in an uncomfortable crossfire from their own lines. It had come from one angle when the first Washington delegates moved in with the Independent Citizens Committee and from another when a clerical employee was dropped because of past associations. Like the question of affiliation with the World Federation of Scientific Workers, these were vexing problems for people accustomed to tolerate some divergence of opinion.

At a time when all their energies were needed to co-ordinate support for the McMahon bill and to combat internal criticism Higinbotham and Rush endured a period of acute anxiety about the security status of FAS. Just as reports were beginning to circulate that the House Un-American Activities Committee was off to investigate Oak Ridge, a dinner was held on March 1 at the home of J. Terry Duce, a vice-president of the Arabian-American Oil Company. The guests included Glenn Seaborg from Berkeley, Albert Cahn and French Hagemann from Chicago, Rush from the federation office, E. U. Condon and his wife, James Newman and his OWMR boss John Snyder, Senators McMahon and Hatch, Representatives Edith Nourse Rogers and Karl Mundt, a few other officials, and several newsmen.

Rush opened the after-dinner discussion with a summary of the scientists' position on international control, emphasizing that they were under no illusions about easy agreement—that, indeed, they felt the odds were poor—but that the appalling consequences of failure impelled them to a desperate effort. Almost immediately the conversation was diverted to Russia with Mrs. Condon in her usual forthright fashion arguing heatedly, for the most part against Representative Mundt, for a more lenient attitude toward the Russians. The scientists, it was noted at the time, did not themselves take part in this discussion and were, in fact, disappointed that so much time was devoted to Soviet relations when they wanted to talk about immediate problems of domestic legislation. Remembering that Mundt was a member of the House Un-American Activities Committee, Rush thought all was lost, but as they were leaving, Mundt spoke to him appreciatively of the views he had expressed, inviting Rush to address the 76 Club made up of surviving members of the Seventy-sixth Congress.[41]

Mundt's good opinion was important. A week later the *New York Times* carried a report that Un-American Activities Committee chairman John S. Wood was leaving for a ten-day trip; his itinerary was secret, but the trip was associated with rumors of espionage links between New York and Oak Ridge.[42] At the same time came private hints that the committee had its eye on the FAS. Higinbotham and Rush decided to make the first move and went to see Attorney-General Tom Clark. Clark was somewhat puzzled at their turning up with no names to report; all they wanted, they explained, was time to make sure that any necessary housecleaning was done. Clark assured them that as far as his office was concerned the FAS was not under any cloud, and the contact, like that with Mundt, later stood them in good stead.

3. The Vandenberg Amendment

The early days of March did not bring much hope that the Senate committee would lose interest in strengthened military liaison. On March 6 newspapers reported not only Churchill's speech of the previous day at Fulton, Missouri, calling for a firmer stand against Russia, but the arrest in England of physicist Alan Nunn May on charges of espionage relating to the Canadian affair. And on March 12 two events intensified the apprehension created in a large segment of the American scientific community by the Canadian spy case and Groves's testimony. The House Military Affairs Committee requested that the revised May-Johnson bill be given priority on the House calendar, and the Senate special committee accepted by a vote of six to one Senator Vandenberg's amendment setting up a military

---

[41] List of dinner guests in FAS XV, 1; interview with Rush, September 7, 1959, and Rush to the author, February 28, 1964; interview with Higinbotham, October 18, 1961. The Duce dinner was recalled in 1948 when Condon's clearance was withdrawn (Peter Edson column, *Washington News*, March 15, 1948).

[42] *New York Times*, March 8, 1946, p. 3.

liaison board and providing that "the Commission shall advise and consult with the Committee on all atomic energy matters which the Committee deems to relate to the common defense and security. The Committee shall have full opportunity to acquaint itself with all matters before the Commission."[43]

To the proposed resurrection of the May-Johnson bill, the FAS responded with an immediate release repeating earlier warnings against its strong military emphasis; if science must be geared to war, it asked, why not all basic industries?[44]

News of Vandenberg's amendment reached Henry Wallace in time for him to denounce it in a speech he was making that afternoon, and this attack from a cabinet member so annoyed Vandenberg that he obtained confirmation of the amendment vote next day in full committee with ten in favor to McMahon's one dissent. As the McMahon bill forces had been urging him to do for some days, the President now reaffirmed his support of civilian control. And from the FAS office Higinbotham issued the second release in two days to deplore the proposed departure from the traditional practice of excluding the military from policy-making. He had to apologize later for acting without authorization, but there is no question that the statement reflected FAS opinion.[45] A more detailed explanation of why scientists found the amendment so objectionable appeared in the next Chicago *Bulletin*. Reiterating the point made in Davies' testimony that the FAS did not oppose efficient or even mandatory liaison with the military, Rabinowitch cited Patterson's own assertion that the military should not be the ones to draw the line between basic research and military applications. A military board lacking expert technical knowledge, said Rabinowitch, cannot avoid playing safe and carving "the largest possible chunk out of the living body of science.... The revolutionary fact of the present situation is that military have ceased to be experts on security."[46]

Running through all the scientists' comments—and the military liaison amendment produced folders of memorandums and analyses —are the dual arguments that military control is contrary to our

---

[43] Byron S. Miller, "A Law Is Passed: The Atomic Energy Act of 1946," *University of Chicago Law Review*, XV (Summer, 1948), 812, n. 16. Copyright © 1948 by The University of Chicago.

[44] FAS press release, March 12, 1946, FAS XVII, 1.

[45] *The New World*, pp. 506–7; FAS press release, March 13, 1946, FAS XVII, 1; Higinbotham to all associations, March 18, 1946, Camb. II.

[46] *Bulletin of the Atomic Scientists*, I (March 15, 1946), 1, 16.

constitution and traditions and that secrecy would stifle scientific progress and thus hamper security. Five scientists on duty in Washington on March 18 issued in their own names an eight-page appeal for civilian control, pointing up the secrecy issue for the ordinary citizen. No group of scientists, they said, proposes to give the world the design or blueprints of any weapon or atomic bomb.

But in the latter case the matter does not stop with blueprints. Suppose that the Garand rifle had involved fundamental scientific discoveries in metallurgy. It would be proper to keep the design—the invention—secret, but if that new metal developed for the M-1 was of such a new and marvelous nature that it would be revolutionary if used in airplanes and motorcars, would the military be justified in keeping the knowledge secret? Would they be justified in insisting that most of that metal in peacetime should be used for guns and not for automobiles?[47]

Before the second FAS council meeting, scheduled for March 23 and 24 in Philadelphia, Higinbotham dispatched a memorandum to all the associations with background information to help them formulate their stand on the Vandenberg amendment and other aspects of the McMahon bill. We cannot afford to appear to be working with McMahon alone, he advised, for other members of the Senate committee and other senators consider him young, inexperienced, and interested in making a name for himself. We must not identify ourselves with any group or party; peace groups and liberals flock to our assistance, and we must retain our objectivity. Higinbotham further reported a very real fear among responsible people, like Forrestal, Patterson, and Vandenberg, that civilian control had been emphasized to a point where our military security was threatened; until world control was achieved the military could not be cut off from weaponeering. Vandenberg claimed that his amendment gave the military liaison committee no power to exercize authority—it could only make recommendations to the commission and advise the President—but this was considered in Washington to be an administrative monstrosity. The Senate committee had not yet come to the secrecy provisions, but there was almost universal confusion between secrecy and security, and it was up to the scientists to emphasize the distinction in all talks and releases.

Higinbotham urged renewed attention to rebutting false statements and rumors. More was heard about this in the next few days. In-

---

[47] FAS press release by A. Cahn, Joan Hinton, W. A. Higinbotham, A. Novick, and J. H. Rush, March 18, 1946, FAS XVII, 1.

a *Washington Post* article Alfred Friendly, in what he called the hardly coincidental series of incidents leading up to the Vandenberg amendment, included the following:

> The House Un-American Activities Committee revealed it had traced a Russian spy link to the great Oak Ridge establishment in the Manhattan Project. So far nothing has been made public on the nature of the evidence.
>
> It was disclosed that the Army is giving lie detector tests to Oak Ridge personnel. In an official statement, the Army declared that the tests were merely experiments to find out more about the lie detector. But again, "reports persisted" that the object was to uncover possible subversion among the employees.[48]

On March 26 the *Washington Post* reported that Ernie Adamson, chief counsel of the House Un-American Activities Committee, had announced a witch hunt among atomic scientists and quoted Adamson as saying that the committee would hold closed hearings in the four research centers in connection with its atomic spy ring investigation. Adamson, according to the *Post*, had been gathering evidence at Oak Ridge. But how had he got in? The *Post* concluded that he must have been working with General Groves; people like Adamson were holding up the development of atomic energy because scientists would not work for the government if they were subjected to the hazards of surveillance, loss of reputation, and idle smearing.[49]

With such rumors abroad it was in a most uneasy atmosphere that the FAS council met on March 23 to discuss the Vandenberg amendment and other aspects of the McMahon bill. But the council could do little more than reaffirm its opposition to reviving the May-Johnson bill and stress its support of civilian control and its desire for a reasonable policy regarding secrecy, for it had no official information as to what amendments to the original McMahon bill the Senate committee would propose. In any case a wide campaign for public support could not be waged on details; but a comprehensive statement on domestic legislation would be useful in explaining the general picture to the public, and the task of drafting one was delegated to the Cambridge Association. Still nursing a strong sense of grievance over the use made of the Canadian spy case by supporters of the military, the council authorized the FAS staff to prepare a sum-

---

[48] Friendly, "Debate over Atom Confused by Clamor for Civilian Control," *Washington Post*, March 21, 1946.

[49] As quoted in "FAS Commentary on Canadian Spy Case," [May 8, 1946], FAS XIII, 1.

mary of the case, based on official statements and the more reliable news reports, and in due course copies of such a summary were widely distributed.[50]

The scientists had one weapon in reserve against controls they considered harmful, and that was not to work. A scientists' strike as a means of curtailing weapons of war was mentioned once or twice in early postwar discussions only to be promptly and firmly repudiated. Besides being thoroughly incompatible with their sense of professional responsibility, scientists well knew that the problem of war and peace was much too complex to be solved by unilateral action of any kind, and in the absence of international agreement most of them believed that continued military development, under proper safeguards, was necessary. Even in their extreme anxiety over the fate of civilian control in March, 1946, scientists did not consider mass action of this sort.[51] If military control was permanently established, however, there was the possibility that by a series of individual decisions enough scientists might choose not to do nuclear research to seriously hamper an atomic energy program. The shaken fabric of civilian control, it was argued, might be strengthened if the aversion of scientists to working under the military was substantiated and publicized.

A poll for this purpose had been proposed by the Chicago executive committee even before Groves made his suggestion about raising scientists' salaries to keep them on the job, and on March 2 George Sacher, a statistician in the biology section of the Met Lab, and sociologist Edward Shils were asked to draw up questions relating to work in government laboratories. This poll was still being prepared when on March 12—the day the May-Johnson bill showed signs of life and Vandenberg introduced his amendment—John Simpson presented to the executive committee three questions on which information was needed in Washington by the end of the week.[52] What was described as a rough compilation of answers from ASC members was as follows:

---

[50] FAS council minutes, March 23–24, 1946, ASC XIV, 2; copy with covering letter to "Dear fellow scientists," May 8, 1946, FAS XIII, 1, and other files.

[51] Michael Amrine, in an interview April 24, 1963, claims that M-Day—the day for moving out of the laboratories—was often mentioned as a possibility, but I have found no other evidence of anything but negative interest in the idea.

[52] Simpson memorandum to ASC members, March 12, 1946, and replies to questions, ASC XIX, 1.

	Yes	No	Perhaps	No Answer
1. Would you like to work on new methods for the production of plutonium and U-235 and the utilization of these substances for peacetime purposes?	93	15	2	2
2. Are you willing to do this under Army control, for instance, such as is exercized at present by the Manhattan District?	16	100	2	5
3. Are you willing to do this in a government laboratory if there is still need to keep technical and engineering information from other nations but no new penalties against violating rules of compartmentalization and sufficient relaxation of secrecy to make intelligent criticism of over-all conduct of projects possible?	69	21	13	6*

*Four said they did not understand the question.

Although hardly an example of sophisticated opinion-taking, this poll clearly showed that a large proportion of those who answered did not want to work under strict military control but that a majority, though a smaller number than those who would not work under army control, accepted the necessity of some restrictions on information.

The more professional poll prepared by Sacher and Shils was distributed at the end of March while the furor over the military liaison amendment was still on; probably most of the replies were made shortly thereafter, although the results were not tabulated until June. The eight-page questionnaire was sent to the two hundred members of the Atomic Scientists of Chicago plus a few non-members on the University of Chicago science faculty. The one hundred and eight answers revealed the scarcely unexpected fact that a substantial majority preferred jobs with a minimum of restrictions; thirty-three admitted that some free time for non-military scientific pursuits would reconcile them to peacetime work in army or atomic energy commission laboratories; forty-one would not choose to work on military research in peacetime regardless of salary or free-time concessions; and thirty-one said these were not factors that would determine their attitude toward military research. A few were undecided on this point.[53]

Two final queries bore directly upon the question at issue in March and are herewith reproduced in full:

[53] ASC XIX, 1, and XXVI, 3; ASC executive committee minutes, March 23, 30, and June 25, 1946, ASC VI, 12, 13. The ASC minutes refer to an earlier poll at Los Alamos, and the Sacher and Shils poll was distributed at Oak Ridge; however, I did not find the results from Los Alamos or Oak Ridge.

Policy-making and administrative power. Indicate if your willingness to work in the nuclear energy field would be influenced by whether civilians or the military controlled policy-making or administration of the National Atomic Energy Commission. Mark (X) before *all* conditions which you would accept, and (?) if undecided.

X	?	
92	3	a) Would work if policy made by a completely civilian commission and executed by civilian administrators (as provided in the original McMahon Bill).
12	24	b) Would work if policy made by a civilian commission, subject to veto by an Army board, and executed by civilian administrators (as provided in the Vandenberg amendment to the McMahon Bill).
3	16	c) Would work if policy made by a part-time Commission and executed by an Administrator who could be a military man (as provided by the May-Johnson Bill).
58	25	d) Would work if policy made by a Commission consisting of full-time civilian members, plus the Secretaries of State, War, Navy, Commerce and Interior, and executed by civilian administrators (as provided by the Ball Bill).

Effect of world conditions on acceptability of security regulations. Mark (X) before *all* conditions of world affairs under which you would, in the national interest, accept any security regulations or restrictions, regardless of your opinion as to the desirability of such restrictions. The alternatives are not arranged in any order of preference.

Would be willing to work in the field of nuclear energy under any security regulations which the National Atomic Energy Commission sees fit to impose:

Yes	?	
17	6	a) in time of peace
65	10	b) in a state of emergency declared by the President.
23	4	c) until a world organization emerges which can prevent wars.
34	6	d) until the United Nations Atomic Energy Commission is set up.
88	2	e) in time of war.
6	0	f) until all nations disarm.
13	4	g) as long as world conditions are unsettled.
3	1	h) under any circumstances.
7	2	i) under no circumstances.

The records do not say what use was made of these polls, but it seems safe to assume that the results were turned over to those planning McMahon bill strategy in Washington. One can guess further that the March 12 answers helped provide background for the eight articles that Alfred Friendly began to publish in the *Washington Post* on March 20 on the scientists' attitude toward working in an atomic energy program controlled by the military.

Friendly's articles were concerned mainly with compartmentation of information and the scientists' certainty that if the military got control, either through the May-Johnson bill or by the more subtle device of the Vandenberg amendment, the compartmentation policy would be continued. Although Friendly mentioned some of the army's arguments for closer military liaison—quoting Patterson as saying, "We don't cotton to the idea of having a bomb handed to us some day and be expected to use it the next day without knowing what it is"—the articles were strongly biased in favor of the scientists' views. Amply furnished with anti-Groves and anti-army stories, which he must have been collecting over the winter, Friendly used them to show that scientists were leaving the Manhattan Project laboratories because of their strong objections to military control.[54]

As motivation for leaving the Project, this feeling was probably not as important as Friendly—and perhaps the scientists themselves —pictured it, for if one thinks of individual cases among both senior scientists and young men and the jobs they left to take in late 1945 and 1946, it seems unlikely that the most idyllic research conditions the government could have proposed would have held many of them. The pull from the opposite direction was too strong. At the University of Chicago, where these polls were taken, there were, for example, the new research institutes that reportedly originated in idle talk between Urey and his friends about establishing in some pleasant and salubrious part of the West a laboratory for exploring interrelations opened up by new scientific knowledge. Although unable to offer a mountain or desert retreat Chancellor Hutchins gave Urey's project a warm welcome at Chicago, where, offering the excitement of a new venture, it attracted a distinguished staff, largely from Columbia, the Met Lab, Los Alamos, and Oak Ridge. E. O. Lawrence's laboratory at Berkeley and the traditional strength of the sciences there were also drawing eminent figures and young men, despite Lawrence's known disapproval of dabbling in politics and his support of the May-Johnson bill. The appeal of old or new teaching and research jobs in Cambridge, Ithaca, or Pasadena was equally strong. Nor should one forget the attractions of more familiar patterns of living. His friends laughed when a Los Alamos scientist summed up his reaction to departure as relief at not having to drive thirty-five miles to get his shoes repaired, but the urge to return to normalcy

---

[54] Alfred Friendly, "Civilian vs. Military Control of Atomic Age," *Washington Post,* March 20–27, 1946.

fortified many a scientist's high-minded objections to working under military control.

These remarks, offered by way of corrective, do not disprove Friendly's major point or the evidence of the polls that a substantial number of scientists were reacting strongly in March of 1946 to the possibility that some form of military control over the atomic energy program would be continued. From this sense of crisis there developed an active collaboration between scientists and other supporters of civilian control that led to an accommodation of the military liaison issue and that also had a marked influence on later stages of the bill.

Within a week of the introduction of the military liaison amendment, the effectiveness of this collaboration was demonstrated in Vandenberg's home state of Michigan, where two meetings on atomic energy, growing out of the Chicago midwest conference of religious leaders of early February, took place in Grand Rapids on March 19 and in Flint on the twenty-first. The meetings had been planned before the introduction of the amendment, and the Atomic Scientists of Chicago when congratulated by the Washington strategists on their timing had to admit that it was quite fortuitous. The five university and Met Lab scientists who went to Grand Rapids and the three who went to Flint included such responsible characters as Kenneth Cole, Thorfin Hogness, Warren Johnson, and Walter Bartky, but they whipped up tremendous feeling against the Vandenberg amendment among the Senator's constituents, who forthwith dispatched resolutions of protest to its author in Washington.[55]

Although this was a small part of the adverse mail reaching Vandenberg's desk, it disturbed him very much. His reply to Rabbi Folkman, one of the sponsors of the Grand Rapids meeting, expressed more sorrow than anger, but he enclosed with it a form letter asserting his entire devotion to the principle of civilian control, his belief that his amendment did no more than insure a sensible regard for national security, and his astonishment at the commotion it had caused. In all his public experience, said Vandenberg, he had "never known anything to be so hysterically misrepresented by propaganda out of Washington as is the action of our Senate Committee" in voting for the amendment. Vandenberg replied even more sharply to a wire from Rabbi Simon of Chicago, like Folkman a member of the continuing committee of the religious leaders conference:

[55] Interview with Katharine Way, April 20, 1959; ASC executive committee minutes, March 2, 23, 1946, ASC VI, 12; reports of the meetings in ASC II, 14, 15.

It seems perfectly obvious to me that you and your associates have been victimized by some of the outrageous misrepresentation to which my amendment to the McMahon Bill has been subjected. On no other possible basis could I explain your "alarm" ... or your suggestion that the amendment violates the "spirit of the Constitution".... To tell you the truth, I am the one who is "alarmed" that public opinion in this country can be so quickly and so effectively misguided as in the present instance.

Rabbi Simon's even tempered reply did not follow the scientists' line about secrecy but explained his objection to having the military liaison committee responsible to the President rather than to the civilian secretary of war. According to the *Bulletin*, it was this feature of the amendment, making the military liaison committee equal in status to the commission, that had produced so many allies among defenders of civilian authority.[56]

4. CITIZENS TO THE RESCUE

With the possible exception of the Friendly articles, these reactions to the Vandenberg amendment had grown out of initiatives taken by the scientists. But at the same time a more deliberately planned phase of scientist-citizen collaboration was being developed in Washington by a small *ad hoc* strategy committee originating in consultations between the FAS scientists, the McMahon committee staff, and the most actively interested members of the National Committee on Atomic Information. One page of minutes of a meeting at 9 A.M. on March 5, a week before the Vandenberg amendment was introduced, probably records the inception of this *ad hoc* committee as the self-appointed guardian of the civilian control issue. After March 12 its immediate objective was the elimination or modification of the Vandenberg amendment. It left no records. Its operations were informal, and so was its composition. The nucleus of it, besides James Newman, Byron Miller, and E. U. Condon, included Mrs. Rachel Bell, Joseph Rauh, a Washington lawyer, Albert Cahn, Higinbotham as FAS representative, and whenever they were in town, Edward Levi and Thorfin Hogness from Chicago. McMahon, Helen Gahagan Douglas, and Holifield sometimes met with it, and so did Friendly whose *Washington Post* articles were closely related to its purpose.[57]

---

[56] Copies of Vandenberg to Folkman, March 23, 1946, and of form letter and correspondence without date between Vandenberg and Simon in ASC X, 8; *Bulletin of the Atomic Scientists*, I (April 1, 1946), 1.

[57] Minutes of meeting, March 5, 1946 in FAS chronological files (Washington, D.C.); those present were, from FAS, Higinbotham, Rush, Phillips, and Novick and,

A most important member of this committee and the leader in mobilizing support for the scientists was Mrs. Rachel Bell, executive secretary of Americans United for World Organization and wife of George Bell of the Commerce Department. Some months earlier Mrs. Bell and two friends had organized the Legislative Information Service, a committee of organizations formed to rally support for the United Nations. It was inevitable, says Mrs. Bell, that the scientists should sooner or later be steered to "movers and shakers" like herself, and she places it in the autumn of 1945 that James Newman asked her and her friends, referred to by their admirers as "Crises Incorporated" and "the three meddlesome matrons," to help promote civilian control. Be that as it may, quite early she met Szilard, Condon, and Wigner and encountered the younger FAS men on occasions such as the Pinchots' parties. Unlike others who describe the scientists as naïve in their political dealings, Mrs. Bell, when pressed to be specific, does not qualify the word away. She found them insufficiently aware of the play of personalities or of the nuances of radicalism and conservatism and tried to prevent them from plunging in and antagonizing people unnecessarily. By the time the issue of civilian control became critical in late February and March, Mrs. Bell was familiar with the subject and the protagonists.[58]

During March and April, and thereafter as the situation required, the *ad hoc* committee met two to five times a week at five in the afternoon to talk about strategy, publicity, and funds for the McMahon bill campaign. References to it are scanty, but its hand is readily detected in Friendly's articles, in the questions circulated at the Met Lab on March 12 about working under the military, and in the announcement at an ASC executive committee meeting that same evening that Edward Levi would go to Washington to arrange interviews between scientists and officials. Four days later the executive committee received a report from Levi, "off-the-record" but almost certainly dealing with the organization of two groups to which the *ad hoc* committee delegated the raising of funds and public support. Recollections are vague, and overlapping terminology—"Emergency Committee for Civilian Control" was loosely applied to all three—

---

from NCAI, Chairman McDonald, Mrs. Reid, Mrs. Bell, Robert Lamb of the CIO, and a few others. References to the *ad hoc* committee in FAS and other files are scarce and confusing; this account is based on interviews with Mrs. Bell, Cahn, Higinbotham, Hogness, Miller, and Newman.

[58] Interview with Rachel Bell, December 29, 1961.

makes it difficult to disentangle the parent *ad hoc* committee and its two offspring. Probably it would be more accurate not to do so.[59] (And a further confusion arises from the formation in the summer of 1946 of the entirely distinct fund-raising group, the Emergency Committee of Atomic Scientists.)

The National Committee for Civilian Control of Atomic Energy, formed of prominent individuals on invitation from former War Production Board chief Donald Nelson, provided funds and publicity. Its membership, as announced on March 28, consisted of some thirty bishops, bankers, university presidents, and other public figures who, in the next few weeks and again when the McMahon bill was before the House in July, placed full-page ads in newspapers and supported the campaign through contributions. Its first press releases and publicity urged defeat of the Vandenberg amendment, which was described as military control in its worst form under cloak of a civilian commission; later statements continued to underscore the importance of an independent civilian agency responsible to the President and Congress.[60]

Albert Cahn became executive secretary of the National Committee for Civilian Control, and his recollections are of a series of proliferating contacts and ever widening circles of influence and support. Probably as early as February he had met Al Friendly through Robert Eichholtz, who became the committee's treasurer. Friendly brought in Leon Henderson; and Henderson brought in Beardsley Ruml. A New York friend took Cahn to the Stork Club as the easiest way to insure a casual encounter with Walter Winchell, and there Cahn also met Jerry Mason, editor of *This Week*, who commissioned an article by FAS publications editor Amrine and was helpful in other ways. Each new contact suggested others—a typical case history, no doubt, of Washington causes, but this was one to which people seemed specially eager to commit their friends, and virtually all Nelson's initial invitations were accepted.

The campaign did not require large funds. Most committee members paid their own expenses; and the newspaper advertisements, office rent, phone bills, and Cahn's salary, guaranteed by the ASC but taken over by the National Committee, were the chief expendi-

---

[59] ASC executive committee minutes, March 12, 16, 1946, ASC VI, 12.

[60] *Bulletin of the Atomic Scientists*, I (April 1, 1946), 1, 18, 19; press releases and related material in ASC I, 5, 20, and FAS XV, 3; Higinbotham memorandum to all associations, March 18, 1946, Camb. II.

tures, totaling, by the time the committee was liquidated in August, just over $6,300. A contribution of $2,500 from the Amalgamated Clothing Workers of America had come at a critical point in early April and was, as Cahn told Sidney Hillman, a lifesaver in enabling the committee to get started and carry on the necessary work with Congress.[61]

The second instrument devised by the *ad hoc* committee for creating public interest in civilian control was a committee of organizations known as the Emergency Conference for Civilian Control of Atomic Energy. On the morning of March 13, the day after Vandenberg introduced his amendment, representatives of eighteen of the organizations affiliated with the National Committee on Atomic Information met in Mrs. Bell's office at Americans United. The tax exempt NCAI could not engage in lobbying, and the solution adopted at this meeting was a parallel organization for political action.[62]

The Emergency Conference began its campaign with two meetings in Washington on Thursday, March 21. In the morning an organization meeting, chaired by Representative Chet Holifield of California, was held in the House caucus room with a large audience—variously reported as one hundred and three hundred—including some thirty congressmen. The president of the conference, the Reverend A. Powell Davies of All Souls Unitarian Church and an NCAI board member, explained the conference aim, and Mrs. Bell, serving as executive secretary, its program. Several scientists and nine congressmen spoke briefly. In the evening a public rally at the Press Club Building auditorium drew an audience of eight hundred. A principal speaker was Thorfin Hogness, just arrived in Washington from the Grand Rapids meeting.[63]

Before a week had elapsed a request had been sent to Chairman McMahon, with copies to Senate committee members, that hearings be reopened so that the public—that is, representatives of organizations such as those in the Emergency Conference—might be heard. Civilian control, the Senate committee was reminded, was a corner-

---

[61] Informal list of expenditures of the National Committee for the Civilian Control of Atomic Energy, and Cahn to Hillman, April 11, 1946, in Cahn's files.

[62] "Summary of Action, Emergency Conference for Civilian Control," April 20, 1946, FAS XV, 3; D. Melcher to NCAI members and friends, March 20, 1946, ASC XVIII, 2; Higinbotham memorandum on tax exemption, December 29, 1947, AORES XVII, 10.

[63] Report of S. G. English to AORS, March 21–22, 1946, AORES V, 2; Emergency Conference for Civilian Control of Atomic Energy press release, March 28, 1946, ASC I, 20; *The New World*, p. 509.

stone of free government and essential for national defense, scientific progress, education, protection of free enterprise, and an adequate program of world control.[64]

Although the National Committee of individuals and the Emergency Conference of organizations were technically separate, with their own letterheads and their own executive secretaries, Cahn and Mrs. Bell worked closely together and policy was co-ordinated by Cahn in the National Committee's office. References in local association minutes and newsletters constantly mixed up the titles of the two groups, and probably in practice there was little distinction.

According to Mrs. Bell there was nothing unusual about the campaign of the next four months except perhaps that the issue of civilian control brought in religious and educational groups, which, unlike labor, were not accustomed to exerting this kind of pressure. The chief device employed—massive assault by telegram—was an established technique.

Mrs. Bell immediately undertook to stimulate action outside Washington. A California committee for civilian control with one hundred participating organizations and a Chicago committee with forty-one were soon reported. The way the job was carried out on the local level can best be followed in Chicago, where the scientists' special interest in legislation, combined with the dynamic leadership of a prominent Chicagoan, Mrs. John P. Welling, produced a prompt response to an opening meeting sponsored jointly by the ASC and the Chicago committee on the evening of March 22.

Thereafter the Chicago committee worked in close association with the Chicago scientists. In the already overcrowded basement office that the ASC shared with the *Bulletin* in the university's Social Science Research Building on the Midway, Mrs. Welling spent many hours in the coming weeks accompanied by a young woman volunteer whose diamonds flashed along the typewriter with unexpected skill. Chic North Side millinery struck a cheerful note among the steam pipes and the surplus filing cabinets, but what really filled the scientists and secretaries with awe was the assurance with which Mrs. Welling and her coworkers conscripted the money, time, and moral support of their fellow Chicagoans. By comparison their own relatively successful public relations seemed halting and clumsy.

In many ways paralleling the activities of the ASC, the Citizens

[64] Unsigned memorandum to McMahon and Senate committee members, March 20, 1946, ASC I, 20.

committee reached a larger and wider audience. It called press conferences for the scientists and sponsored meetings of up to three thousand people, with scientists and others as speakers. At booths manned by the American Veterans Committee cards were collected pledging the signers to write to Washington, and congressional maps were distributed—seventy-five hundred for Chicago and thirty-five hundred for downstate—with instructions on how to do it. Mrs. Welling and her helpers spread around the community fifty thousand fliers headed: "Can You Answer These Life and Death Questions? Atomic Power Threatens You—Your Child—Your Job," and followed by a true-false quiz asking "Is there a defense? Can we keep the bomb a secret? Is this new force only a weapon? And how much time do we have?"

In April and May thousands of letters were sent to pledge-signers informing them of changes in the legislative picture and thousands more to individuals and organizations urging action at critical moments. When the McMahon bill finally passed the House in July, Mrs. Welling could take satisfaction in having "delivered" all seven Illinois congressmen.[65]

It would be easy to conclude, as some have done, that the _ad hoc_ committee took things out of the scientists' hands, exploiting their influence when it was expedient to do so and keeping them out of the way when it was not. Cahn insists that this was not the case, that the collaboration was a genuine one with the committee pitching in to help the hard-pressed scientists carry on what they had started. Nor, Cahn maintains, were the scientists pushed into the background in the lobbying and political maneuvering that was an essential follow-up to the creation of an aroused public opinion.

5. Compromise

Although vigorously beating the drum for civilian control, the scientists recognized all along that the March crisis was more likely to end in compromise than victory. The off-the-record plans relayed by Levi to the ASC on the evening of March 16 probably included the possibility of co-opting the services as intermediary of ASC member Thorfin Hogness, who had often discussed legislation with Miller and Levi and was well versed in what the scientists were fighting for.

---

[65] ASC executive committee minutes, March 20, 23, 1946, ASC VI, 12; Chicago citizens' committee reports and other material, ASC I, 4, 5; interviews with Katharine Way, April 20, 1959, and Mrs. Welling, January 23, 1960.

Then in his early fifties, Hogness had been a member of the University of Chicago chemistry department since 1930. Tall, handsome, with iron-gray hair and bushy eyebrows, he cut a striking, but still an eminently respectable figure. While serving as head of the chemistry division of the Metallurgical Project, he had also been drawn into liaison jobs for OSRD and other government agencies, for which his affable manner in dealing with people eminently suited him.

Hogness recalls being asked by Chancellor Hutchins to go to Washington to see what he could do about the Vandenberg amendment; other sources say he went to work with the Emergency Conference for Civilian Control.[66] No matter under what auspices, immediately after speaking at the Grand Rapids meeting on March 19 he went to Washington and became the principal intermediary between the *ad hoc* committee and Senator Vandenberg in reaching an accommodation on the military liaison issue. His presence there was an acknowledgment that both the impulsive needling of star performers like Urey and Szilard and the earnest representations of youth had served their purpose and that a man with Hogness' well-tailored self-assurance would now be more effective. Mrs. Bell, a normally composed and efficient person, who confesses that exasperation at Szilard's unpredictable behavior once reduced her to tears, found Hogness' conduct of the Vandenberg negotiations absolutely magnificent. "You could send him anywhere," she says, "sure that he would charm and mollify."

But Hogness had not come to Washington in a conciliatory mood. This was evident in the speech he made at the Emergency Conference rally on March 21. Expediency had dictated that bomb development be supervised by the army, he told his audience, because the financing could be covered without explanation by its large appropriations for aviation and because it could arrange priorities in men, materials, and transportation, but given such priorities any other government agency could have developed the bomb at least as well. Hogness advanced the scientists' usual arguments that under the new conditions created by the bomb the military were no longer the guardians of national security because the old concepts of defense were no longer valid; security meant exploring new fields, not simply keeping secrets. If the military remained in control, said Hogness,

[66] Interview with Hogness, January 18, 1960, and letter to the author, November 16, 1962; *The New World*, p. 511.

there would be both an exodus from nuclear research and a reluctance to enter it, for, he added, there is such a thing as free enterprise in science as in business.[67]

In the days that followed Hogness remembers frequent consultations with McMahon, Newman, and Condon. One of his first interviews was with General Eisenhower, then chief of staff. Hogness was familiar with the General's liberal views about the proper limits of the army's concern for security, for he had served on an ASC committee to consider Eisenhower's proposal, made after the testimony from Forrestal but before that of Patterson, that the Joint Chiefs of Staff should pass on atomic security regulations and that differences between them and the atomic energy commission should be referred to the President.[68] Granted a half-hour interview before a staff meeting by a grudging aide, Hogness found Eisenhower more outspoken than any scientist about excessive military claims and ready to support a modification of the military liaison amendment. Seeing Hogness look guiltily at his watch, Eisenhower said the topic they were discussing was more important than the staff meeting and went on talking; when Hogness walked through the anteroom at the end of an hour and a half he found, as he now visualizes the scene, dozens of three- and four-star generals glaring at him.[69]

It was only after this interview, Hogness recalls, that he saw Vandenberg, who listened to his account of the conversation with Eisenhower and said, "You are the man I have been looking for; you fellows fix it up."[70] Hogness had seen a copy of the Senator's angry outburst to Rabbi Simon, and such eagerness to reach an accommodation was unexpected. If it owed something to Hogness' tact and to Vandenberg's customary pattern of approaching an issue obstructively and then undergoing a statesmanlike conversion to the progressive viewpoint, it doubtless owed even more to what had been happening to the Senator's mail and that of his special committee colleagues. The sudden dearth of letters after the Canadian spy news had not lasted, and communications about the military liaison issue had broken all

[67] Speech by T. R. Hogness before Emergency Conference for Civilian Control of Atomic Energy, March 21, 1946, in *Bulletin of the Atomic Scientists* files.

[68] ASC executive committee minutes, February 9, 1946, ASC VI, 12.

[69] Interview with Hogness, January 18, 1960.

[70] Interview with Hogness, January 18, 1960. On April 3 Vandenberg acknowledged the help of a Grand Rapids official in putting Hogness in touch with him (Vandenberg to Hon. George Welsh, April 3, 1946, in Cahn's files). According to *The Private Papers of Senator Vandenberg* (Boston: Houghton Mifflin Co., 1952), Vandenberg took the initiative in bringing in Hogness, in whom he had confidence (p. 259).

records. Contemporary reports tend to be vague about the period covered or about whose mail is included, but they cite totals of over seventy thousand letters and telegrams in support of the original McMahon bill or opposing the Vandenberg amendment, with a peak day of fifteen thousand on March 19. A mere trickle of letters and telegrams favored the May-Johnson bill or the Vandenberg amendment.[71]

On March 27, while Hogness was still negotiating with Vandenberg, the FAS also released the results of the petition supporting the Mc-Mahon bill that had been circulating for the past two months. Eight thousand signatures had been collected in over a hundred college communities and research centers.[72]

It is worth noting that the volume of public response reached its peak just before the citizens' committees got to work. But the first fifteen or twenty thousand letters and telegrams—many of which must have duplicated the eight thousand petition signatures—probably represented the limit of what the scientists could have accomplished unaided.

Although the account based on Vandenberg's private papers does not throw much light on his change of heart, it quotes him as telling Hogness that the scientists could write their own ticket "as long as it fell foursquare within the purpose of assuring the proper liaison between the military and the ultimate civilian authority, and that the military phases of atomic energy were not to be neglected in an aura of wishful thinking about a brave new postwar world."[73] On Hogness' part the impulse to compromise was fortified by knowledge

---

[71] The Los Alamos Newsletter, No. 25, April 16, 1946, ALAS II, 19, reported that when the Vandenberg amendment first appeared, over 70,000 letters opposing it were received, with the peak day on March 19. An undated summary of activities of the Emergency Conference for Civilian Control in FAS XV, 3, states that by April 10 Chairman McMahon and Senator Connally had received 70,972 letters and telegrams in favor of the original McMahon bill, of which 24,851 objected to the Vandenberg amendment; 6 favored the May-Johnson bill, 12 opposed the original McMahon bill, and 7 favored the Vandenberg amendment. This did not include communications to committee members other than McMahon and Connally. *The New World* account (p. 510), based on Senate committee files states that in the four weeks following the introduction of the Vandenberg amendment the Senate committee received 42,189 pieces of mail, which was almost twice the volume of the three previous months of the committee's existence; again this does not count that received by individual members, and *The New World* does not make clear whether "mail" included telegrams.

[72] FAS press release, March 27, 1946, FAS XVII, 1. A March 28 FAS summary of wires received and an eight-page list of organizations supporting S. 1717 and opposing the Vandenberg amendment are in ASC I, 20.

[73] The Private Papers of Senator Vandenberg, p. 259.

that some at least of his fellow scientists would support him. It is true that the two New York associations passed a joint resolution on March 27 opposing the amendment, but at the same time a wire came from the Oak Ridge Engineers and Scientists strongly urging reconsideration of the FAS stand because the hysterical opposition as noted in the press was detrimental to scientists' prestige and unjustified in the light of their basic aim.[74]

Among Hogness' colleagues in Chicago, compromise was discussed at a general meeting of the ASC at which radio commentator Clifton Utley gave advice on how to conduct a campaign on a political issue. After he had analyzed their problem in terms of what they had to sell—that is, civilian control—and the reasons for sales resistance—chiefly fear of Russia and public apathy—he was asked by Teller whether it would not be better to try to change the Vandenberg amendment in a favorable direction than to keep fighting for the original McMahon bill. Utley advised against compromise at this point, for this would result in a bill perhaps 10 per cent satisfactory, whereas, he said, "if we were to keep insisting that the McMahon bill be passed without the Vandenberg amendment and should ultimately be forced to accept some compromise it would be more likely that the final bill would be something like 40 to 50 per cent agreeable to us."[75]

But Hogness had a pretty good idea of what scientists would accept. Since the federation had never officially supported McMahon in demanding complete exclusion of the military (although individual statements and such interpretations as Friendly's perhaps gave the contrary impression), it was possible for its members to support a compromise that guaranteed that the powers of a military liaison committee would not be arbitrary or unlimited. For spotting legal pitfalls, Hogness relied on Edward Levi, now back in Chicago, and kept in touch with him by phone throughout his talks with Vandenberg. On the basis of discussions with Hogness Vandenberg redrafted his amendment, then submitted it to Hogness for approval. The new version also showed the influence of a competing proposal for military liaison drawn up by Wallace and Eisenhower. Vandenberg

---

[74] ANYS meeting notes, March 27, 1946, FAS VI, 2; Minett to Higinbotham, March 28, 1946, FAS XXI, 2.

[75] ASC general meeting minutes, March 27, 1946, ASC VI, 12. *The New World* quotes this incorrectly as indicating the scientists' belief that a compromise on the Vandenberg amendment would give a bill that was 40 to 50 per cent satisfactory (p. 510).

had no intention of losing the ball at this stage, and having obtained a copy of their amendment through the White House, he had incorporated some of its phraseology with his own.

Vandenberg's final version, approved by Hogness and Levi, made the military liaison committee responsible to the secretaries of war and navy. Its concern was defined as relating to military applications, and the objectionable provision broadly granting the committee "opportunity to acquaint itself with all matters before the Commission" had been replaced by the statement that both commission and committee were to keep themselves "fully informed."[76] When Vandenberg presented this new amendment to the Senate committee on April 2, it was accepted by ten votes, with Chairman McMahon abstaining.

Some observers wondered at the time whether the great public clamor had been necessary to obtain such small concessions. Vandenberg himself referred to the compromise as a mere change in language.[77] The more deliberate conclusion of the authors of the McMahon bill was that although "it might appear that the essential elements of the earlier version escaped significant modification and that public protest was quelled with only a token concession . . . the compromise was a genuine one." With the benefit of still longer perspective, the Atomic Energy Commission historians take the view that the changes were indeed too minor to have produced in themselves the sudden willingness to reach an accommodation but that to McMahon the whole episode was worthwhile, even without much substantive change. Prior to this time, they point out, McMahon had been playing a lone hand in the Senate committee without much outside support. "The dispute had made atomic energy legislation a national issue. With the spotlight focused on the bill, McMahon could afford to compromise and move for quick passage in the Senate."[78]

The amendment negotiations may have affected the fate of the bill in another way, for as they proceeded Hogness developed great

---

[76] For both versions of the Vandenberg amendment, see Miller, "A Law Is Passed," p. 812, n. 16.

[77] "Inasmuch as we all seemed to be addressing ourselves to a common objective, it seemed quite silly that this nationwide controversy should continue if a mere change in 'language' could make everybody happy. That is exactly what finally happened" (Vandenberg to Welsh, April 3, 1946, in Cahn's files).

[78] James R. Newman and Byron S. Miller, *The Control of Atomic Energy* (New York: McGraw-Hill Book Co., 1948), pp. 44–45 (used by permission of the publisher); *The New World*, pp. 512–13.

respect for Vandenberg and began to worry lest his speech at the Grand Rapids meeting should have unfavorable repercussions in an election year. He wrote to Rabbi Folkman, asking that his remarks about the original amendment not be interpreted to reflect personally upon the Senator, who had been most co-operative in straightening out the unfortunate phraseology and later in reaching adjustment of security provisions of the bill. Hogness' letter was prominently quoted in the local press, and even if it changed no votes in Grand Rapids, it put Vandenberg in a friendly mood, a perhaps not insignificant point since it was he, not McMahon, who carried the ball in the later stages of the bill's progress.[79]

As for the scientists, just as they had been divided on whether to compromise, so they were of two minds about the result. An editorial in the *Bulletin of the Atomic Scientists* indicated a generally favorable reaction, especially to the subordination of the liaison committee to the civilian secretaries of war and navy; it was also a great gain, the editor added, that public opinion had been aroused. But some people would have liked a further definition of the term "military applications" to prevent the liaison committee from claiming powers in such areas as allocation of fissionable materials and scientific information; the sections of the McMahon bill dealing specifically with those topics would need to be carefully scrutinized. The fight for civilian control, warned the *Bulletin*, was by no means over.[80]

A few people felt that the concessions, engineered entirely by Hogness (and explained by him to the press without consultation with the FAS office), represented less than could and should have been obtained, and this feeling was sufficiently widespread so that three weeks later the FAS council decided not to endorse the revised amendment. But in general it was accepted among scientists, if not with enthusiasm, at least in the belief that Vandenberg's "mere change in language" provided a safeguard against the subservience of the commission to the military liaison committee that the original amendment had seemed to imply. Ambivalence remains: Hogness' services to the cause are appreciatively remembered; yet some scien-

---

[79] Hogness to Folkman, April 12, 1946, and Folkman to Hogness, enclosing press clippings, April 18, 1946, in *Bulletin of the Atomic Scientists* files. In later correspondence with Hogness, Vandenberg referred to this period of happy collaboration (correspondence in Hogness's files).

[80] *Bulletin of the Atomic Scientists*, I (April 1, 1946), 19.

tists now cite the Vandenberg amendment as chief among the compromises that lead them to wonder whether the final McMahon bill was a vast improvement on the despised War Department measure.

6. IN THE SENATE

Acceptance of the revised military liaison amendment by the Senate special committee took place in the course of its review of a new version of the McMahon bill presented by Newman and his staff on April 1. Reflecting committee discussions the bill now provided a commission of five full-time members and a general manager, all appointed by the President, and directors of research, production, engineering, and military application, appointed by the commission. Included also were a general advisory committee, a military liaison committee, and a joint congressional committee. And there were basic changes, to which we shall return shortly, in the section on information.

During the first ten days of April the Senate committee made further revisions. On some topics the federation scientists continued to maintain a hands-off attitude; even when the committee dropped the provision for commission-sponsored research in the political, social, and economic implications of atomic energy, they decided not to fight the point. But in two areas the FAS did try to influence committee action. The first was a provision requiring monthly reports by the commission to the General Accounting Office, dropped and then restored after testimony from Groves and the Comptroller-General. This was not a question on which there was the slightest grass-roots excitement, but on advice in Washington the FAS administrative committee urged the Senate committee not to subject the atomic energy commission to such detailed supervision and submitted a description of the less cumbersome rules applied to the TVA. This intervention was not successful, and the federation had to be content with assurance that frequent reporting would not be allowed to delay operations.[81] Of far more genuine concern to scientists were the revised information and security provisions, associated closely in their minds with the battle they had just fought over military liaison. These two questions, Byron Miller later pointed out, though logically distinct, "were the beaches upon which the civilian and military

[81] FAS administrative committee to McMahon, and memorandum on GAO-TVA relations, April 10, 1946, FAS XI, 7; FAS History-Diary, April 10, 1946, in FAS files (Washington, D.C.).

control proponents engaged; and while the black sand of one issue was distinguishable from the white sand of the other, the heat of the conflict fused them into a single mass of deep disagreement on the special capacity of the military to preserve the national security."[82]

The military control issue made far more noise partly because it arose first and was one on which public opinion could be mobilized. But to the scientists it was also more basic, for they were asking not that the line between secret and non-secret information be drawn at a particular point but that information and security policies should be guided by considerations of healthy scientific research and the maintenance of peace. Yet they were also deeply concerned about information policy. Scientists had liked the information section of the original McMahon bill because it distinguished between "basic scientific information"—specifically upholding the principle of its dissemination—and "related technical informaton." In the new draft of April 1 Newman and Miller, deferring to the obvious will of the Senate committee, had made drastic changes. Instead of "Dissemination of Information" the title of the section was now "Control of Information." In this draft and subsequent modifications, the distinction between basic and technical information disappeared, and the commission was entrusted with the control of "restricted data," defined as "all data concerning the manufacture or utilization of atomic weapons, the production of fissionable material, or the use of fissionable material in the production of power." It was left to the commission to determine from time to time what was not restricted and could therefore be freely discussed and transmitted. Provisions for enforcement and penalties, which had intentionally been placed in a separate section in the earlier version, were now included in Section 10 on the control of information. The maximum penalty for wilful transmission of information, set at $10,000 fine or five years imprisonment or both in the original McMahon bill, had become $20,000 or ten years or both.[83]

The details of the scientists' involvement in adjustments in Section 10 between April 1 and the Senate committee's final discussion of it on the ninth and tenth are somewhat obscure. Diplomatic

---

[82] Miller, "A Law Is Passed," p. 810. Copyright © 1948 by The University of Chicago.

[83] The McMahon bill as introduced on December 20, 1945, is printed as Appendix 1 in *The New World*; in its final form as the Atomic Energy Act of 1946, it is printed as Appendix A in Newman and Miller, *The Control of Atomic Energy.*

maneuver by one senior scientist having produced a partially satisfactory outcome to the Vandenberg amendment, more were recruited in the hope of a relatively greater accomplishment. Rush reported to Oak Ridge that Urey, Szilard, Hogness, Stearns, Selig Hecht of Columbia, and Morrison had spent much time in Washington in early April and had largely carried the ball in dealings with the Senate. At least one dinner meeting was held at which problems of security were discussed with three Republican and three Democratic senators.[84]

A leading role continued to be played by Hogness, whose files contain typed carbons of Section 10 in various stages of revision and long telegraphic comments and suggestions, dated April 6 and 7, from Levi in Chicago, conveying his own opinions about content and phraseology and also those of Law School colleagues and of the bill's coauthor, Byron Miller. Some at least of Levi's suggested changes carried over to the bill as completed by the committee on April 11. For example, in the section dealing with the penalty for transmitting information, the phrase "where there is a reasonable likelihood that the information will be used to injure the United States" was changed to "with reason to believe that such data will be utilized."[85] If the available evidence is not sufficient to determine the extent of the Levi-Hogness influence, it demonstrates, at least, that the scientists were in close touch with what was going on in the now closed sessions of the committee.

The clearing house for policy and tactics continued to be the *ad hoc* committee, and it was undoubtedly this group's opinion that Higinbotham reported to member associations on April 10. The Vandenberg amendment, even as modified could not be endorsed; hamstringing commission operations by too detailed supervision of the General Accounting Office might spell the failure of civilian control, and then the military would take over after all. Security was still being debated.[86]

As usual Higinbotham asked for considered opinions, and, as usual, there is most to be learned from the Chicago files about how these opinions were pooled and developed. Hogness and Szilard, back and forth between Chicago and Washington, were conferring with Levi, Friedman, and Bernard Weissbourd (who had left the Met Lab in

[84] ASC executive committee minutes, April 6, 1946, ASC VI, 12; Rush to E. Tompkins, April 15, 1946, FAS VII, 1; interview with Cahn, March 5, 1963.

[85] Copies of telegrams from Levi in Hogness' files.

[86] Higinbotham to all associations, April 10, 1946, AORES XVIII, 3.

the autumn to study law) about possible changes, and their evaluations were in turn passed on to the Chicago Committee on Civilian
Control of Atomic Energy by its ASC representatives Maria Mayer
and Aaron Novick. In the scientists' view (which had taken on a
strongly legalistic coloring), the McMahon bill now had three principal shortcomings: prohibition of any activity to the advantage of a
foreign power was too vague and should read "military advantage"
(a point made in Levi's wires to Hogness); it did not insure against
the establishment of different categories of people who might be
permitted to have particular knowledge; and too many arbitrary
reasons were allowed for the commission to deny licenses.[87]

Taken to the FAS council meeting in Pittsburgh on April 20 and
21 by Brues and Simpson, these points became part of the broader
critique developed in discussion there. The council delegates went
through the bill section by section, noting changes from the original.
It was agreed that certain undesirable features, including administrative defects, should be left to others and that the FAS fight should
be restricted to the secrecy provisions and the still objectional Vandenberg amendment.

...We stand on our earlier approval of leaving security to the provisions
of the Espionage Act, and take exception especially to three features of
the present security provisions: that all data in a given field are restricted
automatically until declared otherwise by the commission, instead of the
other way around; that the restrictions in Section 10 would now apply to
data whether obtained on any Commission-controlled project or not; that
the phrase "or to the advantage of any other nation" should certainly read
"or to the military advantage of any other nation." The inclusion of all
data concerning the use of fissionable material in the production of power
as restricted data makes the intent clear, but this should be publicly exposed, as well as the dangers of extending commercial advantage to include humanitarian benefits.

The council had difficulty in formulating the point about information obtained outside the Project, so it was omitted from the policy
statement based on this discussion, with the proviso that the attention
of non-Project scientists be drawn to it.[88]

---

[87] ASC executive committee minutes, April 23, 1946, ASC VI, 12; Mayer and Novick
to Chicago committee for civilian control, April 18, 1946, ASC I, 5.

[88] FAS council minutes, April 20–21, 1946, FAS I, 3. An analysis of S. 1717, based
on committee print No. 6, was mimeographed and copies are found throughout the
files. *The New World*, chap. xiv, n. 54, dates print No. 6 as April 13, 1946, and says
that it contained only minor revisions of print No. 5 of April 11, 1946.

The council's expressed preference for the Espionage Act is at variance with a statement by the bill's authors that scientists did not find it adequate and that the security provisions of the McMahon bill were designed to meet their objections. Perhaps this was true of Miller's Chicago contacts, who made a serious effort to understand legal angles of security, or of Szilard, who constantly looked for some simple radical solution, such as allowing an individual to talk freely to people he trusted but imposing heavy penalties on anyone who gave classified information to an enemy. If memories are not now clear on this matter, says Higinbotham, it is because discussions at the time were confused, and consensus rarely went beyond the point that under the Espionage Act atomic energy would be treated like any other information problem. In every other context, one observes, scientists were intent upon emphasizing its uniqueness.[89]

The council policy statement on the McMahon bill was approved by all fifteen associations represented at Pittsburgh, with the exception of Pasadena, where dissent perhaps originated at a steering committee four days earlier. Oppenheimer, who had just completed three months' work on the State Department international control plan, was present, and his opinion, as reported to Pasadena members, was that the McMahon bill could not be recommended because it allowed too much interference with the work of the commission. The McMahon and May-Johnson bills were both deficient, and it might be wise not to endorse either but to save a fight for something worse. Oppenheimer suggested they concentrate on recommending scientists of courage, initiative, and imagination to serve on the commission, on the passage of science legislation, and on supporting and giving information about international control.[90]

When McMahon reported the amended S. 1717 to the Senate on April 19, it looked as though it might go on the calendar immediately, but the draft, Office of Price Administration, and labor legislation kept pushing it along, and its supporters began to fear that it would not get through the Senate in time for House action in the current session. The FAS staff and the *ad hoc* committee decided that more would be lost than gained by raising issues on the Senate

[89] Newman and Miller, *Control of Atomic Energy*, pp. 235–36; Higinbotham to the author, January 23, 1964.

[90] Association of Pasadena Scientists Newsletter, April 23, 1946, ASC XVII, 4; report of APS steering committee, April 16, 1946, FAS VII, 4.

floor. The authors of *The New World* conclude that the McMahon group was able to keep a firm rein on the scientists, but indeed there are no signs that they were disposed even to take the bit in their teeth. Their correspondence and minutes contain none of the mutterings of discontent of which they had been so full a few weeks earlier. The compromise represented by the committee's revisions had induced a mood of discouragement, and the nearest thing to protest was divided opinion in a May 20 meeting of the AORS executive committee, where political action had once been launched so briskly, on whether to try to get the bill passed in the current session or let it die. Once the bill was in the Senate the local groups seem to have abandoned it to the experts, including their own representatives, Cahn and Hogness.[91]

In a *Bulletin* editorial entitled "A Dangerous Lull," Rabinowitch tried to counter this defeatism: failure of the bill in this session would mean delay in conversion of the great laboratories to fundamental research; the army would be left to plan peacetime developments. Congress may want to forget about atomic energy, said Rabinowitch, but we must make it clear that the nation remembers and expects action.[92]

From the Washington office on May 6 Melba Phillips wrote to twenty-five senators on the "OK list" and seven others, enclosing the changes in the bill recommended by the FAS council and offering to discuss these further. Apart from briefing of friendly senators on what steps to take in the event that certain amendments came up on the floor, there is little evidence of other lobbying activity in late April and May, but Cahn says this documentary gap is misleading—that he, at least, was extremely busy with congressional contacts directed chiefly at what lay ahead in the House, for once the bill got on the Senate calendar there was never any doubt that it would go through.[93] Connecticut legislators, with whom Cahn had personal acquaintance, provided a nucleus from which other contacts fanned out. California Representatives Holifield, Voorhis, and even Knowland, were helpful, and the principal House ally continued to be Helen Gahagan Douglas.

---

[91] FAS memorandum on S. 1717, May 14, 1946, AORES XVII, 9; *The New World*, p. 515; AORS executive committee minutes, May 20, 1946, AORES IV, 4.
[92] *Bulletin of the Atomic Scientists*, I (May 15, 1946), 1.
[93] Letters Phillips to "Dear Senator," May 6, 1946, FAS XI, 7; Cahn to ASC executive committee, May 12, 1946, ASC VI, 13; interview with Cahn, March 5, 1963.

Trying to keep fingers on the legislative pulse, Higinbotham and Rush found that the operations of special deputies like Hogness and Cahn, whose instructions came from Chicago or the *ad hoc* committee, put them in an awkward spot, but this was one of the drawbacks to so spontaneous and unautocratic a movement, and frank talk with Cahn and his Chicago sponsors produced better co-ordination.

By mid-May, when the bill had been in the hands of the Senate for a month, the strategists decided on more drastic action, and pressure from the citizens committees, more broadly based and more disinterested than that of the scientists, was solicited. Cahn, for the National Committee for Civilian Control, and A. Powell Davies, for the Emergency Conference for Civilian Control of Atomic Energy, sent out wires urging letters and telegrams. Mrs. Welling of the Chicago citizens committee, with her usual dispatch, phoned Majority Leader Alben Barkley and got his promise to try to fit the McMahon bill into the calendar. Within a week the local associations were assured that the bill was on Barkley's "must" list, along with OPA and the draft law, but Mrs. Welling took no chances. On May 24 her Chicago committee appealed to its members for letters and wires to Barkley and Truman.[94]

Barkley was under strong pressure from other directions as well, and with scarcely a quorum present he brought the bill before the Senate on Saturday afternoon, June 1, postponing the draft bill until Monday and giving McMahon two hours to get it through before the Senate turned to agricultural appropriations. All members of the Senate special committee were there except Democrats Byrd and Tydings. Vandenberg, as the senior Republican member, exchanged compliments with McMahon about the non-partisan unanimity with which the committee presented the bill; he did not gloss over the difficulties, though he somewhat overstated satisfaction with the results. "Not only were there tremendous differences within the committee," said Vandenberg,

but also in the scientific world, as well as differences between the scientific world and the congressional viewpoint. Those differences often flamed during the course of the five months into what sometimes promised to be almost a fatal difficulty. But there again we reached unanimity . . . and I

---

[94] Wire Davies to Mrs. Welling, May 16, 1946, ASC I, 28; *The New World*, p. 516; FAS memorandum to all associations, May 23, 1946, in *Bulletin of the Atomic Scientists* files; Mrs. Welling to members of Chicago Committee for Civilian Control of Atomic Energy, May 24, 1946, ASC I, 22.

think the scientific world approves the proposed legislation as completely as does the committee.

Debate was brief, the chief participants being western senators concerned with mining claims. Those awkward but significant questions, about which the scientists had been so exercized—the conduct of research, compartmentation of information, military influence—were mentioned only cursorily in McMahon's opening speech, and the bill passed by voice vote.[95]

7. IN THE HOUSE

"The Committees on Civilian Control of Atomic Energy and the other organizations which have been so successful in bringing the McMahon bill through the Senate, have one more task cut out for them—to pilot the bill through the House before the summer recess," said the *Bulletin of the Atomic Scientists* in announcing Senate passage. The Chicago scientists promptly took up the challenge by wiring Speaker Rayburn, Majority Leader McCormack, and Minority Leader Martin, urging action; and their newly hired public relations director peremptorily demanded that the FAS office "inform us what is being done in Washington and keep us informed each twenty-four hours."[96]

Actually for some days there was little to report. Then on June 10 the bill went, like its predecessor, to the House Military Affairs Committee, where ordinarily little help could have been expected from Chairman May, whose efforts of the previous autumn had been so ill-rewarded by the administration; but Speaker Rayburn let it be known that he favored prompt action, and May's involvement in a Senate investigation of defense contracts during the first week of June made him unexpectedly pliable.[97]

May held open hearings on the McMahon bill on June 12 and 13; Secretary Patterson, the principal witness, was closely examined by a skeptical Republican minority as to why he had shifted his support from the May-Johnson to the McMahon bill. Republican members also challenged exclusive government ownership of materials and the absence of military men on the commission, and contrary to May's

---

[95] *Congressional Record*, 79th Cong., 2d sess., 1946, XCII, Part 5, 6076–98.
[96] *Bulletin of the Atomic Scientists*, I (June 1, 1946), 11; wire Skinner to Higinbotham, June 3, 1946, FAS XI, 7.
[97] Throughout this section I rely for the background of political events on the account in *The New World*, pp. 516–30; May's difficulties were reported in the *New York Times*, July 2, 1946, p. 1.

wishes, the committee went into executive session on June 14 to discuss these matters further. What the federation learned about the ensuing deliberations was, of course, unofficial. Through "leaks," wrote Higinbotham on June 18 to a member of the Philadelphia association, we find that the Military Affairs Committee is amending the bill in a consistently bad way, including putting one and perhaps two military men on the commission; he concluded gloomily, "We may have to make the whole military control fight over again."[98]

Gloom also stamped the diary that Higinbotham had started a month earlier when the danger of communist infiltration began to worry him. Lunching with Oppenheimer on June 18, he found him very pessimistic about the UNAEC and emphatic about the need for more education. Learning that the Military Affairs Committee was doing violence to the bill, he desperately concluded that the only thing to do was work over the whole House. The emergency committee was going into action, which meant hours on the phone. "What I'd give for more help," wailed Higinbotham. As usual he worked late into the night with Amrine and five volunteers to put out a press release on S. 1717 and a legislative memorandum to the sites. The next two days were "killers"—tasks relating to the bill, an NCAI meeting, and one with Newman, Miller, and Mrs. Bell; a beer with Stewart Alsop and a conference with a Chicago *Sun* reporter about Bikini tests; an article for the CIO, foreign visitors, more reporters, calls from Tass and the *Daily Worker* for comments on Gromyko's speech in the United Nations, and capping it all on the second evening a dinner with Representatives Douglas, Holifield, and others to discuss strategy on the bill.[99]

As more "leaks" opened up, the rumored amendments that most alarmed the federation scientists provided that the five-man commission include two military men, that a military man be director of the division of military application, and that an unspecified number of army and navy officers serve on the military liaison committee. The President would be permitted "to authorize the armed forces to manufacture, produce, or acquire any equipment or device utilizing fissionable material or atomic energy as a military weapon." Except that the final recommendation was for one military man on the commission instead of two, these reports were well founded.[100]

On June 21—with the House committee still revising—three hun-

[98] Higinbotham to W. C. Michels, June 18, 1946, FAS XI, 7.
[99] Higinbotham diary, entries for June 18–20, 1946.
[100] *Bulletin of the Atomic Scientists*, II (July 1, 1946), 23.

dred American Physical Society members, meeting in Chicago, passed a resolution urging that the McMahon bill be accepted by the House without crippling amendments, and so did the FAS council, held on the two days following. "Action clear—no argument," read the council minutes on this point. In Washington the National Committee for Civilian Control of Atomic Energy issued a statement deploring the Military Affairs Committee action in discarding "the careful balance of military and civilian participation worked out so laboriously by the full Senate Committee and approved by all the public officials directly responsible for the nation's military defense and security."[101]

Local associations, their interest revived by the crisis, went through the now familiar routine of contacts and telegrams. Representatives of the Philadelphia scientists, local United Nations supporters, and the American Veterans Committee met with congressmen from eastern Pennsylvania to urge immediate passage of the McMahon bill with amendments to give the commission power to define military matters, to redefine restricted data, and in sections relating to security, to substitute "military advantage" of other nations for advantage."[102]

The Association of New York Scientists, which now included the remnants of the disbanded SAM group, did some letter-writing. One candid reply came from a Democratic member of the Military Affairs Committee, Representative J. Leroy Johnson of California, who as the record would eventually show, was trying hard to moderate Committee action. He had voted against most of the amendments, his letters explained, though he disagreed with ANYS that they would result in military control. But, wrote Johnson,

frankly I am wondering who is spending all the money on the bill as I read the full-page ads. Also I sometimes wish that the scientists would be as dispassionate in their appraisal of what Congress is trying to do as they are in their scientific problems. Generally speaking, I have taken the viewpoint of the scientists on this question, but it strikes me that in many of those actions the scientists have been rather partisan and even intolerant. I hope you will accept this frank statement in the spirit in which it is sent to you.[103]

---

[101] FAS council minutes, June 22–23, 1946, p. 2, ASC XIV, 2; *Bulletin of the Atomic Scientists*, II (July 1, 1946), 23.

[102] Memorandum from the Association of Philadelphia Scientists, June 20, 1946, FAS VII, 5.

[103] J. Leroy Johnson to ANYS, June 22, 1946, FAS VI, 3.

With the bill more than two weeks in committee the National Committee for Civilian Control and the Emergency Conference for Civilian Control on July 2 denounced Republican members for filibustering away the chances of passage, but that same day it was accepted, with many amendments, by the Military Affairs Committee, twenty-four to three. The committee report on the bill was published on the eighth, and on the tenth the bill was reported to the House, going as a matter of course to the Rules Committee.[104]

The prospect of this usual bottleneck does not seem to have alarmed supporters of the McMahon bill, perhaps because Chairman Adolph J. Sabath of Illinois had been the object of special attention from Mrs. Welling's Chicago citizens committee as well as from Albert Cahn, who had met Sabath through Representative Herman Kopplemann, whose office Cahn was now using as Capitol Hill headquarters. Nevertheless the four days the bill was in the Rules Committee were critical ones, for Representative J. Parnell Thomas, though not a committee member, brought to its attention the report of Ernie Adamson, chief counsel to the House Un-American Activities Committee, on suspected subversion among scientists at Oak Ridge, offering it as reason for sidetracking the McMahon bill in favor of firmer military control of atomic energy.

Representative Thomason of Texas, who took over floor management of the bill from May's faltering hands, later remarked that he could recall no legislation that had had as many red herrings drawn across its trail.[105] In terms of what was of real importance to the McMahon bill, these alarms and excursions of Representative Thomas took up an excessive amount of House time, and a similar imbalance is permitted in the present account because the episode seemed exceedingly ominous to the scientists in its bearing on civilian control and on the prospect of their ever being able to play a useful role in political decisions requiring technical knowledge.

The scientists and engineers at Oak Ridge—and others on their behalf—had been uneasy about the intentions of the Un-American Activities Committee ever since the March rumors of laboratory visits. Wood and Adamson had not talked to members of the Oak

---

[104] Committee action was reported in *New York Times*, July 2, 1946, p. 2, and *Washington Post*, July 2, 1946, p. 9, and July 3, 1946, p. 17. For further details of what went on in the closed committee hearings, see *The New World*, pp. 519–20.

[105] *Congressional Record*, 79th Cong., 2d sess., 1946, XCII, Part 7, 9340.

Ridge organizations at that time, but on June 4 they had come to Oak Ridge, and officers of the AORS and ORES (currently arranging their merger into the Association of Oak Ridge Engineers and Scientists) were summoned for interviews. Adamson was in charge and startled the scientists by announcing that he had avoided the use of subpoenas in order to keep the atmosphere friendly; they had the distinct impression that they were being "grilled." Questions that were not malevolent were merely stupid, and much familiar ground about scientists not wanting to give away secrets and estimates as to when other nations might get their own bombs had to be covered again. Adamson was especially interested in communication with foreign scientists and was told that material was prepared by the associations that members could send if they wished. Constitutions, bylaws, membership lists, and samples of literature were sent to him as requested.[106] These interviews were reported in the AORS-ORES Newsletter of June 8 as follows:

Rep. Wood of the House un-American Activities Committee visited Oak Ridge on June 4 along with committee counsel Ernie Adamson. Walter Beard of ORES and Jim Stangby, Lyle Borst, and Spoff English of AORS were questioned for an hour about the groups; do you have foreigners as members, do you correspond with Russian scientists, did you sign the petition last summer about bomb use, etc.

What will come of it is not known, but several members are making inquiries about what we may expect from past actions of the committee and its counsel, and possible action on our part. One question Adamson asked was about the McMahon bill and it was feared the committee might be seeking some material for pro-army anti-civilian publicity.[107]

This hardly inflamatory item caught the eye of someone on the mailing list outside Oak Ridge, and a New York paper printed a garbled account of the committee's visit there. Oak Ridge scientists thought Adamson had planted it, and Stangby wrote him on June 26 to protest it as a vicious distortion and to request a transcript of the June 4 interviews. Adamson's reply expressed equal displeasure. He had not written the article, he informed Stangby, and had talked only to congressmen about the Oak Ridge visit. Chairman Wood had suggested that there be no news announcements, but Adamson

[106] Beard to Adamson, June 12, 1946, AORES VII, 5.
[107] AORS-ORES Newsletter, June 8, 1946, p. 3, and Stangby to C. Utley, August 15, 1946 (in response to a request for the facts of the Oak Ridge interviews), AORES XVI, 2; interview with Stangby October 18, 1961; interview with Henshaw, December 27, 1961.

had before him "a bulletin of one of your associations" that he considered very critical. After this was sent out from the reservation, Adamson said, there was little or no hope of maintaining secrecy.[108]

The requested transcript is not in AORES files, but they do contain a "Preliminary Report," dated June 26 and based upon talks with army men and others at Oak Ridge, including officers of the two scientists' associations. Adamson made fourteen comments, of which numbers eight and nine were deleted; the others contained the following information: the two Oak Ridge societies were composed of young engineers and scientific researchers whose activities supported world government and international civilian control of the manufacture of atomic materials. These societies were opposed to army supervision and were impatiently waiting for the military administration to be thrown out. The officers of the associations admitted communication with persons outside the United States and intended to continue this. The security officers at Oak Ridge thought the peace and security of the United States was definitely in danger. A list of active members and samples of literature had been obtained. The CIO was now making a desperate effort to organize all workers at Oak Ridge. If the jurisdiction of Oak Ridge went into civilian hands the "political plans for exploiting the place are well advanced," and there would be trouble there in six months. "One of the most suprising comments," said the report, "was an expression from one of the young scientists to the effect that the power of the atomic bomb was much greater from a political viewpoint than from its physical aspect." Chairman Wood planned a bill to make Oak Ridge a permanent army reservation outside atomic control legislation, and Adamson's own conclusion was that the army should control the manufacture of atomic energy indefinitely.[109]

It is not clear whether Adamson himself or one of the scientists' Washington allies sent them this report or how long they had it before Thomas used it in the Rules Committee on July 11. His attack in the committee was widely but not very fully reported except in the *Chicago Tribune*, which quoted Aaron Novick of the ASC as declaring the charges to be ridiculous. Mrs. Welling, for the Chicago Committee for Civilian Control of Atomic Energy, used

---

[108] Stangby to Adamson, June 26, 1946, and Adamson to Stangby, July 1, 1946, AORES XVI, 2.

[109] Preliminary report of House Committee on Un-American Activities by Ernie Adamson, counsel to the committee, June 26, 1946, copy in AORES X, 3.

the Thomas attack as an excuse to urge support of the bill as passed by the Senate upon Illinois Representative Leslie C. Arends, a Republican member of the House Military Affairs Committee.

> In view of Rep. Thomas' attack on those favoring civilian control as un-American, we hope the House will be reminded that the Founding Fathers were clear[ly] and firmly determined to establish civilian authority over the military.
> In view of his attempt to make civilian control appear leftist, our sponsor list of sixty-four distinguished Chicagoans, including presidents of corporations and of universities, lawyers, bishops and other civic leaders, obviously refutes such charges.
> We are counting on you![110]

Clearly the scientists could count on Mrs. Welling!

AORES, now established as the single organization at Oak Ridge, issued a press release on July 12 pointing out that Thomas' accusations had been timed to coincide with consideration of the Mc-Mahon bill and inquiring why Adamson had not also accused the President, the State Department, and Mr. Baruch of subversion since they too were supporting international control. An AORES executive committee wire to Chairman Sabath branded Thomas' action as typical of the delaying tactics of those who opposed civilian control of atomic energy and urged passage of the McMahon bill so that international control negotiations and scientific research could proceed. As for Representative Thomas' charges, said the telegram,

> it should be sufficient to point out that since their inception the actions of these groups have been within the jurisdiction and under the surveillance of the security division of the Manhattan district. At no time have the activities of these organizations been criticized or questioned as being subversive by the Manhattan district or anyone. Therefore we respectfully urge that the Rules Committee report the McMahon bill to the House for prompt action so that the Members of the House may have the opportunity to make themselves heard on the unsatisfactory amendments to the original bill which have been made by the House Military Affairs Committee.[111]

Although explosions of righteous wrath had in the past constituted some of the scientists' politically most effective gestures, those in

---

[110] *Chicago Tribune*, July 12, 1946; *Washington Post*, July 12, 1946, p. 1; Welling to Arends, July 12, 1946, in Mrs. Welling's files.

[111] AORES press release, July 12, 1946, AORES XV, 7; *Washington Post*, July 13, 1946, pp. 3, 6; *Congressional Record*, 79th Cong., 2d sess., 1946, XCII, Part 7, 9136.

the Washington office who were trying to cloak the movement in a measure of consistency and maturity were beginning to be dubious about the technique of lashing out. Three days after the Rules Committee episode Rush sent Lyle Borst in Oak Ridge a lot of clippings about it and a résumé of reactions. One newspaper friend thought the Thomas-Adamson combine should be given both barrels; the head of the British information unit thought the charges beneath notice; but Rachel Bell had "heard from her witnesses at the hearing that members of the Rules Committee were quite impressed with the statement and visibly alarmed about the scientists' activities. Reporters I spoke to, traditionally blasé, thought it more likely that most congressmen would dismiss it as politics and hot air. . . ." Rush was disturbed by inconsistency in what the different groups had said about communication with foreign scientists, and henceforth releases must be better co-ordinated. "Personally," he said,

I feel sending the telegram and making public the text was the very limit we should have gone to on these silly charges. We are naturally through one source or another giving friendly congressmen all kinds of information for use in debate and the McMahon committee and cohorts are busy as bees writing speeches. I have one yet to do tonight for a congressman supporting the original bill as passed by the Senate.[112]

Thomas' attempt to stall the bill in the Rules Committee did not succeed, and Chairman Sabath, though by a slim vote, got it out of committee on July 13. Cahn claims that an important factor in this success was an interview Mrs. Douglas had with Speaker Rayburn, but in his report to the House Sabath made much of the enormous number of letters and telegrams he had received urging prompt action. As but a sample he placed in the record the names of thirty-two organizations, including FAS affiliates, labor, church, and educational groups, and thirty-eight individual sponsors of the National Committee for Civilian Control of Atomic Energy; an analysis of the effect of the House amendments, sent to him by Cahn for the National Committee, also went into the Record.[113]

Debate on the floor of the House began on July 16, with Sabath taking up the cudgels for the bill and also for the Oak Ridge scientists. Denouncing Adamson's ignorance of the provisions and objectives

---

[112] [Rush] to Lyle [Borst], July 14, 1946, FAS VI, 5.
[113] *Congressional Record*, 79th Cong., 2d sess., 1946, XCII, Part 7, 9138.

of S. 1717 and declaring that he had neither time nor energy to point out all the foolish things Adamson had said, Sabath continued:

Adamson is trying to suggest that these brilliant scientists, who risked their lives every moment in the long, dangerous, and incalculably important experiments to develop the means of generating atomic energy, who worked day and night under the utmost strain, are not wholly and unimpeachably loyal to this country. It is character assassination by innuendo, by insinuation, by association of ideas.

On the basis of a phone call from E. E. Minett of AORES, Sabath was able to tell the House that two Manhattan Engineer District officers at Oak Ridge, one of them in charge of security, had denied making or authorizing the statements quoted by Adamson about the breakdown of security there.[114]

This phase of House debate covered five days. Before he was through Representative Sabath got a great many other items into the record: the text of an AORES telegram, parts of the Alsop's article in the current *Saturday Evening Post*, "Your Flesh Should Creep," and a mock indictment by columnist Thomas L. Stokes, in the Adamson vein, of all supporters of the McMahon bill, including the United States Senate. Representative Thomas considered himself indirectly insulted by Sabath's remarks and was a long time accepting a blanket apology. Next day he read Adamson's report into the record but with no mention of the two deleted points, and for good measure attacked two individual scientists, Harold Urey and E. U. Condon, whom he erroneously described as coauthors of the McMahon bill. According to Thomas, Urey had written to Mrs. Luce the previous November that he would like to see all the penalty and security violations deleted from the May-Johnson bill. "You can just imagine from this," said Thomas, "what would happen if this civilian commission ever got the atomic bomb secret or if Dr. Urey became one of the commissioners."[115]

For Urey these insinuations had no serious sequel. For Condon it was a different story. Thomas' statement that he was an appointee of Henry Wallace (to the Bureau of Standards) and had been prevented from going to a conference in Russia prior to V-J Day formed the prelude to Condon's clearance troubles—the scientists' cause célèbre until the Oppenheimer case overshadowed it. Except for the

---

[114] *Congressional Record*, 79th Cong., 2d sess., 1946, XCII, Part 7, 9135–40.
[115] *Congressional Record*, 79th Cong., 2d sess., 1946, XCII, Part 7, 9257–58.

concluding remark—"He is one of those who helped write S. 1717"—
Thomas' information was correct. The curious thing was that he
had it. As vice-president of the American Physical Society, Condon
had indeed been invited to join a delegation of American scientists
at a conference in Moscow in June, 1945, and on the eve of departure
was told that as a Manhattan Project consultant he could not go.
A rumor soon reached him that a Soviet plane had been grounded
just after leaving the United States because a Project official feared
he might be on it. Condon's enforced withdrawal had received no
public notice, but Representative Thomas had somehow become
privy to it.[116]

In support of Thomas, Representative Rankin of Mississippi, also
on the Un-American Activities Committee, spoke long and vitupera-
tively. In response AORES chairman Minett (not yet in receipt of
Rush's advice or ignoring it) sent a long telegram to Speaker Rayburn demanding that if Rankin had information about spies at Oak
Ridge he turn it over to the more capable hands of the FBI or
the Project's security division. "Except for the Rankin-Wood-Thomas
charges," said the wire with a touch of bravado,

> we have heard no implications that these agencies have been negligent.
> . . . We note with tongue in cheek that earlier similar charges by members
> of the Wood Committee have still not resulted in arrests. If these charges
> are true and spies and traitors really exist in Oak Ridge then obviously
> military control is no solution to the problem and a change must be made
> since military control has always existed in Oak Ridge.

The charge that the bill was communist-inspired was an insult to
the Senate special committee, and Wood, Rankin, and Thomas
were either completely uninformed or maliciously trying to mislead
their fellow congressmen in whose hands the bill now rested.[117]

The tone of this telegram correctly suggested growing confidence
that the House leadership was not going to be stampeded by the
Thomas-Rankin hue and cry. Representative Estes Kefauver of Tennessee rose to the defense of the Oak Ridge scientists, adopting their
own view that if they were guilty of subversion so was the President,
and other speakers took a similar line. Friendly reporters and commentators prevented the Thomas charges from becoming a national
sensation. *New York Times* dispatches referred only vaguely to his

---

[116] Interview with Condon, July 29, 1962.
[117] Wire Minett to Rayburn, July 18, 1946, FAS VI, 7.

attacks on scientists while giving front-page coverage at the height of the House debate to the War Department's discharge of five civilians at the Aberdeen Proving Grounds and highlighting the claim of a union leader that their discharge was timed to create a spy scare during discussion of the bill.[118]

The relative ease with which the Adamson report was pushed into the background relieved anxiety, but Project scientists were not so innocent as to suppose that his charges had been finally laid to rest (indeed Thomas revived them in June, 1947), and they restrained any impulse to gloat. The AORES Newsletter referred to Sabath's speech on Adamson's warped mind and dropped the subject. Four months later the Woods committee "found" that it had no evidence of subversive activity at Oak Ridge.[119]

What was happening to the bill itself during the five days of House debate from Tuesday July 16 through Saturday the twentieth was also of great concern to its scientist supporters. Administration forces began with the intention of trying to substitute the Senate version of the bill for one reported out by the Military Affairs Committee and to this end tried to draw back to Washington some of the one hundred twenty-five Democrats who had left town for campaigning and other reasons. House opposition to the Senate version came in part from uncompromising supporters of military control like Thomas and Rankin, whose several attempts to bury the bill by recommitting it to committee were narrowly defeated, and in part from those who thought the bill concentrated far too much power in the hands of government. As the strength of these two groups became clear, the bill's supporters adopted the tactic of not fussing over much about undesirable amendments but of getting a bill of some kind passed and trusting to conference with the Senate to salvage as much as possible.[120]

New York Times' Anthony Leviero reported that the debate "degenerated at times into unintelligible arguments, caused the House Chamber to reverberate with angry shouts, and gave the gallery customers a laugh." Perhaps there were groans too, when Representa-

---

[118] New York Times, July 19, 1946, p. 1; July 20, 1946, p. 3.

[119] AORES executive committee notes, November 7, 1946, AORES VIII, 3.

[120] Congressional Record, 79th Cong., 2d sess., 1946, XCII, Part 7, 9135–44, 9249–75, 9340–86, and XCII, Part 8, 9463–93, 9545–63; New York Times, July 17, 1946, p. 6; for the House amendments and the political forces behind them, see The New World, pp. 522–28.

tive Lanham described the original patent section as "a-bomb-inable!" By Saturday the House had attached seventy-one amendments. Many were minor, mere changes in wording, but some were basic.[121]

Lyle Borst of the AORES legislative committee arrived in Washington in the middle of the House debate, and when it ended on Saturday he drafted a seven-page analysis of the amendments. Noting that some congressmen still seemed to be confused about different levels of secrecy and obsessed about the "giving away" of secrets, he selected for comment thirteen of the seventy-one amendments that seemed significantly to modify the structure of the bill without improving it. The federation objected to the inclusion on the commission of a member of the armed forces, a military man as director of military application, the production of bombs by the military, the dropping of grants-in-aid for research, congressional supervision over exchange of information about industrial uses, the striking-out of the dissemination-of-information provisions, declassification of data by unanimous vote of the commission, imposition of the death penalty for revelation of restricted data, and too broad an application of FBI investigations. The changes regarding information policy were especially alarming because they struck at the pooling of research results on which the United States plan for international control was predicated. Amendments relating to subcontracts and the drastic change in the patent provision, which abandoned the principle of absolute government ownership of patents, Borst thought undesirable as leaving the way open to private control of military patents, but the federation took no position on these points.[122]

Although supporters of the McMahon bill had not foreseen quite such slap-happy revision, the general tenor of House action was entirely expected. The division of labor to meet the crisis was by this time fairly well understood. The National Committee for Civilian Control of Atomic Energy had led off with a large newspaper advertisement, supported by many signatures, urging that the bill be passed without the May committee amendments, and an FAS friend, Representative Andrew J. Biemiller of Wisconsin read it into the *Congressional Record* on July 18.[123] Recollection persists—though the exact occasion

---

[121] *New York Times*, July 21, 1946, p. 1; *Congressional Record*, 79th Cong., 2d sess., 1946, XCII, Part 7, p. 9258; *Washington Post*, July 20, 1946, pp. 1, 3.

[122] Analysis by Borst, July 20, 1946, FAS XI, 5. The folder also contains an analysis by Edward Levi.

[123] *Congressional Record*, 79th Cong., 2d sess., 1946, XCII, Part 7, 9343.

has not been pinpointed—of a southern congressman converted overnight by receipt of two thousand telegrams unleashed by a word from Mrs. Bell's office to a few clergymen in his constituency. Albert Cahn, for the National Committee for Civilian Control, and Higinbotham, for the FAS, worked closely together. The anonymous advice that Higinbotham quoted to the associations came, as on earlier occasions, from Newman, Mrs. Bell and other members of the *ad hoc* strategy committee. They advised against a large-scale descent of scientists upon Washington during the committee stages of House action, but Hogness' earlier success with Vandenberg made his presence desirable. He was still in Chicago on June 12, when he was elected chairman of the new ASC executive committee, but left shortly for Washington and spent most of a particularly hot and steamy July talking with congressmen or with people who might influence them.[124]

Borst and Henshaw of AORES and other FAS representatives who attended the House debates were dismayed by the ignorance of the subject in general and of the bill in particular displayed by some of the speakers and, in the early stages, by the lack of floor leadership,[125] but as it proceeded they derived no small satisfaction from the fact that the most eloquent defenders of the bill were those whose company they had cultivated in the past months—Sabath of Illinois, Mrs. Luce of Connecticut, and Mrs. Douglas and Voorhis of California.

Mrs. Luce's support was accompanied by expressions of hearty dislike for the bill, which was, she said, more appropriate to the Soviet Union than to the United States. But many familiar ideas cropped up in her speech. She viewed as redeeming features its reasonable research provisions and its open doorway to international control; security was not to be found in secrecy, and key nuclear scientists would not work under the military. "We want, if we can," she continued, "to avoid the abyss of atomic warfare. It seems that the only road home does skirt that abyss; and unhappily it is the totalitarian road of the legislation before us. Let us take it if we must. But, in the name of all our liberties, let us take it with our eyes wide open. I arise in support of S. 1717 ... with a very heavy heart, indeed."[126] Helen Gahagan Douglas, in addition to her crucial work with Rayburn and other House leaders, was a principal speaker. And it was perhaps a

---

[124] Interview with Hogness, January 18, 1960; ASC executive committee minutes, June 12, 1946, ASC VI, 13.
[125] AORES Newsletter, July 26, 1946, in AORES XX, 4.
[126] *Congressional Record*, 79th Cong., 2d sess., 1946, XCII, Part 7, 9261.

plea from Congressman Jerry Voorhis, one of the scientists' first and staunchest friends in Washington, that narrowly saved the bill from recommitment in the final moments of debate. If, a year after the atomic bomb had dropped, declared Voorhis, any member says he doesn't know enough to vote, he is striking a blow at democratic government itself; not to pass a bill would be to repudiate the Baruch proposal (for international control) and put the stamp of approval on continuation of the arms race.[127]

With its seventy-one amendments the McMahon bill passed the House on Saturday afternoon, July 20, by a vote of 265 to 79, and was scheduled for consideration by a joint Senate-House committee the following week. On Monday Albert Cahn, for the National Committee for Civilian Control, issued a press release giving the reasons for opposition to the House version, based on the Borst analysis of the amendments.[128] Higinbotham wired the local associations:

Please promote an avalanche of telegrams to conferees Brien McMahon and Andrew May recommending Senate form of bill. Urge your sending two best contact men with American names arriving Monday for individual congressional contacts to insure passage of final conference report. Also urge that public figures make strong appeals against isolationism and military control.

And as soon as the names of Senate-House conferees were announced, Higinbotham sent telegrams to thirty-three scientists and other influential individuals asking them to wire or visit the conference committee members.[129]

Oak Ridge had not needed this prodding, and on July 19 wires had gone to Rayburn, McCormack, and Martin from the division directors at Clinton Labs—seven senior men headed by Eugene Wigner—declaring that in their experience only a civilian administration could maintain and guarantee United States leadership in nuclear science and development and that the provisions further weakening civilian control would make it difficult to maintain personnel at even reasonably high scientific standards. AORES forwarded a copy of this wire to Secretary of War Patterson on Monday, July 21, with a statement that AORES members, constituting most of the technical staff of the

---

[127] Congressional Record, 79th Cong., 2d sess., 1946, XCII, Part 8, 9555.
[128] National Committee for Civilian Control of Atomic Energy press release, July 22, 1946, FAS XV, 3; Washington Post, July 21, 1946, p. 1.
[129] Wire Higinbotham to Cohn, July 20, 1946, AORES XVI, 7; Higinbotham wire and list of recipients, July 22, 1946, FAS III, 1.

Clinton Engineering Works, were alarmed by the House amendments and urged a strong statement from the War Department. The Manhattan Project has always trusted its civilian scientists and engineers, said the communication. If legislation threatening their personal security as well as their work and influence is enacted, these men, in the order of their capabilities and rank, will leave for other employment.[130]

AORES followed this up next day with another long wire in the same vein to Speaker Rayburn and a release to the press commenting in detail on the amendments. At the same time there was prepared for AORES, perhaps by Borst in Washington, a three-page memorandum entitled "Basic Considerations Involved in Domestic Legislation." Copies were to be sent to each member of the Senate-House conference committee.[131]

In Chicago the ASC executive committee instructed Novick to keep in daily touch with Hogness and Cahn in Washington and concentrated with considerable success on getting members and non-members to write and wire the Senate-House conferees. Enrico Fermi, who six months earlier had refused to support the McMahon bill, now complied by directing attention to a specific point on which he was willing to commit himself:

I must stress great harm that would be done to science and indirectly to the common security of this country if provisions that hamper dissemination of non-military information were written into atomic bill. A narrow-sighted interpretation of security in this field would discourage American scientists and endanger the source of our present supremacy in this field. Therefore I urge you not to compromise on this part of the original Senate bill.[132]

Other associations joined in the letter and telegraph campaign. About the dispatch of representatives with good American names, or what they did if they got to Washington, there is less evidence. Four more Oak Ridge men were reported in Washington during the week of July 21—M. D. Peterson, Vernon Cannon, Alvin Weinberg, and

---

[130] Wires to Rayburn et al., July 19, 1946 in AORES XVI, 4. The signers were E. Wigner, director; E. J. Murphy, assistant director; L. W. Nordheim, director, physics division; J. Coe, director, chemistry division; M. C. Leverett, director, engineering division; J. E. Wirth, M.D., director, medical division; C. R. McCullough, director, power pile division. AORES statement to Secretary Patterson, July 21, 1946, FAS VI, 7.
[131] AORES wire to Rayburn and press release, July 22, 1946, FAS VI, 5; "Basic Considerations . . . ," July 21, 1946, FAS VI, 7.
[132] Wire Fermi to Hon. Charles B. Clason and others, July 23, 1946 (copies of Fermi's wires and many from other people are in ASC X, 7).

Jerry Coe—but there was not much to be done except await the outcome of the Senate-House conference.[133]

Over these joint discussions, which began on Tuesday, July 23 and ran through Thursday, the twenty-fifth, the Senate conferees kept a firm hand. Vandenberg and Millikin, if their views were not always to the scientists' liking, had at least become ardent supporters of the McMahon bill. Their strategy was to give way on the lesser points in order to win on the major ones; they not only broke precedent by holding the first session on the House side of the Capitol but on the first day let the House conferees have things entirely their own way. The second meeting drew concessions from both sides, the senators yielding to House demands on several of the points on which the federation felt strongly, including the death penalty for giving information and wide FBI powers, and the House members conceding that information on industrial applications might be exchanged once Congress was convinced that effective international control of the bomb had been established. The chief topics on the third and final day were the patent section and military participation, and with Millikin playing a key role on the first and Vandenberg on the second, the Senate version won out in both cases.[134]

There was some last-minute resistance in the House, not from the old antagonist Chairman May, who after the combined strain of McMahon bill hearings and his implication in the defense contract enquiry was plainly ill and indeed suffered a heart attack after he had whispered his assent at the second day of conferences, but from Congressmen Charles R. Clason and Thomas, who refused to sign the conference committee report. Clason gave way during the floor debate; Thomas held out. Nevertheless on Friday, July 26, both houses accepted the bill by voice vote, the Senate without discussion, the House after an hour's debate. It was signed by President Truman on August 1.[135]

8. CONCLUSION

Minding its manners the FAS wrote to members of Congress thanking them for efforts on behalf of suitably drawn atomic energy legislation. Editorial comment in the *Bulletin of the Atomic Scientists* indi-

---

[133] AORES Newsletter, July 26, 1946, in AORES XX, 4.

[134] *New York Times*, July 24, 1946, p. 12; July 25, 1946, p. 1; July 26, 1946, p. 1; *The New World*, pp. 529–30.

[135] *Congressional Record*, 79th Cong., 2d sess., 1946, XCII, Part 8, 10168, 10189–99; *New York Times*, July 27, 1946, p. 3; *Washington Post*, July 27, 1946.

cated satisfaction, if not jubilation, over the end result and proffered the scientists' thanks to those who had helped in the campaign, especially the citizens' committees and Senators McMahon and Vandenberg. "Gradually, imperceptibly, even the most stubborn and reluctant of the senators on [the] Committee," said the *Bulletin* complacently, "appreciated the novel 'facts and implications' of atomic energy, and during the last week of the session they were defenders of reason and moderation against conferees on the House side, who had not benefited from a six months course in physical and political atomistics.[136] Success in mobilizing public opinion against military control was only possible, continued the editorial, "because the apprehension of a possible atomic attack on our cities, had not yet engulfed . . . traditional beliefs in civil liberties and human rights. . . . It is easy to predict that the mass-psychological reaction to a growing feeling of danger and insecurity—a development which will be inevitable if the armaments race is permitted to gain momentum—will be the gradual muffling of the voices of the defenders of civil liberty and democratic freedoms, and a rising clamor for vigorous police action and military leadership of the country." This did not mean that scientists should now stop frightening people, as they had been accused of doing; they must continue to speak the truth as they saw it and must take up the challenge offered by the current deadlock in the UNAEC negotiations.

Off-the-record, scientists held many a private post-mortem, or rather diagnostic and prognostic session, on the meaning of the bill and the part they had played. For the character of the McMahon Act, they could claim a great deal of credit and responsibility. However far short it came of perfection, it was thoroughly imbued with their ideas on the importance of research and the conditions under which it could be effectively conducted. Checks, brakes, and balances had been appended, but they had not been allowed to alter the basic fabric. "It is doubtful," said the authors of the bill, "that the Senators' zeal for education carried them very deeply into the theory of nuclear fission or made them technical experts in the assembly of the bomb. It can be said, however, that the bill they unanimously reported demonstrated a grasp of those fundamental factors that determine to a considerable degree the necessary framework of the control system."[137]

---

[136] Correspondence in FAS XI, 7; *Bulletin of the Atomic Scientists*, II (August 1, 1946), 1.

[137] Newman and Miller, *The Control of Atomic Energy*, pp. 48–49. Used by permission of McGraw-Hill Book Co.

To what extent this general understanding came through Condon, through Newman, through the testimony of individual scientists before congressional committees, or through the collective advice and pressure from the FAS, it is impossible to say. The scientists, said Byron Miller, were "a major factor in the formulation of atomic energy legislation."[138] But one cannot isolate their contribution or give it quantitative value, and the same must be said when it comes to specific points in the passage of the bill. One can affirm with some confidence that the fight for a substitute for the May-Johnson bill would not have been carried so far without pressure from scientists and that without them so strong a stand on military control would not have been made, but one cannot say how many votes they delivered at crucial points in committee or floor debate. Albert Cahn estimates that the alliance of the FAS and the *ad hoc* and citizens' committees changed the votes of at least ten Senate and fifty House members. In neither case was the final vote close enough to make this decisive, but Cahn's estimate does not take account of the numerous instances where legislators had since the early autumn been favorably disposed to the principals embodied in the McMahon bill through the scientists' direct or indirect influence.

The scientists readily admitted the limits of their contribution. The FAS could be proud of its part, Higinbotham reminded its members, but it was the citizens' organizations that produced those seventy thousand telegrams.[139] However, it was the scientists who alerted public opinion in the first place, who requested professional advice in public relations, who sponsored the National Committee for Atomic Information from which the citizens' committees sprang, and who, by establishing good relations with press and radio, insured that the bill and its sponsors were presented in a generally favorable light. Vandenberg, guiding the bill through the Senate and the conference committee, was fully aware of the strength of this body of opinion; and Mrs. Douglas, bringing pressure upon Rayburn and other House leaders, also made full use of it.

In a study of lobbies made five years after the war, Karl Schriftgiesser devoted a chapter to "Lobbying and the Atom" and described the combined forces behind the McMahon bill as a people's lobby that

---

[138] Miller, "A Law Is Passed," p. 800. Copyright © 1948 by The University of Chicago.

[139] Higinbotham probably meant letters and telegrams (memorandum on tax exemption, December 29, 1947, AORES XVII, 10).

might someday be recognized as a classic of its kind—"a thrilling and heartening example of how a democratic government can function in behalf of the general welfare."

The victory of the scientists was a great one, and even more astounding when we realize that here was a pressure group that had come into being for no reason except the general welfare, that was without private ambitions, that had no profit motive, and that was able to put to rout the well-organized private interest lobbies. Whether these latter failed to recognize the profitable implications of atomic energy or whether they were merely temporarily stunned and impotent in the face of an aroused citizenry is difficult to determine. It probably was a little of both.[140]

It may seem that Schriftgiesser mistook the character of the opposition, overemphasizing the importance of vested industrial interests and underplaying military and international factors; one might suggest that a vested interest in research policy leavened the scientists' altruistic concern for the general welfare. But his view of the popular nature of McMahon bill support still seems sound. As a student of lobbies, what impressed Schriftgiesser was the scope and co-ordination of the forces mobilized by the scientists, and even writing so close to the event, he did not attempt to single out what their own contacts with congressmen might have accomplished. What was important was the inspiration and, in some measure, the leadership they had provided.

Both Newman and Miller later expressed the view that the real "control" issues—public ownership, private research, emphasis on peaceful uses, and above all, whether the act should give wide discretion to the administering body, as the May-Johnson bill had done, or explicit instructions—were never properly discussed, partly for escapist reasons and partly because they were dull and colorless subjects for debate. Both sides, concluded Miller, found support in the simpler symbols of military versus civilian control.[141] It is understandable that lawyers and administrators should feel that the scientists' passionate concern about international and military implications distorted the picture. And yet the experience of two postwar decades has not perceptibly altered the balance or placed the "real control issues" in the center of the stage.

The danger that the bill might not pass in any form, plus some battle

---

[140] Karl Schriftgiesser, *The Lobbyists: The Art and Business of Influencing Lawmakers* (Boston: Little, Brown, 1951), pp. 237–38, 249.

[141] Newman and Miller, *The Control of Atomic Energy*, p. 19; Miller, "A Law Is Passed," pp. 817–18.

fatigue, reconciled scientists to deficiencies in the act over which they would have haggled stubbornly a few months earlier. Beyond this, how did they feel about this legislation, which appeared, even to those who approved its passage, as "perhaps the most austere guardianship ever attempted in peacetime" and as "in some respects as radical and unprecedented as the scientific discovery that occasioned it"?[142]

By and large scientists were not much alarmed by the act's potential for radical change in public administration and in business relations, not because they were political or economic radicals, which—judged by any standards—few of them were, but because these areas were unfamiliar, even alien, and it was easy to say that a radical approach was needed, especially when politicians and industrialists seemed so ready to agree. But loudly as they cried that everything was altered by the bomb, in their own field scientists did not want radical change; they wanted rather a return to what they regarded as normal conditions of research and communication. Or perhaps one should say they accepted the fact that conditions under which research was carried out must change but hoped that the basic principles might not. In the two closely related areas about which scientists had been most deeply concerned—military influence and dissemination and control of information—the McMahon bill offered some latitude for the fulfilment of this hope. How science fared under the act would depend much on international events and upon how the Atomic Energy Commission interpreted the research and information sections, but at least doors had been left open for the encouragement of basic science and for its free discussion should external conditions permit.

Gratified as they were at the victory for a civilian commission, the more farsighted among the scientists knew that they had won a battle, not a war. Implicit in their fear of an atomic arms race was a realization that in the continuing conflict between civilian and military interests their antagonists would cease to be military men and would become the weapons of destruction themselves. In retrospect some see themselves as naïve in thinking that the AEC could be a kind of glorified TVA and not a civilian arm of the military establishment. Perhaps far too much reliance was placed upon the bill and its provisions. You cannot, they now say, legislate the allocation or the transfer of power in the body politic. Others, admitting all this, think the fight for civilian control of atomic energy was supremely important—that scien-

[142] William S. White, New York Times, July 27, 1946, p. 3; Newman and Miller, The Control of Atomic Energy, p. 3.

tists' own morale as well as their influence has been vastly stronger because it was made.

The qualified triumph was full of ironies of which perhaps the sharpest was that the bill passed only because usually conservative legislators viewed it as essential to national defense. To this conviction the scientists had substantially contributed by their insistence on the horrors of atomic warfare; yet the lesson they themselves drew from the possibility of mutual destruction was not nationalism, but internationalism. At least this was true in the summer of 1946. In time the divergent views would be reflected in the scientific community itself.

CHAPTER 14

Science Legislation

C HIEF AMONG several problems that federation scientists had chosen to subordinate to international and domestic control of atomic energy was legislation to establish a national science foundation. The controversy that delayed passage of a bill until April, 1950, hinged not upon the desirability of a foundation, which was widely acknowledged, but on whether control of it should be exercized through a board of scientists insulated from political interference—largely self-governing and independent—as Vannevar Bush recommended, or through the normal channels of government operation, as was considered essential by Budget Director Harold Smith and other influential people within the administration. Behind the scenes in Washington, and unknown to most American scientists, the lines of this controversy had been laid down before the war ended on exactly the same principles and reasoning that would shortly create a division within the administration over the May-Johnson bill.[1]

In July, 1945, Bush released his proposal for a national science foundation, later published as *Science—the Endless Frontier*, and

---

[1] Richard G. Hewlett and Oscar E. Anderson, Jr., *The New World, 1939–1946* (University Park: Pennsylvania State University Press, 1962), pp. 409–11 (referred to hereinafter as *The New World*).

scientists were just becoming familiar with its contents—a meeting for this purpose took place at the Met Lab on August 2—when Hiroshima and Nagasaki pushed other matters from their minds. On July 19 Senator Warren C. Magnuson introduced a bill to establish a science foundation based on the Bush report, and on July 23 Senator Kilgore, who as chairman of a Senate subcommittee on war mobilization had studied the government technical program, introduced a second measure more closely in line with Smith's views. Both bills provided for federal civilian sponsorship of research under the supervision of highly qualified scientists through grants to public and private laboratories and through fellowship programs to encourage new talent. The most important difference was in the mechanics of administration. The Magnuson bill provided for a part-time nine-man board that chose its own executive; the Kilgore bill had a single director, appointed by the President and responsible to him, with a large advisory board of private individuals as well as representatives from interested government agencies. The bills also differed on patents—the Magnuson bill following the established OSRD practice of permitting private interests to patent work done with federal funds and the Kilgore bill prohibiting it—and after October, on the inclusion of research in the social sciences, which was added to the Kilgore bill at that time.[2] According to Don K. Price, who represented the Bureau of the Budget view, the two camps

were in full agreement that the Science Foundation should have a coherent program, and that its head should be in a strong enough position to develop one. But they differed—and, as it turned out, irreconcilably—over the question of the relation of the Foundation to the rest of the government. The Magnuson bill . . . gave the Foundation board and its executive director enough authority to keep their divisions in harmony, but it denied the President enough authority to keep the Foundation in harmony with the rest of the Executive Branch. It did so by putting control of the Foundation in a part-time board, with power to elect its own executive director. By contrast the Kilgore bill made a single administrator, appointed by the President, responsible for the direction of the Foundation, but with the assistance of an advisory board.[3]

On September 5, 1945, President Truman endorsed the Kilgore bill. On October 8 Senate committee hearings began on both bills, during

---

[2] For a clear account of developments through July, 1946, see Talcott Parsons, "National Science Legislation: Part I. An Historical Review," *Bulletin of the Atomic Scientists,* II (November 1946), 7–9.

[3] Price, "The Deficiencies of the National Science Foundation Bill," *Bulletin of the Atomic Scientists,* III (October, 1947), 293.

which some compromise was effected, and on December 21 Senator Kilgore introduced another bill, S. 1720, which retained the single administrator but gave the advisory board more power, as in the Magnuson bill, by making it smaller and able to make recommendations to President and Congress. But the continued existence of two opposing views was pointed up in *Science* on November 30 by the publication of a letter from a self-appointed "Committee Supporting the Bush Report," of which the chairman was geographer Isaiah Bowman, president of Johns Hopkins. A month later a "Committee for a National Science Foundation," headed by Harold Urey and Harlow Shapley, issued a statement with two hundred signatures that by implication supported the compromise Kilgore measure of December 21.

Further work in the Senate committee during January produced still further compromise, and on February 21, 1946, still another bill was introduced by Senator Kilgore as S. 1850, which had the approval of the Bush group and the support of Senator Magnuson. This bill reached the Senate floor in April, where, like the McMahon bill, it had to compete on a crowded calendar; it passed the Senate early in July though shorn by amendment of its provision for social science research.

Meanwhile on May 15 Representative Earle W. Mills had introduced into the House as H.R. 6448 a bill very like the original Magnuson bill. Hearings were hastily arranged, initially leaving no chance for opponents to testify. Bush and President Bowman let it be known that they preferred this bill to Kilgore's S. 1850, which they had earlier approved. The hand of those who opposed the Kilgore bill on administrative grounds was strengthened by dislike in other quarters of its patent provisions and by a small knot of opposition to any kind of national science foundation. Considering the Mills bill in July, the House Committee on Interstate and Foreign Commerce decided that it did not have before it sufficient information and by tabling the whole subject removed any chance that science legislation would be enacted by the Seventy-ninth Congress.

From the files of the FAS and its branches one can reconstruct an outline, and a good deal more, of the course of atomic energy legislation during 1945 and 1946; but for science legislation, this is far from the case. References to congressional action and injunctions to read bills and form opinions have an almost perfunctory tone. Until November, 1946, the *Bulletin of the Atomic Scientists* carried no news about the progress of science legislation, and the speeches on research by Ridenour and DuBridge that it printed were chiefly concerned with secrecy, not at all with organization.

The FAS did not, however, completely ignore the science bills. All the local groups discussed them during the winter months while analyzing the McMahon bill and arguing over FAtS and FAmS. On December 28 the Cambridge association heard Lee DuBridge present the case for the Magnuson bill and Harvard astronomer Bart J. Bok for the Kilgore bill but without, apparently, any strong partisan reaction in the audience. The Clinton Labs scientists, so quick to man the barricades on atomic energy questions, discussed the bills and preferred not to take a stand.[4] The Kilgore bill of December 21 was distributed to the site organizations and attention directed to the administrative setup, the inclusion of the social sciences, distribution of funds by states, the patent provisions, and the international exchange of scientific and technical information.[5]

After the second Kilgore compromise of February 21 (S. 1850) received the approval of the Bush group, the FAS office began to suggest more positive action on the grounds that favorable treatment of science legislation might have a corresponding effect upon the McMahon bill, then having heavy sledding in the wake of the Canadian spy affair. The March council, much concerned about the Vandenberg amendment, did not even discuss the science bills, but the April one adopted a resolution supporting S. 1850. This was not, however, followed up by any concerted action, the local associations being left to do as they saw fit. Philadelphia addressed letters to two senators and fifteen representatives pointing out that its five hundred members favored S. 1850; Clinton Labs noted that the bill was in danger of dying of neglect but left expression of opinion to individual members.[6]

After introduction of the Mills bill on May 15 so clearly augured trouble in the House, correspondence from the FAS office reminded key congressmen that the Kilgore bill had wide support among scientists; but at the same time the federation was also pressing for Senate action on the McMahon bill, and a fight on both fronts was considered politically unwise as well as impractical. A few FAS members conducted personal campaigns. Hugh Wolfe of the Association of

---

[4] Roberts to Goldsmith, January 8, 1946, Camb. I; FAS council minutes, January 5, 1946, ASC XIV, 2.

[5] FAtS Newsletter, January 3, 1946, FAS XIV, 8.

[6] Letters to members of Congress from Association of Philadelphia Scientists, May 15, 1946, FAS VII, 5; AORS executive committee minutes, May 20, 1946, AORES IV, 4.

New York Scientists wrote letters to congressmen early in July claiming that Bush and Bowman, in throwing their influence against the Kilgore bill, spoke for a minority of scientists. Wolfe expressed a view common among natural scientists when he regretted the Senate amendment dropping social science research. What was now needed, he declared, was intensive studies in patterns of social behavior so that we can learn to live together in peace.[7]

The main reason for this half-hearted support of science legislation is obvious. The majority of scientists outside the government who were taking an interest in politics were convinced that the need to control atomic energy constituted an emergency so great that even the related problem of a national framework for research should be subordinated to it; if military control of nuclear research was established, freedom of investigation in other areas would be endangered. The curious thing is that these same scientists failed to make any capital of—or even to spell out among themselves—the connection between the issue of part-time or full-time administration of an atomic energy authority, about which they were so exercized, and a science foundation. Nor, except for those in the Washington office, do recollections of this period include a clear definition of the administrative issue that scientists and science-oriented people in the government considered so important. Scientists who testified at the first hearings on science legislation—Langmuir, Shapley, Bush, Oppenheimer, Bowman, Curtis of AORS, and Wilson of ALAS—expressed strong approval of a science foundation and even more emphatically underlined the importance of freedom of basic research and communication, but except for Bush and Bowman, they did not appear to have taken sides on the question of administration as represented in the Magnuson and Kilgore bills.[8]

Not until the spring of 1946, when a division of military research within the foundation was under discussion, is any explicit reference found to the close relation between science foundation legislation and control of atomic energy. The March 1 FAS Newsletter urged its members to obtain copies of S. 1850 and prepare to take action for the following reason:

The battle over administration, a part-time commission versus a responsible administration with an advisory committee of scientists, as well

---

[7] Wolfe to Senator Magnuson, July 5, 1946, and to other congressmen, in FAS X, 7.
[8] U.S. Senate, Committee on Military Affairs, Subcommittee on War Mobilization, *Hearings on Science Legislation*, October 8, 1945–March 5, 1946, 79th Cong., 1st and 2d sess.

as the fight over security provisions, may be one and the same for both pieces of legislation. Both are involved in the vital decision as to whether science is to be used for preparation for war or to advance cooperation for peace.[9]

It seems curious also that those who were deeply concerned about military control of research did not recognize earlier that failure to push hard for a civilian science foundation might leave a dangerous gap. Not until the FAS council meeting in late June was concern explicitly expressed that army and navy contracts might fill the vacuum if science legislation did not pass. The excuse for this lapse of attention was doubtless that until the latter half of May chances for the Kilgore bill seemed fairly bright and that by the time its plight became critical FAS scientists were too involved with the tribulations of the McMahon bill in the House to attempt its rescue.

It should be emphasized that this myopia in regard to atomic energy, if such it was, did not extend to scientists within the government, whichever view they took of the administrative question. According to Don K. Price, the emphasis among government scientists immediately after the war was quite in the other direction and so continued. Higinbotham—taking a rare half-day off, just after the Mills bill was introduced, to go canoeing with Lawrence Hafstad of the Applied Physics Laboratory at Johns Hopkins—noted in his diary that Hafstad was very much interested in science legislation and thought the FAS was going overboard on the United Nations and the McMahon bill.[10]

FAS scientists argued that science legislation was a problem for the scientific community as a whole, which to a certain extent did keep an eye on it, chiefly through the American Association for the Advancement of Science and its journal *Science*. Howard A. Meyerhoff, executive secretary of the AAAS, went to the October hearings armed with the results of a poll of the AAAS council, to which 65 per cent of the 258 members had replied. Only 3 per cent expressed any opposition to federal support of science, but fear of a politically controlled science foundation seemed to be widespread. Questions about how funds should be spent and about the structure of a foundation showed no unanimity. Relevant articles and legislative news appeared in the pages

---

[9] FAS Newsletter, I (March 1, 1946), AORES XXI, 5.

[10] Interview with Price, June 27, 1962; Higinbotham diary, May 19, 1946. Mrs. Margaret Stahl also found that non-Project scientists were more interested in science legislation than in the McMahon bill; see her unpublished dissertation, "Splits and Schisms, Nuclear and Social" (University of Wisconsin, 1946).

of *Science* with increasing frequency as the various compromise measures were introduced. After S. 1850 was reported out of committee in April, the overwhelming support of the AAAS, as indicated in its council vote of 230 to 10, was communicated to all members of the Senate by the AAAS president James B. Conant.[11] But the professional societies like the AAAS were neither inclined nor prepared for the kind of action that the FAS was taking in regard to the McMahon bill.

Is it possible that the failure of any large body of American scientists to concern themselves actively with science legislation stemmed also from lack of preparation? When Newman and Miller tried to acquire some background for drawing up the research provisions of the Mc-Mahon bill, they found much critical analysis by British scientists in the prewar period but almost none by Americans prior to the Bush report and only the 1938 report of the National Resources Planning Board (*Research—a National Resource*) to mark the development of any national science policy.[12] They concluded that after the war American scientists failed to grapple or concern themselves publicly with research problems because excessive secrecy stood in the way of rational solutions and had to be disposed of first.

The records of the scientists' movement, with their paucity of discussion of research in general, their very considerable discontent with existing secrecy, and their preoccupation with information policy, do not contradict this contemporary impression. And the same preoccupation characterized most of the statements of leading scientists not committed to the federation program. Many of these same scientists, and those in the federation as well, completely agreed with Vannevar Bush about the value of avoiding monolithic control of basic research and permitting a given problem to be worked on from many angles, but his efforts toward rapid decentralization of the huge complex of government research projects were attracting little public comment.

This does not, of course, obviate the possibility of a good deal of private talk. The memorandum on fundamental and programmatic research that Robert Wilson of ALAS had ready for the Kilgore committee on October 17 was thoughtful and specific, but as Wilson discovered, the other young scientists collected in Washington expected him to be talking about the evils of secrecy as represented in the May-

---

[11] *Science*, CIII (May 10, 1946), 590.
[12] James R. Newman and Byron S. Miller, *The Control of Atomic Energy* (New York: McGraw-Hill Book Co., 1948), p. 172.

Johnson bill, and much constructive thinking on the subject was diverted in the same way in the coming months. In the closing weeks of the Seventy-ninth Congress, the crisis that marked the fight for civilian control of atomic energy so absorbed the more articulate members of the American scientific community that the tabling of science legislation caused no great outcry.

CHAPTER 15

International Control

Reviewing FAS policy for administrative committee members in the summer of 1947, Higinbotham reminded them of the rationale of earlier action, "We felt," he recalled,

that there were many things we could do which might improve the chances of control. This is one reason why we were interested in good domestic legislation. This is one reason why we have been anxious to get basic science out from under the military. This is why we have been interested in setting up a Committee for Foreign Correspondence. This is why we have tried to promote maximum freedom of science and communication, consistent with security, and urge world distribution of isotopes. I am afraid there is sometimes a tendency to approach these problems from a selfish point of view. But the real justification must be their contribution to world peace and security.[1]

1. Control Problems Crystallize

With little debate the federation scientists had decided that control of atomic energy could best be handled by the United Nations, and for the first year unanimity on this point remained virtually unbroken. Two activities in the fall of 1945 had been directly related to this primary goal: seeking congressional support for talks with Russia and

---

[1] Higinbotham to FAS administrative committee, July 14, 1947, in Rush's files.

initiating the studies on feasibility of inspection. The next objective was a UN atomic energy commission, but with negotiations proceeding satisfactorily at the January UN General Assembly in London, federation circles were content with general expressions of support. A press release by the two New York associations declared that secrets of technical know-how need not be fully revealed to a UN commission and that scientists could probably do an effective job of policing if political machinery were established in a spirit of mutual trust. On January 21, after Senator Connally had placed on record the United States' insistence on guarding atomic bomb secrets, the UN Political and Security Committee adopted a resolution setting up the UN Atomic Energy Commission.[2]

The FAS scientists never intended to develop their own scheme of international control but limited themselves to preparation of the technical studies of inspection and to advising political scientists at Columbia and Chicago. Any need or temptation to go farther than this was removed by the appointment in mid-January of a State Department committee under Undersecretary of State Dean Acheson's chairmanship to draw up a control plan and its choice of a board of consultants headed by David Lilienthal and including Oppenheimer as a member. The almost simultaneous appointment by General Groves of the Benedict committee to integrate inspection studies and the understanding that its report would be available to the Lilienthal board guaranteed that the viewpoint of scientists and such specific ideas as they had thus far developed on the subject of control would be adequately represented.

The best guide to scientists' thinking when these two committees began to work in late January, 1946, was the Federation of Atomic Scientists' December 10 memorandum summarized earlier in connection with the feasibility of inspection reports. Most of its contents was not suitable for public discussion, but a few points received some elaboration in the three months that elapsed before the Acheson-Lilienthal Report on International Control was ready. The use of checks on scientific and technical personnel as a supplement to physical inspection

---

[2] ANYS and AMPS release, *New York Times*, January 12, 1946, p. 5. The most complete account of the first year of negotiations in the UNAEC and the United States political background is to be found in Richard G. Hewlett and Oscar E. Anderson, Jr., *The New World, 1939–1946* (University Park: Pennsylvania State University Press, 1962), chaps. xv and xvi (referred to hereinafter as *The New World*); see also Bernhard G. Bechhoefer, *Postwar Negotiations for Arms Control* (Washington, D.C.: Brookings Institution, 1961).

of plants could be partially explored without revealing secrets, and all agreed that such checks were important. Urey had earlier pointed out that during the war any scientist could deduce that an atomic bomb was being attempted just from knowing that certain specialists had disappeared from other projects. As Philip Morrison put it, scientific personnel, like capital equipment, is conspicuous.[3]

Scientists were also interested in how technical personnel could be encouraged to report violations of a control treaty and protected in so doing by national and international law, a subject that required delicate handling because it violated traditional concepts of national loyalty. Minett had raised this question with the engineers at Oak Ridge, and Szilard proposed that the President of the United States call on all American engineers and scientists to pledge themselves to report violations committed on United States territory, adding an idea to which more than any other he remained consistently faithful, that engineers and scientists from all countries be invited to spend a four to six weeks' annual vacation abroad with their families to promote among them a truly international viewpoint. In their January endorsement of a UN atomic energy commission the New York associations suggested enforcement by mutual agreement among scientists. Nor did this idea appeal only to insurgent opinion, for Vannevar Bush would shortly point out to the Acheson committee and the Lilienthal board that, during the ten or fifteen years it would take for a control system to evolve, "a new class of international servants" might come forward who were sufficiently loyal to the international authority to refuse to "leak" its information to their own governments.[4]

Scientists were also keenly aware of the limitations of their own viewpoint and contributions. The December 10 inspection memorandum began with the reminder that the problem of control was primarily political, but it went on to explore technical possibilities on the theory that political agreement was more likely if it were known that the technical hurdles were not insuperable. Scientists needed no prompting from skeptical politicians to recognize that effective control of the type they envisaged depended upon the opening of Russia and communication with her scientists. Bush and Oppenheimer constantly

[3] Urey to the editor, *New York Herald Tribune,* November 19, 1945; Morrison speech to ALAS, December 29, 1945, Los Alamos Newsletter, No. 12, January 8, 1946, ALAS II, 19.

[4] Minett memorandum, November 9, 1945, AORES VI, 8; Szilard, "We Turned the Switch," *Nation,* CLXI (December 22, 1945), 718–19; *The New World,* p. 546.

warned against overoptimism in this respect. Still scientists did need to keep a firm rein on their tendency to feel that problems were solvable. Technical feasibility, Philip Morrison reminded ALAS members on December 29, was not a primary question or even a clear one, for behind it lay the practical conditions of politics and finance under which a control agency must operate. Abstract speculation about these conditions was not very helpful because a control agency would be a developing, evolving institution, and the course of this development would determine what technical questions came up. Morrison urged his listeners vigorously to discredit the notion that scientists had a set of tricks that would guarantee successful control. "Success," he said, "will be an achievement of statesmanship, exploiting fully the strategic advantages which the situation itself affords."[5]

Morrison, with a mind both fertile and receptive, is a center of talk about any topic of current interest to scientists; his remarks are a dependable clue to what was being said in the upper echelons of politically alert scientists about the prospects for international control and show that they were not unaware of political complexities or entirely optimistic. But to have held all consideration of technical problems in abeyance until political problems were solved would have been to abandon their principal contention that men must now order their political and social relations in the light of new scientific knowledge.

And during this period of waiting for an official proposal to emerge from the Acheson committee, in addition to reaffirming their support for international control, scientists frequently had occasion to emphasize certain negative points, chief among which was their opposition to giving up secrets of the bomb until controls were established and to an unpoliced ban on its manufacture. When the possibility of a ban was seriously raised, it was not by the younger element in the federation but by senior faculty members at Columbia University, representing science, law, history, sociology, and economics, who recommended that the President declare a bomb holiday so that discussion in the newly established UNAEC might proceed in "an atmosphere of full good faith and of confidence in their successful outcome for international peace." Of the five scientists who framed this proposal in a letter to the *New York Times*—Selig Hecht, Edgar Miller, George B. Pegram, I. I. Rabi, and Jan Schilt—only Hecht was an active supporter of

---

[5] Morrison's speech is summarized in Los Alamos Newsletter, No. 12, January 8, 1946, ALAS II, 19.

the FAS. Their specific proposals were (1) that the United States immediately stop production of bombs from material in hand, including the preparation of subassemblies and other fabrication procedures; (2) that for one year the United States stop accumulating purified plutonium and U-235, that plants producing these substances be kept in merely stand-by condition, and that materials produced while running at this minimum rate be dumped in the oceans or returned to the original mixture; and (3) that the United States state its willingness to have the disposition of its present stockpile of bombs considered as an item to be negotiated with other governments.[6]

The editor of the Oak Ridge Engineers and Scientists' newsletter found it "strangely disturbing" that sane and responsible men were daring to face a fundamental problem and carry through to a logical conclusion.[7] The conclusion was less strikingly logical, however, to most readers of the letter, for by coincidence it was printed on the day the Canadian spy scare broke; good faith and confidence sank to a very low ebb, and even the control-minded FAS leaders did not see fit to support so self-denying a policy. Nor did they come out in favor of the related proposal for a moratorium on industrial atomic power, which, in view of the relative ease with which fissionable materials could be converted from a power source to bombs, seemed to provide one answer to an extremely ticklish inspection problem. An unsigned editorial, written by Eugene Rabinowitch for the second issue of the *Chicago Bulletin*, pointed in this direction:

An ideal control system would be one which operates successfully even when all countries are permitted to build large power plants and other installations containing more fissionable material [than] is required to produce one or more bombs. The controls would probably be much simpler, and the security afforded the people of all nations much greater, were industrial developments limited, at least temporarily, to the production of radioactive elements. Many scientists believe that this will not be too great a price to pay for security against atomic warfare. The question of technical feasibility may thus involve a decision to postpone the benefits accruing from large scale industrial use of atomic energy.[8]

6 *New York Times*, February 16, 1946, p. 12; dated February 13, 1946, the letter was signed by L. C. Dunn (sociology), Irwin Edman (philosophy), A. P. Evans (history), Selig Hecht (biophysics), P. C. Jessup (public law), R. M. McIver (sociology), Edgar Miller (biochemistry), F. C. Mills (economics), George B. Pegram (dean of the graduate facilities), I. I. Rabi (physics), Jan Schilt (astronomy), and C. S. Shoup (economics).

7 Atomic Engineer and Scientist (newsletter), II (March 2, 1946), AORES XX, 3.

8 "Technical Feasibility of Atomic Energy Controls," *Bulletin of the Atomic Scientists*, I (December 24, 1945), [1].

Economists in the University of Chicago's Office of Enquiry into the Social Aspects of Atomic Energy were currently studying probable costs of atomic power, and the results would show, said Rabinowitch, whether such postponement would entail great sacrifice. The unofficial control scheme on which Rabinowitch shortly began to collaborate with Professor Quincy Wright suggested such a moratorium. The proposal did not produce much reaction in the spring of 1946, when even normally conservative officials and political scientists were inclined to think daringly, but a year later the idea of a power moratorium was attacked as communist-inspired.[9]

Federation scientists also refused to consider seriously the various formulas—Stassen's, for example—for a quick transfer of bombs to an international authority. Oppenheimer, it will be remembered, had reprimanded a fellow witness at October hearings for implying that atomic bombs could be used as police weapons, and scientists tended more and more to share his view as they considered the chain of events that such use might precipitate. They did not yet use the word escalation, but fear of the phenomenon, both physical and psychological, was real enough. Urey's statement of November, 1945, has needed no modification: "The danger to peace," he said, "lies not so much in a nation making deliberate preparations for world conquest by atomic weapons, as in all nations drifting toward an atomic war which nobody wants, in the wake of an armament race."[10]

The most widely appealing of the panaceas with which the FAS refused officially to fall in line was a campaign for immediate establishment of world government. The site organizations were given every encouragement to listen to the various proposals, and no objection was raised to individual adherence to them, but when, just as the UNAEC was being set up in London, the Clinton Labs group announced, through Americans United for World Organization, that the only real solution to the problem of the bomb was world government, considerable dismay was registered in the Washington office. It was quickly made clear that statements using the name of the federation did not go further than control under the United Nations. Some of the federation's most effective outside support came from individuals active

---

[9] For later discussions of a power moratorium, see Cuthbert Daniel and Arthur M. Squires, "The International Control of Safe Atomic Energy," *Bulletin of the Atomic Scientists*, III (April–May, 1947), 111–16, 135; and David F. Cavers, "Atomic Power versus World Security," *Bulletin of the Atomic Scientists*, III (October, 1947), 283–88, 302.

[10] Urey to the editor, *New York Herald Tribune*, November 19, 1945.

in the world government movement, such as Norman Cousins, Rachel Bell, and Raymond Swing; cordial relations were maintained, and observers at meetings and advice were freely exchanged, but anything approaching formal affiliation was avoided.

At the other extreme of policies that scientists did *not* accept was the possibility of preventive war to take advantage of the temporary monopoly of atomic weapons. It was referred to in federation circles only as one of the excesses of which military zeal might be capable rather than as an even remote alternative.

2. THE LILIENTHAL PLAN

While the Benedict committee was studying inspection techniques and the Lilienthal board was considering the over-all control problem, a few scientists in New York and Chicago were acting as consultants on unofficial control schemes. One of these was developing under the auspices of the Carnegie Endowment for International Peace with the guidance of political scientists James Shotwell and the Committee to Study the Organization of the Peace, the research branch of the American Association for the United Nations. To give stature to the Carnegie project a high-level atomic energy committee of twenty-five members was appointed, which included Harold Stassen, Sumner Welles, Judge Manley O. Hudson, and James B. Conant, but the effective working group was made up of Shotwell and other political scientists, technical experts, and a legal subcommittee, which drafted a plan during the early months of 1946. Back in October Shotwell had gathered a group of Project scientists for control discussions at Columbia, and a month later, shortly after the Truman-Attlee-King conference, he met in Washington with Urey, Szilard, and the current federation delegates; the following day they all conferred with State Department officials, who were then preparing for the Moscow conference.

Further exchange of ideas with physical scientists took place at a Carnegie-sponsored conference in New York on January 4 and 5, 1946, in conjunction with American Physical Society and FAS council meetings. Scientists who took part were Clarke Williams of the SAM Lab and its director, R. H. Crist, Manson Benedict of Kellex, who would shortly head the inspection study, Eugene Rabinowitch and Thorfin Hogness of Chicago, and John A. Wheeler of Princeton. Columbia geologist Paul F. Kerr presented results of a study indicating that inspection of ores at the mine was technically feasible; outright ownership of mines by an international authority was also considered. The difficulties of detecting illegal diversion of material in well-established plants was discussed at some length. The conclusions offered were tentative and of interest chiefly as showing the level at which scientists and political planners were communicating. Much conference time was spent on reports of Russian and European attitudes, the structure of the United Nations, and international angles of the control problem.[11]

The link between the Carnegie group and the FAS was maintained by SAM Lab scientists, principally Irving Kaplan and Clarke Williams, who wrote for the Carnegie atomic energy committee an unclassified report on the feasibility of inspection. Kaplan served for a time as secretary because the political scientists had such trouble with technical terms. The scientists, he recalls, thought the political scientists too cautious, and they in turn thought the scientists' ideas lacked political realism.

The Carnegie committee produced a progress report in April and a draft convention in June, 1946. Compared with the Acheson-Lilienthal Report, which had appeared in the meantime, its recommendations were conservative, allowing national governments to operate atomic energy establishments subject to quotas and to inspection by an international commission under UN auspices; atomic weapons could be manufactured and used subject to the authority of the UN Security Council. Scientists did not have a decisive voice in the final version; it was not considered satisfactory either by the young federation men or by their senior advisers, and fear was expressed lest its influential backing might make it a serious rival to the more imaginative State Department proposal.[12]

In Chicago ASC members, in particular Eugene Rabinowitch, worked on another proposal with Professor Quincy Wright, eminent authority on international law, and with the university's Office of Enquiry into the Social Aspects of Atomic Energy. The resulting "Draft for a Convention on Atomic Energy," completed in April, 1946, also provided for a control authority under the United Nations, with three separate commissions: an atomic energy commission for political

---

[11] Carnegie conference material in ASC II; reported in *Bulletin of the Atomic Scientists*, I (January 10, 1946), [6].

[12] Carnegie Endowment for International Peace, atomic energy committee progress report, April 5, 1946, ASC XXII, 1; interview with Kaplan, April 3, 1962; related correspondence in FAS VI, 2, and FAS XIII, 2.

planning; an inspection commission to police national activities, associated perhaps with the World Court; and an administrative commission with authority to own and operate mining and production facilities and to sponsor research. The draft recommended a five-year moratorium on large-scale production of fissionable materials, with existing facilities maintained in stand-by condition; if after five years the world situation seemed to warrant termination of the moratorium, the development of industrial atomic power would then be supervised by the administrative commission. The draft also proposed that individuals be responsible for violations to an international court of law.[13]

But despite their eminent sponsorship, in the end the Chicago draft and the Carnegie plan were to serve as yardsticks rather than as serious competitors to what was essentially the scientists' plan evolving under the aegis of the State Department. "Guys like Finney [a reporter for Cowles publications] say there wouldn't have been any Lilienthal report but for us," Higinbotham later wrote to revive the flagging spirits of an associate.[14] In a general sense this was probably true, for it was the federation scientists who had given wide currency to the concept of international control and had then pressed hard for studies of inspection and for collaboration of experts at a high level of planning. But there is no evidence that they had specifically demanded the appointment of an official drafting committee to prepare a United States position for negotiation in the UNAEC.

Insofar as records are a reliable guide in an area where there was much informal passing on of suggestions, the initiative in proposing an official study committee seems to have been taken by Vannevar Bush. Prompted by Carroll Wilson, his executive assistant at OSRD, who had helped prepare for the Moscow talks, Bush early in January urged Secretary Byrnes to appoint a committee to study outstanding questions—the release of information in planned stages, inspection techniques, and United States technical strength. Byrnes seems to have responded the more willingly to Bush's suggestion because a State Department committee would help the executive keep the initiative in the field of international control, which was threatened with invasion both by the Senate guardians of foreign policy and by

---

[13] Preliminary version of Chicago draft, *Bulletin of the Atomic Scientists*, I (April 1, 1946), 11–13; for summaries of the Carnegie and Chicago proposals, see *Minutes to Midnight*, ed. E. Rabinowitch ("Atomic Science and Education Series," No. 1; Chicago: *Bulletin of the Atomic Scientists*, 1950).

[14] Higinbotham to Robert Wilson, January 15, 1947, FAS I, 8.

Chairman McMahon, who had announced post-Christmas Senate committee hearings on international aspects of atomic energy.[15]

On January 7 Secretary Byrnes announced the appointment of the State Department committee under the chairmanship of Undersecretary of State Dean Acheson; its other members were Bush, Conant, Groves, and John J. McCloy. This list of names caused no great jubilation in federation circles since they misunderstood Bush's and Conant's ideas on international control and thoroughly mistrusted Groves's, but they were delighted with the composition of the five-man board of consultants that the committee announced on January 23. Oak Ridge scientists had already sought out David Lilienthal, its chairman, for counsel on control problems; Chester I. Barnard, president of the New Jersey Bell Telephone Company had had recent experience in international co-operation with the United Nations Relief and Rehabilitation Administration; Harry A. Winne, vice-president in charge of engineering at General Electric, was regarded as Groves's appointee, though his attitude as a board member quickly dispelled prejudice; Charles A. Thomas, vice-president of Monsanto Chemical Company, was a highly respected chemist, widely and favorably known as co-ordinator of plutonium chemistry for the Manhattan Project; Oppenheimer's fervent pleas for international control had largely neutralized his unpopular support of the May-Johnson bill, and the admiration of Los Alamos for its wartime leader was spreading.

Meeting with this board of consultants on January 23, the Acheson committee gave it a free hand to determine the nature and scope of its report. Groves had opposed appointment of the board; he and Bush and Conant, he said, knew more about the problem than any panel that could be assembled, and he had access to all the scientific advice that was needed.[16] But he now promised the necessary information from the Manhattan Project, especially the co-operation of the committee he had just appointed to study the feasibility of inspection. This diversion of the study originally intended for the McMahon committee seems to have been agreeable to its federation sponsors since they let it pass without comment.

Six weeks of concentrated effort went into the board's consideration of how to control atomic energy. "The consultants talked atomic

---

15 *The New World*, pp. 531–32.
16 Leslie R. Groves, *Now It Can Be Told* (New York: Harper & Bros., 1962), p. 411.

energy in offices, in Pullman compartments, and aloft in an Army plane," wrote Daniel Lang in his *New Yorker* article entitled "Seven Men on a Problem." "Sometimes they deliberated for as long as eighteen hours in a day. They ate and slept and wrangled late at night in places that weren't home to any of them, and then, as soon as they rose in the morning, they would meet again at the breakfast table and resume their marathon discussion."[17]

Lang, drawing on contemporary interviews with participants, and the AEC historians, on the basis of the board's records, both portray a remarkable exercise in collective thinking and formulation, to which Carroll Wilson of Bush's staff, who served as secretary, and Herbert Marks, secretary to the Acheson committee, also made significant contributions. By March 7 the board had a tentative report for the Acheson committee. A conference on that day and the following one was generally encouraging, but a few thorny questions were raised by committee members, and the board spent a final week of hard labor trying to resolve them. When the two groups met again on March 16 and 17 the principal difference of opinion related to a schedule for turning over information to an international authority. Bush wanted the timing, Groves the steps, specified in advance, whereas other members of the committee and the board were anxious to keep things flexible. Bush agreed to compromise statements that a schedule was feasible and that all information should not be released at once, and in forwarding the report to Secretary Byrnes on March 17 the Acheson committee gave it full support: "We lay the report before you as the Board has submitted it to us 'not as a final plan, but as a place to begin, a foundation on which to build.' In our opinion it furnishes the most constructive analysis of the question of international control we have seen and a definitely hopeful approach to a solution of the entire problem."[18]

The board had begun with the commitment of the UN Assembly to establish a system of international control primarily concerned with developing atomic energy for peace, not for war, and to this end it proposed that an atomic development authority should be set up as a subsidiary of the United Nations with powers "to own and lease property and to carry on mining, manufacturing, research, licens-

[17] Daniel Lang, "Seven Men on a Problem," *New Yorker*, XXII (August 17, 1946), 49; see also *The New World*, pp. 534 ff.
[18] *A Report on the International Control of Atomic Energy*, Department of State Publication No. 2498 (Washington D.C.: Government Printing Office, March 16, 1946), p. viii.

ing, inspecting, selling, or any other necessary operations." In its search for ways to eliminate international rivalry, the Board reached two conclusions: "(*a*) that only if the dangerous aspects of atomic energy are taken out of national hands ... is there any reasonable prospect of devising safeguards against the use of atomic energy for bombs, and (*b*) only if the international agency was engaged in development and operation could it possibly discharge adequately its functions as a safeguarder of the world's future."[19] This distinction between dangerous and safe activities was central to the scheme they proposed. Dangerous ones—the control of raw materials, the construction and operation of production plants, the conduct of research in explosives—would be the exclusive province of the atomic development authority, research, apart from that on explosives, and the construction and operation of "non-dangerous power producing piles" would be left to individual nations under moderate atomic development authority controls.

The board's second conclusion, that the atomic development authority should have powers of development and operation, stemmed from its thinking about inspection. Starting from the generally held assumption that an uninspected agreement not to use atomic weapons placed too great a burden on international good faith, the consultants had gone on to consider the dilemma presented by the close relationship between the processes required to produce atomic energy for industrial power and for bombs, namely, whether to sacrifice most of the beneficial applications to insure against secret diversion to weapons or to adopt a cumbersome system of inspection. Acknowledging a great debt to the uniquely qualified group of experts currently studying inspection under Benedict's chairmanship, the report declared:

As a result of our work with this Committee, we are clear: That every stage in the activity, leading from raw materials to weapon, needs some sort of control, and that this must be exercised on all of the various paths that may lead from one to the other; that at no single point can *external* control of an operation be sufficiently reliable to be an adequate sole safeguard; that there is need for a very extensive and technically highly qualified and varied staff if the job is to be done at all; that the controlling agency must itself be active in research and development, and well informed on what is an essentially living art; and that, for effective control, the controlling organization must be as well and as thoroughly informed

---

[19] *Ibid.*, pp. 23–24.

about the operations as are the operators themselves. Finally—and this we regard as the decisive consideration—we believe that an examination of these and other necessary preconditions for a successful scheme of inspection will reveal that *they cannot be fulfilled in any organizational arrangements in which the only instrument of control is inspection.*[20]

Inspection must be supplemented, the board concluded, by more positive functions, not only so that the authority would know what was going on, but so that it could attract to its staff the kind of research men and administrators for whom merely negative police action would hold no appeal.

One technical point was to cause a stir in scientific circles. Picking up a suggestion in the Franck Report of the previous year, the board of consultants offered the possibility of denaturing fissionable material by the addition of an isotope of uranium, which would leave it still useful for producing power but ineffective for making bombs. The denaturing substance, it was believed, could be removed only by so complicated a process as to be readily detected.

By intention the report left much for later decision—a charter would specify organizational details; the exact line between dangerous and safe activities would need revision from time to time; such questions as compensation for material and plant turned over to the atomic development authority, the allocation of material, the location of dangerous installations would have to be determined according to political and strategic considerations. The stages by which the United States would turn over information were tentatively suggested, but the details in this area too were left for further study and negotiation.

No brief summary is a substitute for reading this particular report. It was not merely compiled; it was written with distinction and without taint of officialese. Skilful use of repetition and clarification suggested the hope of its authors that it would be widely read and understood. Its singular tone—at once rational and idealistic—reflected a duality in the professional milieu from which it sprang.

To trace the genesis of the ideas it contains, if indeed this could be done with meaningful precision is a job for a book, not a few pages, and one might even dismiss the attempt as contrary to the spirit in which the concept of international control had developed. The inspiration of Niels Bohr, the thesis of the Franck Report, and its elaboration by the federation scientists were important compo-

---

[20] *Ibid.,* p. 6.

nents,[21] though unrecognized at the time. Also unrecognized were Bush's ideas, shared over a long period with Conant; identification of them has, in fact, made some aspects of the Lilienthal proposal less original than they at first appeared. Benjamin Cohen, Herbert Marks, and others at the State Department had drawn on experience in international planning. Once the war ended much cross-fertilization among these various strains had taken place. Of the Lilienthal board, it was Oppenheimer who had been in closest touch with them all and who through his intimate connection with the final achievement of the bomb was most deeply committed in a personal way to finding a solution. Although his contribution was by no means minor, it now appears that to a degree rare in the annals of committees this group engaged in a co-operative venture of the mind to which all members contributed creatively and critically—Thomas from his wide experience in industrial research and the bomb project, Winne and Barnard as managers of large corporations and, in Barnard's case, as an administrator of UNRRA, and Lilienthal from his unique experience in the Tennessee Valley Authority. Much of the writing and revision were done by the board's two assistants, Marks and Wilson.

But if it is not reasonable to say that any one individual or group served as a source or channel for the proposals of the Lilienthal board, it would be a denial of the central purpose of this book not to show the relationship between its recommendations and what scientists had been trying to tell policy-makers and public for the past seven months.

Like all the manifestos of the scientists' movement, the Acheson-Lilienthal Report was pervaded by confidence in the beneficent powers of science and by the belief that its practitioners, accustomed to the unifying experience of a common intellectual adventure, could contribute significantly to a novel experiment in co-operation. It was based on the assumption, the importance of which its authors were careful to emphasize, that an apprehension of technical facts was the foundation of a sound plan. Applying these principles to the problem at hand, the report took over unchanged the Franck committee's technologically-based arguments, repeated in so many state-

---

[21] According to Oppenheimer, Bohr was never happy with the Acheson-Lilienthal Report because "it was not centered enough on the absolutely central theme of openness" (J. R. Oppenheimer, "Three Lectures on Niels Bohr and His Times," Part III: "The Atomic Nucleus" [unpublished manuscript], p. 14).

ments and speeches, of no defense, no monopoly, and the vast potential of atomic weapons for destructiveness and surprise. Carried over, too, was the familiar plea that the risk for the United States in turning over information to an international agency was negligible compared with that attending the only foreseeable alternative—a nuclear arms race. Nor was it a new idea that the close interrelation between the techniques of bomb and power production made a mere ban on atomic weapons impractical, dependent as this would be upon comprehensive yet detailed inspection.

The Federation of Atomic Scientists' December 10 memorandum on inspection and control, the earliest unclassified statement on what scientists were thinking at so specific a level, is a record—probably not a primary source—of ideas that went into the Acheson-Lilienthal Report. It had stressed the importance of supplying the international negotiators with adequate information on which to base decisions. It had indicated as precisely as an unclassified document could do the processes upon which continuous and detailed checking was necessary—the germ, though not the explicit statement, of the board's distinction between dangerous and safe activities. And it contained the germ of the other essential Acheson-Lilienthal Report feature, the developmental function of the atomic development authority, in the statement that an international authority must engage in continuing research so that inspection procedures should not become obsolete.

As the report freely acknowledged, the board of consultants had been in frequent touch with Groves's technical committee on inspection and control, which was working concurrently in the Kellex offices in New York. Its chairman, Manson Benedict, had sessions with Oppenheimer in Washington, and at least once the board sent an emissary to New York for consultations. The report did not refer, however, to the part played in the establishment of this commission by the demands of the federation or the existence of its preliminary studies. The work of two other official committees of scientists was mentioned. One was the outline of peaceful applications of atomic energy (based in turn on earlier wartime studies) made in the early autumn of 1945 by the Interim Committee's scientific panel;[22] the

---

[22] Panel members were A. H. Compton, E. Fermi, E. O. Lawrence, and J. R. Oppenheimer; their consultants in this study included S. K. Allison, Zay Jeffries, C. C. Lauretsen, I. I. Rabi, C. A. Thomas, and H. C. Urey (*A Report on the International Control of Atomic Energy*, p. 18 n).

other was the declassification committee report of February 4, 1946, prepared by R. C. Tolman and his associates at the direction of General Groves.

Because the final report seemed so plainly to bear the imprint of Oppenheimer's mind and spirit and to contain so many of the ideas they had shared with him, his scientist colleagues have always credited him with the major responsibility for it. And indeed it was Oppenheimer, according to the board minutes, who visualized the international agency as a dynamic creative force and who formulated the affirmative emphasis upon development and research that gave the plan such wide appeal. But Oppenheimer would be the first to acknowledge that whatever he and his fellow scientist, C. A. Thomas, contributed to the board's thinking stemmed from the exchange of ideas with members of other advisory panels and from countless casual and unrecorded conversations at Chicago, Oak Ridge, and Los Alamos. The FAS office journal for these early weeks of 1946 shows that busy as he was Oppenheimer had time for numerous friendly chats with Higinbotham, through whom he learned what the younger federation men were saying. The scientists' grasp of technical realities, their happy experiences in international collaboration, and their strong compulsion to find solutions all left their mark upon the report, representing, as do so many advances in science itself, a joint contribution, in this case from the large segment of the scientific community that had taken to heart the lesson of the bomb.

It later turned out that scientists in Britain were thinking along very much the same lines. At the February conference in London, it had been agreed that British and American scientists should both prepare statements for the UNAEC. The FAS found its task taken care of by the Benedict and Acheson committees, but the British Atomic Scientists Committee had already completed their study when they received the Acheson-Lilienthal Report, containing, they observed with satisfaction, all the control features that they considered most essential plus the unique emphasis on research and development. Of this the British committee heartily approved, and the statement that it forwarded to the UNAEC in May consisted of its original proposals supplemented by comments on and a strong endorsement of the Acheson-Lilienthal Report.[23]

---

[23] "Memo to the UN Atomic Energy Commission from the Atomic Scientists Committee of Great Britain," *Bulletin of the Atomic Scientists*, I (June 1, 1946), 6–8.

3. THE UNITED STATES POSITION

In order not to circumscribe the action of the as yet undesignated United States representative to the UNAEC, the Acheson committee recommended the report to Secretary of State Byrnes for consideration rather than adoption. Most of the members opposed its immediate publication, but Acheson and the board of consultants believed the report should be released so that public reaction could be a guide to how far official policy should go. The decision was left to Byrnes, who, taking Acheson's advice, decided to make it public as soon as key officials had seen it. On March 21 it went to the President and the secretaries of war and navy, and on Monday, March 25, Acheson discussed it with members of the Senate committee and gave them copies. That afternoon a leak occurred, and summaries of the report appeared in the press next day although it was not released officially by the State Department until March 28.

The public reaction that Acheson had sought to stimulate was in general a highly favorable one, though at one extreme there was editorial clamor against giving away secrets and at the other dismissal of the plan as admirable but visionary. Letters and telegrams were still pouring into Washington offices protesting Vandenberg's military liaison amendment, and the National Committee on Atomic Information and the National Committee for Civilian Control of Atomic Energy, which had precipitated this avalanche, immediately tried to launch a similar demonstration on behalf of the State Department report, running off copies and summaries and distributing them widely to individuals and organizations.

For the scientists in the federation, the State Department proposals exceeded anything they had hoped for from an official report, especially one bearing the signature of Bush or Groves. Coming at a time when they were faced with drastic changes in the original McMahon bill, the international control proposal gave an enormous lift to their spirits. "For the first time since the end of the war," Higinbotham later recalled, "we began to feel hopeful. We clasped the new bible in our hands and went out to ring doorbells."[24] No scientist was so rash as to express unalloyed hope—"I should not want to have said anything that sounded cheerful." Oppenheimer told a Cornell audience when he discussed the report a few weeks later. But

---

[24] Higinbotham to FAS administrative committee, July 14, 1947, in Rush's files.

the site organizations, which had "viewed with alarm" on so many occasions in the past months, did not try to hide their enthusiasm and their relief. Calling the report an act of statesmanship, Chicago warned that concern for short-term security should not obscure long-term dangers. The Oak Ridge Engineers and Scientists urged a skeptical approach to the question of denaturing; otherwise ORES considered the proposal, so far as it went, technically workable but questioned whether its political assumptions were as sound as its technical ones.[25]

Gathering in local reactions, the Washington office issued a release on April 11 proclaiming the overwhelming support that the State Department proposal was receiving from American scientists. Many had been worried, declared an FAS administrative committee statement, by the political rather than the technical drawbacks to inspection and were reassured by the manner in which the report linked inspection to the development of peaceful uses.

Permitting national rivalries in this field while still fearing secret development of bombs is a negative answer based essentially on fear. The Acheson Report proposals on the other hand are positive, affirmative, and constructive. They seem to be based on the belief that hope can be as compelling a motive as fear. We may say that so far as atomic energy is concerned, fear of its power is the beginning of *wisdom*. But only hope and faith in man's future can be the beginning of *action*.[26]

Hailing the report as the first step toward preventing atomic war, the *Bulletin of the Atomic Scientists* presented some of the individual opinions that had helped to shape this collective approval. Edward Teller considered the proposal the "first ray of hope that the problem of international control can, actually, be solved." Teller listed five technical "facts or assumptions" made by the framers of the report. He thought those relating to the adequacy of present knowledge and to the possibilities of inspection and control and the immediate conclusions drawn from them were well founded; none were absolutely certain, but "no progress could be made in the difficult question of international control if only foolproof arguments were admitted." But Teller had reservations about two of the report's technical assumptions: he thought the statement about denaturing was too optimistic

[25] ASC executive committee minutes, April 3, 1946, ASC VI, 12; ORES statement on the Acheson report, April 16, 1946, FAS XXI, 2.

[26] FAS press release, April 11, 1946, FAS XVII, 1; *Bulletin of the Atomic Scientists*, I (April 15, 1946), 12.

since it could only impede, not prevent, the use of materials for bombs; and the statement that another nation could catch up in a year, if given theoretical information, he considered too definite. If a competitor did not draw the same conclusions from the theoretical knowledge that Manhattan Project scientists had done, it might take more time; if, unknown to us, they already possessed certain pieces of information, it might take less.[27]

Harold Urey was delighted with the report; after all the talk about keeping the secret, it was like waking from a bad nightmare to see the emphasis on positive objectives. But Urey, too, thought denaturing had been overemphasized. The report did not solve the essential problem, the control of dangerous materials, but this was a job for the United Nations. At present, short of war, the UN had no means of enforcing control, but Urey was hopeful that this shortcoming might be surmounted.[28]

The skepticism about denaturing was so widely expressed among scientists that General Groves appointed a committee of Manhattan Project leaders, including Oppenheimer, who immediately turned in a reappraisal. It did not reject the Acheson-Lilienthal conclusion but explained and cautioned. If plants for reprocessing denatured material had to be built, it would take several years to produce enough material for a significant number of bombs, but without "reasonable assurance that such plants do not exist it would be unwise to rely on denaturing to insure an interval of as much as a year." The experts added that the denaturant had a different effect on the various atomic explosives, and research and experience were needed before precise estimates could be made. They concluded, however, that within the framework of the State Department proposal denaturing would play a helpful part. They also confirmed the board's assertion that there was no forseeable method of releasing atomic energy without uranium, though thorium could be used with it.[29]

In Washington members of the board of consultants and the Acheson committee freely confirmed for the press their support of the State Department plan, but other officials were notably silent. The

[27] Teller, "The State Department Report—a Ray of Hope," *Bulletin of the Atomic Scientists*, I (April 1, 1946), 11, 13.

[28] Urey's comment, *Bulletin of the Atomic Scientists*, I (April 1, 1946), 13.

[29] Signers of the denaturing report were: L. W. Alvarez, R. F. Bacher, M. Benedict, H. A. Bethe, A. H. Compton, Farrington Daniels, J. R. Oppenheimer, J. R. Ruhoff, G. T. Seaborg, S. H. Spedding, C. A. Thomas, W. H. Zinn (see *Bulletin of the Atomic Scientists*, I [April 15, 1946], 11).

federation (which frequently used the monthly recurrence of the Alamogordo test date to warn the public of the fatal passage of time) issued a statement on April 16 deploring the lack of discussion of the report at high government levels, although FAS spokesmen doubtless knew that the silence was related to the delicate situation that had arisen in connection with the appointment of Bernard Baruch as the United States delegate to the UNAEC.

Federation delegates had, of course, recognized the importance of this appointment, but in addition to their preoccupation with Mc-Mahon bill problems, they had faced the dilemma that if they urged the appointment of a scientist the choice would probably fall on one of the advisers whom they associated with the conservative information policies of the Manhattan Project. Deciding that a non-scientist might be safer—they had spoken among themselves of Lilienthal —they had let the matter ride.[30] Perhaps they also thought that the Acheson and Lilienthal groups would have a decisive voice; but it seems that on March 17, unbeknown to the Acheson committee and its consultants, who were busy conferring about final points in the report, Secretary of State Byrnes had obtained from Baruch his consent to serve as United States delegate, and on March 18 the White House announced that his name had been sent to the Senate for approval. The following week when Baruch read in the papers the unofficial versions of the Acheson-Lilienthal Report and references to the committee's strongly commendatory letter of transmission, he angrily concluded that he was to be handed a ready-made policy and requested that Senate action on his appointment be delayed while he obtained assurance from Byrnes and Truman that he would have some control over the position from which he was to negotiate. Apparently satisfied, Baruch allowed his confirmation to go through on April 5. But it was his anxiety about the status of the report that inhibited official discussion.

The FAS release of April 16 refrained from comment on Baruch's appointment, but it was no secret that he regarded publication of the State Department report as a tactical blunder, and federation scientists saw in this an ominous sign. In addition they were keenly disappointed in his choice of the advisers, whose names he had ready for reporters when the White House announced his appointment

---

[30] Kaplan for AMPS to Higinbotham, February 5, 1946, and Higinbotham to Kaplan, February 11, 1946, FAS VI, 1.

on March 18. Three of them were banking associates: John M. Hancock, Fred Searls, and Ferdinand Eberstadt; the fourth, Herbert Bayard Swope, was a journalist who for some years had headed the New York State Racing Commission. As possible scientific advisers, but not apparently to be included in the inner circle, Baruch mentioned Bush, Conant, and A. H. Compton. Even before they learned much about his opinions on specific issues, federation scientists among themselves were frank in expressing their dismay at the choice of champion.

Nor were they entirely alone. Senate supporters of the Acheson-Lilienthal Report tried to neutralize Baruch's reported hostility to it by a resolution "that negotiations within the United Nations be undertaken immediately upon the basis of the report to the end that its provisions be adopted. . . ." In the federation some groups wanted to endorse this resolution, but the FAS council, meeting in Pittsburgh on April 20 and 21, decided not to underwrite the Senate resolution but passed one of its own confirming earlier statements of support for the State Department plan and recommending that it be made the basis for the program of the United States representative rather than the basis for negotiations.[31]

Although resisting the temptation to tie Baruch's hands, federation scientists were determined to see that he got sound technical advice. The Association of New York Scientists in a resolution of March 27 had already conveyed its opinion to the Washington office that the scientists who had developed the bomb were inadequately represented among Baruch's advisers. Not only, said ANYS, were his first-string associates all financiers and industrialists, but the scientists mentioned by Baruch had been of the minority supporting the May-Johnson bill. ANYS recommended that two scientists who had opposed military control be added to the advisory group and that the scientist advisers be elevated to the top level.[32] ANYS left the disposition of this resolution to the FAS office, and it is not clear what use, if any, was made of it or how direct an influence the FAS had on Baruch's final selection of science advisers. The skill that its members had so recently demonstrated in mobilizing public opinion on the military liaison issue cannot have failed to impress those making the appointment, and the spirit, if not the letter, of the ANYS resolution was, in fact, carried out.

[31] FAS council minutes, April 20–21, 1946, FAS I, 3.
[32] ANYS resolution and Wolfe to Higinbotham, March 27, 1946, FAS VI, 2.

It now appears that Baruch had suggested to Byrnes that both the Acheson committee and its board of consultants continue in an advisory capacity. Groves and McCloy were willing, but Conant would have only limited time, and Bush was not interested in a subordinate position under Baruch's financial experts. The board of consultants unanimously declined because as official advisers they would be unable to express independent critical opinions. Baruch next considered a single science adviser. Bush, he learned, would be unacceptable both to the President and to McMahon. For several weeks Oppenheimer seemed the likely choice, but he had reservations both about Baruch's own appointment and about his other advisers, and Baruch himself began to see that he and Oppenheimer differed on some important points. On the advice of Conant and Groves (and quite likely of Oppenheimer, too) the choice fell upon Richard C. Tolman of California Institute of Technology, who had already headed a wartime study of the future of atomic energy and more recently the committee on declassification. Tolman accepted the job just before the middle of May.[33]

Among scientists Tolman's appointment was greeted with relief. Although he had been in the Project's inner councils, he bore none of the onus for unpopular policies and in his tours of duty as consultant, as in his earlier career as teacher and graduate dean at Cal Tech, he had acquired the confidence of many younger men. This soon seemed justified by the associates he chose. Those who served most prominently in this capacity in the coming months were Oppenheimer and Robert F. Bacher, former associate director at Los Alamos, who had recently served on the committees on declassification, on inspection and control, and on denaturing. Tolman also named A. H. Compton, Charles A. Thomas of the Lilienthal board, and Harold C. Urey, who with Oppenheimer provided a close link with federation scientists, as did Philip Morrison and Victor Weisskopf, who served as part-time consultants during the summer. Baruch's choice of military adviser, Major General Thomas F. Farrell, was also welcomed by the scientists who had come to know him as Groves's deputy in activities relating to delivery of bombs in the Pacific. That General Groves should represent the Joint Chiefs of Staff in Baruch's entourage seemed a natural if not a popular move.

That these appointments went so much the way federation scien-

---

[33] *The New World,* pp. 559–62.

tists wanted them to go can scarcely have been unrelated to the satisfactory relationship established with Baruch in late April and May by Albert Cahn, the young Met Lab mathematician who had been playing such an active role in the civilian control fight as a member of the *ad hoc* strategy committee and as executive secretary of the National Committee for Civilian Control of Atomic Energy. Cahn had learned a lot about the value of personal commendation in his earlier experience in Kansas City machine politics. During a phone call to Albert Lasker, retired advertising executive and supporter of the National Committee, Cahn mentioned Baruch's coolness to the Acheson proposal, and Lasker and Anna Rosenberg, then his guest in LaJolla, offered to arrange a meeting with Baruch.[34] After some discussion about suitable people to join Cahn in the first interview, Harold Urey and Philip Morrison were chosen, having both shown skill in impressing unpromising audiences. Cahn vividly remembers how, arriving first at the Baruch establishment on Fifth Avenue, he found Baruch standing on the sidewalk, his arm thrown fraternally around the shoulders of Billy Rose, the theatrical producer. Cahn was quickly sheltered under the other arm of the towering Baruch, and he remained a self-conscious member of this unlikely tableau when Urey and Morrison drove up a few minutes later.

Cahn, usually accompanied by one or two other federation scientists, saw a good deal of Baruch in the next few weeks. Often Morrison went along, for like most people Baruch was charmed by his lively mind and clear and vivid speech, but his interest cooled when he learned that Morrison had once had left-wing connections. Cahn himself established excellent rapport with Baruch and in the middle of May joined Tolman's staff while continuing as executive secretary of the civilian control committee.[35] The topics covered in these interviews are not a matter of record, at least on the FAS side, but once the question of scientific advisers was settled, they centered on whether Baruch would support the State Department proposal, especially that part of it so appealing to scientists, the powers of research and development it bestowed on the atomic development authority. The gap between Baruch's views and the Acheson-Lilienthal Report was

---

[34] Interview with Cahn, March 5, 1963; Cahn to Lasker, April 23, 1946, in Cahn's files.

[35] ASC executive committee minutes, May and June, 1946, ASC VI, 12, 13; Higinbotham to C. Williams, May 8, 1946, FAS VI, 2; interview with Higinbotham, October 18, 1961; interview with Cahn, March 5, 1963.

obvious, and those who returned from these conferences were consistently reported as discouraged and of the opinion that prospects would have been brighter with some other representation in the United Nations.

But they did not say so publicly. On other occasions the politically minded scientists had made angry outbursts their stock in trade; now they were very discreet. They left the talking to Oppenheimer, who, on May 14, in the last of six lectures at Cornell, explained with his usual eloquence why a development authority was to be preferred either to a purely regulatory agency or to one armed with a stock of atomic bombs for retaliatory purposes, and spoke with great feeling of the hope that co-operation in the control of atomic energy might serve as a pattern for other areas.[36]

Although Oppenheimer did not minimize the obstacles to international agreement, he tactfully ignored the struggle already shaping up behind the scenes between proponents of the State Department proposal and the United States delegate to the UNAEC.[37] At first things had gone smoothly. Byrnes and Truman had agreed that Baruch should be the one to announce United States policy when the UN negotiations opened, and Baruch and Acheson were in complete accord as to procedure, with Baruch's staff making the necessary further studies and drafting a statement for the UN Security Council. By the middle of May Baruch and his advisers had a good idea of how they thought the Acheson report should be modified or supplemented, and a conference with the Acheson committee and the board of consultants was held on May 17 and 18 at the Blair-Lee House in Washington. With Hancock in the chair, the consultants were asked if, on further consideration, they would now change any parts of the report. As summarized from the meeting notes by the authors of *The New World*, the replies were as follows:

Lilienthal would change nothing. Barnard said he would modify only Section IV; it implied too much holding back by the United States. Oppenheimer had more second thoughts than anyone else. Like Barnard, he thought Section IV came too close to saying, "This is what the United States wants to do." It might have been better to stress minimum steps to be taken in some certain order. But there were other things that might be improved. The section on denaturing had stimulated too much hope.

---

[36] J. Robert Oppenheimer, "The International Control of Atomic Energy," *Bulletin of the Atomic Scientists*, I (June 1, 1946), 1–5.

[37] For the detailed account on which the following summary is based, see *The New World*, pp. 562–74.

The report might have been more clear about the ownership or control of raw materials. Finally, it said nothing about the relation of the atomic development authority to the veto question (he was thinking of a veto on day-to-day operations, not punishment).[38]

But these exercises in self-criticism by the authors of the report were modest compared to the changes that Baruch and his advisers wished to make. Their general criticism of the State Department proposal related to the quality that most excited admiration in others—its flexibility. Much more should be specified in advance, said the Baruch supporters, noting in particular the absence of any provision for punishing violators of an international agreement. The report rested on the assumption that a year, more or less, would elapse between the seizure of the authority's installations by a nation bent on aggression and the point when it could mount a war with atomic weapons giving opportunity for arbitration and negotiation. Baruch and his friends thought this a hopelessly inadequate safeguard; outlawry and penalties must be provided. (The report did provide a penalty for violation, commented Oppenheimer, namely, war.) The Baruch solution was to abolish the UN Security Council veto, not merely on day-to-day operations but on all questions relating to atomic energy, so that a violator could not interfere with sanctions. The veto question was to be a crucial one.

Baruch also wanted an immediate world-wide survey of raw materials, but Acheson, Lilienthal, and others thought this would only alarm the Russians and arouse resistance before negotiations began. Baruch and his advisers did not want the development authority to have outright ownership of ores in the ground (federation scientists attributed this to private enterprise bias) but were prepared to rely more fully than the Lilienthal board upon licensing as a means of control; they, too, doubted the value of denaturing.

Behind these differences lay a commonly shared objective—peace and security—and a recognition that the ultimate aim was the abolition of war. But unhappily, there was also mutual suspicion. When it was suggested during ensuing discussions that the board of consultants be recalled to advise the State Department, Hancock objected because, he said, it was difficult to confine scientists to technical questions and in politics and negotiations they were too inelastic.[39] In scientists' circles the criticism of Baruch that cropped up more

[38] *The New World*, p. 564 (parentheses as given).
[39] *The New World*, p. 568.

often than any other throughout his tenure as United States delegate was his rigidity.

It is interesting to observe that the federation scientists, so quick to detect military influence on the domestic front, did not at any point suggest that it was responsible for the stiffening of the United States position in the UN negotiations, which they were shortly to deplore. Here they were on firm ground, though whether they knew it is another matter, for it appears that until Baruch himself took the initiative on May 24 the Joint Chiefs of Staff had not been consulted about the United States position in the forthcoming negotiations. General Spaatz, General Eisenhower, and Admiral Nimitz were in general accord with what Baruch intended to propose, though they expressed varying opinions on the nature or usefulness of penalties. What the chiefs had to say, comment the AEC historians, was less interesting than

their apparent isolation from the process of decision making. Far from dictating policy, they had some difficulty in discovering what policy was. Though Baruch sought out the opinions of Eisenhower and his colleagues, though he unquestionably had a sure sense of where they stood, neither he, nor Byrnes, nor the President, waited on their views. Eisenhower did not finish his statement until the very day Baruch formally announced American policy.[40]

The opening session of the UNAEC was set for June 14. In the four weeks that remained after the Blair-Lee House meeting, conferences were held and drafts of a United States position exchanged between Baruch and Acheson, with Hancock and Marks as their principal collaborators. Toward the end of May Baruch agreed that the Acheson proposal should be his point of departure, but no progress was made in reconciling differences on penalties, the veto, ownership of ores, and licensing. Baruch continued to feel constrained by the widespread tendency at home and abroad to regard the State Department report as official policy, and it was only a few days before he was to go before the UNAEC that he received really satisfactory assurances that the President approved his stand on penalties and the veto and that he would give Baruch a decisive voice in policy as negotiations proceeded. This assurance meant that where they differed it would be Baruch's views, not those of the Acheson group, that would be offered to the UNAEC. On June 12 Baruch testified before the Senate special committee, whose own investigation of

---

[40] *The New World*, pp. 575–76.

international control had been several times postponed at State Department request, and received its approval of what he intended to say.

In these final preparations even the scientists on the Acheson committee and the Lilienthal board seem to have played a minor role and those outside the inner circle none at all. But through Albert Cahn the federation had continued to make representations to Baruch. On May 16 Cahn consulted Higinbotham about a conference of scientists, sponsored by the FAS or the University of Chicago, to get Baruch to say what he wanted, but the course adopted was to request the FAS and its member associations to submit their views in writing. In doing so Tolman asked that these not be made public since circulation of divergent opinions could only embarrass the United States negotiator.[41] A cynic might wonder if this move was not designed to keep the rebellious scientists quiet, but it showed at any rate that the error of the previous autumn, when official advisers had proved to be out of step with general scientific opinion on the May-Johnson bill, was not to be repeated. There would be no excuse for another uprising on the ground that this wider opinion was being ignored.

For the FAS Higinbotham, Rush, and Melba Phillips immediately replied with a strong endorsement of the Acheson-Lilienthal Report. The practical steps of control were political problems and must be negotiated, but they hoped that the United States would try to foster genuine co-operation, free from pressure for nationalistic advantage. The development of confidence in the technical field required the removal of censorship on pure science, and the UNAEC would need some technical know-how in order to plan; this might mean the concession of some immediate military advantage on our part but not much, in view of the present United States monopoly of plants.[42]

The site groups did not respond as promptly, and Higinbotham and Rush sent them a reminder on June 7, accompanied by cautionary words urging patience and good will. The meeting of the UNAEC a week hence would provide both an opportunity and a responsibility in public relations. We cannot keep quiet, they advised, but we must be very careful what we say, make our criticisms constructive, and display a sympathetic attitude toward our own delegation.[43]

---

[41] Phillips to all associations, May 23, 1946, in *Bulletin of the Atomic Scientists* files.
[42] Higinbotham, Rush, and Phillips to Baruch, May 15, 1946, FAS XXII, 1.
[43] Higinbotham and Rush to all associations, June 7, 1946, AORES XVII, 9.

Comments from the Northern California and Cornell associations were already on the way. The Cornell scientists concentrated on six points on which they had learned that Baruch's opinions differed from their own. "Dangerous" activities, said the Cornell memorandum, must not be left to national or private enterprise, even under licensing; the constructive activities of the atomic development authority were vitally important; the control of atomic energy was a significant step toward world peace; the United States must be ready to compromise on the speed with which we relinquished our special position; and the United States delegation should avoid nationalistic positions on related economic and political questions.[44]

The communication to Tolman from the Association of Los Alamos Scientists was in the same sense and in the same tone, a more deferential one than a curt summary implies. It was not a question of whether, but when, our monopoly would expire, said the ALAS memorandum, and in the transition stage it was important that the United States representative display initiative and flexibility, beginning, for example, with discussion of control of uranium sources. "Nothing," it declared, "could be more damaging to the advantages of our present position than a 'take it or leave it' attitude toward specific American proposals." The continued production of bombs, said ALAS, was much discussed by scientists, though with sharp disagreements. The advantages of stockpiling were largely illusory; the question could not be isolated from continued production of fissionable materials. But

no single act can so dramatically establish the seriousness of our aims in the field of international control as the cessation of bomb production. We do not attempt to say at what stage this act should be taken; but we deplore the lack of political insight and seriousness implied in the view that it should be taken only after the success of international control is in some absolute sense "guaranteed."[45]

Federation scientists did not publicly discuss a moratorium on atomic weapons during the summer of 1946. As the ALAS statement suggested, they could not have reached agreement. But they were clearly interested in the several forms that it might take from

[44] S. H. Bauer, H. A. Bethe, and R. S. Rochlin for the Cornell association to R. C. Tolman, June 4, 1946, and Rochlin to Higinbotham, June 5, 1946, FAS VIII, 3; memorandum from Northern California association to Tolman, June 4, 1946, FAS XXIV, 4.
[45] D. Flanders for ALAS to Tolman, June 11, 1946, ALAS V, 5.

the extreme measure of destroying existing stockpiles of fissionable materials and bombs, through the intermediate one of fixing the status quo by halting the production of bombs and fissionable materials (as the Columbia University professors had suggested back in February), to the less drastic decision not to assemble any more bombs. Lack of unanimity on this point among scientists was a large straw in the wind. Just before the Oak Ridge organizations merged in June, the world government committee of the Oak Ridge Engineers and Scientists circulated to other associations a proposal that included destruction of bombs and was met by ALAS with arguments straight out of the Acheson report: *de facto* equality in atomic energy would not be achieved by lowering the potential of the United States; nor would a mere policing of dangerous activities be enough; military applications could be controlled only to the extent that peaceful uses were vigorously pushed. The Philadelphia association, with many medical and biological research people among its three hundred and more members and few "atomic" scientists, was more dogmatic and on June 5 prepared letters to the President and other officials containing a resolution that "the manufacture of fissionable materials for war purposes be discontinued and all stocks of such material on hand be denatured immediately."[46]

Two comments from individual scientists appeared while Baruch and Acheson were working over the United States proposal, one by David Inglis, the other by Edward Teller. At Los Alamos they had often hiked and skied together; in June, 1946, both warmly supported the Acheson proposal, but their comments were perhaps prophetic of their later diametrically opposite views on a test ban, since Teller's aimed at strengthening controls whereas, Inglis indicated a willingness to take something on trust.

Teller's suggested amendment to the Acheson-Lilienthal Report contained a Szilardian gimmick—not by accident, perhaps, since these old friends were now fellow members of the University of Chicago faculty. To give the atomic development authority more concrete power Teller recommended that "every country be permitted to send to any country as many agents as it pleases." Chosen and paid by the country they represented, these agents would be responsible to the development authority and could freely inquire into any

---

[46] D. Hawkins to W. R. Kittredge, July 15, 1946, ALAS IV, 1; Philadelphia association to President Truman *et al.*, June 5, 1946, FAS VII, 5 (it is not certain that these letters were sent).

activity they considered inimical to their own country or to world peace. It would be the duty of every citizen to give information and he would be protected by world law. Under this system all secrecy would cease, but the United States would still have its production plants and—its most valuable secret—experience. The atmosphere of freedom would create confidence, said Teller, whereas the giving of information piecemeal, as provided in the Acheson report, would prolong the period of uneasiness and mutual suspicion.[47]

Inglis' remarks were essentially a plea for flexibility and ingenuity, foreshadowing the main theme of FAS comment on the negotiations in the months to come. Rephrasing a familiar text, Inglis said, "Many of us have come out of our war experience with a feeling of having shared in the process of doing the nearly impossible and are impatient with public thought which seems to be fettered by tradition and limited by the horizons of past experience." East and West had co-operated well enough when community of interest required the defeat of Germany, and community of interest was plainly indicated in controlling atomic energy. It was to be hoped that a statute of limitations could be devised within which an atomic development authority board of directors could act effectively by majority agreement. "Our present efforts should not be directed toward imagining monkey wrenches that others might want to throw in the machinery," concluded Inglis, "but rather toward influencing our representatives in the Atomic Energy Commission to approach their task in a spirit of sincerely cooperative study, and with a determination that the final result of the compromising must be an ADA that works."[48]

---

[47] Teller, "A Suggested Amendment to the Acheson Report," *Bulletin of the Atomic Scientists*, I (June 1, 1946), 5.

[48] Inglis, "The ADA and the Veto Power," *Bulletin of the Atomic Scientists*, I (June 1, 1946), 15.

CHAPTER 16

The Apogee
of Hope

BARUCH PRESENTED the American plan to the opening session of the UNAEC on June 14, 1946. On a note of apocalyptic foreboding that rivaled the scientists' own warnings, he addressed his fellow commission members and the citizens of the world:

> We are here to make a choice between the quick and the dead.
> That is our business.
> Behind the black portent of the new atomic age lies a hope which, seized upon with faith, can work our salvation. If we fail, then we have damned every man to be the slave of Fear. Let us not deceive ourselves: We must elect World Peace or World Destruction.
> Science has torn from nature a secret so vast in its potentialities that our minds cower from the terror it creates. Yet terror is not enough to inhibit the use of the atomic bomb....
> Science, which gave us this dread power, shows that it can be made a giant help to humanity, but science does not show us how to prevent its baleful use. So we have been appointed to obviate that peril by finding a meeting of the minds and the hearts of our peoples. Only in the will of mankind lies the answer.[1]

Declaring that this will could be made effective only by swift and sure punishment of violators of a control agreement, Baruch then outlined the essential features of the Acheson-Lilienthal Report.

---

[1] *International Control of Atomic Energy: Growth of a Policy.* Department of State Publication, No. 2702 (Washington, D.C.: Government Printing Office, n.d.), Appendix 13, pp. 138–47.

Scientists attached to the various delegations listened to Baruch with intense interest and with mixed reactions, which they shared next evening when the FAS and the New York association were hosts at a reception for foreign scientists at the American Physical Society's headquarters in New York. The majority thought Baruch's speech a good beginning, but Higinbotham, perhaps taking a pessimistic cue from Oppenheimer, was appalled that so many accepted the Baruch proposals without trying to understand them, some even prophesying agreement within a matter of days. The general good fellowship that pervaded the gathering, which included Soviet delegate Dmitri Skobeltsin, was at any rate a happy omen for those who regarded technical agreement as basic.

On June 19 Andrei Gromyko, without explicitly rejecting the American plan, offered a Soviet counterproposal—a pledge by participating nations not to use atomic weapons under any circumstances, to prohibit their production and stockpiling, and to destroy all stocks in whatever stage of production within three months. By June 25 the Baruch plan had been approved by nine of the twelve nations represented on the UNAEC. Russia and Poland supported the Soviet proposal; Holland did not commit herself. During the next three weeks the United States delegation submitted three explanatory memorandums. Gromyko, though requested by several delegates to be more explicit about the international convention he demanded, did little more than denounce the United States plan. He shifted his ground from time to time, but the main point of his attack was Baruch's proposal to abolish the veto.

This issue was complex and easily misunderstood by the public. The first step toward control was obtaining consent to an agreement, and there was no question about any nation's right to withhold it. The next stage would be implementation of a treaty involving decisions about day-to-day operations; on such questions Russia did not suggest applying the veto. It was in relation to the third stage, when parties to the treaty might wish to impose penalties on a violator, that Baruch had at once insisted on dropping the veto and Gromyko had as promptly declared it to be impossible. Disagreement over the veto blocked further progress in settling the relation of the development authority to the Security Council, but other aspects of the Baruch proposal were referred to the UNAEC's Committee 2, which in turn appointed a scientific and technical subcommittee to study inspection and control. Under the chairmanship of the Dutch physicist, H. A. Kramers, this group held its first meeting on July 19 with Tolman, Oppenheimer, and Bacher as the United States members.

Meanwhile other issues that could conceivably affect the outcome of the control talks were commanding public attention. On June 13, the day before Baruch's first speech at the United Nations, the McMahon bill had gone to the House Military Affairs Committee. The anxiety of scientists about what might happen to it there stemmed partly from their conviction that its passage in the form accepted by the Senate on June 1 would favorably affect the international control picture. Though less desirable from their point of view than the original, the Senate version still assured civilian control of domestic policy, relaxed some information restrictions, and granted priority in certain areas to a future international agreement. News from the Military Affairs Committee vied for scientists' attention with what was happening in the UNAEC.

At the same time many supporters of international control, scientists included, viewed with dismay the final preparations for the naval tests at Bikini, believing them to be a tragically inappropriate backdrop for the offer to share our knowledge of atomic energy, which Baruch was currently making. The federation staged a briefing session for newsmen at the home of Nat Finney of the *New York Times* to help them interpret what they would see and hear at Bikini, carefully choosing representatives likely to make a good impression. But the affair left a *Washington Daily News* reporter unconvinced and his dispatch from Honolulu on June 21 bitterly attacked the scientists for their cry-baby attitude toward the tests, which, he claimed, was spreading panic among crew members and rapidly draining the reservoir of good will they had commanded six months ago. On the other hand, Sam Shaffer, who had done the sympathetic *Newsweek* article on the atomic scientist delegates the previous November, phoned the FAS office when he got back from Bikini and said, "Call me Paul; I have seen the light." He had not really understood, he said, what his friends the scientists were talking about.[2]

On July 1 (on the far side of the date line) the United States dropped its fourth atomic bomb. Full-width headlines in the *New York Times* contained just the kind of reassuring news that critics of the tests had foretold: "Atom Bomb Exploded over Bikini Fleet;

[2] Jim G. Lucas, "Long Faces," *Washington Daily News*, June 21, 1946, p. 31; Amrine memorandum on Lucas' report, June 21, 1946, FAS II, 7.

2 Ships Are Sunk; 19 Damaged out of 73; Blast Force Seems Less Than Expected." *Times* reporter William L. Laurence, a witness of Alamogordo and Nagasaki, sent another vivid firsthand account, and related articles studded the back pages.[3] An FAS release repeated the refrain made familiar by earlier warnings that scientists "in the main . . . already know what the bomb will do. . . . The great crossroads before mankind is not whether navies can survive, but whether civilization can survive."[4] Federation scientists were not surprised when next day the ships sunk had risen to five, with thirty-one fired by the blast. K. T. Compton was quoted as saying that the damage was mounting, and a *Times* editorial urged caution in interpreting the results. A dispatch from CBS representative George Moorad sourly reported the imposition of censorship. The test had been unsatisfactory to the authorities, he claimed, adding cynically that the full story of the bomb damage would doubtless foster the impression that atomic power was nothing more radical than the refinement of TNT over Chinese gunpowder. Having seen Nagasaki, he believed this to be a wrong conclusion and that the test should be repeated under conditions of full public scrutiny.[5]

Censored or not, Bikini news filled the papers for days. Whereas some of it modified the early reports in the direction of greater damage, scientists feared that the first impression would remain in the public mind. Joe Rush, who saw a special showing of an official film in company with members of the McMahon committee and Commerce Department officials, reported the results to be about what scientists expected, that is, visually not very impressive but clearly not telling the whole story.[6]

The fears felt in federation circles about the effect of the tests on world opinion seemed fully justified when *Pravda* declared on July 3 that the Bikini tests had shattered faith in United States intentions, proving that she was interested in perfecting the weapon, not in restricting it. The Soviet Army's *Red Star* also referred scathingly to United States belligerence.[7] Comments from other nations, though made more in sorrow than in anger, were generally in the same vein.

Laymen had scarcely begun to make sense of the conflicting head-

[3] *New York Times*, July 1, 1946, p. 1.

[4] FAS press release, July 1, 1946, FAS XVII, 5, quoted in *New York Times* editorial, July 14, 1946, sec. E, p. 2.

[5] *New York Times*, July 2, 1946, pp. 1, 18, 19, 24.

[6] *Washington Post*, July 11, 1946, p. 3.

[7] Dispatches from Moscow in *New York Times*, July 4, 1946, p. 4; July 5, 1946, p. 3.

lines, dispatches, and special articles on the first Bikini test when the second, a slightly subsurface explosion, took place on July 25. After each test preliminary reports were issued by the President's evaluation commission and by the Joint Chiefs of Staff evaluation board. The two evaluations agreed that the tests had been admirably executed and were worth the effort and expense, but whereas the board reporting to the Joint Chiefs of Staff concluded that the national safety required further large-scale research and development, the President's commission drew from the tests the lesson that "if there is to be any security or safety in the world war must be eliminated."[8] These dual conclusions, around which scientific opinion would tend to polarize in the coming years, were strengthened by mounting evidence, especially after the second test, that widespread and persistent radioactivity would eventually have rendered "vessels within a mile of an atom bomb air burst . . . inoperative due to crew casualties." The observers for the Chiefs of Staff declared:

It is too soon to attempt an analysis of all of the implications of the Bikini tests. But it is not too soon to point to the necessity for immediate and intensive research into several unique problems posed by the atomic bomb. The poisoning of large volumes of water presents such a problem. Study must be given to procedures for protecting not only ships' crews but also the populations of cities against such radiological effects as were demonstrated in Bikini lagoon.

Critics of the tests could find no fault with the frankness of these conclusions but still doubted that they would circulate widely enough to counteract the first impression. And the dangers of radioactivity, emphasized publicly for the first time, did not immediately command widespread attention. William L. Laurence, whose vivid description of his third mushroom cloud on July 1 had prepared his readers for greater devastation, addressed himself a month later to the question of what the public had learned from the Bikini tests. In the view of scientists and others closely connected with the atomic bomb, said Laurence, it was far less important to evaluate the physical data obtained from the tests than to gauge their effect on the public attitude.

Considered from this point of view, the Bikini tests add up to a tragedy of errors for which the world may pay a heavy price unless measures are taken in time to counteract them.

---

[8] Excerpts in *Bulletin of the Atomic Scientists*, II (August 1, 1946), 26; see also W. A. Shurcliff, *Bombs at Bikini* (New York: Wm. H. Wise & Co., Inc., 1947), Appendixes 10 through 13.

On returning from Bikini, one is amazed to find the profound change in the public attitude toward the problem of the bomb.

Before Bikini the world stood in awe of this new cosmic force. . . . Since Bikini this feeling of awe has largely evaporated. . . . [The average citizen] had expected one bomb to sink the entire Bikini fleet, kill all the animals aboard, make a hole in the bottom of the ocean and create tidal waves that would be felt for thousands of miles. He had even been told that everyone participating in the test would die.

Since none of these happened, he is only too eager to conclude that the atomic bomb is, after all, just another weapon. As such it is a problem concerning only the military and nothing for the average citizen to be worried about.

Laurence was alarmed to think what a potential enemy must have learned from the tests about damage to ships and crews from blast, heat, and radiation and about the ten million tons of radioactive water that had turned even undamaged ships into radioactive stoves. An enemy had been given a good blueprint of how to decimate a fleet. He advised statesmen to keep these things in mind and to heed the scientists' warning that the only defense against the bomb was effective international control and elimination of war.[9]

The third test in the Bikini series was never held. Its indefinite postponement was announced on September 7, 1946, with the explanation that in view of the successful completion of the first two the Joint Chiefs of Staff believed the additional result would not be sufficient to justify it.[10]

After its July 1 release the FAS made no further comment on these events, having observed on other occasions that ideas were more effectively disseminated by a reputable journalist like Laurence. But some scientists still wonder whether historians of postwar diplomacy looking for more subtle springs of Soviet action may not underestimate the significance of Bikini in stiffening the Russian attitude at the very beginning of the control talks.

On June 22 and 23—a week after the opening session of the UNAEC and a week before the first Bikini test—the FAS council met in Chicago. The speeches of Baruch and Gromyko were discussed; even the purposes of a control agreement were to some extent reexamined. Delegates were exhorted to report fully to their associations and to encourage careful study of all proposals. The Federation's role,

---

[9] *New York Times*, August 4, 1946, p. 3; reprinted in *Bulletin of the Atomic Scientists*, II (September 1, 1946), 2.

[10] Shurcliff, *Bombs at Bikini*, pp. 205–6.

it was agreed, was to clarify and inform, but any statement that might magnify existing differences should be avoided and every effort made to promote the realization that present positions did not represent last-ditch stands. A continuing committee, with the New York association as a nucleus, was authorized to observe events at the United Nations and to supply technical information to reporters but not, insofar as it could be avoided, evaluation. The resolution embodying these points did not touch upon substantive questions relating to control.[11]

Aided by the *Bulletin of the Atomic Scientists*, which filled its pages with UNAEC reports and excerpts of speeches, the local associations heeded, in some measure at least, the council's behest and carried on discussions. The views dispatched to Tolman's office during the summer showed that interest revolved chiefly around the abolition of the veto, the adequacy of information given to the UNAEC, and actions, such as the Bikini tests or continued production of bombs, that seemed to make other countries doubtful about our pacific intentions. Many doubted the wisdom of Baruch's demand to abolish the veto, but this was an unequivocally political topic, and for the time being most scientists confined their strictures to regret that the question had been raised so soon. Their attitude about penalties at this period was later reconstructed by Eugene Rabinowitch:

At the bottom of the Acheson-Lilienthal plan lay the belief that participation in the common development of atomic energy for peaceful purposes would prove so advantageous to all nations—both from the point of view of national security and that of technological advancement—that they would have no inducement to break away. If this hope should fail, the authors of the Report expected only one advantage from the international control set up; that violations would not remain secret, and that "danger signals" would be raised in time for other nations to prepare for individual or collective security measures. The Acheson-Lilienthal Report recognized that the only reliable guarantee of continued adherence of all nations to the control convention would be the creation of a common vested interest in its success. In the eyes of many, Mr. Baruch's emphasis on sanctions brought a note of realism into the otherwise unrealistic Acheson-Lilienthal dream of world cooperation; but others believed, to the contrary, that reliance on sanctions (which could be imposed—except in the unlikely case of a small nation being the culprit—only through a major war) was a legalism divorced from reality. Mr. Baruch's answer to this criticism was that his provision would have made war against the violator nation a

[11] FAS council minutes, June 22–23, 1946, FAS I, 3; council resolution in *Bulletin of the Atomic Scientists*, II (July 1, 1946), 23.

"legal" war; but the practical importance of this point seemed doubtful to his critics.[12]

In retrospect Rabinowitch regarded the insistence on sanctions as the only significant change made by Baruch in the Acheson-Lilienthal Report. But, to judge by the summer memorandums to Tolman, even the veto was subordinate in the minds of FAS scientists to the question whether the United States was doing all it could to establish an atmosphere of confidence—whether, in fact, the United States delegation was not more concerned to allay the fears of congressmen and the American public than of those with whom we were negotiating. In the tactfully phrased comments submitted to Tolman the principal emphasis was on the need to release enough information to the UNAEC so that the technical advisers of other nations would feel confident they were not merely accepting a dictated control plan but were making sound decisions. In a second ALAS note to Tolman this necessary information was defined as (1) certain detailed basic scientific facts, (2) some idea as to the probable direction of future developments, and (3) the basis on which the distinction between dangerous and non-dangerous activities had been drawn in the American plan.[13]

And adequate information, thought most scientists, would not only create confidence; it would affect the end result. Study of the facts concerning atomic energy, claimed the State Department report, had inescapably driven the members of the Lilienthal board, despite their diverse backgrounds, to the same conclusions. In the same way some scientists fondly hoped, and others like Rabinowitch firmly believed, that, as he put it, Russian experts could not help arriving at the same diagnosis as their American and British colleagues.[14] It must be said once again that scientists were not recommending that anyone be told how to make an atomic bomb. As we have seen, they could not even agree that the United States should halt bomb production. But they were deeply troubled because—despite such lucid explanations as Ridenour's *Fortune* article of how secrecy often decreased security—many people in a position to influence decisions still did not seem to understand that where technical information was concerned secrecy and security were not synonomous.

[12] *Minutes to Midnight*, ed. E. Rabinowitch ("Atomic Science and Education Series," No. 1; Chicago: *Bulletin of the Atomic Scientists*, 1950), p. 47.

[13] D. Flanders to Tolman, June 26, 1946, FAS XXIV, 4.

[14] "A Victory and an Impending Crisis" (editorial), *Bulletin of the Atomic Scientists*, II (August 1, 1946), 24.

In private the local associations explored other preconditions for agreement. The attitude toward atomic energy, argued the executive committee of the Cornell association in a late August memorandum, could not be divorced from the tensions and conflicting aims in other areas of international relations; not only in the UNAEC but through such bellicose gestures as continued production of bombs, extension of military bases, development of long-range rockets, and the Bikini tests, the United States was showing far too little regard for the apprehensions of other nations, especially during the delicate transition period when it still had its atomic monopoly. The Cornell executive committee recommended agreement on the early abolition of atomic weapons from national armaments, halting our own preparations for warfare, making available to the UNAEC all necessary basic scientific data, and developing a more consistent foreign policy.[15]

The Cornell executive committee in this first draft was clearly overstepping the bounds within which scientists could speak from professional knowledge, and the statement it sent to Tolman, if still not strictly technical, was much more guarded, urging that the United States delegation should endeavor to clarify what it was willing to do and adopt every means to mitigate distrust. Before negotiating further on details of control and development, the UNAEC should agree on the abolition of atomic weapons from national armaments, and the United States should make available information for a *complete* discussion.[16] How or when atomic weapons should be eliminated even the less cautious Cornell memorandum did not presume to say. Scientists were continuing to talk about a moratorium as a means of lessening tension without reaching any consensus.

In formal FAS communications United States intransigence was referred to impersonally; in private Baruch was held chiefly responsible for it, and his attitude was attributed variously to pique at not having himself devised the Acheson plan and to a deepseated dislike of international ownership; his motives in introducing the veto issue so early were questioned. In other quarters Baruch's contribution was regarded more favorably. Bernhard Bechhoefer, a member of Baruch's staff and a chronicler of later arms control developments, credits Baruch with a genius for gauging and responding to currents of world opinion. "It was Baruch's decision," says Bechhoefer,

---

[15] Memorandum of the executive committee, Association of Scientists of Cornell University, August 29, 1946, FAS VIII, 3.

[16] Cornell association to Tolman, September 12, 1946, FAS VIII, 3.

that the United States, at the outset of the negotiations, should present a full plan providing answers for any anticipated questions rather than merely a framework for future negotiators. It was he who set the tone of almost religious fervor that prevented the negotiations from degenerating immediately into vituperative propaganda. Baruch could convincingly call on Americans, despite past isolationist sentiment, "to start freeing ourselves from the fetish of national sovereignty.[17]

August and early September were uneventful at the UNAEC. The scientific and technical committee was quietly preparing its report, which was awaited with intense interest by American scientists. The international control issue had proved a rallying point for some of the newer associations of the FAS and had brought recruits into the movement, but to some of the earliest enthusiasts for international control, the Soviet reaction seemed a sure prelude to failure, for it meant a delay in which atomic energy negotiations could be infused with all the old political tensions. John Simpson, who had been largely responsible for the Federation of Atomic Scientists' inspection studies, now concluded that a plateau had been reached and gradually reduced his FAS commitments. Others followed the lead of Higinbotham and Oppenheimer, who, though at times deeply discouraged, saw no alternative to continued support of the United Nations.

On September 17—nine days before the technical committee's report was ready—the federation's overt adherence to the Baruch proposal was tested with the publication of a letter that Henry A. Wallace had written to President Truman two months earlier criticizing the rigidity of the United States position as represented by Baruch and objecting to its step-by-step feature. Policies outside the UNAEC —the thirteen-billion-dollar army and navy budget, the Bikini tests, continued bomb production—Wallace said, must strike the world, especially Russia, as inconsistent with international control. This letter was the culmination of a long-standing difference between Wallace and majority opinion in the administration on the posture to be maintained toward Russia, and on September 20 he resigned as secretary of commerce.[18]

Though there is no evidence of direct communication, it is clear that some scientists shared some of Wallace's views: Teller had also

---

[17] Bechhoefer, *Postwar Negotiations for Arms Control* (Washington, D.C.: Brookings Institution, 1961), pp. 37–38.

[18] For an account of the Wallace episode and Baruch's part in it, see Richard G. Hewlett and Oscar E. Anderson, Jr., *The New World, 1939–1946* (University Park: Pennsylvania State University Press, 1962), pp. 597–606 (referred to hereinafter as *The New World*).

questioned the step-by-step procedure; and the Cornell group, and others as well, regarded United States policy as inconsistent. Wallace's letter and the questions it raised were foremost in the minds of delegates who assembled for the FAS council in New York City on Sunday and Monday, September 22 and 23, especially at the Sunday morning session, which was attended by foreign scientists associated with the UNAEC. The visitors included L. Kowarski, who had been at the Met Lab in Chicago during the war, and Frederic Joliot, both associated with the French delegation, P. M. S. Blackett of Manchester, and Captain Raymond Blackburn, Labour Member of Parliament and chairman of the parliamentary and scientific committee of the House of Commons. Of the scientists associated with the United States delegation, Oppenheimer and Urey were there, as well as Morrison and Cahn, both members of the FAS administrative committee.

Reporting on progress in the UNAEC, Oppenheimer pointed out that Wallace had made two substantial errors of fact, first, in supposing that the United States intended unilaterally to determine the timing of each stage of control and, second, in stating that the Russian proposals went further than the Baruch plan in punishing violators. Kowarski confirmed this statement of Wallace's factual errors, but he thought his over-all criticism of the United States position was justified. He admitted, however, that there was no assurance that a more conciliatory attitude on the part of the United States delegation would produce the desired results.[19]

Blackett thought it a mistake to try to separate atomic energy from other international problems, and other speakers agreed. Questions raised earlier by the local associations were explored. In regard to release of information—a matter of primary concern—Oppenheimer told the council that negotiations thus far had not been impeded by lack of it but that a control treaty could not be drafted on the basis of what was now available. The issue of a bomb moratorium elicited contradictory opinions, as it had in the association memorandums; Szilard thought that halting production might have been effective a year ago but would now seem a trivial gesture, whereas Joliot, whose Communist affiliation made his opinions, especially on this point, suspect to many American scientists, argued that to stop assembling bombs, though a minor part of the whole process, would greatly ease tensions and strengthen the moral position of the United States.

---

[19] FAS council minutes, September 22–23, 1946, FAS I, 4.

Much of this discussion would have taken place had there been no Wallace letter. There seemed to be little, if any, disposition to throw organized support behind him, whether because his statement of the case was extreme, because the issues were so manifestly political, or because the presence of foreign guests checked criticism of the United States position. What Rabinowitch took back to Chicago and included in the next *Bulletin*, along with the text of Wallace's letter, was the judgment that national unity was vitally important in the fight for international control. This did not mean, he said, that suggestions for amendment or even a new plan should not be welcomed. It meant that the only thing on which no bargaining was possible was the principle of effective international control. One reader protested that if scientists were to become merely another arm of nationalistic self-righteousness they would be relegated to their traditional position of makers of tools and become tools themselves; but in the site groups Wallace's letter was discussed with no more than a show of sympathetic interest. FAS leaders observed that Wallace had made a tactical error in publicly attacking Baruch without making sure that his attack had adequate support within the administration, and they profited by the lesson.[20]

On September 26, a few days after this meeting between federation and UNAEC scientists and while Baruch was still trying to repair the damage to his position caused by publication of the Wallace letter, the scientific and technical committee turned in its report. It had been ready since September 3, but Russia had delayed a vote on its contents until other committee members had finally threatened to proceed without her. The vote, when it came, was unanimous. The initial request from the parent Committee 2 had called for a report on "whether effective control of atomic energy is possible, together with an indication of the methods by which the Scientific and Technical Committee considers that effective control can be achieved." But the scientific subcommittee decided at the outset that methods of control would involve problems of a non-technical nature that were largely within the jurisdiction of other committees and limited itself to the scientific and technical aspects.

As American scientists had fondly believed would be the case,

---

[20] *Bulletin of the Atomic Scientists*, II (October 1, 1946), 1; Carl Dreher to editor, *Bulletin of the Atomic Scientists*, II (November 1, 1946), 30–31; Higinbotham to the author, January 27, 1964.

these discussions with their foreign counterparts had taken place in an atmosphere of increasing confidence, reasonableness, and even harmony. Tolman, Oppenheimer, Bacher, and Sir George Thompson of Great Britain were in the best position to answer the questions posed chiefly by the chairman, Kramers, and the Soviet member, Dmitri Skobeltsin. To supplement the widely available Smyth and State Department reports, Tolman's staff had collected two volumes of material entitled "Scientific Information Transmitted to the United Nations Atomic Energy Commission by the United States Member" and made them available on June 14 and July 10. They contained unclassified articles, special releases, and some specially prepared material. In the latter category was an unclassified version of the earlier report on the feasibility of inspection from the technical committee on inspection and control, prepared by Manson Benedict and two committee members, Philip Morrison and Colonel J. R. Ruhoff.

Even if, as Oppenheimer had assured the FAS council, this information was adequate, the United States scientists felt the awkwardness of the one-sided exchange. While they, and to a certain extent the British, had their own considerable experience and that of hundreds of colleagues to draw on, other members had to rely on conjecture and were handicapped by having few knowledgeable experts available.[21] Chairman Kramers later told Committee No. 2 that to scientists the limitation on information was far from agreeable but that the opportunity of speaking frankly and informally had been of great value; and Captain Alberto of Brazil remarked upon how tactfully the American scientists had handled what he described as a delicate and difficult situation. In answer to sometimes indiscreet questions, he told Committee 2, "they furnished us information in keeping with the standard of truthfulness among real men of science, and all this within the limits imposed by their duty to their country."[22]

The report of the scientific and technical committee summarizing these amicable exchanges dealt with the production and utilization of nuclear fuels, peaceful applications of atomic energy and their bearing on control problems, possible clandestine activities to be guarded against, and probable future developments. Far more limited in scope than the Acheson-Lilienthal proposal this international report yet managed to include some of the points that constituted for scientists

---

[21] Interviews with Bacher, July 29, 1962, and Benedict, September 13, 1962; *The New World*, pp. 593–94.

[22] Excerpts from statements made before UNAEC Committee 2 on October 2, 1946, *Bulletin of the Atomic Scientists*, II (November 1, 1946), 16.

the special virtues of the earlier statement. Among these were the following:

The maintenance and strengthening of the international community of scientists, the free exchange of scientific information and an increasing awareness among all scientists of one another's research activities would assist in making less likely the application of research talent to clandestine activities.

It is clear that the major assurance against clandestine activities would lie in the existence of effective safeguards applied to known peaceful activities.

... Whatever the future may bring, those charged with responsibility for maintaining safeguards on atomic energy will best be able to make necessary adaptations in these safeguards if they are intimately associated with and participating in new developments in the entire field.

The committee's final conclusion was that

with regard to the question posed by Committee 2, "whether effective control of atomic energy is possible," we do not find any basis in the available scientific facts for supposing that effective control is not technologically feasible. Whether or not it is politically feasible, is not discussed or implied in this report, nor is there any recommendation of the particular system or systems by which effective control can be achieved.[23]

On October 1 Higinbotham on behalf of the FAS wrote to congratulate Baruch on the fine report of the technical and scientific committee, with its hopeful implications that atomic energy could be controlled, and expressed gratification over the important contributions of the American representatives. FAS members had recently discussed progress in the UNAEC, said Higinbotham discreetly and without reference to the Wallace letter, and believed that further good will would be created if certain points were clarified, namely, the sequence and timing of transitional steps, and the attitude of the United States delegation to control the American stockpile of ore and fissionable materials by an international authority. Higinbotham cited seemingly contradictory or unclear statements by the United States delegation.[24] The letter failed by a great deal to cover all that had been said within the privacy of the FAS circle in the past few months and of necessity represented a basic minimum of critical comment.

The success of the scientific and technical committee in reaching agreement encouraged a certain degree of optimism during the autumn

---

[23] *International Control of Atomic Energy: Growth of a Policy*, Appendix 24, pp. 261–78.
[24] Higinbotham to Baruch, October 1, 1946, AORES XVIII, 5.

of 1946. The next step in the UNAEC was a study of safeguards against clandestine activities, of which the technical committee had warned. As a partly political problem this was taken up in Committee 2, which chose to adopt, however, the informal procedure that the scientists had found natural and productive. Experts in various fields were called in at this stage, and the American scientists became gradually less active as consultants; Bacher's services terminated when he was appointed to the United States Atomic Energy Commission at the end of October. The results of the safeguards study formed part of the first UNAEC report, submitted to the Security Council on December 31, 1946.

While these developments were taking place, the question of general disarmament, upon which Gromyko had placed primary emphasis in his response to the United States proposal, was discussed in the autumn sessions of the UN General Assembly, meeting now in its temporary quarters at Lake Success, New York. The result was a disarmament resolution adopted by the Assembly on December 14. During the debates both Soviet and U.S. delegates made concessions in relation to a possible disarmament agreement on just those points that had prevented them from getting together on atomic energy control. The United States granted that control organs should operate within the framework of the Security Council and did not mention the veto in relation to violations. Russia agreed to discuss inspection and that the veto should not apply to day-to-day operations. But these conciliatory steps did nothing toward reconciling the Soviet insistence that atomic energy control should be part of a general disarmament settlement with United States determination to carry through with a carefully thought out and implemented atomic energy agreement.

Of the scientific and technical committee's report Bernard Bechhoefer has said that "for the first and almost the last time the Soviet delegation had agreed with the United States. Even today [1961], when both the Soviet Union and the United States have recognized that changed conditions have destroyed the possibility of complete accountability for nuclear materials, the principle of accountability still forms the basis of the most important proposals to lessen the dangers of nuclear war."[25]

One cannot claim that the scientists in the federation were directly

[25] Bechhoefer, *Postwar Negotiations for Arms Control*, p. 43.

responsible for policy decisions in this area during the summer of 1946 or for what went into the scientific and technical committee's report. But they helped to determine who represented American science, and they could with some justice regard the report as the culmination of their insistence, first expressed in their inspection studies nearly a year before, that control be based upon scientific and technical considerations. The solid achievement of the scientific and technical committee, nurturing the promise of emulation in other areas, does much to explain the steadfastness with which the majority of scientists continued to support the negotiations in the UNAEC through the disheartening months ahead. The scientific and technical report stands at the apogee of scientists' hope for international control.

PART VI

Hope Deferred

CHAPTER 17

The Long Haul
1946–47

A LOGICAL stopping place in the history of a continuing movement is hard to find. This chapter rounds out the period when FAS
scientists felt they were dealing with an emergency and indicates the
direction of their activities as they adjusted to the loss of initial
fervor and unanimity and assumed a long-term, watchdog role over
the relation of science and scientists to government.

1. WAYS AND MEANS

The autumn of 1946 was a critical time for the FAS and the movement
it represented. Not all of its founders had thought of it as a permanent
organization; but those who saw its main function as educational now
knew that the job had just begun, and those who regarded it as a
political pressure group foresaw that it might still be needed as the
McMahon Act was implemented and as the UNAEC tried to bring
its technical agreement to a political conclusion. As the first anniversary of the federation approached the question was not so much
whether it should but whether it could continue and how its limited
resources could best be employed.

From the beginning the organization had scraped along in hand-to-
mouth fashion. Its leaders had succeeded remarkably well in not
letting ends be submerged by ways and means, but far more time

than the foregoing account suggests had been spent by Higinbotham, Rush, and others in exploring sources of revenue, in discussion with tax experts, and in explaining to members what the FAS could and could not do to influence political decisions if it became eligible for tax deductible contributions. Some money had come from foundations, but this had to be assigned to special educational projects. Norman Cousins' fund-raising dinners in New York had brought several gifts ranging from fifty to a thousand dollars, and more would have been forthcoming had they been tax exempt. Royalties assigned to the FAS by contributors to *One World or None* brought in a few thousand more. Annual dues of two dollars a member were paid by the local associations but were often in arrears.

The scale of operations was not lavish; for the first eight months of 1946—a period of maximum activity—expenditures totaled $23,368.24, but the deficit mounted. By September, 1946, it had reached $10,000, of which some $4,000 was owed to the local associations; another $4,000, chiefly in unpaid salaries, to individual members; $1,000 to the NCAI for furniture and equipment; and $1,000 in unpaid bills. An emergency appeal to members, bringing in $500 from each of the larger associations, provided temporary relief; external debts were discharged, and the administrative committee was able to insist that Higinbotham, who had not been paid since he arrived from Los Alamos a year before (and offered to continue that way), should receive back salary at the token rate of $250 a month and a future rate of $500. A year later Higinbotham's parting present from the staff was, appropriately enough, an empty wallet. Rush and Amrine had also worked along with no assurance of payment, and Higinbotham's sacrifice for the cause, though the outstanding example, was not unique.[1]

Thoughtful scientists were well aware in the autumn of 1946 that the movement that had so absorbed them for the past year faced a crisis that went deeper than finance and organization, but it was natural to attack the practical problem first. Early in the summer hope of financial relief had risen with the formation of the Emergency Committee of Atomic Scientists, which, as explained earlier, bore no relation to the Emergency Conference for Civilian Control of Atomic

---

[1] FAS financial statements in ASC XIV, 4, and FAS IV, 4; Higinbotham to all associations, October 11, 1946, AORES XVII, 9; FAS administrative committee minutes, December 15, 1946, in Rush's files; AORES Newsletter, January 17, 1946, FAS VI, 8; Higinbotham to Meier, December 10, 1947, FAS XV, 5.

Energy but had its origin in a fund-raising campaign undertaken for the National Committee for Atomic Information by Harold Oram of New York. With Einstein as an actively interested chairman, the Emergency Committee consisted of Leo Szilard, Hans Bethe, Thorfin Hogness, Harold Urey, and Victor Weisskopf; Selig Hecht of Columbia, Philip M. Morse of Brookhaven, and Linus Pauling of Cal Tech later joined them. Except for Einstein the original members were affiliated more or less closely with the FAS, and its hard-pressed leaders, observing the rich yield of some $85,000 that the committee's prestige immediately attracted, naturally wondered why some of the one million that it hoped to raise should not come to the federation. But Urey explained to the September FAS council that the Emergency Committee was in process of incorporating as an educational organization and that although it wanted to support the federation it could do so only if the FAS adjusted its activities so as to be eligible for tax deductible funds.[2]

Pending such adjustment, the Emergency Committee, in addition to supporting the NCAI, allocated sums of a few hundred dollars each to the local associations for educational work, the Atomic Scientists of Chicago with the most ambitious program receiving a thousand. The *Bulletin of the Atomic Scientists*, whose finances had been separated from those of the ASC some months before, was considered by the Emergency Committee as the most valuable single scientists' activity, and with ECAS aid it now paid off some of its debts and was assured of six months continuance.[3]

Meanwhile in line with Urey's advice, Rush pursued the question of tax exempt status for the FAS and shortly reported to the administrative committee that "educational" organizations were permitted to engage in propaganda on issues and for objectives broadly political in character but not yet embodied in legislation. The FAS could probably continue to campaign for international control during negotiations, but it could not lobby for Senate ratification of a control treaty. It could disseminate information on legislative issues if balanced pro and con; its representatives could testify before congressional committees by invitation, as they had done before the McMahon committee, but they could not demand to testify. Members could still lobby as individuals or through other organizations.[4]

[2] FAS council minutes, September 22, 1946, FAS I, 4.
[3] Correspondence relating to ECAS allocations, November, 1946, FAS XV, 4.
[4] Rush memorandum to administrative committee, October 9, 1946, FAS II, 2.

Rush, Higinbotham, and the others who bore the brunt of making ends meet saw no alternative to making the FAS educational and to having the local associations also obtain educational status. Among the various reorganization schemes considered, the one favored in Washington was to have the FAS become educational and to set up independent local councils for political action, but this proposal was voted down by the member associations. The FAS therefore remained political, and a new organization was incorporated in December, 1946, the Association of Scientists for Atomic Education. At a two-day meeting in Washington in January a provisional ASAE board of directors, composed of eight FAS members, endeavored to integrate all the educational projects of the local associations. It was an ambitious program, testifying to the steadfast purpose of a core of true believers. At the base would be seven study committees to maintain a continuing up-to-date analysis and to supervise activity in the areas of international control, domestic developments, the implications of preventive war, security and secrecy in science, educational policy, educational techniques and evaluation of results, and a committee on foreign contacts that would supervise the successful Committee for Foreign Correspondence and set up an International Information Center.[5]

The organization of the ASAE was based on eight regional councils within which membership was on an individual basis. Each region contained a center of FAS activity, and it was assumed that parallel FAS and ASAE groups would be maintained. The Atomic Scientists of Chicago, which had recently been granted educational status on the basis of its close links with the University of Chicago and the *Bulletin of the Atomic Scientists,* opposed this arrangement, wishing, as Goldsmith told the January board meeting, to concentrate on function and avoid an elaborate organizational structure. What was really needed, Chicago thought, was several well-qualified scientists working full-time for several months, not an extensive organization. The ASC became an affiliate of the ASAE, but its members did not set up an independent educational group.

The Emergency Committee, which raised more money during the

---

[5] The provisional board consisted of E. E. Minett, Bernard Feld, J. H. Rush, W. A. Higinbotham, A. A. Brown, L. Marchi, H. H. Goldsmith, and David Hawkins (ASAE minutes, January 11–12, 1947, ASC XII, 5). For other material, see ASC XIII, 1; FAS VI, 8; XVII, 4; XIX, 4; and Rush's files. A file of ASAE material in the FAS Washington office has not been used for this book.

autumn, launched the ASAE with a lump sum of $13,600 and the promise of $7,150 a month. E. E. Minett, as ASAE chairman, and some of the regional directors put tremendous effort into the new operation, and for a time educational activity did indeed seem to acquire new vitality. A start was made on community programs in co-operation with the NCAI. The ASAE at Oak Ridge took over the AORES southern state conferences and kept them going through 1947; and during that summer Philip Kennedy, the English teacher who had organized the Youth Council in Oak Ridge, was given $600 for a tour of New York State teachers' colleges and for demonstrations of atomic energy discussion material to three thousand high-school teachers, which were reported to be uniformly successful.

The new organization was not, however, so wildly successful as to provoke the charge of disrupting the old. The FAS, in fact, continued to add new affiliates during 1947. A chapter at Fort Monmouth, New Jersey, was admitted in February, the Chicago Association of Scientists and Engineers in March, the Mohawk Valley Association of Scientists and Engineers in August, and in December new groups in Baltimore and at the Brookhaven National Laboratory. The only casualty was Pasadena, where the association had been composed mainly of students with little faculty support. Early in the year the FAS began admitting members-at-large. But these developments resulted in part from the migration of members of the older associations and did not always reflect new and expanding interest.

The office at 1749 L Street, to which the FAS and NCAI had moved in June, 1946, had settled down to a slightly less hectic pace than its predecessors. After passage of the McMahon Act zealous delegates no longer dashed in and out to committee hearings or appointments on the Hill, but the level of demand for liaison and information remained high enough that there was always more work than time and hands to do it. Higinbotham had completed his term as chairman of the FAS and was filling the new post of executive secretary created by the September, 1946, council; Robert Wilson of the Cornell association became chairman. At the same time the job of publications editor lapsed when Mike Amrine left for the Advertising Council in New York. Rush stayed with the FAS until April, 1947, then worked with the Association of Scientists for Atomic Education until September, when he resumed his graduate work. A great source of strength was added in September, 1946, when Dorothy Higinbotham was corralled as a volunteer by her brother; and when Higin-

botham himself left for Brookhaven in December, 1947, he passed on
to his successor, social scientist Richard Meier, what he described as
a flexible, hard-working outfit that could turn out more work than
any group he ever saw, willing to work all night when necessary.[6]

2. No Longer with One Voice

These mechanical adjustments had scarcely been undertaken in the
autumn of 1946 when the more basic problems, of which these
financial and organizational troubles were but symptoms, had to be
faced. "We are having the same sort of difficulty at Los Alamos as
you are in Washington—insufficient manpower," Fred Reines had
written to Amrine in explanation of why he could produce so few
articles for the first anniversary of Alamogordo. "The situation will
take an alarming turn for the worse at the end of this month, and
another in September. I foresee the end of ALAS, and of Los Alamos
as an important scientific laboratory."[7]

In Chicago the manpower problem appeared to be not so much a
matter of interest as of time. People thought it was wonderful that
scientists were recognizing their responsibilities, wrote John Simpson
as he looked back on the first year of federation activity, but they
could not continue what they had done and remain scientists.

The constant stream of interruptions day and night, phone calls,
speeches and strange decisions have made it impossible to think for any
extended periods of time on the subjects with which we are concerned.
At the University of Chicago alone, over twenty-four hundred hours per
month have been devoted by the scientists, in addition to their regular
working hours, to carry on their program of education and political action
during the most active periods of this last year.

For many of us it has meant the postponement or complete loss of a
year of valuable research time out of the productive part of our lives. We
feel this has been justified in the past year, but cannot be justified over
longer periods of time. There are very few scientists and, because of the
last war, not many are joining our ranks.[8]

One way of broadening participation was to permit local associations to take in larger numbers of non-scientists, but this would tend
to weaken the authority of the central organization on technical ques-

    [6] Higinbotham memorandum on tax exemption, December 29, 1947, AORES XVII,
10; the staff at that time consisted of Meier, Mary Bernard (secretary and bookkeeper),
Dorothy Higinbotham (typist and information clerk), and Leon Cunningham (typist
who took care of mimeographing and mailing).
    [7] Reines to Amrine, June 1, 1946, FAS V, 3.
    [8] Simpson, "Scientists in Washington," University of Chicago Magazine, XXXIX
(November, 1946), 7.

tions, a competence that was already threatened as Manhattan Project employees moved into academic and industrial jobs.

But lack of time was only one side of the coin of flagging enthusiasm. The other was uncertainty about policy and a growing sense of futility. Until mid-1947, though despair was sometimes privately confessed, there was little open questioning on the part of the initially committed scientists that international control was still an attainable goal, but there was increasing divergence of opinion on how the federation could now contribute to reaching it. Just how fluid the policy situation appeared to be was demonstrated at the September, 1946, council meeting by the nature and number of the questions tossed at the delegates by Higinbotham. The Sunday morning discussion with foreign visitors about progress in the UNAEC, some of it critical of United States policy, had lent a note of immediacy to council proceedings and to Higinbotham's suggestion at Monday's session that they take a fresh look at what fields the FAS should attempt to cover—atomic energy only, science and society, foreign policy and/or, world organization. What relative weight should be given to self-education and study, to co-operation with foreign scientists, to thorough investigation of pertinent issues, to public education, to co-operation with non-scientific groups, and to direct political activity? What public stand should the federation take? Or none, perhaps, until the issues were clearer? Should it merely repeat basic points about international control? Or should it shift the emphasis to related subjects, such as military financing of science and peacetime applications of atomic energy, or to clarifying statements relating to United Nations and domestic developments?

The generally bland character of such conclusions as the council reached suggested considerable doubt if not actual disagreement: there were to be no sensational statements or releases; educational campaigns of the NCAI, Advertising Council, and other groups should be encouraged, with emphasis upon the basic points of no defense, no monopoly, and international control; statements on UN activities should not denounce or idealize particular proposals; and groups should seriously consider the federation position in the event that UN negotiations bogged down. Amrine pointed to the ironical fact that public interest in atomic energy, resulting from discussions in Congress and the UN and tests at Bikini, was reaching a peak just as the scientists were deciding they did not want to say very much.[9]

---

[9] FAS council minutes, September 22–23, 1946, FAS I, 4.

An important inhibiting factor, partly responsible for the mood of restraint that Amrine noted, was a growing uncertainty on scientists' part as to whether the fear they had stimulated had in fact done more to scare men into rationality, as they had hoped, or to provoke the favorable view of preventive war that rumor from time to time attributed to certain circles and individuals. Back in the spring of 1946 the FAS had sought help on this point and had been advised by a special committee of the American Psychological Association that crippling, panicky fear was undeniably bad, but that healthy action-goading fear could lead to an understanding of the dangers of atomic energy, encourage its constructive use, and promote progress toward control and international co-operation.[10] Federation leaders at first accepted this confirmation of their own instinctive approach, but as the latter months of 1946 brought the realization that things were not going well in the UNAEC and that the American public did not care very much, they began to wonder if emphasis on the dangers of nuclear war had indeed created paralysis. At an NCAI meeting in Washington in February, 1947, Luther Evans, the librarian of Congress, accused the scientists of having tried to panic the public by use of tactics worthy of ham actors, of displaying abysmal ignorance, and as amateurs, of contributing little but confusion. Higinbotham replied that scientists now realized that the "fear business" had been overdone, or at least done enough, but that at first it had seemed necessary to dispel the public inertia. Evans' sharp rebuke, coming from usually sympathetic intellectual quarters, perhaps moved Higinbotham and W. C. Beard of the Association of Scientists for Atomic Education to consult a group at Columbia Teachers College that was preparing to re-evaluate education in the light of atomic energy. Less cholerically than Evans, this group also questioned the value of the fear approach.[11]

In the weeks following the September, 1946, council, reappraisal was also made of the balance of effort to be made at home and abroad. Individual decisions taken at this period showed how the wind was blowing. Edward Tompkins had agreed to try to revive the editorial committee of AORES but found that scientists at Oak Ridge just

---

[10] Summary of report of committee of American Psychological Association, printed in *Atomic Information*, I (June 17, 1946), 10.

[11] The *Houston Chronicle*, February 22, 1947, quoted the Evans episode as added evidence of scientists' desire to rule not only the United States but the world. Material relating to the Teachers College discussion, March–June, 1947, FAS XXI, 8.

wouldn't write articles and reported to Amrine that those who were competent had done all the writing they were willing to do, partly because a lot of work had gone into things that never got published. The United States now had its own domestic atomic energy policy with 80 per cent of the people behind it, said Tompkins, and as for future developments scientists were leery of risking their reputations by speculating. He himself would rather spend his time writing to scientists in other countries. Simon Freed had recently returned from conferences in Europe, convinced that much could be accomplished toward international control by personal communication leading toward a strong scientists' organization. So Tompkins was giving up editorial activity and joining the Committee for Foreign Correspondence.[12]

A certain amount of collective soul searching on this question also took place—in its most pronounced form at Oak Ridge, where AORES members were constantly taking polls and exhorting each other to decide where they were going. Perhaps this was a matter of record-keeping, but more likely the merger of the small nucleus of world government enthusiasts in ORES with the political action group in AORS actually made the definition of objective more difficult there. The Cornell association, on the other hand, had immediately taken the international problem as its chief concern, but without apparent conflict later adopted the question of personnel clearance as its special responsibility. In Chicago the initial emphasis on public and self-education continued to find expression in the *Bulletin*, and the city and nearby communities continued to offer opportunities for as much educational work as the scientists were willing to do.

Interspersed with repeated calls for stocktaking, the definition of federation policy was tailored to what it was wise, expedient, or possible to attempt. In the international context the story concerns not so much what scientists did as what they did not do. If a theoretical problem or experiment does not yield to one approach, a scientist admits temporary defeat and tries another—more radical or conservative as suits his experience and intuitions—or even chooses for the time being some less awkward problem. Following the heartening agreement in the UNAEC's scientific and technical committee, the stalemate in the UNAEC negotiations presented scientists with a dilemma to the resolution of which their professional skills could

---

[12] Tompkins to Amrine, October 15, 1946, FAS V, 3.

in no way contribute. Although some of the FAS leaders, as well as those less deeply involved in the organization, early recognized the probability of failure, they could not openly admit this without substantially diminishing such chance of success as still remained. Both the dilemma and the pessimism were apparent in late 1946 and 1947. "The possibility of achieving world control never seemed very great to me," wrote Higinbotham to Edward Tompkins in a comment on his decision to turn from domestic to foreign education, "but I could see no other acceptable course and still can't. That possibility can be affected by us through our influence on public opinion, both here and abroad."[13]

But as each piece of good news from the UNAEC was followed by a reversal, even such guarded optimism was hard to maintain. To the federation leaders progress toward international agreement was intimately linked with loss of momentum in the scientists' movement. "I'm sure disgusted with everyone," Higinbotham noted in his diary on March 5, 1947, the day Gromyko rejected the United States plan. "The groups have failed on questionnaires, nominations, ASAE and about everything else." And a week later: "Feeling discouraged. . . . Saw Oppie at five. We think nothing FAS or educational groups can do. UN in good hands. . . . Moped around. Told Joe [Rush] how I feel and so does he. The end is in sight unless Lilienthal is not confirmed and then?"[14]

To the local associations Rush wrote that Gromyko's speech raised the question of the federation's future course, for no one would listen if it continued to press for an impossible solution. We in Washington, he said, are increasingly disturbed by loss of enthusiasm, unwillingness to give time, and failure to respond to ballots and to pay dues. "It will be tragic indeed," he concluded, "if the effort we have undertaken, which has gained such universal confidence and approval, is allowed to die because scientists themselves have become indifferent to the urgency of the situation."[15]

To Oppenheimer in Berkeley, Higinbotham confided that in the aftermath of Gromyko's rejection he had doubted that the FAS should continue, but then he had thought of all the problems facing the domestic Atomic Energy Commission for which a sympathetic and intelligent body of scientific opinion might be needed, of the confirmation a year hence of the original members, and of other

---

[13] Higinbotham to Tompkins, October 23, 1946, FAS V, 3.
[14] Higinbotham diary, March 5, 11, 12, 1947.
[15] Rush memorandum to all associations, March 8, 1947, AORES XVII, 10.

questions, such as radio isotopes, on which there was a straightforward job to be done, and decided it should. But the problem was to develop a unified purpose. Some people wanted to interfere in all kinds of questions, Higinbotham complained; some were very critical of United States foreign policy, and many were exceedingly suspicious of anyone in a top position. Some wanted to stop all educational activity for fear of frightening the public; others said, "Now is the time to get on the ball and make a break with the conservatives." The rowing in every direction worried Higinbotham, who thought scientists could still do a good job if they would get together and stick to their chief concern.[16]

In reply Oppenheimer expressed little hope for the success of UN negotiations—no one involved officially seemed to have any, he said—but he saw no alternative to continuing to work for international control. As far as the FAS was concerned, he thought the rowing in all directions almost inevitable. The federation could be useful but only

if there is a clear recognition that so far we have not succeeded, and if it is recognized that in laying the foundation of a future hope our role can no longer be that of the prophets of doom coming out of the desert, but rather that of a group of specialized and, in their way, competent, men who must be sensitive to all new avenues of approach which are hopeful and who are after all intellectuals and not politicians. If you can help to achieve this, you will have not only my support but my warm and I hope, useful assistance.[17]

Higinbotham's anxiety about the related problems of purpose and program—and this was fully shared by others—did indeed presage a more serious crisis for the federation and its related organizations than that provoked by the Wallace episode because this time the challenge came from within. The crisis came to a head in the early summer of 1947 when Harold Urey announced his conviction that international control was a lost cause, a step for which he had been preparing for some months. A year before in a commencement speech at Swarthmore College he had spoken of alternatives to international control and mentioned preventive war as one that he did not advocate. The speech, as Urey remarked later, did not disturb his Quaker audience, but when it was printed in the August, 1946, issue of *Air Affairs*, the press picked up the preventive war angle. To one of the frantic wires from FAS members complaining that such talk undermined all the work they were doing, the Washington staff replied: "Urey speaks for Urey. Too bad press gave headlines to one of his three logical

---

[16] Higinbotham to Oppenheimer, May 12, 1947, FAS XXI, 4.
[17] Oppenheimer to Higinbotham, May 20, 1947, FAS XXI, 4.

alternatives which must be faced." Urey tried to set the record straight in an October speech to the American-Scandinavian Foundation in which he denounced preventive war and gave a general endorsement of world government; but by the following spring he had abandoned hope for the United Nations negotiations and was ready to advocate immediate federal union of all nations willing to sacrifice sovereignty in the interests of self-defense against totalitarianism. He stated his arguments for such a limited world government in the June, 1947, issue of the *Bulletin of the Atomic Scientists*.[18]

Urey was answered by FAS chairman Robert R. Wilson and Philip Morrison of its administrative committee in the next issue, their title, "Half a World . . . and None," showing what they thought of Urey's acquiescence in a divided world. He was taking refuge, they claimed, in a patently unworkable scheme, and his partial world government was but another name for a defensive military alliance. Scientists must not abandon hope for the imaginative, constructive Lilienthal-Baruch proposals.[19]

Another significant defection began a few months later when Edward Teller read to the executive committee of the Atomic Scientists of Chicago a statement, "Challenge to Atomic Scientists," in which he pointed out that of their two main goals, domestic and international control, the first had been satisfactorily reached, but the second remained, for the time being at least, unattainable. Under such conditions one could not deny the importance of keeping this country in the lead in atomic energy developments both for war and for peace. As Teller's views were shortly presented in the *Bulletin*, the point about defense, so prophetic of his later public stand, though clearly stated, was subordinate to his advocacy of world government, not the limited variety proposed by his close friend and colleague Urey, but one that would assume full responsibility for political and civil rights. Not only, said Teller, was such world government inevitable, either by agreement or force, but it alone could give peace and freedom.[20]

---

[18] Rush to B. Shank in Hollywood, August 19, 1946, FAS XXV, 6; Urey speech to American-Scandinavian Foundation reprinted in *Bulletin of the Atomic Scientists*, II (November 1, 1946), 2–3; Urey, "An Alternative Course for the Control of Atomic Energy," *Bulletin of the Atomic Scientists*, III (June, 1947), 139–42, 166.

[19] Morrison and Wilson, "Half a World . . . and None; Partial World Government Criticized," *Bulletin of the Atomic Scientists*, III (July, 1947), 181–82.

[20] ASC executive committee minutes, October 7, 1947, ASC VI, 13; Teller, "Atomic Scientists Have Two Responsibilities," *Bulletin of the Atomic Scientists*, III (December, 1947), 355–56.

These published views, especially when attached to memorable names, were the ones that caught the eye both of laymen and of fellow scientists, and they have since been used as evidence of emerging schools of thought in the scientists' movement.[21] But the tidy generalizations of political scientists should not be allowed to obscure the fact that for several years after the initial unanimity on international control was broken, discussion among scientists continued and a good deal of flexibility of viewpoint was maintained. Committee minutes, memorandums, or printed articles record only a small fraction of the discourse that took place at evening parties in Chicago, Ithaca, or Cambridge or around the fringes of technical gatherings. For scientists to toss ideas around, even after they had agreed to disagree, was so normal a part of their scarcely separable professional and social lives that the dialogue continued even after the eruption of the hydrogen bomb issue made the recognition of two camps unavoidable. It was only after the Oppenheimer case, which evoked such intense personal feeling, that communication was to a certain extent interrupted. And even since that time, the division has been between those who believe in negotiating from strength and those who continue to exchange doubts rather than between two well-formulated orthodoxies. And it should also be remembered that the division of scientists into groups according to expectations of Russian co-operation did not reflect standard ideological views about communism. Conservatives and liberals in the government and the country at large united behind the attempt to obtain international control through the United Nations and the same was true of the scientist supporters. To those who had known each other before the war the way in which the international control issue brought together people of differing views on other questions was a constant source of wonder. Among its most stubborn advocates were a few who had toyed with communism in the Depression period and men like Eugene Rabinowitch, a refugee from Bolshevist Russia. One could make a pretty good case for the proposition that advocacy of continued negotiation depended more upon temperament than upon politics.

With these caveats in mind let us explore further the emergence of divergent views in 1947, the existence of which was frankly recognized by Hans Bethe when he explained to Harrison Brown that he

---

[21] I refer particularly to Robert Gilpin's division of scientists into control, finite containment, and infinite containment schools in *American Scientists and Nuclear Weapons Policy* (Princeton, N.J.: Princeton University Press, 1962).

could not attend the June conference at Lake Geneva, Wisconsin, to discuss what scientists should be saying to the American people. Bethe was a fellow member with Urey on the Emergency Committee of Atomic Scientists, a good friend of Teller's, and a much respected slightly senior colleague of Wilson and Morrison at Cornell. He knew very well what was being said behind the printed page, and the views that he wanted Brown to convey to the conference were probably more representative of the way many scientists were beginning to feel, and certainly more soundly predictive of how the majority would behave in the next few years, than the position either of the moderates who were running the federation or of the individuals who called for more radical measures. In view of the deadlock in the United Nations —the reasons for which he thought Urey had correctly analysed— Bethe thought that continued advocacy of international control would only make more evident the hopelessness of the situation and perhaps lead to increased demand for preventive war. In their attitudes toward foreign policy scientists were now deeply divided, with a majority of the younger men advocating a friendly attitude toward Russia in the hope of inducing co-operation and an older group, of whom Urey was one, expecting no co-operation from Russia and advocating the union of democratic countries in a partial world government. Even if they could agree on a plan, Bethe doubted the wisdom of presenting it as coming from the scientists. It was true that they had acquired considerable political prestige, but past success had depended upon having a clear case that they could prove with almost scientific logic, on their enthusiasm, and on the absence of an official strategic plan.

... Now, on the other hand, we propose to bring to the public a purely political issue. . . . The public will soon see that this time we do not have a clear case and will also soon discover the lack of the spontaneous enthusiasm which marked our previous campaigns. Therefore, the only result we shall achieve will be to lose our present prestige in politics.

I believe the time may come again when we shall need this prestige, and when we shall again have a message which is spontaneous and which we can carry with enthusiasm. It is most important to preserve our ability to act at such a time.[22]

The Lake Geneva conference, to which Bethe's letter referred, met June 18 to 21. It was called by the Atomic Scientists of Chicago at the

---

[22] Bethe to Brown, June 13, 1947, Appendix IV of "A Report on a Conference of Scientists held at Lake Geneva, Wisconsin, June 18–21, 1947," FAS XIV, 1.

request of the FAS, NCAI, and ASAE, for the purpose of elaborating a new program of action for scientists, but it produced instead a re-affirmation of the responsibility to provide information and scientific insights that had led them to organize in the first place. It was agreed that they would continue to warn about the deceptiveness of security based on atomic weapons, to urge the establishment of international control, to work for peacetime benefits, to point out the dangers to scientific and civil liberties inherent in military control of science, and to appraise American policy in the light of those technical considerations that were increasingly affecting its course. The final section of the statement marked the triumph of those who wanted to maintain the unity of the movement and keep the FAS and its associated organizations as comprehensive as possible. For those who wanted expanded activity, it denounced preventive war, admitted the eventual necessity of a world government "with powers adequate to maintain a peace based on the rule of law," urged that the United States support the UN agencies for international collaboration and, through the United Nations, contribute to a program of world economic reconstruction; for the benefit of the more cautious, these objectives were phrased in very general terms. The Lake Geneva statement was approved by the local associations at the August FAS council and has proved a serviceable frame of reference down to the present day.[23]

A characteristic incident, to which the prima donna syndrome, the exigent demands of public relations, and sheer thoughtlessness on the part of busy men all contributed, nearly wrecked the unity that the Lake Geneva conferees had labored so hard to encompass. The Emergency Committee of Atomic Scientists, which had acquired during its year of operation, in addition to its fund-raiser, a Madison Avenue office with executive secretary and clerical staff, asked that it be allowed to release the Lake Geneva statement to the press to inaugurate a new drive for funds for the organizations backing the conference. This reasonable request was readily granted, but when the Emergency Committee made the release on June 29, it also issued a statement of its own; this upheld the principle of international control but asked if thoughtful and well-informed men could any longer expect fruitful results from UNAEC negotiations and dwelt at some length

[23] "Statement of the Lake Geneva Conference," *Bulletin of the Atomic Scientists*, III (August, 1947), 217.

upon the necessity of "a supra-national government, with powers adequate to the responsibility of maintaining peace." Nothing was said about the part that scientists might play, and the Lake Geneva statement was effectively buried in the flood of rhetoric about world government and in the reporters' concern with big names.

The young men on the FAS administrative committee were shocked and angry. They refrained from public comment but they did not hesitate to give their elders a thorough dressing down for having subordinated "the broadest formal consensus of scientists' views to date" to their independent expression of opinion. All ECAS members had been invited to Lake Geneva; only Urey and Szilard had gone. The protest that Rush sent to the ECAS on behalf of the FAS administrative committee on July 17 read in part as follows:

> More serious even than this lapse of responsibility to other scientists is the impact of the Emergency Committee's statement on public opinion. The persistent and concerted effort of scientists has been a major factor in the progress toward world control of atomic energy—and that progress has been by no means trivial. Discouragement with the UNAEC proceedings is now general, and there is grave danger that the U.S. may withdraw its proposals, with unforeseeable consequences. Denunciation of the UNAEC effort at such a time by scientists removes the only remaining substantial body of opinion which stands in the way of such a breakdown.
>
> Moreover, the Emergency Committee seems to us to take a needlessly defeatist attitude in disavowing any competence to suggest means of attaining even its own proposed objectives. The Committee did not hesitate to assume competence in assaying the political effectiveness of the UNAEC and other UN functions; it seems to us inconsistent in refusing to face the political consequences of the alternatives it proposes.
>
> ... We feel that you who constitute the ECAS must recognize that the prestige of your names and the activities of the Committee give to your utterances a special authority. You have access to publicity; and, whether you will it or not, to the public you speak for all scientists.[24]

In the hope of healing the breach and because the international situation seemed to be deteriorating, the Emergency Committee called another conference in Princeton for the end of November, which was attended by representatives of the fourteen larger FAS groups and individuals with special interest in atomic problems. Agreement on a definite program proved impossible, Philip Morrison reported to the December FAS council; the mood of the meeting was one of frustra-

---

[24] "Statement of the Emergency Committee," *Bulletin of the Atomic Scientists*, III (August, 1947), 216; Rush for the FAS administrative committee to members of the Emergency Committee of Atomic Scientists, July 17, 1947, FAS XV, 5.

tion and confusion and action was chiefly negative in blocking extension of scientists' efforts to less directly related fields. The only positive agreement was that the UNAEC ought to continue. Sentiment on this point, Morrison said, was overwhelming and had forestalled collapse of the conference. To his diary Higinbotham confided that he had never seen such a disgusting performance by any group anywhere; he was ashamed that reporters and other visitors had witnessed it.[25]

The fiasco at Princeton was the prelude to revision of the organizational structure of the scientists' activities, which had become dependent upon the Emergency Committee for funds. There was no lack of public support, fund-raiser Harold Oram had told Einstein apropos of the disappointing spring campaign; the trouble lay in lack of agreement within the committee.[26] When the autumn campaign also petered out, leaving in fact a slight deficit after filling commitments to local associations and the *Bulletin*, the Emergency Committee decided to taper off its activities and to devote whatever surplus might result from another campaign in the spring of 1948 to support of the *Bulletin*.

Correspondence of December, 1947, reflects the dismay this decision caused. The younger men working in the FAS and on local educational programs showed considerable understanding of the predicament of the committee—of how hard it was to take time for meetings speeches, and dinners, and above all, of the difficulty of saying anything "in these confusing times." But they also felt bitter about the arbitrary unilateral decision. The diversion of senior talent and well-known names to the Emergency Committee had weakened the FAS and made it unable to compete for funds; the Chicago and Northern California associations had been asked to call off plans for local fund-raising and work with the ECAS, and now the whole thing had collapsed.[27]

The scientists felt responsible for the National Committee on Atomic Information, whose fund-raising operations with Oram had led to formation of the ECAS in the first place, but NCAI leaders were philosophical about impending change. The executive committee of the NCAI was deeply sensible of the contributions of lead-

[25] Correspondence in FAS XIV, 3; FAS council minutes, December 27–28, 1947, FAS I, 6; Higinbotham diary, November 28–30, 1947.
[26] Oram to Einstein, May 27, 1947, in Hogness' files.
[27] Higinbotham memorandum on tax exemption, December 29, 1947, AORES XVII, 10; correspondence in FAS XIII, 7; XV, 5; XVI, 7.

ing scientists, wrote its chairman Ralph McDonald to Einstein, but
the educational effort had passed into a new phase; the questions confronting citizens were now political, economic, and social, and as it
had seemed logical in 1945 to turn to scientists, it now seemed logical
to turn to men and women of broader experience in public affairs. The
cost of fund-raising by ECAS was too high; the NCAI should set up
a broader fund drive of its own and try to co-ordinate its activities with
those of the FAS and its educational affiliates along simpler lines. The
leadership of NCAI, said McDonald diplomatically, is ready to relieve
you and carry on.[28] Although its leaders and supporting organizations
did maintain their interest in atomic energy on the broader base suggested by McDonald, the drying up of ECAS funds proved fatal to the
organization as such, and it ceased to function within the next few
months.

The Emergency Committee's decision also gave the *coup de grace*
to the Association of Scientists for Atomic Education, which despite
a brave start in a few places had never fulfilled the hopes of its back-
ers. Collaboration with the NCAI had gone smoothly, but duplication of FAS effort had proved confusing and unworkable. E. E.
Minett, one of the chief supporters of ASAE, resigned as chairman
in the summer of 1947 when he left Oak Ridge to work full time
with the Emergency Committee. At the same time the AEC refused
permission to make Oak Ridge the national ASAE headquarters on
grounds of security and housing, and the New York and Washington
offices stayed open only through the summer of 1948. The community projects collapsed with the NCAI early in 1948, and the activities that had real support from scientists, such as the Committee for
Foreign Correspondence, reverted to the FAS or its local branches.[29]

The Emergency Committee's fund-raising campaign in the spring
of 1948 enabled it to pay its obligations and to ensure publication
of the *Bulletin* for another year or so. In May of 1949 its supporters
were told that it would become dormant, and they were urged to
support the *Bulletin*. It was clear, the announcement said, that international control was only obtainable within the framework of a
general settlement; this would involve taking a stand on many controversial issues, and this was not the task of the committee. It was
formally disbanded in September of 1951, with Einstein and Szilard

---

[28] McDonald to Einstein, December 17, 1947, FAS XIX, 2.
[29] Higinbotham to ECAS members, May 15, 1947, FAS XV, 5; Rush to Beard,
September 28, 1947, in Rush's files.

wanting to turn remaining funds over to the Quakers but with other committee members successfully arguing for the *Bulletin*.[30]

The FAS was not directly affected by the drying up of Emergency Committee funds, but it, too, narrowly escaped extinction in the spring of 1948. One weekly payroll had been met only through a $200 loan from an administrative committee member, and it was decided to close the Washington office as of May 1. Richard Meier, who had succeeded Higinbotham as executive secretary in December, 1947, arranged to leave, but the office was kept open by a last-minute decision to set up an executive secretariat of three or more volunteers living in the Washington-Baltimore area. Meier's salary was somehow scraped together, and he stayed on as a member of the secretariat until early 1949. The unexpected reprieve and subsequent stabilization of the FAS were entirely due, Meier later noted, to the devotion and perseverance of three people—Clifford Grobstein, a biologist with the Public Health Service, Alan Shapley, a physicist at the Bureau of Standards, both members of the secretariat, and Dorothy Higinbotham, who had been helping in both the FAS and ASAE offices.[31]

During this period the membership of the FAS had shown a marked decline from a high of over three thousand. Dropping to just over one thousand in mid-1949, it was up to fifteen hundred by the end of that year and slowly climbed to a fairly stable level of about twenty-five hundred. A constitutional revision of November, 1949, provided that only two-thirds of the federation members need be natural scientists; a few months later nine-tenths were scientists and engineers. For some time members-at-large had been encouraged, and the revision of 1949 made everyone a member of the national organization. The local associations, however remained a vital part of the federation. In April, 1949, there were still eighteen of them, but by the end of the year the number listed was down to ten, with other so-called informal branches. By 1951 such old stand-bys as ALAS and AORES were virtually defunct, but new groups were forming at the University of Illinois and Stanford, and those at the Argonne and

[30] Einstein to "Dear Friend of the Emergency Committee," May 20, 1949, as reproduced in *Bulletin of the Atomic Scientists*, V (June–July, 1949), back cover; Otto Nathan and Heinz Norden (eds.), *Einstein on Peace* (New York: Simon & Schuster, 1960), p. 558.
[31] Unsigned carbons from an administrative committee member to ECAS members (apparently not sent), December 5, 1947, FAS XV, 5; Rush to R. McConnell, April 1, 1948, in Rush's files; FAS administrative committee order, June 6, 1948, FAS I, 7; Meier to D. Higinbotham, November 15, 1951, FAS XII, 7.

Brookhaven national laboratories contributed a great deal to FAS leadership in the years ahead.[32]

The federation had early adopted the practice of assigning topics for intensive study to particular local groups, and the continuation of this policy not only relieved the Washington office, but at the same time stimulated interest in new problems as chances for the Baruch plan diminished. The Cornell association's year-long study of clearance procedures, the Washington group's reports on science legislation, bacteriological warfare, and similar projects helped both to keep scientists themselves informed about new or changing fields and to provide a sound basis for FAS recommendations. After 1948 the Mohawk Valley Association of Scientists took over the educational activities that had previously been handled from the Washington office and later undertook the project of technical aid to foreign scientists, once hopefully discussed by the Committee for Foreign Correspondence, by collecting periodicals and funds for technical literature. For several years the Rochester chapter staffed an FAS committee on aid to foreign scientists, which concentrated on obtaining graduate science fellowships and assistantships in the United States for foreign students.

As this program indicates, the FAS by 1948 had accepted a role in which politics and public education went hand in hand, and it stopped worrying about tax exempt status. Atomic education did not come to a halt with the collapse of the NCAI and ASAE. Where there was patent opportunity to co-operate with other groups and individuals, scientists could still be found to speak at conferences and participate in planning, as members of the Atomic Scientists of Chicago continued to do in the Midwest. By 1947, and continuing for some time thereafter, the offices of the FAS and the local associations, especially Chicago, were flooded with pencilled scrawls from school children across the country expressing with varying degrees of conviction and literacy their consuming sense of the importance of atomic energy and their desire for information. When the NCAI dissolved the New York Committee on Atomic Information was formed by scientists, lawyers, and educators to stimulate rather than

   [32] FAS newsletters for 1949–50, FAS files (Washington, D.C.); W. A. Higinbotham, "The Federation of American Scientists," *Bulletin of the Atomic Scientists*, IV (January, 1948), 21–22; Clifford Grobstein, "The Federation of American Scientists," *Bulletin of the Atomic Scientists*, VI (February, 1950), 58, 61; Grobstein and A. H. Shapley, "The Federation of American Scientists," *Bulletin of the Atomic Scientists*, VII (January, 1951), 23–25.

carry out local programs. With Hugh Wolfe of ANYS as vice-chairman, it continued for several years to distribute reports, provide speakers and exhibits, and through special committees—religious and welfare, legal, and medical—to study social and ethical implications, the working of the McMahon Act, and medical uses of atomic energy. The most durable of several co-ordinating groups formed after the war was the Council on Atomic Implications, which began in 1946 at the University of Southern California and, staffed by faculty and students in the natural and social sciences, continued to provide a reference library, films, and speakers in the Los Angeles area, where a more limited scientists' organization had proved shortlived.[33]

3. CONTINUING RESPONSIBILITIES

From these organizational readjustments the FAS emerged with clipped wings but with sufficient vitality to maintain its place as the organization primarily concerned with the relation of atomic energy, and increasingly of science, to public policy. As far as its own goals and program were concerned the crisis of 1947 had no definitive conclusion. No break occurred with world government enthusiasts. In the following fall and winter all FAS groups were importuned to support plans for a constituent assembly in Geneva in 1950, but adherence to such projects remained an individual matter, and the scientists who thought it worthwhile to work for world federation either divided their efforts or transferred them while others, similarly disenchanted with international control, took refuge in inactivity. But with varying degrees of commitment and conviction a core of FAS members continued to follow with proprietary interest negotiations in the UNAEC as they reached acknowledged deadlock in the spring of 1948, were brightened now and then by hints of progress, and finally merged in 1951 in the work of the UN Disarmament Commission. There was little scientists could do beyond keeping themselves informed and maintaining their insistence that satisfactory agreement depended upon the broadest possible factual understanding. It was not an exhilarating role, nor was accomplishment easy to measure. From time to time federation scientists tried to check their own technical statements, some of which they now admitted had been little more than hastily improvised collective hunches. In July,

---

[33] Reports on the NYCAI and the Council on Atomic Implications appeared in *Bulletin of the Atomic Scientists*, VI (February, 1950), and VII, 1 (January, 1951); for early material relating to the Council on Atomic Implications, see ASC XI, 2, and FAS XXV, 5.

1947, when Urey was quoted as saying that it would take Russia ten years to make a bomb Higinbotham warned Secretary of State Marshall that this statement did not reflect the considered opinion of all scientists, but, he added, since no real investigation of the question had been made, neither individual nor group estimates were very significant. Russia might have decided to make one bomb as quickly as possible, and for this an industrial plant of only moderate size would suffice. Further investigation was desirable.[34] Periodically the FAS urged intensified study by the UNAEC of technical and economic aspects of the control problem and authorized investigation by its own members of biological warfare with special reference to how its development might affect United States policy on control of atomic weapons.

In the effort to keep the record straight and the factual base expanding, the FAS had firm support from the *Bulletin of the Atomic Scientists*, although its editorial views did not agree on all points with those of FAS leaders or local groups. The *Bulletin* regularly printed United Nations reports and official comments, as well as discussions of the increasingly complex ramifications of atomic energy and of the usefulness of science and technology to government. By June, 1947, its circulation was nearing twenty thousand, and it was reaching scientists in seventeen different countries.

This period of transition also saw some review of the premises on which scientists had based their entry into politics two years earlier. Then they had said that "faced with the same set of facts, we have all reached certain conclusions." Now from the same set of facts different conclusions were being drawn. Their dismay at this awkward development was compounded by a more vivid realization of complexity. True, they had from the beginning described atomic weapons as but the most sinister manifestation of the larger problem of war; at the same time, by their own admission, they had tried to treat international control as an isolated problem.[35] "It is a custom in science—and perhaps a principle," James Franck once told a Chicago audience, "to select from the infinite reservoir of unsolved problems only those simple ones whose solution seems possible in terms of available knowledge and skills. We are trained to subject our results to the most severe criticism. Adherence to these two principles results in our knowing very little, but, on the other hand,

---

[34] Higinbotham to Marshall, July 14, 1947, FAS XXIV, 2.

[35] See speech by M. S. Freedman to National Association of Public Relations Counsels, April 30, 1946, text in ASC II, 2; and Geneva Conference Report (June 18–21, 1947), Appendix II, FAS XIV, 1.

being very certain that we really know this little."[36] It was in this spirit that the FAS had initiated the study of inspection and control, and it was the triumph of this method that the report of the UNAEC scientific and technical committee in September, 1946, had seemed for a time to symbolize. "We need not deny that the issues that have arisen are serious ones," said an FAS policy statement shortly after that report was completed. "But we know that in the sphere where we are competent there is a solution; we must have confidence that in other spheres also solutions can be found."[37] Subsequent lack of progress led to doubts of the applicability of this principle to politics and contributed to the decision of some scientists to drop organized activity, and yet the belief that the isolation and solution of a limited problem might serve as a pattern for attack on more complex and difficult ones has never been entirely abandoned by American scientists, some of whom, in recent years, have worked stubbornly for a test ban, less from belief in its intrinsic importance than because they hoped to establish a prototype for a broader agreement on arms control.

Another readjustment closely related to their habitual behavior as scientists had to do with their growing remoteness from the "facts" as members of the original Manhattan Project site groups left for other jobs. The self-education programs of the local associations and the tireless efforts of the *Bulletin* to provide information about new developments were designed to help close the factual gap. In the field of biological warfare the FAS had few specialists and made a specific effort in 1947 to get qualified biologists to join. But in the field of particular concern—atomic weapons—the requirements of military security vitiated all such efforts, and the gloomy prediction that the military would soon say "Only we can judge," was in some measure to be fulfilled.[38] Increasingly scientists found themselves without the kind of information on which a conscientious member of the profession likes to base an opinion, and this contributed to a temporary retreat from the field of international politics.

Inevitably, American scientists turned more and more to domestic problems although their concept of the implications of atomic energy as a seamless web made the distinction dubious. Of central impor-

[36] Speech to an Emergency Committee of Atomic Scientists luncheon, February 8, 1947, *Bulletin of the Atomic Scientists*, III (March, 1947), 70.
[37] FAS policy statement, December 9, 1946, ASC XIII, 16.
[38] M. S. Freedman to ASC executive committee, April 8, 1949, in Jaffey's files.

tance obviously would be the composition of the domestic Atomic Energy Commission and how it interpreted its sweeping mandate. Officially, the federation expressed great satisfaction over its membership as announced by President Truman on October 28, 1946: David Lilienthal, who resigned as director of TVA to accept the chairmanship, Rear Admiral Lewis L. Strauss, a Wall Street investment banker, Sumner T. Pike, formerly of the Securities and Exchange Commission, William T. Waymack, editor of the Des Moines *Register and Tribune,* and as the one scientist member, physicist Robert F. Bacher, once of Los Alamos, now back at Cornell.[39] Compared with the fury of their intervention at certain stages in the legislative battle, the scientists' role in these appointments was a passive one, limited to lists of possible candidates from local groups and individuals and official FAS backing of Lilienthal as chairman. However, when the question of Lilienthal's confirmation provoked a long fight in the Senate in early 1947, the FAS revived on a modest scale the tactics that had saved the McMahon bill and promoted telegrams to wavering senators. "I don't believe official FAS statements changed one vote for Lilienthal," Higinbotham later remarked in arguing that the FAS need not retain its lobbying function, "but the united stand of all scientists and the thousands of personal letters were effective.[40]

A united stand again proved its value in the summer of 1949 when the AEC rode out charges of "incredible mismanagement" precipitated by the granting of a fellowship for non-secret work to a Communist. An FAS administrative committee defense of commission policy was supplemented by individual endorsements. When these came from people of such stature in the atomic energy program as Enrico Fermi and Walter Zinn, they may well have carried more weight than statements by an organization. But individuals rarely undertake extensive investigations or maintain the kind of steady pressure that the FAS did at this period on such questions as FBI investigation of non-secret fellowships, the distribution of radioisotopes to foreign scientists, and security and clearance procedures.

Distribution of isotopes was of particular interest as a gesture that might assure scientists in western Europe who were dismayed by

---

[39] *New York Times,* October 29, 1946, pp. 1, 3; for background of appointments and sketches of commissioners, see Richard G. Hewlett and Oscar E. Anderson, Jr., *The New World,* 1939–1945 (University Park: Pennsylvania State University Press, 1962), pp. 620–22, 639–40 (referred to hereinafter as *The New World*).

[40] Higinbotham memorandum on tax exemption, December 29, 1947, AORES XVII, 10.

continued bomb production. In June, 1947, after some months of discussion the FAS made public a letter to the AEC requesting such distribution, and President Truman's September announcement that export would be permitted was welcomed. Local associations were asked to look for ways of improving the service, and on the basis of reports from Washington, D.C., and Berkeley, the FAS proposed that distribution be turned over to a United Nations agency to avoid complaints of discrimination. This did not happen, and the FAS continued to view critically the isotope export policy of the AEC, with some federation members protesting vigorously when Commissioner Strauss later stopped a shipment of radioactive iron to Norway.[41]

The twin problems of security and clearance were more complex. In accepting the principle that information about weapons technology should be withheld until international agreement was reached, American scientists had committed themselves to some measure of secrecy, but their wartime experiences, plus the Canadian spy affair and the rumblings of the House Un-American Activities Committee, made them extremely sensitive to the manner in which this policy of partial secrecy was handled by its new guardian, the AEC. When the first instances of refusal of clearance on seemingly inadequate grounds or without due regard to civil rights were brought to the attention of the FAS council in February, 1947, its members disclaimed competence to consider facts but recognized the federation's responsibility for insuring decent procedures. It therefore authorized studies of the whole problem of security and personnel clearance, and these were eventually concentrated in the hands of a committee of nine members of the Cornell association. Mindful of the difficulties facing the commission in this area, the FAS avoided public comment and pending completion of the study merely made representations to the commission about a scientist's right to know the grounds of clearance refusal and to have a hearing.

For nearly a year the Cornell committee studied procedures, collected case histories, talked with lawyers, conducted a poll, and in December, 1947, recommended a clearance policy that the FAS council accepted and forwarded to the AEC. In the case of unclassified research carried out in university, industrial, or government

---

[41] FAS council minutes, February 1–2, 1947, FAS I, 5; other material in AORES XVII, 10, and XVIII, 4; news items in *Bulletin of the Atomic Scientists*, IV (May, 1948), 138, and IV (August, 1948), 248.

laboratories, no loyalty check should be required of employees or applicants, and such laboratories should isolate their secret projects. For classified work, the committee did not attempt to set down precise criteria but deplored the use of guilt on the basis of association or of unsubstantiated rumor. Refusal of clearance should not be made public or communicated to a prospective employer unless classified work was involved. Hearings should be held before a jury of working scientists in the field involved; the defendant should be given a detailed statement of charges, and other normal safeguards should be maintained. Richard Meier forwarded these recommendations to Chairman Lilienthal on January 9, 1948. Ten days later the AEC announced the appointment of the Personnel Security Review Board under the chairmanship of former Supreme Court Justice Owen J. Roberts and with President K. T. Compton of M.I.T. representing scientists. Beginning on February 1 the whole question was opened up for discussion in the *Bulletin of the Atomic Scientists* with articles on AEC interim procedures, on the Cornell report, and on specific clearance cases. In October, 1948, the FAS set up a scientists' committee on loyalty problems, with headquarters in Princeton, to provide information and advice to scientists with clearance problems.[42]

When the AEC finally issued its permanent clearance procedures in September, 1950, it was noted by the FAS chroniclers of an otherwise discouraging year that they included almost all the improvements recommended by the federation's committee on loyalty problems and that rules adopted by other government agencies reflected the same influence.[43] Renewed activity by the House Un-American Activities committee after 1948, especially the recurrent charges against Bureau of Standards director E. U. Condon, kept FAS interest in the subject of clearance alive and vigorous through the period of the Oppenheimer case and the McCarthy era.

Scientists naturally took a keen day-to-day interest in the workings of declassification. Satisfaction with the volume of material released by the Manhattan Engineer District after the Tolman committee

---

[42] FAS council minutes, February 1–2, March 15–16, and May 4, 1947, FAS I, 5, and August 9–10 and December 27–28, 1947, FAS I, 6; Meier to Lilienthal, January 9, 1948, ALAS II, 6; memorandum from FAS committee on security and clearance to members of FAS, November 22, 1947, AORES XVII, 10; articles and news items in *Bulletin of the Atomic Scientists*, IV (February–November, 1948).

[43] Grobstein and Shapley, "The Federation of American Scientists," *Bulletin of the Atomic Scientists*, VII (January, 1951), 23–25.

report of February, 1946, was tempered by annoyance that official lists were not distributed and could not be circulated outside the Project. For this reason the *Bulletin of the Atomic Scientists* printed long lists of declassified documents in its December, 1946, and January, 1947, issues. Victor Weisskopf reported that copies of declassified papers were not reaching scientists abroad, who concluded, therefore, that American science was more rigidly under guard than was actually the case.

When the new Atomic Energy Commission took over in January, 1947, it continued for some months to operate under the declassification system inherited from the Manhattan District, but it was observed that scientists' nerves were frayed by "bureaucratic obstructions and legalistic uncertainties" and that, however liberal the policy, some curtailment of discussion was inevitable because no scientist could become "a walking encyclopedia of declassification" and remember at a moment's notice whether he could legitimately take part in a certain discussion.[44] Inequalities between one field and another were attributed to the exercise of personal influence. On the whole, however, it was considered that the AEC took a sensible attitude and that declassification went along about as well as could be expected. Therefore, although it was much discussed by scientists and continued to be a matter of interest to the FAS, it was not a major issue. One aspect of the information question caused considerable chagrin—that under the McMahon Act, for which scientists had worked so hard, it was impossible to talk with British friends and associates even about those subjects on which they had worked together during the war. This, like many other problems in their book, could be settled satisfactorily only when international agreement reduced the need for secrecy.

"An Atomic Development Authority will never live in a world where American science has become the armorer of war," declared an FAS policy draft of December, 1946. "We saw that when we fought for the principle of civilian control of atomic energy. In the same way we must speak against military support of research and for a National Science Foundation. Last year this issue was peripheral for us; this year it lies squarely in our path." Breaking its silence on

---

[44] Bart J. Bok, Francis Friedman, and Victor Weisskopf, "Security Regulations in the Field of Nuclear Research," *Bulletin of the Atomic Scientists*, III (November, 1947), 321–24, 344.

research and science legislation, the *Bulletin of the Atomic Scientists* had devoted most of its November issue to scientific demobilization, the role of large nuclear laboratories, the army's research program, Manhattan Project declassification, and a history of the Magnuson and Kilgore bills, which had failed to pass the Seventy-ninth Congress.[45]

With new science foundation bills scheduled for introduction when the Eightieth Congress convened early in 1947, the FAS took two steps to affirm its increased interest. One was participation in the Inter-Society Committee, formed in December, 1946, with some sixty representatives of scientific groups at the invitation of the American Association for the Advancement of Science. Higinbotham and Morrison represented the FAS, and Higinbotham reported regularly to the FAS council on the legislative picture as it appeared to the Inter-Society Committee.[46]

The other step taken by the FAS was to encourage a study of research patterns and science legislation by the local Washington association, whose members, mostly government employees, were inhibited in some kinds of political activity, but on this particular subject had much firsthand knowledge. Periodic reports of this study group, headed by Clifford Grobstein of the U.S. Public Health Service, appeared in *Science* and the *Bulletin* during the next few years.

The most promising science measure of the Eightieth Congress, Senator Alexander Smith's S. 526, was vetoed by President Truman in July, 1947, because its large unwieldy board was responsible to neither President nor Congress. Two more bills failed in the Eightieth Congress, and it was May, 1950, before a bill setting up a science foundation became law. Discussion of these various measures and of the August, 1947, report on scientific manpower by the President's Scientific Research Board under the chairmanship of John R. Steelman broadened enormously the familiarity of all scientists with the problems relating to federal sponsorship of research. Yet no group

---

[45] FAS administrative committee draft statement, December 9, 1946, ASC XIII, 16; articles in *Bulletin of the Atomic Scientists*, II (November 1, 1946) included Philip Morrison's "The Laboratory Demobilizes" and Lee A. DuBridge's "The Role of Large Laboratories in Nuclear Research."

[46] Higinbotham and Philip Powers of the Washington FAS group had talked earlier about the need for a committee to work out compromise legislation and lead a political campaign, with the FAS perhaps putting a scientist on its staff to act as executive secretary. Higinbotham memorandum to FAS administrative committee, November 21, 1946, in Rush's files; *Science*, CV (January 3, 1947), 7, and CV (January 31, 1947), 117.

stood ready to put behind the passage of science legislation the concentrated effort that the FAS had put into the McMahon Act. Indeed, the federation itself immediately sidestepped the issue of a federal research policy, which it had described as squarely in its path, and gave top priority to security and clearance, in which as a consequence it was able to point to substantial results. Its members did show some interest, to be sure, in certain topics relating to the organization of research and the allotment of funds, but they continued to regard the question of administrative responsibility, which seemed to be the chief stumbling block to passage of legislation as lying largely outside their field of competence. By this time most scientists, even those hitherto engrossed in problems of atomic energy, had read Vannevar Bush's *Science—the Endless Frontier,* and the realization of how well its author understood the basic character of science— its dependence upon freedom, its capacity for self-management, and its relation to human welfare—made even those who had disliked his Project research policies reluctant to take issue with his view that the administration of a science foundation must be independent of political pressures.

The first report submitted by the Washington association study group in the autumn of 1947 took FAS scientists sternly to task for this attitude, claiming that the difference of opinion on how the foundation should be administered was not a superficial matter but stemmed from a conflict of fundamental philosophies—the one conceiving of science as a national resource, with the nation's scientific manpower as its raw material, for which elected representatives should be responsible; the other regarding science as an auxiliary to the development of industry, medicine, and the national defense and wishing to expand research and development within the existing haphazard structure. Almost everyone wanted science to be controlled by civilians, the study group reported, but while the argument dragged on, military control was increasing and fundamental science, in which America was weakest, was being neglected for applied. The report continued:

As scientists we cannot escape our share of responsibility for the present hazardous state. Congressmen who were interviewed displayed a flattering interest in the views of scientists and their organizations on national science legislation, but many confessed their lack of knowledge of details of the legislation and stated that they had had little advice from home to guide them. One remarked ruefully that, if this were a labor issue, he would have heard from every labor leader in his district. He was forced to conclude that scientists were not very much interested one way or the other.[47]

The study committee did not refer to the McMahon bill campaign, but the contrast was obvious, consisting partly in what scientists themselves had done to "educate" and prod legislators but quite as much in what they had inspired others to do. It would indeed have been difficult to present to citizens' committees the character of a research establishment either as so sharp an issue or as one so patently their concern as the civilian control of atomic energy. But even more important, scientists themselves conspicuously lacked the certitude and unanimity of the earlier occasion. Their attitudes toward increased government control were now undergoing the kind of readjustment that had taken place in the American business community fifteen years earlier. But the process was neither so long nor so painful, and in a very short time suspicions of government sponsorship of science were allayed by the extremely enlightened handling of research funds in the newly established Office of Naval Reseach. At the same time the transformation under the Atomic Energy Commission of the wartime atomic research centers and the establishment of the Brookhaven National Laboratory gave reassuring evidence of support for basic science. Government was evidently to be a far more benign and generous patron than most scientists had believed possible. And far less dictatorial, for the rapid incorporation of scientists into government in an advisory role meant that they themselves were to a large extent able to call the tune. Then, too, scientists began more honestly to face the fact that what they had to fear was not so much the voracious desire of military men to control them as their own technological skills in devising destruction. Such changing viewpoints—and these merely suggest some facets of a large and important subject—speeded the return to normal divergencies of opinion on the social and political implications of science, which had been temporarily submerged in the common anxiety about the release of atomic energy.

Further developments in the scientists' movement can here be indicated only in the most general terms. After 1948 it meant virtually the *Bulletin of the Atomic Scientists* and a hard core of a hundred or so among the federation membership. By this time the exaggerated

[47] As printed in *Bulletin of the Atomic Scientists*, III (December, 1947), 357–58, 369.

acclaim bestowed upon scientists had begun to subside. Russia—even earlier than most scientists had foreseen—exploded her own atomic bomb, and in the absence of agreement in the United Nations the armaments race that scientists had predicted picked up momentum. Two scientists abroad, and later two less prominent technical men in the United States, were convicted as traitors, and the varying degrees of internationalism to which American scientists subscribed made them tempting if not in the end very satisfactory targets even before the climax of the McCarthy hysteria. Those who remained committed to political activity through the FAS were principally engaged in defending members of their profession and the integrity of science.

Certain issues relating to security, such as declassification of information, were peculiarly the scientists' problems. So was the Astin case of 1953, in which the Secretary of Commerce overruled the judgment of the Bureau of Standards that a certain battery additive was useless and dismissed Director A. V. Astin when he protested. With a unanimity reminiscent of the autumn of 1945, and prophetic of the response to the Oppenheimer case, American scientists raised such an outcry that Astin was reinstated. Other problems, such as passport and visa restrictions and loyalty investigations, of which Condon's, beginning in 1948, and Oppenheimer's in 1954, provided the two most publicized cases, gave scientists a common cause in the field of civil liberties with other intellectuals.

Although scientists' anxiety about these matters was not confined to the FAS, it found a focus there and was in some cases first alerted by the federation's Washington office, which still maintained useful contacts with people in the press and in government and kept a watchful eye on the utilization of science, particularly of atomic energy, and such questions as the development of atomic power, other peaceful applications, the wisdom of a crash program for an H-bomb, and UNESCO's technical aid to underdeveloped countries. But except where some strong consensus existed among scientists, the FAS was no longer in a position to do much but provide information, warn of impending trouble, and formulate positions. In the seven or eight years following 1947 even the successful battles were fought in a mood of disenchantment with public affairs, and perhaps this was why scientists did not demand a positive role in policy-making with the same vigor they showed in defending the integrity of science and scientists. The FAS had early called for science advisers on the President's staff and in the State Department, but when the first moves in this direction miscarried, protests from the scientific community at large were mild and sporadic.

And yet in retrospect the period of diminished influence was by no means unfruitful. Writing in 1956, Edward Shils, University of Chicago sociologist and a sympathetic if sometimes critical ally of the local scientists, concluded that the anti-scientific bias in the anti-intellectualism of the preceding years had been the Parthian shots of an adversary in retreat. Scientists both in and out of government, Shils believed, had acquired greater influence in the previous decade. He viewed the scientists' movement as a unique phenomenon that had introduced a new element into American public life.

On almost every issue which has aroused the interest of our scientists' movement, something arising from the efforts of the scientists has stuck and deflected the course of political or administrative action toward what was almost always a more reasonable course—through prodding, reminding, pointing out, through the embodiment of an outlook or state of mind which reasserted the values of detachment and generosity of judgment, of freedom from tyrannous passion, and of the desirability of objective inquiry and of calm reflection.[48]

The year 1955 now appears to have represented a peak of anti-scientific feeling, but the relaxation of tension that came with the decline of McCarthy brought not a return of the overinflated prestige of post-Hiroshima days but rather a more sensible expectation in both scientists and public of what their contribution to public life might be. The channels through which scientists now try to make that contribution have changed with a renewal of communication with scientists abroad, greater unofficial participation in discussion of policy, and a much enlarged role in official decisions. In August, 1955, a Conference on the Peaceful Uses of Atomic Energy was held in Geneva, initiated by the United States Atomic Energy Commission as part of the international atoms for peace program. For the first time in many years, scientists from both sides of the iron curtain heard each other's papers and chatted informally in corridors; and although they talked about research, not politics, implicit in the title of the conference was a concern with how science is applied. It was a highly reassuring occasion, not only because the United States government sponsored the exchange of information over a wide field and included in its large delegation many scientists who had con-

---

[48] Shils, "Freedom and Influence: Observations on the Scientists' Movement in the United States," *Bulletin of the Atomic Scientists*, XIII (January, 1957), 13–18.

sistently challenged official policy, but because the meeting demonstrated that science still carried within itself the seeds of a genuine world community.

Shortly before the Geneva conference Bertrand Russell, Albert Einstein, and other Nobel Prize winners had appealed to their fellow scientists to take a more active part in solving problems of war and peace. From this appeal developed the Pugwash Conferences on Science and World Affairs, named for the Nova Scotia village where the first meeting took place in 1957. At least once a year since then scientists from east and west have met in Canada, western Europe, Moscow, or the United States to talk with relative frankness about the technical and political angles of biological warfare, radiation, the banning of nuclear tests, the avoidance of accidental war, the social responsibility of scientists, and their contribution to underdeveloped societies.

More formal international organizations have also gathered strength in recent years. The Society for Social Responsibility in Science includes those who refuse to work on research with direct military application. The American Association of Scientific Workers, although overshadowed in the political field by the FAS and on a broader level by the growing acceptance of responsibility by the professional societies, is affiliated with the World Federation of Scientific Workers, whose influence is very strong, especially in the Asiatic countries. Thus through a variety of media scientists continue to assert the faith in an international fraternity of science and in its contributions to peace that was so strong a motivating force in what they tried to do after the war.

In July, 1960, the preface to a long report from the Committee on Science and Human Welfare of the American Association for the Advancement of Science made what was to some a declaration of the obvious fact "that scientists bear a serious and immediate responsibility to help mediate the effects of scientific progress on human welfare, and that this obligation should be reflected in the program of the AAAS." Yet coming from the organization most broadly representative of American science which had hitherto studiously ignored non-scientific questions, it meant that the entire profession had responded to the stirrings of conscience that had moved some of its members for many years.

Even before the post-McCarthy thaw the FAS and a few individual voices had tried to revive something of the earlier idealism on specific issues: in 1954 David Inglis, Argonne Laboratory physicist, and an FAS committee suggested a test ban; Ralph Lapp, a physicist turned writer, tried almost alone for a time to publicize the dangers of excessive radiation; and Linus Pauling, a Nobel prize-winning chemist at Cal Tech, fascinated large audiences with his descriptions of the wonders of science and the horrors of its misuse, and his petition to stop nuclear testing eventually bore the signatures of thousands of scientists around the world.

The FAS has consistently supported test ban negotiations and the establishment of a United States arms control agency and has opposed the spread of nuclear weapons. It has undertaken or encouraged studies of detection techniques, of radiation effects, of the value of the "clean bomb," and of a shelter program. Quite as important is the work done in areas relating to arms control by members, or former members, under other auspices, official or private. Scientists criticize themselves for having rendered little more than lip service to the international atoms-for-peace program and to the science-related side of UNESCO's work, but, in fact, the spirit of the postwar Committee for Foreign Correspondence was perpetuated in the FAS programs of fellowships and technical aid for foreign scientists.

The sharpened sense of responsibility has led some scientists to work for peace and security not through negotiation and accommodation but through stronger armaments. Many, indeed, have found it possible to follow both paths at once, hoping that they will reach the same destination, a schizophrenic reaction that is only more obvious among scientists than among others, not more common. It has, in fact, become official policy.

But by far the greatest change in the relation of scientists to public affairs has been their incorporation into the fabric of government, a development that owes as much to the reliance of Soviet leaders on their technical men as it does to the intrinsic merits of the counsel given by our own. Not so much because scientists have demanded a part as because their technological skills have become indispensable, a vast web of advisory channels now exists through which thousands of scientists on a part-time and *ad hoc* basis feed facts and opinions to those who annually dispense billions of dollars in research funds and fellowships and those who write party platforms, define goals of national policy, or negotiate with foreign countries. Added to these are a growing number of full-time science posts in government—assistant secretaryships in important departments capped by the President's own scientific adviser and advisory committee. Those who have pioneered in this advisory role feel that the specialist serving in an *ad hoc* capacity does not adequately fill the need and that what the times now require is, in the words of George Kistiakowsky, one-time science adviser to President Eisenhower, "a new kind of public servant, who combines scientific training with the skills of policy maker and diplomat."

James R. Killian, Jr., Kistiakowsky's predecessor as presidential science adviser, also challenged his fellow scientists and engineers to give serious thought to the spirit in which they performed their new duties in a speech to the American Association for the Advancement of Science:

The growing linkage of science and technology with government demands of science a new order of poise, steadiness, and statesmanship. It demands of scientists who serve in advisory capacities a deep understanding of the role and limitation of the adviser.

The current emphasis on science, if it is not to cause reactions adverse to science, also requires of the scientific community humility and a sense of proportion. It requires of scientists a recognition that science is but one of the great disciplines vital to our society and worthy of first-rate minds, a recognition that science is a partner—sharing and shouldering equally the responsibilities which vest in the great array of professions which provide the intellectual and cultural strength of our society.[49]

Judged by this definition the efforts of the atomic scientists to influence public opinion and public policy after the Second World War seem fumbling and crude, but if most scientists were then unprepared by the suddenness of the change to play a more mature role, government was equally unprepared to receive them. To what will be a continuing process of individual and collective adjustment, the story of these critical years may lend some perspective.

---

[49] Killian, "Science and Public Policy," reprinted in *Bulletin of the Atomic Scientists*, XV (April, 1959), 168–72.

CHAPTER 18

In Conclusion

To INVEST THE skeleton of fact with the flesh and blood of motive, personal reaction, and minor incident we have followed in great detail a phenomenon without precedent in the annals of the scientific profession, when some three thousand members of it abandoned their customary role as fashioners of tools of social and political change and tried to direct that change toward a particular end. Numerically the three thousand were a small proportion of the country's scientific and technical workers, but by virtue of their recent technological triumph, they enjoyed extraordinary individual and collective prestige; and although there were many who remained outside the movement because they found political activity uncongenial and others who frankly disapproved, yet it was the views and the actions of the articulate minority that now seem to have represented the prevailing mood and temper of American scientists.

The principal motive power behind the scientists's movement was the feeling of responsibility, and in some sense and in some people of regret, for the part played by science and technology in the orgy of destruction that had just ended and a fervent hope that controlling the atom might be a step toward the elimination of force as a means of settling international disputes. Whether this acceptance of responsibility resulted from a gradual awakening or whether it came with traumatic suddenness, it was the most powerful of the influences that drew people into the movement. Many men of good will at this period followed a natural instinct toward healing by subscribing to some form of international collaboration, but for scientists who had worked on the bomb, there was particular appeal in corporate activity, especially in something that could be openly avowed and freely discussed. After the pressures and the externally imposed goals of the war years, it was not easy, especially for the young men, to return to normal routines of research, and this period of self-initiated involvement in a common cause provided a salutary transition to less rigidly controlled conditions of work. Although it may at first appear that the evangelical zeal with which scientists embarked on public education and lobbying was entirely out of character with the rationalist temper of their calling, yet their moral earnestness often had deep roots in backgrounds of Judaism or evangelical Protestantism, for whose creeds and tenets had been substituted the no less compelling obligation of the scientist to find and disseminate truth. The sense of mission—the impulse to use their special knowledge to save mankind from disaster—was strong enough to overcome normal reluctance to join and organize for any but strictly professional purposes.

Although this study has centered on a group rather than on individuals, it indicates that one cannot generalize about the aptitude of scientists for politics. Some showed a great deal, some very little. But evaluations have often ignored the fact that they were not trying to be politicians; they were trying rather to be lobbyists and publicists. Collectively, they brought to this task experience in working together, in analyzing problems and laying out a course of action, and in devising ways (if not always means) to carry it out. They brought certain skills in explication and communication. And they brought the flexible approach that good research men and good engineers must have. But although conviction that their ideas sprang from incontrovertible scientific facts enabled them to speak with moving sincerity, it also led to a certain inflexibility in ideas once adopted. Insofar as scientists did become politicians and try to get things done, their tendency to concentrate on an objective was both a strength and a weakness. And it is noteworthy that men who could accept with reasonable equanimity the ups and downs of research plunged more easily from hope to despair when faced with disappointment in the unfamiliar world of politics and that customary tolerance of diversity of opinion sometimes gave way to warm and far from dispassionate judgments.

One tends to assume that any general lessons in lobbying and education offered by the scientists' movement of 1946 must by now have been absorbed by those in a position to profit from them, but as one observes the emergence in 1964 of a broadly based effort by intellectuals aggressively to promote the cause of peace, it seems possible that certain points about the earlier period might serve as warnings and guide lines. "The FAS has been able to exert an influence on public policy out of all proportion to its numerical strength," wrote J. H. Rush in early 1947 in commenting on demands for broadened objectives,

and that success has been due in large measure to its refusing to take sides on any issue except atomic energy control and directly related matters such as the Science Foundation. We have thus been able to draw support from an amazing variety of people and organizations, from the CIO to the Educational Committee of the NAM and from Baptist preachers to Catholic bishops by saying in effect, "You argue over your differences later; but first we all must survive."[1]

Unity and concentration, as Rush indicated, were immensely important; they attracted support and bolstered internal morale. It is worth noting, too, that scientists probably made their most useful contribution to civilian and international control by an extension of their customary functions of collecting and providing information; and by enlisting the aid of existing organizations, their own initial effort was multiplied many times. Their influence was also greatly magnified by their wooing of the press and radio, but their success with the mass media was limited by failure to make as strong an impression on editors and producers as they did on reporters and commentators. Familiar as were their techniques to experienced lobbyists, there is still perhaps a lesson for amateurs in the skillful use of prestige, in the cultivation of a few receptive people in Congress and the supplying of them with copious quotable evidence of voter interest in the form of mail and petitions, in the repetitive harping on a few points, and in the judicious use of outbursts of anger and impatience.

What did this unusual manifestation of interest in politics actually accomplish, and was the contemporary impression that it had a revolutionary effect upon the thinking and behavior of American scientists indeed a valid one? Granting that there is room for some

---

[1] Draft of letter from Rush to P. Cohen, January 6, 1947, in Rush's files.

qualification on every point, we may legitimately argue that the scientists who subscribed to the views of the Federation of American Scientists succeeded in mobilizing the support that established civilian control of atomic energy, contributed significantly to agreement on technical aspects of international control, and made substantial headway on the vast job of educating laymen in the facts and implications of a particular technological development and hence in a small way of science and technology in general. The scientists had the common experience of finding that the teacher learns more than the taught. And the autocatalytic effect of their efforts to make others understand the impact of science, particularly on international relations, can be traced in the later behavior of certain individual scientists who have been in close touch with those who determine national policy. Because of the professional stature of those in whom this new sensitivity was evoked, an interest in public affairs no longer requires apology. Although scientists freely acknowledged that political problems were more stubborn than technical ones, some of them learned much from the actual experience of political complexity.

In the Federation of American Scientists, the movement produced a watchdog over the relations of science and public policy that has done a good deal over the years to protect science and scientists from attack and also, by providing a medium for self-criticism, from the temptations of their own success. By guarding the rights of a particular profession in a dangerous period in the 1950's the FAS contributed to the general cause of civil liberties. The impulse that produced the federation has also generated and fostered a series of projects to answer particular needs—the *Bulletin of the Atomic Scientists*, the Pugwash Conferences on Science and World Affairs, numerous non-government studies of arms control and defense—and has initiated one step toward agreement, the test ban treaty of 1963. Scientists with their fingers on the pulse of power have sometimes tended to write off the FAS and its satellite activities as less effective than their own more direct pressure, but its ability to mobilize opinion in a time of crisis has been on many occasions a bulwark to their own influence.

When an organization has once been dynamic, a levelling-off of interest is often regarded as a sign of failure, but the static condition that the FAS has maintained for the past fifteen years represents not so much failure as the fact that a majority of scientists still find political activity unappealing and that for those with a developed taste for helping to mold decisions a more congenial means of doing so has opened up. The greater participation of scientists in government as advisers and even as policy-makers that has been such a marked phenomenon of the mid-twentieth century is linked with the intense postwar interest in control of atomic energy in ways that defy an easy attribution of cause and effect. It is possible to conclude that this development received some impetus from increased interest on the part of scientists themselves; it is quite probable that their insistence that atomic policy be decided on the basis of the fullest possible technical information left its mark on other fields of science. Or one can argue that these changes were hastened only slightly by the war and subsequent readjustments, and that science and government have been drawn together far more by mutual need—for technical advice, on the one hand, and for research money, on the other—than because scientists have demanded a voice in determination of policy. Indeed it seems clear that they would now be sitting on Washington panels, advising the President and his cabinet, and testifying before congressional committees had there been no war and no scientists' movement. What has drawn most scientists to Washington is a sense of duty to see that science is wisely used or fairly treated (fortified, to be sure, by satisfaction in finding their services in such demand), and this would have operated at any time that was technologically ripe.

But if the flurry of organized activity after the war was a response to unusual circumstances and if it was only a minor factor in the new official status of scientists, one can at least say that the experiences of the first two postwar years amply highlighted certain difficulties that the new relationship would entail. First there was the relatively simple one of time that was in part responsible for the manpower shortage that so early reduced the vigor of the federation. In some intellectual fields practical experience and breadth of responsibility add both to professional prestige and to competence, but in a rapidly advancing area of science even a few months absence can leave a man far behind. Far more than a lawyer or an economist, a scientist who becomes a government adviser or administrator loses touch with his own research and his authority as a scientist is likely to diminish. For the young this is professionally fatal; for their elders it is at best a deflating experience and at worst a heartbreaking one. A few with special luck and special gifts emerge with on aura of scientific statesmanship, but this is ephemeral and for many not worth the risks.

There was also the problem of leadership. Those who had stimulated others to think about the implications of atomic energy were not the type to organize and provide consistent guidance, whereas those equipped to organize and administer were already identified with official policy and therefore unable or unwilling to lead an essentially insurgent movement, however sympathetic they might be with its goals and principles. Others were inhibited by tradition and personal tastes, so that when the young men in the federation office were asked whether senior scientists supported their efforts they answered that certain well-known figures had indeed helped to write statements or signed petitions but had to admit that they were not in Washington spearheading action. And when things seemed to be going badly in Congress or the UNAEC, critics within the federation would demand that one mature leader be chosen. But again no one was available, ostensibly for reasons of time but quite as much because of reluctance to direct and organize opinion and tell others what to do in this new and uncertain field. Several of those best equipped for leadership were already serving as confidential advisers to White House and State Department and could not speak publicly on the issues to which the federation was addressing itself. In 1945 and 1946 this handicap was, perhaps, more apparent than real, for to outsiders the youth, spontaneity, and anonymity of spokesmen for the federation distinguished the movement from the ordinary run of causes and gave its pronouncements authority of a novel kind. But in the long run, as people with special technical knowledge, wise understanding of non-technical problems, or marked ability to explain technical matters to laymen have been seized upon by official agencies, the rank and file have been left without natural leaders and spokesmen.

It also became clear in the early months after the war that the formulation of opinion on issues involving science by any large segment of the scientific community was going to be increasingly difficult. When the war ended a substantial number of people possessed up-to-date information about atomic energy, radar, or other wartime research and as they turned to other subjects, despite security restrictions, they still constituted a body of reasonably well-informed external observers of policy. But this situation did not last long, and as time went on there were few technical problems among the growing number of interest to government upon which scientists and engineers outside the confidential inner circle felt confident they knew enough to offer valid opinions. As with the inspection studies that the Federation of Atomic Scientists so hopefully initiated in November, 1945, responsibility had to be delegated to a small group but without the checks that we like to think operate in a democracy. The FAS has tried to provide or inspire critical appraisal on such topics as radioactive fallout, test detection, and a shelter program, only to be faced with the dilemma that on many questions involving science and public affairs those who know cannot speak whereas those who are free to speak often will not do so for fear that their information is not adequate.

Still another difficulty centered around the question of unanimity. Because scientists have claimed to provide the medium for revelation of truth about the physical world, one answer to any given question is expected of them, as, indeed, they have come to expect it of themselves; and when they disagree publicly, the authority of science is undermined to a greater degree than is that of other disciplines. In the process of reaching a consensus scientists tolerate uncertainty and even disagreement; the essence of science is, in fact, a curious mixture of certainty and doubt. But when scientists began speaking to a wider public, doubts had to be suppressed and certainties emphasized. For the first year after the war they were able to speak unanimously and therefore confidently about the facts of atomic energy and even about what these facts meant, but as they admitted first to divided opinion about the implications and later, on occasion, to disagreement about the facts, their authority suffered a grievous blow.

But of the problems confronting the scientists who wanted to influence atomic energy policy, the central and most thorny one was where to draw the line between those questions on which their opinion had a special value because they were scientists and those on which it counted simply because they were informed and greatly interested citizens. The easy answer—that the line fell between fact and interpretation—turned out to be a trap for the unwary and one not easy to avoid even with foresight. Oppenheimer's comment when he was appointed to the Interim Committee's scientific panel in the spring of 1945 was, "Now we are in for trouble." His fellow panel member A. H. Compton tried to settle the matter with the scientists-and-citizens formula, but his proposal to critics of the May-Johnson bill that they should speak as scientists about the research provisions but as citizens when they criticized the makeup of the commission struck them as a meaningless distinction. All scientists expected to draw the line somewhere, but those who challenged Compton's formula wanted a broader definition of the area in which scientific fact gave special insight. So did the young men at Oak Ridge who so vigorously took issue with the *New York Times* for questioning their fitness to express views about international affairs. Wherever the line was placed scientists were sure to cross it in private speculation. When they did so publicly it was as likely to be at the invitation of the very people who questioned their political competence as through their own indiscretion, and they did not always show the resolution of the federation witnesses who ignored the request of the Senate special committee to prepare a list of specifications for international control. In two decades the complexity of this problem about the nature of scientists' advice and the limitations of their roles as scientists and citizens has been demonstrated time and again with little serious effort to resolve it by either the scientists themselves, the government agencies who hire them, or the public which alternately reveres and repudiates what they say. It is, of course, but a latter-day manifestation of an old, old problem of the intellectual in society exacerbated by a new and awful immediacy.

Appendixes

Prospectus on Nucleonics
(the Jeffries Report)

I. Introduction

Many of us have watched the birth and development of the electronics industry. From laboratory experiments a few decades ago electronics has developed into one of the most lusty of the sciences and industries. In *Electronics*, a trade and technical publication, 1618 companies are listed as electronics companies. Billions of dollars are being spent for electronic devices for war. The field seems to be headed for great post-war developments.

The word "electronics," as is well known, relates to electrons, the negatively charged particles whose normal home is in the outer parts of atoms. As is likewise well known, the center or core of every atom is an exceedingly small but relatively heavy positively charged group of particles called its nucleus. In this prospectus, we are going to present some thoughts on the potentialities of that expanding field of science and industry which deals with atomic nuclei.

We propose to use the word "nucleonics" as a name for this field.

Submitted to Arthur H. Compton, November 18, 1944, by the committee consisting of Zay Jeffries (chairman), R. S. Mulliken (secretary), Enrico Fermi, James Franck, T. R. Hogness, R. S. Stone, and C. A. Thomas (in Manhattan Engineer District files). The following sections are omitted: II. The Early History of Nucleonics; III. Nucleonics since 1939; IV. The Dawn of the Nucleonics Age.

Reflecting the modern trend toward close correlation between science and industry, and following the lead of "electronics," we propose that the word "nucleonics" shall refer to both science and industry in the nuclear field.

The science of nucleonics began with the discovery of natural radioactivity by Becquerel in 1896 and it is, therefore, about the same age as the science of electronics. There is also a nucleonics industry which is as old as the commercial production of radium. The radium, radon, mesothorium, and polonium industries may be regarded as parts of the nucleonics industry.

Major steps forward in the science of nucleonics were the first achievement of transmutation of the elements in 1919, the discovery of artificial or induced radioactivity, and the development of the cyclotron in the early nineteen-thirties.

Then, during the winter of 1938–39, when Hahn and his associates discovered atomic fission, the horizons of nucleonic science were so greatly enlarged that, even now, no one can foretell the consequences. It was discovered that the nucleus of uranium can be split in two and that the splitting is accompanied by the evolution of energy tens of millions of times larger than that of the most energetic chemical reactions. Soon afterwards, some observations on the details of this "nuclear fission" led to the faint hope that a means could be found to utilize the liberated energy for practical purposes. This was the reason for the establishment of the Metallurgical Project and other related projects in this and other countries. How the hope of releasing at will and utilizing nuclear energy, which had seemed fantastic only four years ago, has now been realized, and what problems for the future arise from this momentous discovery, will be discussed in several sections of this prospectus.

The Metallurgical Project was established for military purposes and has been operated as a secret military research and development project. The field of nucleonics, however, embraces a scope far greater than the military. In this prospectus, we shall make the attempt, speculatively, to foreshadow something of the immensity of the future development of nucleonics and of its effects on mankind.

As a springboard for our excursion into the future, we shall review in Section II the pre-war history of nucleonics, including the discovery of fission. In Section III we shall outline the crescendo of the wartime history of nucleonics within the Metallurgical Project, culminating in the first achievement of a nuclear power plant.

In Sections IV and V we shall speculate freely about what it may be possible to achieve with the new methods and new tools that we can now visualize. In Section VI we shall try to assess the political implications, both national and international, of the coming age of nucleonics; and we shall conclude in Section VII with a discussion and suggestions on the post-war organization of nucleonics research and industrial nucleonics in this country.

V. The Nearer Future of Nucleonics

We have attempted to give, in the preceding section, a general idea of the tools which the development of nucleonics promises to give mankind: a new source of energy, a source of radiations of extraordinary intensity, several new heavy elements of exceptionally interesting properties, and a vast assortment of radioactive isotopes of ordinary elements. Let us now survey a few of the infinite number of possible applications of these new tools in different spheres of science and technology.

Many of the suggestions enumerated below are speculative and we do not wish to imply that we expect that all will be put into practice. Nevertheless we believe that this group of suggestions, including the most speculative ones, does give a correct and not exaggerated impression of the *type* of development which is in store.

Physics.—Striking changes can be expected to follow from the availability of nuclear energy in both pure and applied science. The construction of the chain-reacting pile is a notable example of how disinterested research in a field of physics apparently far remote from any practical interest can suddenly yield results of tremendous technological value. The potential practical importance of pure research is likely to be shown in this case even more clearly than in the well-known example of the development of the electrical industries from the discovery of electromagnetism by Faraday.

In the haste of wartime development, further basic experimental and theoretical research on the true nature of atomic nuclei, although it provided the basis for the realization of the nuclear chain reaction in the pile, has of necessity been neglected. After the war, this type of research will come into its own again. Making use of the powerful tools for nuclear transformation made available by the industrial development of the pile, the science of nucleonics will strive to penetrate deeper into the mystery of the nucleus. A better understanding of nuclear structure, acquired in this way, is certain to open new ways for the practical mastery of nuclear forces. The old story of science and technology mutually assisting and promoting each other is likely to be repeated in nucleonics on a more spectacular scale than ever before. We have witnessed a development of this type in the wartime history of nucleonics, where the study of minute quantities of plutonium made accessible by the cyclotron technique has revealed the potentialities of this material as a source of nuclear power, and thus provided the incentive for the construction of large-scale plutonium-producing piles.

While nucleonics promises to become, after the war, the most lively part of theoretical and experimental physics, other branches of physics will undoubtedly benefit from the possibility of using the radiations from the pile, as well as pile-produced radioactive tracers. This will be particularly true of all studies of migration and exchange processes of the type of diffusion or evaporation, as well as of the investigations of the general properties of the crystalline and liquid states.

Chemistry and Chemical Engineering.—Pure and applied chemistry are likely to make an even wider use than physics of pile radiation and pile products. In the realm of inorganic chemistry, the study of the transuranic elements is certainly going to be eagerly pursued, particularly when these elements become more readily available. Suffice it to recall that the discovery of a single new element has always been considered an important step forward in the history of chemistry. The cyclotron and the pile have already made possible the discovery and production of two new elements, neptunium and plutonium, and may provide several more. The position of these elements at the extreme end of the periodic system makes their study very important for the better understanding of the latter.

The radiations of an operating pile are known to produce pronounced chemical and other changes in graphites, water, and other materials. In the future, these radiations can be used to bring about transformations of various materials which may be difficult or impossible to obtain in any other way. Such materials could be irradiated inside or outside the pile. A new "super-photochemistry" already is emerging from studies of this type. In contrast to light, the pile radiations (consisting of gamma rays and neutrons) are absorbed by every kind of matter. One may therefore anticipate difficulties in producing selectively the desired transformations; but certainly this will be found possible in some cases. As a result, pile irradiation may replace catalyst action or high temperature in various important chemical or physicochemical processes, such as nitrogen fixation, hardening of metals or plastics, cracking of petroleum oils, and chain polymerization as in making synthetic rubber.

An improved method of making liquid fuels from coal, lignite, cellulose, and the like, could perhaps be obtained. Natural gas with or without other added constituents, for example, water, carbon dioxide, ammonia, hydrogen sulfide, and so on, could be circulated over artificial radioactive material or through a pile, to produce synthetic rubbers, plastics, lubricating oils, fuels of special characteristics, and so on. It may prove feasible to synthesize certain low volume, high-priced organic chemicals by exposure to pile radiation.

The use of radioactive tracers also will become important for both pure and applied chemistry. In pure chemistry, the possibility of providing a radioactive "stand-in" for practically every ordinary element will give entirely new possibilities for all studies in the field of reaction kinetics, enabling the chemist to follow the fate of all components throughout a chemical process, and to detect transfers of atoms from place to place within a molecule, or from one molecule to another, even in the state of chemical equilibrium, where ordinary chemical methods show no change at all.

The use of the radioactive carbon isotope C^{14}, in particular, promises to create for the first time the possibility of investigating directly the mechanism of organic reactions, and of verifying the concepts which organic chemists have widely used in their work.

In applied chemistry, tracer methods will be important for the study of such processes as corrosion, diffusion, adsorption, and formation and destruction of colloids. They will be used for studying the performance of distillation columns and other equipment used in chemical engineering, for example in the oil industry. Particularly important as a tracer in the oil industry will be the carbon isotope C^{14}. Experimental chemical engineering, including research and development work on the unit operations, general trouble shooting work on chemical processes, and correlation of performance data on chemical process equipment, offers a wide variety of possibilities for useful applications of the tagged atom technique as an analytical method. In the rare gas industry, radioactive rare gases obtained as pile fission products will be very valuable.

In the study of fluid flow, radio-compounds can serve as metering fluids in the usual method of dilution measurement; they have a decided advantage in ease of analysis. Again, the linear velocity of liquid flow in a pipe can be measured by timing the successive appearance of activity at two points along its length. This method is of special value where circumstances are such that sampling is impossible; the activity can be detected through the pipe walls.

Biology and Medicine.—In medicine and in biological science, both the intense radiation emitted by the pile or by products made in it, and the radioactive tracer isotopes, will be of utmost usefulness. As we have stated before, a working pile may well become a center of biological radiation research and therapy. Radioactive fission products, as well as radioactive isotopes prepared "to order" from pile-irradiated materials, will be widely used for medicinal purposes. Not only will they be available in quantities vastly greater than those in which radium or mesothorium can be obtained now, but they will also allow a much wider selection of radiations with respect to both type of radiation and penetrating power; and they will often permit localized treatment of the type which was illustrated in Section II by the example of radioactive iodine absorbed selectively in the thyroid. One could also produce a radiation center directly in the tissue where irradiation is desired, by introducing locally an element such as boron which strongly absorbs neutrons, and irradiating it with a stream of neutrons.

The use of tracer elements is even more important for biology and medicine than it is for physics and chemistry. In biology, such isotopes as radioactive phosphorus and the non-radioactive rare isotopes of hydrogen, carbon, oxygen and nitrogen have already been used with conspicuous success in determining the mechanism of many complex steps in metabolism. They have also been used in finding out how single atoms or large atomic groups are exchanged in living tissues for fresh ones—a process which goes on continuously even in such permanent structures as teeth or bones. When radioactive carbon (C^{14}), nitrogen, and hydrogen become easily available, the usefulness of the radioactive tracer technique will be vastly increased. It will be applied to the solution of the basic problems of animal and plant metabolism, such as respiration, photosynthesis, fat and protein metabolism, as well as to minor puzzles presented by the metabolic role of "micro-nutrients," such as cobalt, whose absence has caused widespread losses of cattle in New Zealand.

Photosynthesis, that is the building up, through the action of light in green leaves, of complex organic compounds such as form the structure of plant and animal tissues, is the most important single biochemical process in nature. No life at all would be possible on earth if we did not have plant life to synthesize organic matter from the inorganic materials carbon dioxide and water. In this process, plants use the energy of sunlight—which as we have seen is itself derived in the final analysis from nuclear energy—and convert it into the chemical energy of combustible organic matter. Not only all animal life, but also all technological developments based on coal and oil, are possible only because of this function of plant life.

Despite extensive studies, we still know practically nothing about the mechanism of this most fundamental process of life, which nobody has yet succeeded in repeating outside the living plant cell. We do not know what intermediate chemical compounds are formed in the course of photosynthesis, nor what is the first product of it. All these questions could perhaps be answered by using tagged radioactive atoms of carbon.

The animal organism reverses the process of photosynthesis; sugar is oxidized to carbon dioxide and water, liberating energy. In this case the process, although it involves a great number of steps, is comparatively well understood, but its understanding has required the work of hundreds of investigators for several decades. By the use of tracers the effort to obtain this knowledge would have been greatly reduced; and much additional information (for example, concerning the role of copper and other metals in respiration) can still be expected from the application of the tracer technique. Comparatively little is known about the metabolism of fats and proteins; in these fields, more complex than that of sugar metabolism, tracer techniques hold great promise.

Once we understand the oxidation and breakdown of proteins in the animal body, the solution of the reverse problem, that of growth, will be greatly aided. The problem of normal growth is fundamental to that of abnormal growth or cancer.

It is known that plants require some twenty or more elements for their growth, including such "micronutrients" as boron, manganese, or cobalt. Because micronutrient experiments on animals are practically impossible, we have no similar information on them. Tracers, however, will make the study of this field easily possible.

What is the mechanism of nerve action? How do pathogenic bacteria carry out their poisonous missions? What is the mechanism of immunological reactions? What is the chemical reaction which controls the beating of the heart? What is the mechanism that stops and starts growth? These are only a few of the current questions to which prompter answers will very probably be obtained by the use of tracers.

In medicine, many artificially activated substances are now being used as tracers, particularly diagnostic work. Radioactive iron, for example, is being used to label and trace red blood cells in shock cases. Activated sodium metaborate is used to check blood circulation time in cases of "immersion foot," diabetes, hardening of the arteries, etc. The strontium isotope Sr^{89} is used as a tracer for calcium to determine the healing of bone fractures. The iodine isotope I^{161} is used for measuring the functioning of pathological thyroid glands.

Another primary biochemical use of tracers is in analysis, for which such adaptations have been made as the radioautograph to determine the actual cells involved in an accumulation or secretion process; the use of gamma radiation to analyze for a tracer species without destruction of the animal or tissue analyzed; and analyzing quantitatively by the "isotope dilution" technique for chemical or cellular constituents which cannot be isolated or separated in a quantitative manner.

All these methods and procedures will be facilitated and many new ones will be made possible by the abundantly available isotopic tracers derived from the pile.

Scientists have already induced mutations by means of radiation, so that it is not improbable that geneticists may now be able to produce many more new and economically important types of plant and animal life.

Metallurgy.—In metallurgy, the use of radioactive tracers has many possible applications. Some of these are as follows:

Diffusion of an element into itself and into alloys in which the element in question is a component, can be followed if the diffusing atoms are radioactive.

Inclusions, that is small bits of foreign matter in metals, could be identified by adding a radioactive form of suspected components to the melt. The inclusions could furthermore be photographed by microradiographic techniques.

Minor constituents often markedly affect the properties of metals and alloys. Positive identification and location of these minor constituents is usually very difficult by microscopic methods. Microradiographic method could be used in studying the distribution of these minor constituents among different phases in a piece of metal.

Engineering and Construction.—In the design and testing of machinery and in many phases of engineering and construction, radioactive tracers and other pile products have promising applications.

They could be applied to problems of wear and lubrication of moving parts. Wear problems are concerned with pick-up of metal or other material from one surface to another. By introducing tracers, the effect of pick-up under various conditions, such as surface treatment, lubrication, loading, temperature, and so on could be studied.

One might introduce small amounts of radioactive gaseous fission products into tanks and other equipment to test for leaks; use the same kinds of active gas for determining convection and air removal rates in ventilation problems for buildings; or use the active gases to determine the permeability of relatively impervious membranes and structures.

Radioactive tracers have already found use in the field of geophysics for tracing flows of liquid or gaseous materials in subterranean deposits, and this use can be extended. Tracers might also be used in measurements of flow in sewers and over dams where the volume is high and ordinary chemicals would have to be used in too large a quantity. Radioactive sodium or other material could be added to drilling muds pumped into oil wells to establish whether the mud is reappearing in adjacent intersecting wells. Questions of underground drainage of oil across property lines could also be attacked by adding oil-soluble active material in one well and looking for it in neighboring ones.

Radioactive materials could be embodied into paints and floor coverings for cutting down static. These paints and coatings might be made using either beta or very soft gamma emitters. They would be particularly useful in explosive plants and in the printing industry.

Hard and soft gamma emitters of reasonably long life made up into radiation "sources" could be used as substitutes for industrial and clinical X-ray machines. The possibility of putting a gamma ray source into body cavities is attractive since better pictures could be obtained than is now possible in some cases. The same would be true of X-ray pictures made of machinery, castings, etc. The small size of the source required would permit its insertion into the inside of complicated hollow castings, and so on.

In the lighting field one can visualize a cold light that would last for many years, produced by mixing radioactive material with luminescent material.

The field of instruments relating to nucleonics will be very large. The need for instruments in this field is, perhaps, greater than that of any other so far uncovered by man.

Prospecting for minerals should be a fruitful field for nucleonics applications. For instance, the presence of beryllium might be determined by the emission of neutrons upon irradiation by gamma rays, and the fluorescence of many minerals under gamma irradiation might likewise be used. In any case where specific nuclear reactions are involved, a suitable device could be set up which would specifically determine these elements.

Agriculture.—Nucleonics even promises to go out on the farm and help the farmer of the future, both by irradiation and by the application of tracers. Commercial growers are already producing superior pineapples from a mutation obtained by irradiation. The detection of selenium in fodder plants in certain South Dakota counties where animals have been poisoned because plants they ate had absorbed selenium from the soil, is a typical problem which can be studied by the radioactive tracer technique. The same applies to other poisons, as well as to "micro-nutrients" which are important for the growth of plants. Small amounts of radioactive material might be sprayed on migratory insect pests to aid in determining their origins, routes, and migration speeds. Radioactive isotopes could be used to test fertilizer materials for immediate availability.

Power.—We have spoken so far in this section only of the use of the "by-products" of the pile development—radiation and new isotopes. The present quantitative limitation and the immense intensity of nuclear power have been described in the preceding section. These two characteristics determine the uses to which nuclear power may be put in the immediate future, that is before pile materials other than uranium are utilized.

The limited amount of available uranium precludes a widespread use of pile power for energy production in competition with coal, oil or falling water. However, the tremendous heat generated by a working pile built primarily for other purposes, for example plutonium production, can certainly be utilized in such ways as the central heating of large areas, thus freeing oil for premium uses (aircraft, automobiles, and so on). Since the petroleum supply is definitely conceded to be critical by even the most optimistic geophysicists, plutonium plants might, despite their cost, become an economic necessity on the east coast where oil is now being used for heating both public buildings and private homes. While it is unlikely that piles will be constructed for heating purposes alone, it is quite probable that waste heat will be an important by-product of piles constructed for other purposes such as the fission process itself, or for supplying power for mining or irrigation in inaccessible places.

Piles built with material capable of sustaining high temperatures, for example with beryllium metal as moderator, will offer improved thermodynamic possibilities for power production. Even without such radical efficiency improvement, the pile may conceivably prove useful as an energy source until special conditions where its freedom from fuel supply limitations may outweigh all other considerations, particularly those of costs. That cost is not always the decisive factor in the selection of methods of energy generation, is illustrated by the following example.

If electrical energy is to be used in the manufacture of metallic aluminum, the cost should be in the neighborhood of 0.2¢ per kilowatt hour. Electrical energy for many industrial uses is practical at around 1¢ per kilowatt hour. Electrical energy for home lighting is economical at 5¢ per kilowatt hour. Large amounts of power are used in automobiles, trucks, buses and airplanes at a cost of around 20¢ per kilowatt hour, without including any labor or up-keep items. We would willingly pay $1 per kilowatt hour, or more, for electrical energy with which to start our automobiles rather than return to the old handcrank. The public also consumes a substantial amount of power for electricity to operate flashlight lamps from small dry batteries. A round figure for the cost of this power is $30 per kilowatt hour. Thus, it is seen that the value of power is not a fixed thing, and it may be that many uses will be found for pile power in which the overall cost of the power is not the controlling factor. On the other hand, we should not conclude that the cost of pile power is necessarily going to be high as compared with other power sources. This is one of the great uncertainties of the future which can only be answered by further experimentation and experience.

Let us consider some aspects of the power situation. It might be possible to put in power plants in the Far North, in the Antarctic, or in desert regions adjacent to important mineral deposits. Other sources of power might be practically unavailable to these areas and piles might make it possible, therefore, to gain added mineral resources for mankind. While these mineral resources were being made available for man's use, one or more of the other by-products might also be produced, which could have the result of making the entire operation economical.

Pile power may also be used for transportation, particularly in regions far distant from fuel supply bases. While pile-powered interplanetary ships still belong to the realm of scientific daydreaming, pile-powered battleships or submarines have been considered as likely applications of nuclear power in the relatively near future.

It is not impossible to hope that a submarine powered by a pile could make a round trip across the Pacific without once having to surface for refueling or for recharging of its batteries. Of course, much experimentation will have to be completed before a small compact unit of relatively large capacity can be produced for this purpose, but the total uranium needed is so little compared with the reserves available that this application appears to be among the most promising ones.

The generation of nuclear power for driving a fleet of 30 modern battleships would require 30 power plants of roughly 500,000 KW capacity (heat rate) each. Assuming that these operate at only 10% of rated capacity on the average, the total heat dissipation rate would be 1,500,000 KW; the known North American uranium reserve could support such a fleet for about 470 years. Thus the uranium supply is large enough to warrant discussion of its use in battleships. The great weight of the pile and the fact that this weight must necessarily be concentrated in one part of the ship probably will lead to structural design changes in the ship itself, since at present the fuel reserve is widely distributed over the ship.

Explosives.—It is clear from what was said in Section IV what terrifying results can be expected from the use of plutonium or other pure fissionable isotopes as explosives. The possibility of their use for military or political purposes inevitably dominates not only the war-time development of nucleonics but also all discussion concerning its post-war future.

This is the main reason why, unlike most other scientific discoveries and inventions, the pursuit and organization of nucleonics after the war cannot be left entirely to private scientific and industrial initiative without bringing mankind and our nation in particular into the gravest jeopardy. This consideration has caused us to devote to the military and political implications of nucleonics a separate Section VI, and to present in the final Section VII, a series of recommendations as to how the development of nucleonics should be organized in this country after the war emergency is over.

It is, of course, our most ardent hope that nuclear explosives will never be used to annihilate cities or whole nations. One can hope that if they are used at all, it will be for peacetime engineering undertakings on a scale deemed impossible until now. The development of such peacetime applications of nuclear explosives will hinge on methods of controlling the time and violence of the explosions. When nuclear explosives are brought under control, one may be able to consider seriously such spectacular things as changing the direction of sea currents, destroying or diverting tropical hurricanes, removing the danger of earthquakes or volcanic eruptions by timely release of the accumulated pressure or strain, or of reducing to a few days the time required for the blasting of such waterways as the Panama Canal.

VI. The Impact of Nucleonics on International Relations and the Social Order

Military Implications.—It is the unanimous opinion of observers acquainted with the active work in nucleonics that developments in this field will be of extraordinary importance in connection with the post-war security problem. We know that the British are actively engaged in this work. A reasonable surmise is that the Germans are about as far along as ourselves and are pressing the subject most vigorously. It would be surprising if the Russians are not also diligently engaged in such work. Until the peace has become stable, we can afford no relaxation in our present developments. Rather, we have to broaden them, so as to include possibilities hitherto neglected under the pressure of immediate needs imposed by the war. Otherwise, we may find to our surprise that our present strong hand is covered by a stronger.

While it is our duty to our nation to see that no such surprise ever takes place, by preserving and extending in the post-war period the lead in the field of pure and applied nucleonics which we believe we have established now, it cannot be emphasized too strongly that no lasting security against a national and international catastrophe can be achieved in this way. Peace based on uncontrolled and perhaps clandestine development of certain phases of nucleonics in a number of sovereign nations will be only an armistice. It is bound to end, sooner or later, in a catastrophe, particularly because nuclear power, beyond any older means of warfare, holds out to the aggressor the temptation of being able to make a successful sudden stroke, even against a vastly more powerful and well-prepared nation. Nuclear weapons might be produced in small hidden locations in countries not normally associated with a large scale armament industry, thus evading surveillance. A nation, or even a political group, given the opportunity to start aggression by a sudden use of nuclear destruction devices, will be able to unleash a "blitzkrieg" infinitely more terrifying than that of 1939–40. A sudden blow of this kind might literally wipe out even the largest nation—or at least all its production centers— and decide the issue on the first day of the war. The weight of the weapons of destruction required to deliver this blow will be infinitesimal compared to that used up in a present day heavy bombing raid, and they could easily be smuggled in by commercial aircraft or even deposited in advance by agents of the aggressor.

If a war should start with both sides unprepared for immediate use of nuclear weapons, the nation which has accumulated the larger reserves of critical materials or developed the best ways for their conversion into nuclear explosives will have in exaggerated form the same type of advantage that this country has had in the present war because of superior capacity for airplane construction.

The situation as it has been developing may be described by an analogy somewhat as follows. Since the area of the earth does not increase, the advantage of the attacker constantly increases with increasing technical development. If two people are in a room of 100 by 100 feet and have no weapons except their bare fists, the attacker has only a slight advantage over his opponent. But if each of them has a machine gun in his hands the attacker is sure to be victorious. Similarly, as long as the weapons of war were of the caliber of rifles and guns, the act of attacking gave very little advantage. The situation had already changed substantially with the advent of the airplane; the present war illustrates this point clearly. With the production of nuclear bombs, however, the world situation approaches that of two men with machine guns in a 100 by 100 foot room.

The problem of the elimination of aggression will no doubt be solved eventually in the same way in which modern society has solved the problem of machine guns. It has given the privilege of possessing machine guns only to a well-disciplined group responsible to established authorities. Similarly a central authority must be set up to exercise the necessary control over nuclear power.

Until such an authority is established, even the most intense and efficient "nucleonic re-armament" of a nation will not be able to give this country enduring safety from a sudden devastating blow. The most that an independent American nucleonic re-armament can achieve is the certainty that a sudden total devastation of New York or Chicago can be answered the next day by an even more extensive devastation of the cities of the aggressor, and the hope that the fear of such a retaliation will paralyze the aggressor. The whole history of mankind teaches that this is a very uncertain hope, and that accumulated weapons of destruction "go off" sooner or later, even if this means a senseless mutual destruction.

The Dilemma of Technological Progress in a Static World Order.— As we approach the nucleonics age, the existing gap between continued technological progress and our relatively static political institutions tends to widen. The tension impelling us toward a solution of this problem on a world-wide scale may rise to extreme heights. As recently stated by Dr. L. L. Mann, "technological advances without moral development are catastrophic. Thus brotherhood, once a vision, is now a necessity."

Two types of solution seem possible. These may briefly be described as forward-looking and backward-looking. The backward-looking approach would call for a moratorium on the progress of science and industry, and in particular nucleonics, in order to give social, economic, and political development a chance to catch up. The forward-looking approach would combine an intensive development of nucleonics, because of its immense potential benefits to humanity, with an even more intensive effort to solve the most crucial of existing political problems on a world-wide scale. In this approach, widespread scientific education must go hand in hand with education of the general public. *The moral development necessary to prevent the misuse of nuclear energy can only be achieved if public opinion becomes fully aware of the catastrophic possibilities inherent in the development of nucleonics, and thus prepared to give its support to the decisions required to prevent the danger.* Public opinion will agree to the abandonment of cherished old traditions only if it becomes absolutely clear that their retention will of necessity release forces that will bring about self-destruction of civilization, if not of mankind.

Neither of the two approaches can succeed without international cooperation, and both involve great risks. The backward-looking approach, if adopted by any individual nation, will inevitably mean national suicide for that nation. For there will be other nations which will be willing and glad to take advantage of this situation by arming themselves for modern and in particular for nucleonic warfare.

Thus, the forward-looking approach, providing for the maximum intensity in the development of nucleonics, appears the only one feasible. But it must be continuously kept in mind that without a worldwide organization for the maintenance of peace, this approach will hasten the coming of the most destructive war in history. In this war, if all are not destroyed, it is likely that one nation will acquire global dominance so that a world organization will in the end be established, but probably in a form not to our liking. *To sum up, we believe that the inevitability of the development of nucleonics by some if not all nations shows compellingly, because of its potential military consequences, the necessity for all nations to make every effort to cooperate now in setting up an international administration with police powers which can effectively control at least the means of nucleonic warfare.*

The Control of Critical Materials.—Among the ways by which the worldwide development of nucleonics can be kept under control, one of the most important is the supervision over critical materials, particularly those which are of crucial value for military purposes. Even within a nation this is of particular importance, since any group gaining control over such materials might seize and hold power in that nation.

In the first place, worldwide prospecting for the ores of such critical metals as uranium, thorium, beryllium (which may be very important in nucleonics), and perhaps bismuth, will be needed. In addition to prospecting the rocks and earth, sea water, and the sea floor, salt lakes and fossil salt lake beds should be examined as possible sources of these raw materials. Careful studies on the mining of these ores, and the stockpiling of the resulting metals and perhaps also of heavy water (which may be important for use in future piles), will need to be instituted. It is probable that U^{235} and such pile products as U^{233} and plutonium will be rated as vital national or international assets such as gold has been in the past.

If so, it might be possible to work out plans whereby these materials would be made in greater quantities during times of low employment than during times of high employment. Projects for the recovery of uranium and thorium from low-grade deposits may likewise be made part of a sound program for employment in times of low industrial activity. It now seems that there will be no possibility of acquiring too much U^{235}, U^{233}, or plutonium for generations. No one yet knows what other elements may also be valuable in nucleonics, and should also be stockpiled. Future research alone can answer these questions.

In the future nucleonics industry in America it will be possible to give considerable scope to free private enterprise activity and still have the government hold a tight rein on important factors in the nucleonics field. Control of end products need not be so far different from that of gold, except for safety measures. No one may hoard gold, yet the gold industry is quite free. Gold production is in private hands and any one may purchase it for use in the industries and arts. Industrial ethyl alcohol has been in the hands of private enterprise, but its production and sale are under government observation.

Researchers normally have little difficulty in getting gold or ethyl-alcohol for experimental purposes. Similar arrangements could be made if the government had control of all potentially dangerous nucleonics end products. The same might be true of certain of the raw materials involved. While stockpiles are being built up there will be a continuous and steady market for all such materials. The military needs could always be given first preference.

In spite of the need of an unusual degree of governmental or international control over materials used in nucleonics, because of their exceptional possibilities for destruction, this control could be kept at the minimum level consistent with safety.

VII. The Post-War Organization of Nucleonics in America

In the preceding section, we have emphasized the imperative necessity for a worldwide organization to prevent nucleonics from becoming the destroyer of our civilization. Before such an organization is established, as well as later within its framework, it will be of vital importance for this country to retain its leading position, both in nuclear research and in the nucleonics industry. The present section deals with the probable development of nucleonics in America after the war and with the measures which should be taken to strengthen it.

It will be impossible to stop the scientific world from tackling the whole nucleonics field feverishly in the post-war period. With so many things unknown, there will always be the feeling that something big can come from further studies in the nuclear field. Finding of new facts in this field is of the utmost importance in order that we may achieve as good an understanding of the structure of nuclear matter as now obtains for the electron atmosphere surrounding the nucleus. Our present theory is definitely not sufficient for that purpose. When this understanding has been achieved, who knows what sweeping predictions may be made to guide experimenters straight to goals otherwise attainable only by slow and costly cut-and-try methods?

There should, therefore, be government-supported nucleonics laboratories having ample facilities for both fundamental and applied research. A legitimate side-line of such laboratories would be the supplying of special materials to other research centers and to industry.

It seems, however, both unlikely and undesirable that the whole development of nucleonics should be restricted to these government-sponsored laboratories, under the protection of continued wartime secrecy. On the contrary, full information on most phases of the subject should be released just as soon as possible from the standpoint of national security. Probably this would mean soon after the close of the war, for, as recently remarked by Rear Admiral J. A. Furer, "There is no such thing as permanent secrecy of ideas, or even very much lag in the flowering of the same ideas in the brains of the enemy. I plow through vast heaps of intelligence reports and I am pretty well convinced the enemy is trying to do all—or most all— of the things we are, and is certainly thinking along virtually the same lines. True security lies in speed of accomplishment. It is the only way we can keep ahead of the enemy in this complex technical war of measure and counter-measure."

It is inevitable that differences of opinion shall arise over the question of admitting industrial groups to full participation in the development of nuclear power and its by-products. However, without a healthy development of nucleonic *industry*, nucleonic research alone will be insufficient to guarantee the leading position of this country and its full preparedness for all emergencies.

In the first forty odd years of the history of nucleonics, up to the discovery of atomic fission, practically all work in this field was done at the universities. The discovery of fission laid the groundwork for the Metallurgical Project and other related projects based on cooperation of universities and industrial concerns. Because of the war and the possible important military uses of the pile products, the government took over the support of this work. In doing so, it gained a patent position in this field which is far more comprehensive than is warranted by its own participation in the development and its legitimate interest in that part of the results which are vital for the security of the nation.

By this cooperative wartime effort the progress of nucleonics has been pushed forward greatly with respect to both science and the groundwork for industrial success. No one can say just to what extent the normal development has been accelerated; but we may well be several years ahead of where we would have been had the war emergency not caused the government to press for full exploitation of this field, and science and industry to place all its facilities at the service of the government.

The best way to maintain the lead which America has acquired in this field probably lies in a combination of (a) extensive nuclear research work in universities and specially created nucleonics laboratories, with (b) continued government-sponsored study and development of the problems directly related to military matters, and (c) a healthy growth of an independent nucleonics industry.

A well-developed nucleonics industry will be the best insurance for military potency in the nuclear field, and will strengthen America's hand in its attempts to achieve an international understanding to make impossible the use of nuclear power for destructive purposes.

It may turn out that the first problem of industrial participation in nucleonics development will be not how to exclude undesirable industrial concerns, but how to induce any concern at all to step into a field which, at least at present, offers little prospect of early profit. Probably only large concerns, able to support long-range research programs, will be interested at all, and these only if normal patent claims may be made on bonafide company developments. Objectors to this point of view will speak of monopolies contrary to public interest. The answer is that not one but several independent concerns must become active in the field. The resulting diverse viewpoints, healthful competition of ideas, and the economic urge to develop and produce useful things (as against the scientific aim to discover and develop new things) should result in the growth of a nucleonics industry which, in future emergencies, will be as necessary to the security of the nation as the automotive, the airplane, the metal working, the chemical, and the electronics industries are in this war. This point deserves emphasis: the nation will need pure scientific ability and creative talent in nucleonics; but it will also need the physical plant—piles, radiochemical plants and whatever else may develop—in *quantity*, and this will come only if there is a nucleonics *industry*. Research alone is not enough, essential though it is.

Public education in the scientific and technical field on the significance of nucleonics, and enlightenment on its consequences in the national and international situation, are urgently needed in order to prepare for the post-war readjustment. After our weapons have once been demonstrated, a calm appraisal of the realities widely spread before the public will help to obtain full support of the work. What will then be most required is wise judgment in determining how the national effort in this direction can be encouraged and guided. For such guidance our democracy must rely upon the common sense of a generally informed public and the expert opinions of a fully informed group of technical men.

The nations putting in the most effort in nucleonics after the war may be expected to succeed ahead of the lagging nations. The nations which establish conditions favorable to extensive research and industrial development in nucleonics may be expected to show a greater advance in the science and art than nations which, intentionally or otherwise, have policies or laws which discourage research and development in this field. As Americans, we have an important stake in the future of nucleonics from the military, industrial, and scientific standpoints. It is, therefore, of vital importance to the future of the United States that proper relationships be established between governmental and non-governmental agencies in this field.

The broad objectives, in our opinion, should be:

1. To STIMULATE WIDESPREAD RESEARCH IN NUCLEONICS IN THE UNITED STATES.

2. To ENCOURAGE THE DEVELOPMENT OF A FREE NUCLEONICS INDUSTRY IN THE UNITED STATES.

3. To COORDINATE THE GOVERNMENTAL ACTIVITIES IN NUCLEONICS WITH THE SCIENTIFIC AND INDUSTRIAL DEVELOPMENTS IN THIS FIELD IN SUCH A WAY AS TO INSURE MAXIMUM NATIONAL SECURITY.

4. To STRIVE FOR THE ESTABLISHMENT OF AN EFFICIENT INTERNATIONAL SUPERVISION OVER ALL MILITARY ASPECTS OF NUCLEONICS.

While the procedures necessary for the accomplishment of these objectives may not now be fully obvious, and while they may be expected to be changed as experience is gained, we believe these objectives can be substantially achieved. Some suggestions are offered for consideration:

a) THE PROJECTS RELATING TO PLUTONIUM, U^{235}, and PERHAPS U^{233} SHOULD BE PROSECUTED BY THE GOVERNMENT, NO MATTER WHEN THE WAR ENDS, to a point sufficient for military appraisal.

b) THE DEVELOPMENT OF THE NUCLEONICS INDUSTRY BY PRIVATE ENTERPRISE SHOULD BE ENCOURAGED. The military by-products of the industrial developments should be made available to the government, and the use of government information and patents should be made available to industry so far as the military situation may permit.

c) SCIENTIFIC EDUCATION AND RESEARCH SHOULD BE ENCOURAGED IN EXISTING UNIVERSITY LABORATORIES, AND NEW RESEARCH LABORA-TORIES for nucleonics with special facilities SHOULD BE CREATED at universities.

d) A SUITABLE AGENCY, with both government and non-government representatives, SHOULD BE ESTABLISHED to guide and coordinate such nucleonics activities as may affect the military or other interests of the nation.

e) ENLIGHTENMENT OF PUBLIC OPINION ON THE SCOPE AND SIGNIFI-CANCE OF NUCLEONICS SHOULD START AS SOON AS POSSIBLE to bring about realization of the dangers for world security caused by the new scientific and technical developments, and to prepare for decisions which will have to be taken to meet this danger.

f) COOPERATION WITH FRIENDLY NATIONS IN all these problems—particularly the last named one—SHOULD BE GIVEN SERIOUS AND PROMPT ATTENTION.

The Franck Report
June 11, 1945

I. PREAMBLE

The only reason to treat nuclear power differently from all the other developments in the field of physics is the possibility of its use as a means of political pressure in peace and sudden destruction in war. All present plans for the organization of research, scientific and industrial development, and publication in the field of nucleonics are conditioned by the political and military climate in which one expects those plans to be carried out. Therefore, in making suggestions for the postwar organization of nucleonics, a discussion of political problems cannot be avoided. The scientists on this Project do not presume to speak authoritatively on problems of national and international policy. However, we found ourselves, by the force of events during the last five years, in the position of a small group of citizens cognizant of a grave danger for the safety of this country as well as for the future of all the other nations, of which the rest of mankind is unaware. We therefore feel it our duty to urge that the political problems, arising from the mastering of nuclear power, be recognized

---

This text is taken from an untitled, undated carbon in Hogness' files. The same version was declassified by the Manhattan Engineer District after deletion of about one-eighth of the text and was published by the *Bulletin of the Atomic Scientists*, I (May 1, 1946), 2–4, 16, as "A Report to the Secretary of War—June, 1945."

in all their gravity, and that appropriate steps be taken for their study and the preparation of necessary decisions. We hope that the creation of the Committee by the Secretary of War to deal with all aspects of nucleonics, indicates that these implications have been recognized by the government. We believe that our acquaintance with the scientific elements of the situation and prolonged preoccupation with its world-wide political implications, imposes on us the obligation to offer to the Committee some suggestions as to the possible solution of these grave problems.

Scientists have often before been accused of providing new weapons for the mutual destruction of nations, instead of improving their well-being. It is undoubtedly true that the discovery of flying, for example, has so far brought much more misery than enjoyment and profit to humanity. However, in the past, scientists could disclaim direct responsibility for the use to which mankind had put their disinterested discoveries. We feel compelled to take a more active stand now because the success which we have achieved in the development of nuclear power is fraught with infinitely greater dangers than were all the inventions of the past. All of us, familiar with the present state of nucleonics, live with the vision before our eyes of sudden destruction visited on our own country, of a Pearl Harbor disaster repeated in thousand-fold magnification in every one of our major cities.

In the past, science has often been able to provide also new methods of protection against new weapons of aggression it made possible, but it cannot promise such efficient protection against the destructive use of nuclear power. This protection can come only from the political organization of the world. Among all the arguments calling for an efficient international organization for peace, the existence of nuclear weapons is the most compelling one. *In the absence of an international authority which would make all resort to force in international conflicts impossible, nations could still be diverted from a path which must lead to total mutual destruction, by a specific international agreement barring a nuclear armaments race.*

II. PROSPECTS OF ARMAMENTS RACE

It could be suggested that the danger of destruction by nuclear weapons can be avoided—at least as far as this country is concerned—either by keeping our discoveries secret for an indefinite time, or else by developing our nucleonic armaments at such a pace that no other nations would think of attacking us from fear of overwhelming retaliation.

The answer to the first suggestion is that although we undoubtedly are at present ahead of the rest of the world in this field, the fundamental facts of nuclear power are a subject of common knowledge. British scientists know as much as we do about the basic wartime progress of nucleonics—if not of the specific processes used in our engineering developments—and the role which French nuclear physicists have played in the pre-war development of this field, plus their occasional contact with our Projects, will enable them to catch up rapidly, at least as far as basic scientific discoveries are concerned. German scientists, in whose discoveries the whole development of this field originated, apparently did not develop it during the war to the same extent to which this has been done in America; but to the last day of the European war, we were living in constant apprehension as to their possible achievements. The certainty that German scientists are working on this weapon and that their government would certainly have no scruples against using it when available, was the main motivation of the initiative which American scientists took in urging the development of nuclear power for military purposes on a large scale in this country. In Russia, too, the basic facts and implications of nuclear power were well understood in 1940, and the experience of Russian scientists in nuclear research is entirely sufficient to enable them to retrace our steps within a few years, even if we should make every attempt to conceal them. Furthermore, we should not expect too much success from attempts to keep basic information secret in peacetime, when scientists acquainted with the work on this and associated Projects will be scattered to many colleges and research institutions and many of them will continue to work on problems closely related to those on which our developments are based. In other words, even if we can retain our leadership in basic knowledge of nucleonics for a certain time by maintaining secrecy as to all results achieved on this and associated Projects, it would be foolish to hope that this can protect us for more than a few years.

It may be asked whether we cannot prevent the development of military nucleonics in other countries by a monopoly on the raw materials of nuclear power. The answer is that even though the largest now known deposits of uranium ores are under the control of powers which belong to the "western" group (Canada, Belgium, and British

India), the old deposits in Czechoslovakia are outside this sphere. Russia is known to be mining radium on its own territory; and even if we do not know the size of the deposits discovered so far in the USSR, the probability that no large reserves of uranium will be found in a country which covers ⅕ of the land area of the earth (and whose sphere of influence takes in additional territory), is too small to serve as a basis for security. *Thus, we cannot hope to avoid a nuclear armament race either by keeping secret from the competing nations the basic scientific facts of nuclear power or by cornering the raw materials required for such a race.*

We now consider the second of the two suggestions made at the beginning of this section, and ask whether we could not feel ourselves safe in a race of nuclear armaments by virtue of our greater industrial potential, including greater diffusion of scientific and technical knowledge, greater volume and efficiency of our skilled labor corps, and greater experience of our management—all the factors whose importance has been so strikingly demonstrated in the conversion of this country into an arsenal of the Allied Nations in the present war. The answer is that all that these advantages can give us is the accumulation of a large number of bigger and better atomic bombs—and this only if we produce these bombs at the maximum of our capacity in peace time, and do not rely on conversion of a peace-time nucleonics industry to military production after the beginning of hostilities.

However, such a quantitative advantage in reserves of bottled destructive power will not make us safe from sudden attack. Just because a potential enemy will be afraid of being "outnumbered and outgunned," the temptation for him may be overwhelming to attempt a sudden unprovoked blow—particularly if he should suspect us of harboring aggressive intentions against his security or his sphere of influence. In no other type of warfare does the advantage lie so heavily with the aggressor. He can place his "infernal machines" in advance in all our major cities and explode them simultaneously, thus destroying a major part of our industry and a large part of our population, aggregated in densely populated metropolitan districts. Our possibilities of retaliation—even if retaliation should be considered adequate compensation for the loss of millions of lives and destruction of our largest cities—will be greatly handicapped because we must rely on aerial transportation of the bombs, and also because we may have to deal with an enemy whose industry and population are dispersed over a large territory.

In fact, if the race for nuclear armaments is allowed to develop, the only apparent way in which our country can be protected from the paralyzing effects of a sudden attack is by dispersal of those industries which are essential for our war effort and dispersal of the populations of our major metropolitan cities. As long as nuclear bombs remain scarce (i.e., as long as uranium and thorium remain the only basic materials for their fabrication), efficient dispersal of our industry and the scattering of our metropolitan population will considerably decrease the temptation to attack us by nuclear weapons.

Ten years hence, it may be that atomic bombs containing perhaps 20 kg of active material can be detonated at 6% efficiency, and thus each have an effect equal to that of 20,000 tons of TNT. One of these bombs could then destroy something like 3 square miles of an urban area. Atomic bombs containing a larger quantity of active material but still weighing less than one ton may be expected to be available within ten years which could destroy over ten square miles of a city. A nation able to assign 10 tons of atomic explosives for the preparation of a sneak attack on this country, can then hope to achieve the destruction of all industry and most of the population in an area from 500 square miles upwards. If no choice of targets, with a total area of five hundred square miles of American territory, contains a large enough fraction of the nation's industry and population to make their destruction a crippling blow to the nation's war potential and its ability to defend itself, then the attack will not pay, and may not be undertaken. At present, one could easily select in this country a hundred areas of five square miles each whose simultaneous destruction would be a staggering blow to the nation. Since the area of the United States is about three million square miles, it should be possible to scatter its industrial and human resources in such a way as to leave no 500 square miles important enough to serve as a target for nuclear attack.

We are fully aware of the staggering difficulties involved in such a radical change in the social and economic structure of our nation. We felt, however, that the dilemma had to be stated, to show what kind of alternative methods of protection will have to be considered if no successful international agreement is reached. It must be pointed out that in this field we are in a less favorable position than nations which are either now more diffusely populated and whose industries are more scattered, or whose governments have unlimited power over the movement of population and the location of industrial plants.

If no efficient international agreement is achieved, the race for nuclear armaments will be on in earnest not later than the morning after our first demonstration of the existence of nuclear weapons. After this, it might take other nations three or four years to overcome our present head start, and eight or ten years to draw even with us if we continue to do intensive work in this field. This might be all the time we would have to bring about the regroupment of our population and industry. Obviously, no time should be lost in inaugurating a study of this problem by experts.

III. PROSPECTS OF AGREEMENT

The consequences of nuclear warfare, and the type of measures which would have to be taken to protect a country from total destruction by nuclear bombing, must be as abhorrent to other nations as to the United States. England, France, and the smaller nations of the European continent, with their congeries of people and industries, would be in a particularly desperate situation in the face of such a threat. Russia and China are the only great nations at present which could survive a nuclear attack. However, even though these countries may value human life less than the peoples of Western Europe and America, and even though Russia, in particular, has an immense space over which its vital industries could be dispersed and a government which can order this dispersion the day it is convinced that such a measure is necessary—there is no doubt that Russia will shudder at the possibility of a sudden disintegration of Moscow and Leningrad and of its new industrial cities in the Urals and Siberia. Therefore, only lack of mutual *trust*, and not lack of *desire* for agreement, can stand in the path of an efficient agreement for the prevention of nuclear warfare. The achievement of such an agreement will thus essentially depend on the integrity of intentions and readiness to sacrifice the necessary fraction of one's own sovereignty, by all the parties to the agreement.

From this point of view, the way in which the nuclear weapons now being secretly developed in this country are first revealed to the world appears to be of great, perhaps fateful importance.

One possible way—which may particularly appeal to those who consider nuclear bombs primarily as a secret weapon developed to help win the present war—is to use them without warning on an appropriately selected object in Japan. It is doubtful whether the first available bombs, of comparatively low efficiency and small size, will be sufficient to break the will or ability of Japan to resist, especially given the fact that the major cities like Tokyo, Nagoya, Osaka and Kobe already will largely have been reduced to ashes by the slower process of ordinary aerial bombing. Although important tactical results undoubtedly can be achieved by a sudden introduction of nuclear weapons, we nevertheless think that the question of the use of the very first available atomic bombs in the Japanese war should be weighed very carefully, not only by military authorities, but by the highest political leadership of this country. If we consider international agreement on total prevention of nuclear warfare as the paramount objective, and believe that it can be achieved, this kind of introduction of atomic weapons to the world may easily destroy all our chances of success. Russia, and even allied countries which bear less mistrust of our ways and intentions, as well as neutral countries may be deeply shocked. It may be very difficult to persuade the world that a nation which was capable of secretly preparing and suddenly releasing a weapon as indiscriminate as the rocket bomb and a million times more destructive, is to be trusted in its proclaimed desire of having such weapons abolished by international agreement. We have large accumulations of poison gas, but do not use them, and recent polls have shown that public opinion in this country would disapprove of such a use even if it would accelerate the winning of the Far Eastern war. It is true that some irrational element in mass psychology makes gas poisoning more revolting than blasting by explosives, even though gas warfare is in no way more "inhuman" than the war of bombs and bullets. Nevertheless, it is not at all certain that American public opinion, if it could be enlightened as to the effect of atomic explosives, would approve of our own country being the first to introduce such an indiscriminate method of wholesale destruction of civilian life.

Thus, from the "optimistic" point of view—looking forward to an international agreement on the prevention of nuclear warfare—the military advantages and the saving of American lives achieved by the sudden use of atomic bombs against Japan may be outweighed by the ensuing loss of confidence and by a wave of horror and repulsion sweeping over the rest of the world and perhaps even dividing public opinion at home.

From this point of view, a demonstration of the new weapon might best be made, before the eyes of representatives of all the United

Nations, on the desert or a barren island. The best possible atmosphere for the achievement of an international agreement could be achieved if America could say to the world, "You see what sort of a weapon we had but did not use. We are ready to renounce its use in the future if other nations join us in this renunciation and agree to the establishment of an efficient international control."

After such a demonstration the weapon might perhaps be used against Japan if the sanction of the United Nations (and of public opinion at home) were obtained, perhaps after a preliminary ultimatum to Japan to surrender or at least to evacuate certain regions as an alternative to their total destruction. This may sound fantastic, but in nuclear weapons we have something entirely new in order of magnitude of destructive power, and if we want to capitalize fully on the advantage their possession gives us, we must use new and imaginative methods.

It must be stressed that if one takes the pessimistic point of view and discounts the possibility of an effective international control over nuclear weapons at the present time, then the advisability of an early use of nuclear bombs against Japan becomes even more doubtful—quite independently of any humanitarian considerations. If an international agreement is not concluded immediately after the first demonstration, this will mean a flying start toward an unlimited armaments race. If this race is inevitable, we have every reason to delay its beginning as long as possible in order to increase our head start still further. It took us three years, roughly, under forced draft of wartime urgency, to complete the first stage of production of nuclear explosives—that based on the separation of the rare fissionable isotope U^{235}, or its utilization for the production of an equivalent quantity of another fissionable element. This stage required large-scale, expensive constructions and laborious procedures. We are now on the threshold of the second stage—that of converting into fissionable material the comparatively abundant common isotopes of thorium and uranium. This stage probably requires no elaborate plans and may provide us in about five or six years with a really substantial stockpile of atomic bombs. Thus it is to our interest to delay the beginning of the armaments race at least until the successful termination of this second stage. The benefit to the nation, and the saving of American lives in the future, achieved by renouncing an early demonstration of nuclear bombs and letting the other nations come into the race only reluctantly, on the basis of guesswork and without definite knowledge that the "thing does work," may far outweigh the advantages to be gained by the immediate use of the first and comparatively inefficient bombs in the war against Japan. On the other hand, it may be argued that without an early demonstration it may prove difficult to obtain adequate support for further intensive development of nucleonics in this country and that thus the time gained by the postponement of an open armaments race will not be properly used. Furthermore one may suggest that other nations are now, or will soon be, not entirely unaware of our present achievements, and that consequently the postponement of a demonstration may serve no useful purpose as far as the avoidance of an armaments race is concerned, and may only create additional mistrust, thus worsening rather than improving the chances of an ultimate accord on the international control of nuclear explosives.

Thus, if the prospects of an agreement will be considered poor in the immediate future, the pros and cons of an early revelation of our possession of nuclear weapons to the world—not only by their actual use against Japan, but also by a prearranged demonstration—must be carefully weighed by the supreme political and military leadership of the country, and the decision should not be left to military tacticians alone.

One may point out that scientists themselves have initiated the development of this "secret weapon" and it is therefore strange that they should be reluctant to try it out on the enemy as soon as it is available. The answer to this question was given above—the compelling reason for creating this weapon with such speed was our fear that Germany had the technical skill necessary to develop such a weapon, and that the German government had no moral restraints regarding its use.

Another argument which could be quoted in favor of using atomic bombs as soon as they are available is that so much taxpayers' money has been invested in these Projects that the Congress and the American public will demand a return for their money. The attitude of American public opinion, mentioned earlier, in the matter of the use of poison gas against Japan, shows that one can expect the American public to understand that it is sometimes desirable to keep a weapon in readiness for use only in extreme emergency; and as soon as the potentialities of nuclear weapons are revealed to the American people, one can be sure that they will support all attempts to make the use of such weapons impossible.

Once this is achieved, the large installations and the accumulation of explosive material at present earmarked for potential military use will become available for important peace-time developments, including power production, large engineering undertakings, and mass production of radioactive materials. In this way, the money spent on wartime development of nucleonics may become a boon for the peacetime development of national economy.

IV. Methods of International Control

We now consider the question of how an effective international control of nuclear armaments can be achieved. This is a difficult problem, but we think it soluble. It requires study by statesmen and international lawyers, and we can offer only some preliminary suggestions for such a study.

Given mutual trust and willingness on all sides to give up a certain part of their sovereign rights, by admitting international control of certain phases of national economy, the control could be exercised (alternatively or simultaneously) on two different levels.

The first and perhaps simplest way is to ration the raw materials— primarily, the uranium ores. Production of nuclear explosives begins with the processing of large quantities of uranium in large isotope separation plants or huge production piles. The amounts of ore taken out of the ground at different locations could be controlled by resident agents of the international Control Board, and each nation could be allotted only an amount which would make large scale separation of fissionable isotopes impossible.

Such a limitation would have the drawback of making impossible also the development of nuclear power for peace-time purposes. However, it need not prevent the production of radioactive elements on a scale sufficient to revolutionize the industrial, scientific and technical use of these materials, and would thus not eliminate the main benefits which nucleonics promises to bring to mankind.

An agreement on a higher level, involving more mutual trust and understanding, would be to allow unlimited production, but keep exact bookkeeping on the fate of each pound of uranium mined. Some difficulty with this method of control will arise in the second stage of production, when one pound of pure fissionable isotope will be used again and again to produce additional fissionable material from thorium. These could be overcome by extending control to the mining and use of thorium, even though the commercial use of this metal may cause complications.

If check is kept on the conversion of uranium and thorium ore into pure fissionable materials, the question arises as to how to prevent accumulation of large quantities of such materials in the hands of one or several nations. Accumulations of this kind could be rapidly converted into atomic bombs if a nation should break away from international control. It has been suggested that a compulsory denaturation of pure fissionable isotopes may be agreed upon by diluting them, after production, with suitable isotopes to make them useless for military purposes, while retaining their usefulness for power engines.

One thing is clear: any international agreement on prevention of nuclear armaments must be backed by actual and efficient controls. No paper agreement can be sufficient since neither this or any other nation can stake its whole existence on trust in other nations' signatures. Every attempt to impede the international control agencies would have to be considered equivalent to denunciation of the agreement.

It hardly needs stressing that we as scientists believe that any systems of control envisaged should leave as much freedom for the peacetime development of nucleonics as is consistent with the safety of the world.

SUMMARY

The development of nuclear power not only constitutes an important addition to the technological and military power of the United States, but also creates grave political and economic problems for the future of this country.

Nuclear bombs cannot possibly remain a "secret weapon" at the exclusive disposal of this country for more than a few years. The scientific facts on which their construction is based are well known to scientists of other countries. Unless an effective international control of nuclear explosives is instituted, a race for nuclear armaments is certain to ensue following the first revelation of our possession of nuclear weapons to the world. Within ten years other countries may have nuclear bombs, each of which, weighing less than a ton, could destroy an urban area of more than ten square miles. In the war to which such an armaments race is likely to lead, the United States, with its agglomeration of population and industry in comparatively few metropolitan districts, will be at a disadvantage compared to nations whose population and industry are scattered over large areas.

We believe that these considerations make the use of nuclear bombs for an early unannounced attack against Japan inadvisable. If the United States were to be the first to release this new means of indiscriminate destruction upon mankind, she would sacrifice public support throughout the world, precipitate the race for armaments, and prejudice the possibility of reaching an international agreement on the future control of such weapons.

Much more favorable conditions for the eventual achievement of such an agreement could be created if nuclear bombs were first revealed to the world by a demonstration in an appropriately selected uninhabited area.

In case chances for the establishment of an effective international control of nuclear weapons should have to be considered slight at the present time, then not only the use of these weapons against Japan, but even their early demonstration, may be contrary to the interests of this country. A postponement of such a demonstration will have in this case the advantage of delaying the beginning of the nuclear armaments race as long as possible. If, during the time gained, ample support can be made available for further development of the field in this country, the postponement will substantially increase the lead which we have established during the present war, and our position in an armament race or in any later attempt at international agreement would thus be strengthened.

On the other hand, if no adequate public support for the development of nucleonics will be available without a demonstration, the postponement of the latter may be deemed inadvisable, because enough information might leak out to cause other nations to start the armament race, in which we would then be at a disadvantage. There is also the possibility that the distrust of other nations may be aroused if they know that we are conducting a development under cover of secrecy, and that this will make it more difficult eventually to reach an agreement with them.

If the government should decide in favor of an early demonstration of nuclear weapons, it will then have the possibility of taking into account the public opinion of this country and of the other nations before deciding whether these weapons should be used in the war against Japan. In this way, other nations may assume a share of responsibility for such a fateful decision.

To sum up, we urge that the use of nuclear bombs in this war be considered as a problem of long-range national policy rather than of military expediency, and that this policy be directed primarily to the achievement of an agreement permitting an effective international control of the means of nuclear warfare.

The vital importance of such a control for our country is obvious from the fact that the only effective alternative method of protecting this country appears to be a dispersal of our major cities and essential industries.

J. Franck, Chairman
D. J. Hughes
J. J. Nickson
E. Rabinowitch
G. T. Seaborg
J. C. Stearns
L. Szilard

Memo to the Committee
on Panel Discussions
July 12, 1945

What we can and should do in attempting to prepare for the impact of nucleonics on the world is a twofold problem:

 1. Immediate Action
 2. Long-range Program

1. IMMEDIATE ACTION

1. With Franck's committee report to the Secretary of War's Nucleonics Committee, we have done all that could be done within the present limits imposed by uncompromising secrecy and security considerations. Szilard's petition to the President will contribute nothing new, and has only strained unnecessarily our relations with the Army. We might not be able to avoid conflicts with the Army in this field, but then let's have them only when fighting for a definite worthwhile objective and not merely for the purpose of "going on the record."

2. The only way in which the present situation could be changed radically, is a limited or unlimited removal of secrecy restrictions, not on technical details, but on the fundamental fact of successful libera-

Memorandum to the Committee on Panel Discussions, July 12, 1945, signed E. Rabinowitch, copy in Simpson's files.

tion of atomic power, *before any use is made of this power*, thus giving us the possibility of discussing the subject with a larger group of responsible people in Washington, and what is more important, giving the public opinion at large the chance to assimilate the facts and to influence the decision as to the best use to be made of the new weapon. Thus, one concrete step to be considered would be a *petition to tell the American people about the problem* instead of committing the nation to a decision in which it has not participated. In contrast to the presently circulated petition, this one would concern itself with a concrete step not recommended or even discussed in the first report of Franck's committee.

An announcement of the fundamental facts of nucleonics to the public in USA may be preceded by a preliminary confidential communication to our allies, so as to avoid shocking them by "learning of the whole thing through the newspapers."

2. LONG-RANGE PROGRAM

The long-range problem is that of education—of making the people of this and other countries realize that nucleonics will not destroy our civilization, only if we change our world-political system so as to make an efficient prevention of nucleonic warfare possible.

The answers to the Daniels poll confirm what I have stated before in a memorandum to the Project Committee on Education—that this education should begin *with the scientists themselves*. Therefore, further panel discussions of this and related subjects are vitally necessary. There should be no objection to these discussions being officially sponsored, if provision is taken to satisfy all reasonable security requirements in respect to:

   a) selection of those admitted; and
   b) topics not to be touched upon.
Security representatives should be present at these discussions to assure that no leaks of information are allowed.

If these conditions are satisfied, the Army should have no reason to hinder our discussions—unless it follows the military censorship in its tendency to use rules established to safeguard secret information to prevent spread of "undesirable" political opinions.

Among the subjects to be discussed in our panel meeting, the following could be mentioned:

   a) Should we advocate a removal of secrecy (to the extent discussed in (1)?

b) Should scientists *as such* take an active role in post-war organization of the world? Should an attempt be made to organize scientists for this purpose?

c) What should be the relation between private and publicly directed research in post-war nucleonics?

3. Organization

While impartial panel discussions of all these problems could be *officially* sponsored, any *action* to be taken will needs be *partisan*, and can therefore be undertaken only in the name of a *group* or *organization*, and not in that of the Laboratory as a whole. We have strained to the utmost our right to speak in the name of the Lab as a whole in the Franck Committee Report, and can go no further without provoking conflict with those who hold different opinion:

Therefore, an organization of those who have made up their mind about certain basic problems and decisions to be made, should be created on the Project, with the intention of spreading it beyond the Project limits to scientists at large, as soon as the secrecy is lifted by announcement, demonstration, or actual use of nuclear power. This "Scientists Action Committee" should have the purpose to act, by open propaganda or lobbying, for the full recognition of the tremendous change in world situation created by the release of nuclear power, for international agreement on control of this power, and for all of the general measures of international policy which may be required to create lasting security against a threatening devastation of this and all the other countries by nuclear bombs; for the most efficient organization of post-war research in nucleonics for the common good of mankind, and for increased influence of scientists on national and international policies.

Suggestions

1. Committee to organize officially sponsored panel discussions in cooperation with army security organs.

2. An organizational group to study the possibility and means of permanent organization of "Scientists Political Action Committee."

E. Rabinowitch

Note
on Sources

Note
on Sources

T HE PRINCIPAL sources for this book are interviews and correspondence with participants in the scientists' movement that developed
after World War II and the files of the Federation of American Scientists, its affiliates, and related organizations. With the exception of
some early material retained by the FAS office in Washington, the
organization files cited in the notes are now in the Special Collections
of the Harper Memorial Library at the University of Chicago. Deposited there, in addition to the bulk of the FAS papers, are the files
of the Atomic Scientists of Chicago, the Association of Los Alamos
Scientists, the Association of Oak Ridge Engineers and Scientists, the
Association of Cambridge Scientists, the *Bulletin of the Atomic Scientists*, and the Emergency Committee of Atomic Scientists. The files
of the National Committee on Atomic Information are in the Library
of Congress. These collections contain much duplicate material, and
the location I cite is not necessarily the only place where a given
document, or a copy of it, can be found.

I am exceedingly grateful to individuals who showed me certain
documents and records in their files. The diaries of W. A. Higinbotham and Lyle Borst and the files of Albert S. Cahn, Paul Henshaw, Arthur H. Jaffey, Byron S. Miller, J. J. Nickson, J. Robert
Oppenheimer, John A. Simpson, and Mrs. John P. Welling remain

in their possession. The files of J. H. Rush and material loaned to me by Thorfin R. Hogness, Robert S. Mulliken, and Eugene Rabinowitch have been deposited in Harper Memorial Library at the University of Chicago.

Published accounts relating to this period, few in number when I began this study, are rapidly increasing. My indebtedness to them, especially to the official AEC history, *The New World,* is acknowledged in the footnotes.

Index

Index